15.95
01 mc

FINITE GROUPS

Harper's Series in Modern Mathematics

I. N. Herstein and Gian-Carlo Rota, EDITORS

FINITE GROUPS

DANIEL GORENSTEIN

NORTHEASTERN UNIVERSITY

HARPER & ROW, Publishers

NEW YORK, EVANSTON, AND LONDON

Library of Congress catalog card number: 68-10195

In memory of my father,
Philip Gorenstein (1888–1951)

CONTENTS

PART II: APPLICATIONS

PART III: GENERAL CLASSIFICATION PROBLEMS

PREFACE

In the past ten years there has been a tremendous surge of activity in finite group theory. The period has witnessed the first serious classification theorems concerning simple groups and the discovery of several new families of simple groups; and, above all, the fundamental question of the solvability of groups of odd order has been answered. Dramatic applications have been made of Philip Hall's earlier basic results on solvable and nilpotent groups and of Brauer's long and continued contributions to the theory of group characters. Out of the work of Feit and Thompson on groups of odd order, of subsequent work of Thompson on the minimal simple groups, and of Suzuki's numerous classification theorems, there is gradually emerging a body of techniques and a series of general methods for studying simple groups. Although the entire field is presently in an excited state of ferment and fluidity, as recent basic work of Glauberman and Alperin clearly indicates, a degree of stability appears to be settling over certain aspects of the subject.

Our primary object will be to present a systematic development of most of these techniques and to illustrate their applicability through the analysis of several classification problems. For reasons of exposition, clarity, and emphasis, we have divided the book into three parts. In Part I we study the total body of material required for the classification problems we shall consider later. Although each of the chapters on representation theory, character theory, p-groups, solvable groups, and transfer includes a considerable number of results which can presently be found only in the literature, it is Chapter 8 on p-constrained and p-stable groups and Chapter 9 on groups of even order that present the new methods in their most developed form.

In selecting or rejecting material for Part I, we have held steadfast to a single-minded purpose: to present only those results deemed essential for application to the study of simple groups. Thus, for example, most of the beautiful and well-worked-out theory of solvable groups has been omitted, and, in particular, the important subclass of supersolvable groups has not even been mentioned. Only by such uncompromising restraint did we feel that we could give the reader a sense of the underlying continuity and interrelationship that exists among the various methods that are used in these classification problems.

There are two omissions that have been caused rather by limitations of space. The first, and for our purposes the more serious, is the theory of modular characters, which is an essential tool for studying simple groups. Fortunately (and also by design) the particular classification problems we have chosen for analysis in Part II require only results of ordinary character theory for their solutions; yet, they are sufficiently complex to illustrate the use of the various methods developed in Part I. Secondly, we have not given a systematic treatment of the known simple groups, apart from a brief outline without proofs in Chapter 17 of Part III. This is another area that has been the subject recently of a great deal of investigation. As a result of the work of Chevalley, Tits, Steinberg, and others on algebraic groups and Lie algebras, the finite simple groups of Lie type are now well understood. However, a precise knowledge of these groups is actually not required for the classification problems that have so far been undertaken (with the exception of certain groups of low rank that can be studied without reference to the general theory). It is quite evident, however, that as the classification problems under consideration become more and more general in the future, this situation will change.

Part I is written on the assumption that the reader has had the equivalent of a standard first-year-graduate algebra course. Thus we assume a familiarity with basic group-theoretic concepts and an understanding of linear algebra, elementary properties of modules and tensor products, and the theory of fields, including Galois theory. In Chapter 1 we list explicitly a number of elementary results about groups without proof. Apart from these specific theorems and the general knowledge we have presupposed, the book is entirely self-contained. All proofs are complete and, with a few trivial exceptions, do not rely on earlier, unproved exercises.

We note also that the development of character theory is confined to Section 6 of Chapter 3, all of Chapter 4, and Section 4 of Chapter 9, and is used elsewhere in Part I only for Burnside's theorem on groups of order

$p^a q^b$ and Frobenius' theorem on transitive permutation groups. Hence if one is willing to accept the last two theorems, it is possible to present the entire non-character-theoretic portion of Part I as an independent unit in approximately one semester or two quarters. To facilitate the development of the material in this way, we have deliberately included certain results in Chapter 3 (excluding Section 6) even though there exist shorter proofs for them using character theory. On the other hand, all the material of Part I, together with a few of the applications of Part II, can easily be covered in a year's course.

The recent advances in our knowledge of simple groups have not been accomplished without great effort, for the papers embodying them are among the longest in all of mathematics, the Odd Order paper alone running to 255 journal pages. Any writer attempting to present this work is thus faced with a very serious problem: Given the limitations of space and energy, how is he to present a body of theorems the complete proofs of which, no matter how efficiently organized, would require perhaps a thousand pages for complete exposition? The compromise we have decided upon is this: On the one hand, to present complete proofs of special cases of these various theorems, which are sufficiently significant to provide meaningful application of the techniques developed in Part I and to give some indication of the nature of the general problems themselves; and, on the other hand, using these special cases as a starting point, to outline in some detail the complete proofs of the general theorems.

Thus in Part II we establish the solvability of CN-groups of odd order (groups in which the centralizer of every nonidentity element is nilpotent) and also determine all simple CN-groups of even order which have abelian Sylow 2-subgroups. The latter argument depends in part on the classification of certain Zassenhaus groups (doubly transitive permutation groups in which only the identity fixes three letters). Our results on Zassenhaus groups also enable us to present a complete analysis of a particular case of the general dihedral Sylow 2-subgroup problem: that of groups which possess a self-centralizing Sylow 2-subgroup of order 4. In addition, we derive a basic structural property of groups which have a generalized quaternion Sylow 2-subgroup of order at least 16. We also establish the solvability of groups which admit fixed-point-free automorphisms of several specified types (our results here are essentially complete inasmuch as they include the only general cases in which solvability has at present been established). Finally, we have included a complete proof of P. Hall and G. Higman's fundamental theorem on p-solvable linear groups. Even though this result is not strictly the solution of a classification problem, it has had a great impact on the study of simple groups and, in addition, provides a number of lovely applications of our earlier results.

In Chapter 16 of Part III we discuss in outline the bulk of the recent general results on the classification of simple groups. In a preparatory section we have tried to indicate the over-all nature of these theorems, the conceptual organization of their proofs, and the way in which the three basic methods of finite group theory—the local group-theoretic, the character-theoretic, and the generator-relation methods—enter into the arguments. This section attempts to bring together within a single unified framework the diverse techniques and procedures developed in Part I. In Section 8 of Chapter 16 we list a number of related unsolved problems.

Chapter 17 contains some highly personal and speculative views of the direction we feel the future study of simple groups may take. In it we have tried to point out some of the difficulties, and at the same time to show how many of the concepts that have played so important a part in recent work have fairly natural extensions that should be useful for investigating other classes of simple groups. In addition, we also present in Section 1 a complete list of the known simple groups together with a summary of some of their properties.

The non-character-theoretic portions of Chapters 1 to 7, 10, 11, and 14 and parts of Chapters 8 and 9 are based on lecture notes of a course in group theory which I have twice given and whose purpose was in a modest way the same as that of this book. A great stimulus for much of this material was a magnificent set of lecture notes by Philip Hall that were presented in a course by John Thompson at the University of Chicago in the fall of 1960. The reader familiar with these notes will realize the extent of their influence on Chapters 2, 3, 5, and 6. For the development of the character theory, I have been fortunate indeed to have had available an outstanding set of notes by Walter Feit, which have been indispensable. My general views on the classification of simple groups have been very greatly influenced by Thompson's forthcoming paper on N-groups, a preliminary version of which I have been studying over the past three years. Together with the Odd Order paper, it has been the underlying inspiration for this attempt to write a book which would make these fundamental works accessible to a wider audience.

I owe special thanks to both J. L. Alperin and George Glauberman, each of whom spent a great many hours on the over-all text, as well as on several specific theorems and points of difficulty, and whose continued interest throughout its preparation has significantly affected its final form. I am also indebted to Paul Fong and Michio Suzuki, who read portions of the manuscript and made a number of helpful suggestions. I should also like to acknowledge my gratitude to I. N. Herstein, who began my education in group theory, to J. H. Walter for a long collaboration which deepened my understanding of the entire subject, and to the University of Chicago and Dean A. A. Albert, in particular, for making possible my participation in the Group Theory Year 1960–1961, which was a milestone in my mathematical development. Finally I wish to express my thanks to the publishers, Harper & Row, and especially to Mrs. Amy Kramer, for their intelligent professional help and guidance; their continued advice and assistance throughout the entire publication of the book considerably simplified my own tasks.

A word about the notation: Theorem 3.4.2 will, as customary, denote the second result of Section 4 of Chapter 3; however, for simplicity, all references to this result *within* Chapter 3 itself will be designated as Theorem 4.2. Furthermore, we emphasize that *all* groups considered in the book are finite.

D. G.

PART **I** METHODS

CHAPTER 1

PRELIMINARIES

In this chapter we list explicitly those basic results of finite group theory which will be assumed without proof. Proofs of the various theorems can be found in any standard text on the subject. Apart from these particular results, we also presuppose a familiarity with various elementary group-theoretic terms and concepts: abelian, order, coset, conjugacy, normal and characteristic subgroups, factor groups, homomorphism, isomorphism, direct products, center, commutator, centralizer and normalizer, permutation, cycle, symmetric group, and so on. In addition, we assume an elementary knowledge of the theory of linear transformations and the theory of fields. In particular, we require an understanding of the definitions and basic properties of tensor products of vector spaces, of modules, of characteristic roots and similarity of linear transformations, on the one hand; and of algebraic field extensions, Galois theory, and finite fields on the other. Thus, in effect, we shall assume a knowledge of most of the material that is customarily covered in a first-year-graduate course in algebra.

Following the listing of the basic theorems, we shall establish a number of additional closely related elementary results with which the reader may perhaps not be fully acquainted.

1. NOTATION AND TERMINOLOGY

It is important to establish at the outset various notational conventions that we shall use throughout the book.

We use the symbol 1 for both the identity element and identity subgroup of a group G. The set of nonidentity elements of G will be denoted by G^*.

If X, Y are subsets of the group G, we write $X \subseteq Y$ if X is a subset of Y and $X \subset Y$ if X is a *proper* subset of Y. $X \cap Y$ is given its customary meaning. If $X \subseteq Y$, $Y - X$ denotes as usual the set of elements of Y not contained in X.

If X is a subset of G, $\langle X \rangle$ will denote the subgroup of G generated by X. Equivalently $\langle X \rangle$ is the intersection of all subgroups containing X. We extend this symbol in the obvious way to the subgroup generated by a collection of subsets of G. It will often also be convenient to write $\langle x \mid x \in X \rangle$ for the subgroup of G generated by the elements of the subset X.

The subset of G consisting of the elements $x_1, x_2, \ldots, x_n$ is denoted by $\{x_1, x_2, \ldots, x_n\}$ or $\{x_i \mid 1 \leqslant i \leqslant n\}$. Similarly, if X is a subset of G, $X = \{x \mid x \in X\}$.

If X, Y are subsets of G, we write XY for the subset consisting of all products xy with $x \in X$, $y \in Y$. Thus $XY = \{xy \mid x \in X, y \in Y\}$. If X_i, $1 \leqslant i \leqslant n$, are subsets of G, we define the subset $X_1 X_2 \cdots X_n$ analogously. Similarly, if H is a subset of G and $x, y \in G$, we write $Hx = \{hx \mid h \in H\}$ and $yHx = \{yhx \mid h \in H\}$. In particular, $x^{-1}Hx$ is the image of H under the inner automorphism of G induced by conjugation by x.

If X is a subset of G, $|X|$ will denote the order of X. For a single element x, we shall use the same symbol $|x|$ for the order of x, that is, the order of the cyclic subgroup $X = \langle x \rangle$. Furthermore, for any prime p, we denote by $|G|_p$ the highest power of the prime p that divides $|G|$.

If π is a set of prime numbers, we say that the element x of G is a π-*element* if $|x|$ is divisible only by primes in π. In particular, we have the notion of a p-*element*, p a prime. Similarly, a group G is called a π-*group* if $|G|$ is divisible only by primes in π. In addition, $\pi(G)$ will designate the set of primes dividing $|G|$. Clearly G is a $\pi(G)$-group; moreover, if G is a π-group, then $\pi(G) \subseteq \pi$. Finally, the least common multiple of the orders of the elements of G is called the *exponent* of G.

The complementary set of primes to π will be denoted by π'. Thus we also have the notion of π'- and p'-elements as well as π'- and p'-groups. For example, a $2'$-element is simply an element of odd order.

If X is a subset of G, $C_G(X)$ and $N_G(X)$ will denote the centralizer and normalizer of X in G, respectively.

We write $H \lhd G$ if H is a normal subgroup of G and H char G if H is a characteristic subgroup of G.

The center of G will be denoted $Z(G)$. We have $Z(G)$ char G.

If $x, y \in G$, we write $[x, y]$ for the commutator $x^{-1}y^{-1}xy$. If X, Y are subsets of G, then $[X, Y] = \langle [x, y] \mid x \in X, y \in Y \rangle$, so that $[X, Y]$ is always a subgroup of G. In particular, $[G, G]$ is the commutator subgroup of G. We have $[G, G]$ char G. As is customary, we also frequently write G' for $[G, G]$.

We shall usually write our operators on the right. Sometimes we shall use the exponential notation H^α for the image of H under the mapping α. In particular, if H is a subset of the group G and x is an element of G, we shall write H^x for the subset $x^{-1}Hx$ and H^G for the subgroup generated by the sets H^x with x in G. Clearly H^G is a normal subgroup of G, which we call the *normal closure* of H in G.

It is also convenient to introduce the following term: We say that a group K is *involved* in G provided K is isomorphic to a homomorphic image of a subgroup H of G. (Such a homomorphic image is called a *section* of G; however, we shall not need this term.)

2. ASSUMED RESULTS

Theorem 2.1 (LaGrange)

The order of a subgroup H of a group G is a divisor of the order of G.

Thus $|G|/|H|$ is an integer, which we designate $|G : H|$ and call the *index* of H in G. $|G : H|$ is the number of right (or left) cosets of H in G.

Theorem 2.2

If X, Y are subsets of G, then $|XY| = |XY| = |X||Y|/|X \cap Y|$. Moreover, XY is a subgroup of G if and only if YX is a subgroup.

Theorem 2.3

Let K_i, $1 \leqslant i \leqslant r$, denote the distinct classes of conjugate elements of G and let x_i be an arbitrary element of K_i. Then we have

(i) $|K_i| = |G : C_G(x_i)|$, $1 \leqslant i \leqslant r$.

(ii) $|G| = \sum\limits_{i=1}^{r} |G : C_G(x_i)|$.

(iii) *If X is a subset of G, then $|G : N_G(X)|$ is the number of distinct conjugates of X in G.*

Equation (ii) is sometimes called the *class equation* of G.

We list next the three standard isomorphism theorems.

Theorem 2.4

Let ϕ be a homomorphism of the group G onto the group G' with kernel K. Then we have

    (i) *G' is isomorphic to the factor group G/K.*

    (ii) *There exists a one-to-one correspondence between the subgroups of G containing K and the subgroups of G'. Such a subgroup H of G corresponds to its image $H' = H\phi$ in G'. Furthermore, $H \lhd G$ if and only if $H' \lhd G'$.*

Theorem 2.5

Let K, H be normal subgroups of G with $K \subseteq H$. Then G/H is isomorphic to $(G/K)/(H/K)$.

Theorem 2.6

Let K, H be subgroups of G with $K \lhd G$. Then we have

    (i) *KH is a subgroup of G.*

    (ii) *KH/K is isomorphic to $H/K \cap H$.*

A chain of subgroups $G = G_0 \supseteq G_1 \supseteq G_2 \supseteq \cdots \supseteq G_n = 1$ is called a *normal series* of G provided each $G_i \lhd G_{i-1}$, $1 \leqslant i \leqslant n$. The factors group G_{i-1}/G_i are called the *factors* of the normal series and the integer n is called its *length*. If each G_i is a maximal proper normal subgroup of G_{i-1}, the normal series is called a *composition series* and the factors G_{i-1}/G_i are called its *composition factors*. In this case it follows at once from Theorem 2.4 that G_{i-1}/G_i has no proper normal subgroups except the identity and hence is a *simple* group.

We have the following two basic results concerning normal and composition series.

Theorem 2.7 (Schreier)

Any normal series of G no two of whose members are equal can be refined to a composition series of G.

Theorem 2.8 (Jordan-Hölder)

Any two composition series of G have the same length and, with respect to a suitable ordering of the composition factors, the corresponding factors are isomorphic.

Thus the composition factors of any group G are completely determined up to isomorphism (and ordering) by any one composition series. It is therefore meaningful to speak of *the* set of composition factors of G.

Theorem 2.9 (Sylow)

Let G be a group and p a prime. Then we have
- (i) *G possesses a subgroup of order $|G|_p$ and every p-subgroup of G is contained in a subgroup of order $|G|_p$.*
- (ii) *Any two subgroups of order $|G|_p$ are conjugate in G.*
- (iii) *The number of distinct subgroups of G of order $|G|_p$ is of the form $1 + kp$ for some nonnegative integer k.*

A subgroup of G of order $|G|_p$ is called a *Sylow p-subgroup* or, briefly, an S_p-*subgroup* of G. As an immediate corollary of Sylow's theorem we have

Theorem 2.10

- (i) *G is a π-group if and only if each element of $G^{\#}$ is a π-element.*
- (ii) *A normal p-subgroup of G is contained in every S_p-subgroup of G.*
- (iii) *G possesses a unique S_p-subgroup if and only if an S_p-subgroup of G is normal in G.*

We also have the following related results:

Theorem 2.11

A p-group G has the following properties:
- (i) $Z(G) \neq 1.$
- (ii) *If H is a proper subgroup of G, then $N_G(H) \supset H$.*
- (iii) *If H is a maximal subgroup of G, then $|G:H| = p$.*
- (iv) *Any group of order p^2 is abelian.*

If $G_1, G_2, \ldots, G_n$ are groups, the set of elements $(x_1, x_2, \ldots, x_n)$ with $x_i \in G_i$ form a group G^* under the operation $(x_1, x_2, \ldots, x_n)(x_1', x_2', \ldots, x_n') = (x_1 x_1', x_2 x_2', \ldots, x_n x_n')$, where also $x_i' \in G_i$ and $x_i x_i'$ denotes the product in G_i. G^* is called the *(external) direct product* of the G_i and we write $G^* = G_1 \times G_2 \times \cdots \times G_n$.

Theorem 2.12

Let G_i be normal subgroups of G, $1 \leqslant i \leqslant n$, which satisfy the following conditions:
- (a) $G = G_1 G_2 \cdots G_n.$
- (b) $G_i \cap G_1 G_2 \cdots G_{i-1} G_{i+1} \cdots G_n = 1, 1 \leqslant i \leqslant n.$

Then we have
- (i) *Each x in G has a unique representation of the form $x = x_1 x_2 \cdots x_n$ with x_i in G_i, $1 \leqslant i \leqslant n$.*
- (ii) *The mapping $(x)\phi = (x_1, x_2, \ldots, x_n)$ of G into $G_1 \times G_2 \times \cdots \times G_n$ is an isomorphism.*

In view of this result we say under these circumstances that G is the (*internal*) *direct product* of its normal subgroups $G_i, 1 \leqslant i \leqslant n$, and with slight abuse of terminology we write $G = G_1 \times G_2 \times \cdots \times G_n$. Of particular importance is the case $n = 2$, in which the conditions reduce to $G_1, G_2 \lhd G$, $G = G_1 G_2$, and $G_1 \cap G_2 = 1$. Then we have $G_1 G_2$ isomorphic to $G_1 \times G_2$.

Theorem 2.13

Let G be an abelian group and let $\pi(G) = \{p_1, p_2, \ldots, p_n\}$. Then we have
   (i) The set of p_i-elements of G forms a subgroup P_i which is the unique S_{p_i}-subgroup of G, $1 \leqslant i \leqslant n$.
   (ii) G is isomorphic to the direct product $P_1 \times P_2 \times \cdots \times P_n$. In particular, $|G| = |P_1| \cdot |P_2| \cdots |P_n|$.

Theorem 2.14

An abelian p-group G is the direct product of cyclic subgroups $H_i, 1 \leqslant i \leqslant n$. Moreover, the integer n and the orders $|H_i|$ are uniquely determined (up to ordering).

We shall denote this uniquely determined integer n by $m(G)$. If $|H_i| = p^{e_i}$, we say that G is of *type* $(p^{e_1}, p^{e_2}, \ldots, p^{e_n})$. In particular, if G is of type $(p, p, \ldots, p)$, G is called *elementary* abelian, while if G is of type $(p^e, p^e, \ldots, p^e)$, G is called *homocyclic*. If $H_i = \langle x_i \rangle$, then the $x_i, 1 \leqslant i \leqslant n$, are called a *basis* of G. We can then write each element x of G uniquely in the form

$$x = x_1^{a_1} x_2^{a_2} \cdots x_n^{a_n},$$

where $0 \leqslant a_i < p^{e_i} = |x_i|, 1 \leqslant i \leqslant n$. We see from this that the elements of G of order p together with 1 form an elementary abelian subgroup of order p^n with basis $x_i^{p^{e_i-1}}, 1 \leqslant i \leqslant n$.

In dealing with abelian p-groups, it is often more convenient to use additive than multiplicative notation, in which case we write mx instead of x^m. Hence if $x_i, 1 \leqslant i \leqslant n$, is a basis of G, each x in G can then be uniquely written in the form

$$x = a_1 x_1 + a_2 x_2 + \cdots + a_n x_n,$$

with $0 \leqslant a_i < |x_i|, 1 \leqslant i \leqslant n$.

We note also the obvious consequence of these results—that an abelian group is simple if and only if it has prime order.

Another basic property of abelian groups that we shall need is the following:

Theorem 2.15

The set E of endomorphisms of an abelian group G form a ring under the operations $\phi + \psi$ and $\phi\psi$, with ϕ, ψ in E, defined by

$$x(\phi + \psi) = x\phi + x\psi \quad and \quad x(\phi\psi) = (x\phi)\psi \qquad for\ x\ in\ G.$$

We conclude with the statements of two other basic results of a different nature.

Theorem 2.16 (Cayley)

Every group of order n is isomorphic to a subgroup of the symmetric group of degree n.

Theorem 2.17

The alternating group of degree n is simple or all $n \geqslant 5$.

3. RELATED ELEMENTARY RESULTS

We present here with proof a number of additional basic results that we shall need. Our first results concern abelian groups.

Theorem 3.1

  (i) *If G is cyclic of order n and m divides n, then G possesses a unique subgroup of order m and it is cyclic. In particular, every subgroup of G is characteristic.*

 (ii) *An abelian group is cyclic if and only if all its Sylow subgroups are cyclic.*

(iii) *If x is an element of the group G and $\pi(\langle x \rangle) = \{p_1, p_2, \ldots, p_r\}$, then x can be written uniquely in the form $x = x_1 x_2 \cdots x_r$, where x_i is a p_i-element and each x_i, x_j commute, $1 \leqslant i, j \leqslant n$.*

Proof

If $G = \langle x \rangle$ is cyclic of order n and $m \mid n$, then the m elements $x^{in/m}$, $1 \leqslant i \leqslant m$, are distinct and form a cyclic subgroup with generator $x^{n/m}$. Since this subgroup clearly consists of all elements of G whose orders divide m, it is the unique subgroup of order m and (i) holds. In particular, the Sylow subgroups of G are all cyclic. Conversely, if G is an abelian group with cyclic Sylow subgroups $P_i = \langle x_i \rangle$, $1 < i \leqslant r$, it is immediate that the element $x = x_1 x_2 \cdots x_r$ has order $n = \prod_{i=1}^{r} |P_i|$. But $n = |G|$ by Theorem 2.12, so G is cyclic. Thus (ii) holds.

Now let the assumptions be as in (iii) and set $G_0 = \langle x \rangle$. The final argument of the preceding paragraph shows that there are p_i-elements x_i' in

G_0 such that $x' = x_1'x_2' \cdots x_r'$ generates G_0. But then $x = x''$ for some t and so $x = x_1x_2 \cdots x_r$, where $x_i = x_i''$ is a p_i-element, $1 \leqslant i \leqslant r$. Furthermore, since each x_i is in G_0, these elements commute pairwise.

Assume finally that $x = u_1u_2 \cdots u_r$, with u_i a p_i-element and u_i, u_j commuting, $1 \leqslant i, j \leqslant r$. Write $|x| = p_i^{e_i}q_i$ for suitable integers e_i, q_i with $(p_i, q_i) = 1$. Then clearly x_i, u_i have order $p_i^{e_i}$ and x_j, u_j have orders dividing q_i for $j \neq i$. Hence $x^{q_i} = (x_1x_2 \cdots x_r)^{q_i} = x_1^{q_i}x_2^{q_i} \cdots x_r^{q_i} = x_i^{q_i}$. Similarly, $x^{q_i} = u_i^{q_i}$ and so $x_i^{q_i} = u_i^{q_i}$. Choosing k so that $q_ik \equiv 1 \pmod{p^{e_i}}$, it follows that $x_i = x_i^{q_ik} = u_i^{q_ik} = u_i$ and hence the x_i are uniquely determined, thus proving (iii).

Theorem 3.2

An elementary abelian p-group G of order p^n is isomorphic to a vector space of dimension n over the field Z_p with p elements.

Proof

We use additive notation for G and let x_i, $1 \leqslant i \leqslant n$, be a basis for G, so that every element x of G has a unique representation in the form $x = \sum_{i=1}^{n} a_ix_i$, where $0 \leqslant a_i < p$, $1 \leqslant i \leqslant n$. If $y = \sum_{i=1}^{n} b_ix_i$, with $0 \leqslant b_i < p$, $1 \leqslant i \leqslant n$, is another element of G, then the product law in G gives $x + y = \sum_{i=1}^{n} c_ix_i$, where $0 \leqslant c_i < p$ and $c_i \equiv a_i + b_i \pmod{p}$, $1 \leqslant i \leqslant n$. Hence if we regard the coefficients a_i, b_i, c_i as elements of Z_p, we have $c_i = a_i + b_i$ and it follows that the mapping $(x)\phi = (a_1, a_2, \ldots, a_n)$ is an isomorphism of G onto the abelian group of the space V of n-tuples over Z_p. Furthermore, G is a Z_p-module in a natural way and $(ax)\phi = (\sum_{i=1}^{n} (aa_i)x_i)\phi = (aa_1, \ldots, aa_n) = a(a_1, a_2, \ldots, a_n) = a(x\phi)$. Thus ϕ also preserves the operation of Z_p on G and so maps G isomorphically onto the vector space V over Z_p.

Lemma 3.3

If A is a cyclic subgroup of maximal order of the abelian group G, then A is a direct factor of G (that is, $G = A \times B$ for some subgroup B of G).

Proof

If G is cyclic, then $G = A$ by the maximality of A and the lemma holds trivially with $B = 1$; so we may assume that G is noncyclic. Then some S_p-subgroup of G is noncyclic by Theorem 3.1(ii) and hence G possesses a noncyclic elementary abelian p-subgroup. But then some subgroup H of G

of order p is not contained in A, whence $A \cap H = 1$. Setting $\bar{G} = G/H$, it follows that the image $\bar{A}$ of A in $\bar{G}$ has the same order as A and so is cyclic of maximal order in $\bar{G}$. But then using induction on $|G|$, it follows that $\bar{G} = \bar{A}\bar{B}$ with $\bar{A} \cap \bar{B} = \bar{1}$ for some subgroup $\bar{B}$ of $\bar{G}$. If B is the inverse image of $\bar{B}$ in G, then $G = AB$ and $A \cap B \subseteq H$, whence $A \cap B = 1$. Thus $G = A \times B$, as required.

Lemma 3.4

If $G/Z(G)$ is cyclic, then $G = Z(G)$ and G is abelian.

Proof

If y is an element of G whose image generates $G/Z(G)$, then every element of G is of the form zy^i for some z in $Z(G)$ and some integer i. But then it is immediate that any two elements of G commute and so $G = Z(G)$ is abelian.

Lemma 3.5

A group of exponent 2 is abelian.

Proof

Let G be of exponent 2. If $x, y \in G$, then $(xy)^2 = x^2 = y^2 = 1$, whence $xyxy = xxyy$ and so $xy = yx$. Thus G is abelian.

We shall need the following condition for a group to be a direct product:

Theorem 3.6

If every Sylow subgroup of G is normal, then G is the direct product of its Sylow subgroups.

Proof

Let $\pi(G) = \{p_1, p_2, \ldots, p_r\}$. By assumption an S_p-subgroup P_i of G is normal in G, $1 \le i \le r$. Thus P_i is the unique S_{p_i}-subgroup of G by Sylow's theorem and so contains every p_i-element of G. But now if $x \in G$, $\pi(\langle x \rangle) \subseteq \pi(G)$ and hence $x = x_1 x_2 \cdots x_r$, where x_i is a p_i-element, $1 \le i \le r$, by Theorem 3.1(iii). Therefore $x_i \in P_i$ and $x \in P_1 P_2 \cdots P_r$. We conclude that $G = P_1 P_2 \cdots P_r$.

Furthermore, any product of the P_i's is a subgroup and repeated application of Theorem 2.2 yields that $Q_i = P_1 P_2 \cdots P_{i-1} P_{i+1} \cdots P_r$ is a p_i'-group, $1 \le i \le r$. But then $Q_i \cap P_i = 1$, $1 \le i \le r$, and now the desired conclusion follows from Theorem 2.12.

Our next theorem is a simple consequence of Sylow's theorem, sometimes called the *Frattini argument*. Despite its simplicity, the result is of fundamental importance.

Theorem 3.7

If $H \lhd G$ and P is an S_p-subgroup of H, then $G = N_G(P)H$.

Proof

For x in G, we have $P^x \subseteq H^x = x^{-1}Hx = H$ as $H \lhd G$. Since $|P^x| = |P|$, P^x is also an S_p-subgroup of H and so is conjugate to P by an element y of H by Sylow's theorem. Thus $P^x = P^y$ and so $P^{xy^{-1}} = P$, whence $xy^{-1} \in N_G(P)$. Since $x = (xy^{-1})y$ and x is arbitrary, the theorem follows.

A related useful result is

Theorem 3.8

If $H \lhd G$ and P is an S_p-subgroup of G, then $H \cap P$ is an S_p-subgroup of H.

Proof

We have $|P| = |H|_p |G/H|_p$. By the second isomorphism theorem, $|PH/H| = |P/P \cap H|$. But PH/H is obviously an S_p-subgroup of G/H. We conclude at once that $|P \cap H| = |H|_p$ and consequently $P \cap H$ is an S_p-subgroup of H.

Theorem 3.9

If G is a group of order pq, where p and q are primes with $p > q$, then an S_p-subgroup of G is normal in G.

Proof

Let P be an S_p-subgroup of G. By Sylow's theorem, the number of S_p-subgroups of G is of the form $1 + kp$ and is also equal to $|G : N_G(P)|$. Since the latter number is 1 or q and $q < p$, we must have $k = 0$ and so $P \lhd G$.

For any group G, we shall denote by Aut G the group of automorphisms of G. The following elementary result is useful.

Theorem 3.10

(i) *If G is cyclic, then* Aut G *is abelian.*

(ii) *If G is cyclic of prime order p, then* Aut G *is cyclic of order $p - 1$.*

Proof

Let $G = \langle x \rangle$ be of order n. If $\phi \in$ Aut G, then $(x)\phi$ also has order n and so $(x)\phi = x^k$ with $(k, n) = 1$. We put $\phi_k = \phi$. Conversely, for each integer k prime to n the mapping $x^i \to x^{ik}$ is an automorphism of G. Furthermore, if ϕ_h and ϕ_k are in Aut G, we have $(x)\phi_h\phi_k = (x^h)^k = x^{hk} = x^{\overline{hk}}$, where $\overline{hk}$ denotes the residue of $hk \pmod{n}$. Thus $\phi_h\phi_k = \phi_{hk}$ and it follows that Aut G is isomorphic to the multiplicative group of residue classes $\pmod{n}$.

Since the latter group is obviously abelian, so is Aut G. Moreover, if $n = p$, the latter group is isomorphic to the multiplicative group of the field with p elements and so is cyclic of order $p - 1$, whence (ii) also holds.

EXERCISES

1. Let H, K be subgroups. For u in G, the set of elements

$$HuK = \{xuy \mid x \in H, y \in K\}$$

   is called a *double coset* with respect to H, K. Prove
   (i) HuK is the union of $|K : K \cap H^x|$ distinct left cosets of H and also $|H^x : K \cap H^x|$ distinct right cosets of K.
   (ii) If two double cosets with respect to H, K have an element in common, they are identical.

2. If H, K are subgroups of G, show that the number of conjugates of H by elements of K is $|H : N_G(H) \cap K|$.

3. If P is an S_p-subgroup of G and H is a subgroup of G containing $N_G(P)$, prove that $N_G(H) = H$.

4. A subgroup H of G is called *pronormal* in G if for any x in G, H is conjugate to H^x in $\langle H, H^x \rangle$. Prove
   (i) An S_p-subgroup of G is pronormal in G.
   (ii) A p-subgroup H of G is pronormal in G if and only if each S_p-subgroup of G contains exactly one conjugate of H.
   (iii) If $H \subseteq Q \subseteq P$ are subgroups of G with H pronormal in G and P an S_p-subgroup of G, then $N_G(Q) \subseteq N_G(H)$. In particular, $H \lhd P$.
   (iv) If H_1 and H_2 are pronormal p-subgroups of G such that $\langle H_1, H_2 \rangle$ is a p-group, then $H_1 H_2$ is pronormal in G.
   (v) If P is an S_p-subgroup of G and $K \lhd G$, then $K \cap P$ is pronormal in G.

5. A subgroup H of G is called *subnormal* if H is a member of some normal series of G. Prove
   (i) If H is subnormal in G and $H \subseteq K$, K a subgroup of G, then H is subnormal in K.
   (ii) If H is subnormal in K and K is subnormal in L, where H, K, L are subgroups of G, then H is subnormal in L.
   (iii) If H is subnormal in the subgroup K of G and L is an arbitrary subgroup of G, then $H \cap L$ is subnormal in $K \cap L$.
   (iv) The intersection of subnormal subgroups of G is subnormal in G.
   (v) If H is subnormal in G and P is an S_p-subgroup of G, then $H \cap P$ is an S_p-subgroup of H.

6. A subgroup H of G is normal in G if and only if it is both subnormal and pronormal in G.

7. Show that a group of order $5 \cdot 7 \cdot 13$ is necessarily cyclic.

8. Let $G = G_1 \times G_2 \times \cdots \times G_n$ with G_i, G_j of relatively prime orders for $i \neq j$ and let H be a subgroup of G. Prove that H is the direct product of its subgroups $H \cap G_i$, $1 \leqslant i \leqslant n$.

9. Let $G = G_1 \times G_2$ and let H be a normal subgroup of G such that $H \cap G_i = 1$, $1 \leqslant i \leqslant 2$. Prove that H is abelian.

10. Let $G = G_1 \times G_2 \times \cdots \times G_n$ and let θ_i be the coordinate mapping of G on G_i, $1 \leqslant i \leqslant n$. A subgroup H of G is called a *residual product* if $\theta_i(H) = G_i$ for all i. Prove the following result: If K_i are normal subgroups of a group G, $1 \leqslant i \leqslant n$, and $K = \bigcap_{i=1}^{n} K_i$, then the group $\bar{G} = G/K_1 \times G/K_2 \times \cdots \times G/K_n$ has $\bar{H} = G/K$ as a residual product. (Here $\bar{H}$ is identified with a subgroup of $\bar{G}$ by means of the map: $xK \rightarrow (xK_1, xK_2, \ldots, xK_n)$.)

11. If G is abelian, then G is the direct product of nontrivial cyclic subgroups G_i of orders m_i, $1 \leqslant i \leqslant n$, with m_{i+1} dividing m_i, $1 \leqslant i \leqslant n-1$. Moreover, the integers $m_1, m_2, \ldots, m_n$ are uniquely determined by G and are called the *elementary divisors* of G.

12. We say that G is *semisimple* if G is the direct product of nonabelian simple groups or if $G = 1$. (In Chapter 17 we shall extend this definition to cover a wider class of groups.) Prove

    (i) Every subnormal subgroup of a semisimple group G is normal and is a direct factor of G.

    (ii) If H and K are semisimple normal subgroups of G, then HK is semisimple and

$$HK = (H \cap K) \times C_{HK}(H \cap K).$$

CHAPTER 2

SOME BASIC TOPICS

In this chapter we consider several primarily unrelated basic topics of finite group theory that we shall need in varying degree throughout the book. These include characteristic subgroups, higher commutators, nilpotent and solvable groups, semidirect and central products of groups, the relationship between groups of automorphisms and groups of linear transformations, and transitive and doubly transitive permutation groups. In the final section we shall discuss the groups of all nonsingular 2×2 matrices over finite fields and an important related class of doubly transitive groups. Later chapters will treat various aspects of these subjects in greater detail and depth. Here we shall be interested only in deriving elementary properties, in introducing various auxiliary concepts, and in developing some important notational conventions.

1. CHARACTERISTIC SUBGROUPS

The following easily verified properties of automorphisms are left as an exercise.

Theorem 1.1

Let A be a subgroup of Aut *G and let H be an A-invariant subgroup of G. Then we have*

(i) $N_G(H)$ and $C_G(H)$ are A-invariant.

(ii) For each ϕ in A, the restriction $\phi|_H$ of ϕ to H is an automorphism of H and the mapping ϕ to $\phi|_H$ is a homomorphism of A into Aut H.

(iii) If $H \lhd G$, the mapping ϕ^* of G/H into G/H defined by $(Hx)\phi^* = H(x\phi)$ for x in G is an automorphism and the mapping ϕ to ϕ^* is a homomorphism of A into Aut (G/H).

We call $\phi|_H$ the *restriction* of ϕ to H and call ϕ^* the automorphism of G/H induced by ϕ. If B is the kernel of the homomorphism of A into Aut H, then A/B is isomorphic to a subgroup of Aut H. For simplicity of exposition we often refer to A as a group of automorphisms of H, even though it is not strictly correct. Likewise, if $H \lhd G$, we speak of A as a group of automorphisms of G/H.

The next result concerning characteristic subgroups follows directly from the definitions and is also left as an exercise.

Theorem 1.2

(i) If H char K and K char G, then H char G.

(ii) If H char K and $K \lhd G$, then $H \lhd G$.

(iii) If $H \lhd G$, then $(H)\phi \lhd G$ for any automorphism ϕ of G.

(iv) If $H \subseteq K$ are subgroups of G such that H char G and K/H char G/H, then K char G.

The next theorem is of a similar nature:

Theorem 1.3

If H is a normal subgroup of G whose order and index are relatively prime, then H char G.

Proof

Let $|H| = m$ and $|G:H| = n$, so that $(m, n) = 1$ and $|G| = mn$. If $\phi \in$ Aut G, then $H' = (H)\phi$ also has order m and HH' is a subgroup of G by Theorem 1.2.6. Setting $d = |H \cap H'|$, we have that $d \,|\, m$, $|HH'| = m^2/d$, and $(m^2/d) \,|\, mn$. Since $(m, n) = 1$, this forces $m = d$ and $H = H'$. Thus H char G, as asserted.

A group with no nontrivial proper characteristic subgroups is called *characteristically simple*. Our next result describes the structure of such groups:

Theorem 1.4

A *characteristically simple group is the direct product of isomorphic simple groups.*

Proof

Let G be characteristically simple and let G_1 be a nontrivial normal subgroup of G of least possible order (possibly $G_1 = G$). Now let H be a subgroup of G of maximal order of the form $H = G_1 \times G_2 \times \cdots \times G_r$, where $G_i \lhd G$ and G_i is isomorphic to G_1, $1 \leqslant i \leqslant r$. Clearly, $H \lhd G$. We shall argue that $H = G$.

If $\phi \in \operatorname{Aut} G$, we have $G_i^\phi \lhd G$ and G_i^ϕ isomorphic to G_i and hence to G_1. Suppose that for some i and some ϕ, we have $G_i^\phi \nsubseteq H$. Then $G_i^\phi \cap H \subset G_i^\phi$, whence $|G_i^\phi \cap H| < |G_1|$. But $G_i^\phi \cap H \lhd G$, whence $G_i^\phi \cap H = 1$ by our minimal choice of G_1. Hence $HG_i^\phi = H \times G_i^\phi$ satisfies the same conditions as H, but has larger order, contrary to the definition of H. It follows that $G_i^\phi \subseteq H$ for all i, $1 \leqslant i \leqslant r$, and all $\phi \in \operatorname{Aut} G$, whence $H^\phi = H$ for all ϕ in $\operatorname{Aut} G$. Thus H char G and, as G is characteristically simple, we conclude that $G = H = G_1 \times G_2 \times \cdots \times G_r$.

But now we see that any normal subgroup of G_1 is, in fact, normal in G, so that G_1 must be simple by our minimal choice of G_1. Thus G is the direct product of isomorphic simple groups, as asserted.

As an immediate corollary, we have

Theorem 1.5

If H is a minimal normal subgroup of G, then either H is an elementary abelian p-group for some prime p or H is the direct product of isomorphic nonabelian simple groups.

Proof

By definition, $H \neq 1$, $H \lhd G$, and no nontrivial proper subgroup of H is normal in G. But then H has no nontrivial proper characteristic subgroups by Theorem 1.1(ii) and so is characteristically simple. Thus $H = H_1 \times H_2 \times \cdots \times H_r$, where the H_i are isomorphic simple groups. If H_1 is abelian, then H_1 has prime order p and H is clearly an elementary abelian p-group. The theorem follows.

Finally we wish to introduce certain important characteristic subgroups of a p-group. If G is a p-group, we shall denote by $\Omega_i(G)$ the subgroup of G generated by its elements of order dividing p^i. In general, $\Omega_i(G)$ may contain elements of order exceeding p^i. However, if G is abelian, the exponent of $\Omega_i(G)$ is at most p^i, as follows immediately from Theorem 1.2.14. In particular, $\Omega_1(G)$ is elementary abelian in this case.

Similarly, we use the symbol $\mho^i(G)$ to denote the subgroup of G generated by the elements x^{p^i} with x in G.

As a direct consequence of the definitions, we have

Theorem 1.6

If G is a p-group, then $\Omega_i(G)$ and $\mho^i(G)$ are characteristic in G for all i.

2. ELEMENTARY PROPERTIES OF COMMUTATORS

The following omnibus result gives a number of basic properties of commutators:

Theorem 2.1

Let x, y, z be elements of G and H, K, L be subgroups of G. Then we have
- (i) $[xy, z] = [x, z]^y [y, z]$.
- (ii) $[x, yz] = [x, z][x, y]^z$.
- (iii) $[H, K]$ *is a normal subgroup of* $\langle H, K \rangle$.
- (iv) $[H, K] = [K, H]$.
- (v) *H normalizes K if and only if* $[H, K] \subseteq K$.
- (vi) $K \lhd G$ *and* G/K *abelian if and only if* $[G, G] \subseteq K$.
- (vii) *If* $K \subseteq H$ *are each normal in G, then* $H/K \subseteq Z(G/K)$ *if and only if* $[H, G] \subseteq K$.
- (viii) *If H, K, L are normal in G, then* $[HK, L] = [H, L][K, L]$.
- (ix) *If* ϕ *is an endomorphism of G, then* $[H, K]^\phi = [H^\phi, K^\phi]$.
  In particular, $[H, K]$ *is normal in G if both H and K are.*

Proof

First, (i) and (ii) follow at once by direct computation using the definitions. To prove (iii), we must show that for each x in $[H, K]$, both x^h and x^k are in $[H, K]$ for each h in H and k in K. Since x is a product of commutators, it will suffice to prove that both $[y, z]^h$ and $[y, z]^k$ are in $[H, K]$ for each y, h in H and z, k in K. But by (i), $[y, z]^h = [yh, z][h, z]^{-1} \in [H, K]$; while by (ii), $[y, z]^k = [y, k]^{-1}[y, zk] \in [H, K]$. Thus (iii) holds.

Now $[h, k] = h^{-1}k^{-1}hk = (k^{-1}h^{-1}kh)^{-1} = [k, h]^{-1}$. Since $[K, H]$ is a subgroup, it follows from this that $[h, k] \in [K, H]$ for all $h \in H$, $k \in K$, whence $[H, K] \subseteq [K, H]$. By symmetry $[K, H] \subseteq [H, K]$ and (iv) holds. Next H normalizes K if and only if $h^{-1}k^{-1}h \in K$ for all h in H, k in K and hence if and only if $h^{-1}k^{-1}hk = [h, k] \in K$ for all h in H, k in K. Since this last equality holds if and only if $[H, K] \subseteq K$, (v) follows.

Since $G/[G, G]$ is abelian, any subgroup K of G containing $[G, G]$ is normal in G and satisfies G/K abelian by the first and second isomorphism theorems. The converse is obvious, so (vi) also holds. As for (vii), $H/K \subseteq Z(G/K)$ if and only if $[Kh, Kx] = K$ for each h in H, x in G, or equivalently if and only if $[h, x] \in K$ for all h in H, x in G, and (vii) follows.

Furthermore, (viii) follows easily from (i), while the first assertion of (ix) is an immediate consequence of the relation $[h, k]^\phi = [h^\phi, k^\phi]$ which holds for all h in H, k in K. Taking for ϕ the inner automorphisms induced by the elements x of G, the second statement of (ix) follows also as a corollary.

The next lemma will be useful for studying p-groups of class 2.

Lemma 2.2

Let $x, y \in G$ and suppose $z = [x, y]$ commutes with both x and y. Then we have
  (i) $[x^i, y^j] = z^{ij}$ for all i, j.
  (ii) $(yx)^i = z^{(1/2)i(i-1)}y^i x^i$ for all i.

Proof

Since $x^{-1}y^{-1}xy = z$, we have $y^{-1}xy = xz$, whence $y^{-1}x^i y = (y^{-1}xy)^i = (xz)^i = x^i z^i$ as x and z commute. Conjugating by y gives $y^{-2}x^i y^2 = y^{-1}x^i z^i y = y^{-1}x^i y z^i = (x^i z^i)z^i = x^i z^{2i}$ as y and z commute. Repeating this argument j times, we conclude that $y^{-j}x^i y^j = x^i z^{ij}$, whence $[x^i, y^j] = z^{ij}$, proving (i).

Clearly (ii) holds for $i = 1$. Assuming the result for $i - 1$, we have $(yx)^i = (yx)^{i-1}(yx) = z^{1/2(i-1)(i-2)}y^{i-1}x^{i-1}yx$. Since $x^{i-1}y = z^{i-1}yx^{i-1}$ by (i), (ii) follows at once.

We now extend the definition of the commutators $[x, y]$ and $[X, Y]$ to arbitrary numbers of elements or subsets of a group G:

If $x_i \in G$, $1 \le i \le n$, $n \ge 2$, we define $[x_1, x_2, \ldots, x_n]$ recursively to be $[[x_1, x_2, \ldots, x_{n-1}], x_n]$. Similarly, if X_i, $1 \le i \le n$, $n \ge 2$, are subsets of G, we define $[X_1, X_2, \ldots, X_n]$ to be $[[X_1, X_2, \ldots, X_{n-1}], X_n]$.

The following result will be important for our later work:

Theorem 2.3 (Three-Subgroup Lemma)

Let x, y, z be elements of G and H, K, L subsets of G. Then we have
  (i) $[x, y^{-1}, z]^y[y, z^{-1}, x]^z[z, x^{-1}, y]^x = 1$.
  (ii) If $[H, K, L] = 1$ and $[K, L, H] = 1$, then also $[L, H, K] = 1$.

Proof

$$[x, y^{-1}z]^y = y^{-1}[x^{-1}yxy^{-1}, z]y = y^{-1}(yx^{-1}y^{-1}x)z^{-1}(x^{-1}yxy^{-1})zy$$

$$= x^{-1}y^{-1}xz^{-1}x^{-1}yxy^{-1}zy.$$

Set $a = xzx^{-1}yx$, $b = yxy^{-1}zy$, and $c = zyz^{-1}xz$, and note that b and c are obtained from a by cyclic permutation of the elements, x, y, z. Furthermore, we see that

$$[x, y^{-1}, z]^y = a^{-1}b.$$

But now it follows by cyclic permutation of x, y, z that also

$$[y, z^{-1}, x]^z = b^{-1}c \qquad \text{and} \qquad [z, x^{-1}, y]^x = c^{-1}a.$$

Since $(a^{-1}b)(b^{-1}c)(c^{-1}a) = 1$, we conclude that (i) holds.

Suppose now that $[H, K, L] = [K, L, H] = 1$. Then for all $x \in H$, $y \in K$, and $z \in L$, we have $[x, y^{-1}, z] = [y, z^{-1}, x] = 1$. Hence, by (i) ,we also have $[z, x^{-1}, y] = 1$. But $[L, H, K]$ is generated by the set of all such commutators $[z, x^{-1}, y]$, whence $[L, H, K] = 1$.

We also have the following useful identities whose proof we leave as an exercise.

Lemma 2.4

  If x, y, z are elements of G, we have
    (i) $[xy, z] = [x, z][x, z, y][y, z]$.
    (ii) $[x, yz] = [x, z][x, y][x, y, z]$.
    (iii) $[x, y]^{-1} = [y, x]$.

We conclude with a more specialized result that we shall need in Chapter 8.

Lemma 2.5

  Let $x, y, z \in G$. Then we have
    (i) *If y commutes with z and if $[x, G]$ is abelian, then $[x, y, z] = [x, z, y]$.*
    (ii) *If $[x, y]$ commutes with both x and y, then*

$$[x, y]^{-1} = [x^{-1}, y] = [x, y^{-1}].$$

Proof

First, $[x, y, z] = [[x, y], z] = [x, y]^{-1}z^{-1}[x, y]z = y^{-1}x^{-1}yxz^{-1}x^{-1}y^{-1}xyz$ $= x^{-1}(xy^{-1}x^{-1}y)(xz^{-1}x^{-1}z)z^{-1}y^{-1}xyz$. Furthermore, $xy^{-1}x^{-1}y = [x^{-1}, y]$ $= [x^m, y]$ for some positive integer m; and we conclude easily by induction on m, using Lemma 2.4(i), that $[x^m, y] \in [x, G]$. Thus $xy^{-1}x^{-1}y$, and likewise $xz^{-1}x^{-1}z$, lies in $[x, G]$. Hence by hypothesis these two elements commute. It follows therefore that

$$[x, y, z] = x^{-1}(xz^{-1}x^{-1}z)(xy^{-1}x^{-1}y)z^{-1}y^{-1}xyz.$$

Since y and z commute by assumption, this reduces to

$$[x, y, z] = z^{-1}x^{-1}zxy^{-1}x^{-1}z^{-1}xzy = [x, z, y],$$

proving (i).

We could derive (ii) from Lemma 2.2 provided we first extend that lemma to negative i and j; but it is as easy to apply Lemma 2.4. Indeed, by

Lemma 2.4(i), we have

$$1 = [xx^{-1}, y] = [x, y][x, y, x^{-1}][x^{-1}, y].$$

But $[x, y, x^{-1}] = [[x, y], x^{-1}]$ and $[x, y]$ commutes with x by hypothesis; whence $[x, y, x^{-1}] = 1$. Hence $1 = [x, y][x^{-1}, y]$ and consequently $[x, y]^{-1} = [x^{-1}, y]$. Similarly, using Lemma 2.4(ii), we obtain $[x, y]^{-1} = [x, y^{-1}]$. Thus (ii) also holds.

3. NILPOTENT GROUPS

Using the higher commutators, we now define a sequence of subgroups of a group G, which we call the *lower central series* of G, by the rules

$$L_1(G) = G \qquad L_2(G) = [G, G] \qquad L_i(G) = [L_{i-1}(G), G] \quad \text{for } i > 2.$$

The following properties are immediate:

Theorem 3.1
(i) $L_i(G)$ char G *for all* i.
(ii) $L_{i+1}(G) \subseteq L_i(G)$ *and* $L_i(G)/L_{i+1}(G)$ *is contained in the center of* $G/L_{i+1}(G)$.

Proof
First, (i) follows by induction on i from Theorem 2.1(ix). This in turn implies that $L_{i+1}(G) \subseteq L_i(G)$. But now (ii) is a consequence of Theorem 2.1(vii).

In view of this result, it is natural to consider a second sequence of characteristic subgroups of G, called the *upper central series* of G, defined by the rules

$Z_0(G) = 1$, $Z_1(G) = Z(G)$, and, for $i > 1$, $Z_i(G)$ is the inverse image in G of $Z(G/Z_{i-1}(G))$.

That each $Z_i(G)$ is characteristic in G follows at once from Theorem 1.1(v) by induction on i.

A group G is called *nilpotent* if $L_m(G) = 1$ for some m. If $n + 1$ is the least value of m satisfying this condition, then n is called the *class* of G. For brevity we write $\text{cl}(G) = n$.

The following theorem expresses a basic relation between the upper and lower central series of a nilpotent group.

Theorem 3.2
G *is nilpotent if and only if* $Z_m(G) = G$ *for some* m. *Moreover, if* G *has class* n, *then* n *is the least integer such that* $Z_n(G) = G$.

Proof

Let G be of class n and set $L_i = L_i(G)$, $Z_i = Z_i(G)$. We first argue that $L_{n+1-r} \subseteq Z_r$ for all r. We have $1 = L_{n+1} = Z_0$. Assume by induction that $L_{n+1-i} \subseteq Z_i$. By Theorem 3.1, $L_{n-i}/L_{n+1-i} \subseteq Z(G/L_{n+1-i})$. But under the present assumptions G/Z_i is a homomorphic image of G/L_{n+1-i}, whence $L_{n-i}Z_i/Z_i \subseteq Z(G/Z_i)$. Hence $L_{n-i}Z_i \subseteq Z_{i+1}$ by definition of Z_{i+1}. Since $Z_i \subseteq Z_{i+1}$, we have $L_{n-i} \subseteq Z_{i+1}$, proving the assertion. In particular, it follows that $G = L_1 \subseteq Z_n$ and consequently $Z_n(G) = G$.

Conversely, suppose $Z_m(G) = G$ for some m. We argue that $L_{r+1} \subseteq Z_{m-r}$. We have $L_1 = G = Z_m$; so assume $L_i \subseteq Z_{m+1-i}$. Since $L_{i+1} = [L_i, G]$, we have $L_{i+1} \subseteq [Z_{m+1-i}, G]$. On the other hand, by Theorem 2.1(vii), $[Z_{m+1-i}, G] \subseteq Z_{m-i}$ as $Z_{m+1-i}/Z_{m-i} \subseteq Z(G/Z_{m-i})$. But then $L_{i+1} \subseteq Z_{m-i}$, proving the assertion. In particular, we have $L_{m+1} \subseteq Z_0 = 1$ and hence $m \geqslant n$. Thus n is the least integer such that $Z_n(G) = G$ and the theorem is proved.

We have the following general results:

Theorem 3.3

(i) *Subgroups and homomorphic images of nilpotent groups are nil-potent.*

(ii) *The direct product of nilpotent groups is nilpotent.*

(iii) *Every p-group is nilpotent.*

Proof

If $H \lhd G$, it follows trivially by induction that $Z_i(G)$ maps into $Z_i(G/H)$, whence $Z_n(G/H) = G/H$ for some n and so G/H is nilpotent. If H is any subgroup of $G, L_i(H) \subseteq L_i(G)$, so $L_{n+1}(H) = 1$ for some n and H is nilpotent. Thus (i) holds. Moreover, (ii) follows at once by induction and the fact that the center of a direct product is the direct product of the centers of the individual factors. Finally, (iii) follows also by induction together with the fact that the center of every p-group is nontrivial.

The following properties of nilpotent groups are basic:

Theorem 3.4

If G is nilpotent and $H \subset G$, then $N_G(H) \supset H$.

Proof

Let i be the largest integer such that $Z_i = Z_i(G) \subseteq H$. Then $Z_i \subset G$ and, as G is nilpotent, we have $Z_i \subset Z_{i+1}$. But $[Z_{i+1}, G] \subseteq Z_i$ by Theorem 2.1(vii), which implies that $[Z_{i+1}, H] \subseteq H$. Theorem 2.1(v) now yields $Z_{i+1} \subseteq N_G(H)$. However, $Z_{i+1} \nsubseteq H$ by our maximal choice of i and we conclude that $N_G(H) \supset H$.

Theorem 3.5

A group G is nilpotent if and only if it is the direct product of its Sylow subgroups.

Proof

If G is the direct product of its Sylow subgroups, then G is nilpotent by parts (ii) and (iii) of Theorem 3.3. Conversely if G is nilpotent, we argue that its Sylow subgroups are normal in G. Indeed, if P is an S_p-subgroup of G and $H = N_G(P) \subset G$, then $N = N_G(H) \supset H$ by the preceding theorem. But P is an S_p-subgroup of H and $H \triangleleft N$, so that $N = HN_N(P) = HH = H$ by Theorem 1.3.7, a contradiction. This proves the assertion. But now G is the direct product of its Sylow subgroups by Theorem 1.3.6.

4. SOLVABLE GROUPS

The class of solvable groups which includes that of nilpotent group will be of central importance throughout the entire book.

A group is said to be *solvable* if its composition factors are all of prime order.

We have

Theorem 4.1

(i) *Subgroups and homomorphic images of solvable groups are solvable.*
(ii) *If $H \triangleleft G$ and both H and G/H are solvable, then G is solvable.*
(iii) *Direct products of solvable groups are solvable.*
(iv) *Nilpotent groups are solvable.*
(v) *A minimal normal subgroup of a solvable group is an elementary abelian p-group for some prime p.*
(vi) *If G is solvable, then $[G, G] \subset G$.*

Proof

Let G be solvable and let H be a nontrivial proper normal subgroup of G. Then by the Schreier refinement theorem the normal series $G \supset H \supset 1$ can be refined to a composition series G_i, $1 \leqslant i \leqslant n$, with say $G_r = H$. But then G_i/H, $1 \leqslant i \leqslant r$, is a composition series of G/H. Since $(G_{i-1}/H)/(G_i/H)$ is isomorphic to G_{i-1}/G_i, the solvability of G implies at once the solvability of G/H. Likewise the G_i, $r \leqslant i \leqslant n$, form a composition series of H, so also H is solvable. Conversely, if H is a solvable normal subgroup of the group G such that G/H is solvable, and if G_i, $1 \leqslant i \leqslant n$, is a composition series of G which includes H, then G_{i-1}/G_i is either isomorphic to a composition factor of H or of G/H and so has prime order. Thus G is solvable.

If G is the direct product of the solvable groups G_i, $1 \leqslant i \leqslant m$, then $G_1 \lhd G$ and G/G_1 is isomorphic to $G' = G_2 \times G_3 \times \cdots \times G_m$. By induction on m, G' is solvable and so G is solvable by the preceding paragraph.

Assume next that G is nilpotent. Now $Z_1 = Z_1(G)$ is abelian and it is immediate from the decomposition theorems for abelian groups that every abelian group is solvable. Hence Z_1 is solvable. Since G/Z_1 is nilpotent and has lower order than G, it is solvable by induction and it follows that G is solvable.

Now the direct product of isomorphic nonabelian simple groups clearly has composition factors that are not of prime order and so is nonsolvable. Hence by Theorem 1.5 a minimal normal subgroup of a solvable group is an elementary abelian p-group for some prime p.

If G is solvable, the second term G_2 of a composition series G_i, $1 \leqslant i \leqslant n$, of G is normal in G and G_1/G_2 is of prime order, whence abelian. But then $[G, G] \subseteq G_2 \subset G_1 = G$.

Thus to complete the proof, it remains only to show that any subgroup K of a solvable group G is solvable. Let H be a minimal normal subgroup of G. Then $H \cap K$ is abelian and so is solvable. Furthermore, $KH/H = K/H \cap K$ is solvable by induction on $|G|$. But then K is solvable by the first paragraph of the proof.

We can obtain a slight extension of (v) above. To do so requires the following definition: A normal series G_i, $1 \leqslant i \leqslant n$, of a group G is called a *chief* series provided each G_i is a proper subgroup of G_{i-1} chosen maximal subject to being normal in G. The factor groups G_{i-1}/G_i are called the *chief factors* of the series.

Theorem 4.2

In a solvable group the factors of every chief series are elementary abelian of prime power order.

Proof

Let G be solvable and let G_i, $1 \leqslant i \leqslant n$, be a chief series of G. Then G_{n-1} is a nontrivial normal subgroup of G and contains no nontrivial proper subgroup that is normal in G. Hence G_{n-1} is a minimal normal subgroup of G and so by Theorem 4.1(v) the factor $G_{n-1} = G_{n-1}/G_n$ has the required form. Since the groups G_i/G_{n-1} form a chief series for G/G_{n-1}, which is also solvable, the theorem follows at once by induction.

We want to give one other characterization of a solvable group in terms of the *derived* series of a group G, which is defined recursively by the rule

$$D_0(G) = G \quad D_1(G) = [G, G] \quad D_i(G) = [D_{i-1}(G), D_{i-1}(G)] \quad \text{for } i > 1.$$

It is immediate that each $D_i(G)$ char G, that $D_i(G) \subseteq D_{i-1}(G)$, and that $D_i(G)/D_{i-1}(G)$ is abelian.

Theorem 4.3

G is solvable if and only if $D_n(G) = 1$ for some n.

Proof

Set $D_i = D_i(G)$. If G is solvable, then so is each D_i by Theorem 4.1(i). But then $D_{i+1} \subset D_i$ by Theorem 4.1(vi). Hence $D_n = 1$ for some n. Conversely, if $D_n = 1$ for some n with $D_{n-1} \neq 1$, we have D_{n-1} abelian and so D_{n-1} is solvable. But it is immediate that D_i/D_{n-1} is the derived series of G/D_{n-1}. Hence G/D_{n-1} is solvable by induction on the length of the derived series and so G is solvable by Theorem 4.1(ii).

If G is solvable, the least integer n such that $D_n(G) = 1$ is called the *derived length* of G.

5. SEMIDIRECT AND CENTRAL PRODUCTS

If $H \lhd G$ and if ϕ_x denotes conjugation of H by the element x of G, we know that the mapping $x\psi = \phi_x$ is a homomorphism of G into Aut H whose kernel is $C_G(H)$. Conversely, if K is a group and ψ is a homomorphism of K into Aut H, there exists a fairly natural way of constructing a group G of the form $G = H^*K^*$ with H^* isomorphic to H, $H^* \lhd G$, and G/H^* isomorphic to both K^* and K such that the automorphism $k\psi$ of H corresponds on H^* to the automorphism induced by conjugation by the corresponding element of K^*.

Indeed, we define G to be the set of ordered pairs (k, h), $h \in H$ and $k \in K$. On G, we introduce the operation

$$(k_1, h_1)(k_2, h_2) = (k_1 k_2, h_1^{k_2\psi} h_2) \qquad \text{for } k_i \in K, h_i \in H, 1 \leqslant i \leqslant 2.$$

One verifies that for k_i in K and h_i in H, $1 \leqslant i \leqslant 3$,

$$(k_1, h_1)((k_2, h_2)(k_3, h_3)) = (k_1 k_2 k_3, h_1^{(k_2 k_3)\psi}(h_2^{k_3\psi})h_3)$$

and

$$((k_1, h_1)(k_2, h_2))(k_3, h_3) = (k_1 k_2 k_3, (h_1^{k_2\psi} h_2)^{k_3\psi} h_3).$$

Since $k_3\psi$ is a homomorphism of H and ψ is a homomorphism of K into

Aut H, we have

$$(h_1^{k_2\psi}h_2)^{k_3\psi} = h_1^{k_2\psi k_3\psi}h_2^{k_3\psi} = h_1^{(k_2 k_3)\psi}h_2^{k_3\psi},$$

which proves that the associative law holds in G. Clearly $(1,1) = (1_K, 1_H)$ is the identity of G and one verifies directly that $(k^{-1}, (h^{-1})^{k^{-1}\psi})$ is a left and right inverse of (k, h). Thus G is a group under the given operation.

If we set $H^* = \{(1, h) \mid h \in H\}$ and $K^* = \{(k, 1) \mid k \in K\}$ it is immediate that H^* and K^* are subgroups of G isomorphic to H and K, respectively, that $G = H^*K^*$ and that $H^* \cap K^* = (1, 1)$, so that also G/H^* is isomorphic to both K^* and K. Furthermore, we compute that

$$(5.1) \qquad (k^{-1}, 1)(1, h)(k, 1) = (1, h^{k\psi}) \in H^*$$

for all k in K, h in H. Thus H^* is normalized by K^* as well as H^* and so is normal in G.

Finally, (5.1) shows that the element $(1, h)$ of H^* is transformed into $(1, h^{k\psi})$ by conjugation by the element $(1, k)$ of K^*. Thus G has all the required properties.

It is natural to identify H and K with their images H^*, K^* in G. When this is done we obtain the following conclusions:

Theorem 5.1

Let H, K be groups and let ψ be a homomorphism of K into Aut H. *Then there exists a group G of the form $G = HK$ with $H \lhd G$ and $H \cap K = 1$ such that for h in H, k in K, we have $k^{-1}hk = h^{k\psi}$.*

The group G of Theorem 5.1 is called the *semidirect* product of H by K (with respect to ψ). It is also known as the *split extension* of H by K. In the special case that $K = $ Aut H and ψ is the identity, G is called the *holomorph* of H.

The notion of semidirect product is a generalization of that of direct product. In fact, as a corollary of the preceding analysis we have

Corollary 5.2

The semidirect product G of H by K with respect to ψ is isomorphic to the direct product of H and K if and only if ψ maps K onto the identity subgroup of Aut H.

Proof

$G = H \times K$ if and only if $K \lhd G$, which will hold if and only if $h^{-1}k^{-1}hk = h^{-1}h^k = h^{-1}h^{k\psi}$ lies in K as well as H for all h in H, k in K. Since $H \cap K = 1$, this is equivalent to $h^{k\psi} = h$ for all h in H, k in K, thus proving the corollary.

This construction can frequently be used to prove the existence of groups of a particular form. For example, let H be cyclic of order n and $K = \langle k \rangle$ be cyclic order m and suppose r is an integer such that $r^m \equiv 1 \pmod{n}$. Then it is trivial to verify that the mappings $h^{k^i \psi} = h^{r^i}$ for h in H, $1 \le i \le m$, are automorphisms of H and that ψ is a homomorphism from K to Aut H. Hence the semidirect product G of H by K (with respect to ψ) exists and if h now denotes a generator of H, G is given by the defining relations:

(5.2) $h^n = 1$ $k^m = 1$ $k^{-1}hk = h^r$ with $r^m \equiv 1 \pmod{n}$.

Here every element of G is uniquely represented in the form $h^i k^j$, $0 \le i \le n - 1$, $0 \le j \le m - 1$, and the multiplication table of G is completely specified by (5.2).

In this case G contains a cyclic normal subgroup H such that the factor group G/H is also cyclic. Such a group is said to be *metacyclic*. A case of particular importance is that of a *dihedral* group, corresponding to the case $|K| = m = 2$ and $r = -1$.

Consider once again the situation of a normal subgroup H of a group G. Then there may or may not exist a *complement* for H in G—that is, a subgroup K such that $G = HK$ and $H \cap K = 1$. When such a complement K exists, G will be isomorphic to a semidirect product of H by K (for the appropriate ψ). In the contrary case, G will not be a semidirect product. Thus our construction corresponds only to a particular case of the general situation.

More generally we say that K is a *partial* complement of H in G provided $G = HK$ and K is a *proper* subgroup of G. The subgroup $M = H \cap K$ is normal in K, but is not necessarily the identity.

If ϕ_k denotes conjugation of H by k in K, once again we have that $k\psi = \phi_k$ is a homomorphism of K into Aut H. Furthermore, if we consider M as a subgroup of H and $M\theta$ as a subgroup of K, where θ is the identity automorphism of M, then it is obvious that the following two relations hold for all h, k, m in H, K, M, respectively:

(5.3) $h^{(m\theta)\psi} = h^m$

(5.4) $(m^{k\psi})\theta = (m\theta)^k$.

Conversely, let H, K, M be groups with $M \subseteq H$ and suppose that there exist mappings ψ and θ with ψ a homomorphism of K into Aut H and θ an isomorphism of M into K which satisfy (5.3) and (5.4). We shall construct a group $\bar{G}$ of the form $\bar{G} = \bar{H}\bar{K}$ with $\bar{H} \triangleleft \bar{G}$, $\bar{H} \cap \bar{K} = \bar{M} \triangleleft \bar{K}$ and H, K, M

isomorphic to $\bar{H}, \bar{K}, \bar{M}$, respectively, such that the action of $\bar{K}$ on $\bar{H}$ corresponds to the action of $K\psi$ on H.

To do this, we first consider the semidirect product $G = HK$ with respect to ψ, so that in G we have $h^{k\psi} = h^k$, h in H, k in K. Set $D = \{(m\theta)m^{-1} \mid m \in M\}$. We argue that $D \lhd G$. Indeed, if $m_1, m_2 \in M$, then $(m_1^{-1})^{m_2\theta} = (m_1^{-1})^{m_2}$ by (5.3), whence

$$((m_1\theta)m_1^{-1})((m_2\theta)m_2^{-1}) = (m_1\theta)(m_2\theta)(m_1^{-1})^{m_2\theta}m_2^{-1} = (m_1m_2)\theta(m_1m_2)^{-1}.$$

Thus D is a group. Furthermore, if $h \in M$ and $m \in M$, we have, using (5.3), that

$$h^{-1}((m\theta)m^{-1})h = (m\theta)(h^{-1})^{m\theta}m^{-1}h = (m\theta)(h^{-1})^m m^{-1}h = (m\theta)m^{-1}.$$

Hence H centralizes D. Finally, let $k \in K$ and $m \in M$. Then, using (5.4), we have $k^{-1}((m\theta)m^{-1})k = (m\theta)^k(m^{-1})^k = (m^k)\theta(m^k)^{-1} \in D$. Hence D is invariant under K as well as H and so D is normal in G.

Observe next that as $H \cap K = 1$ and $M \subseteq H$, $(m\theta)m^{-1} \in H$ only if $m\theta = 1$. Since θ is an isomorphism, $m = 1$ and so $H \cap D = 1$. Similarly, $(m\theta)m^{-1} \in K$ implies $m = 1$ and so also $K \cap D = 1$. Hence if we set $\bar{G} = G/D$ and let $\bar{H}, \bar{K}, \bar{M}$ be the respective images of K, K, M in $\bar{G}$, it follows that $\bar{H}$ is isomorphic to H and $\bar{K}$ to K. Moreover, $\bar{G} = \bar{H}\bar{K}$ with $\bar{M} \lhd \bar{K}$ and $\bar{H} \lhd \bar{G}$. By definition of D, m, and $m\theta$ lie in the same coset of D for each m in M and consequently $\bar{M} \subseteq \bar{H} \cap \bar{K}$. On the other hand, $|D| = |M|$, whence $|G/D| = |H||K|/|M| = |\bar{H}||\bar{K}|/|\bar{M}|$, forcing $|\bar{M}| = |\bar{H} \cap \bar{K}|$. Thus $\bar{M} = \bar{H} \cap \bar{K}$. Finally, if $\bar{x}$ denotes the image in $\bar{G}$ of the element x of G, we have

$$\bar{h}^{\bar{k}} = (\overline{h^k}) = (\overline{h^{k\psi}})$$

for all h in H, k in K. Thus $\bar{G}$ exists with the required properties.

As usual, we identify H, K, M with their isomorphic images in $\bar{G}$ and drop the superscript on $\bar{G}$. Thus $G = HK$, $H \lhd G$, $M = H \cap K$, and for h in H, k in K, we have $k^{-1}hk = h^{k\psi}$. We call G the *partial* semidirect product of H by K with respect to $\{M, \theta, \psi\}$.

As an illustration, let $H = \langle h \rangle$ be cyclic of order 2^a, $a \geq 2$, set $m = h^{2^{a-1}}$, and $M = \langle m \rangle$, so that $|M| = 2$. Let $K = \langle k \rangle$ be cyclic of order 4 and let θ be the isomorphism of M into K determined by setting $m\theta = k^2$. Also let $k\psi$ be the automorphism of H which inverts all its elements. Then ψ determines a homomorphism of K into Aut H and one verifies directly that (5.3) and (5.4) are satisfied. Thus the partial semidirect product G exists and is given by the defining relations:

$$G = \langle h, k \mid h^{2^{a-1}} = k^2 = m, m^2 = 1, k^{-1}hk = h^{-1} \rangle.$$

A group G given by such defining relations is called a *generalized quaternion* group. In the special case $a = 2$ ($|G| = 8$), it is called a *quaternion* group.

We remark that a generalized quaternion group of order 2^{a+1} and a dihedral group of the same order are never isomorphic, as the first possesses a unique element of order 2 (namely, m), while the second always possesses more than one such element.

There is a particular case of a partial semidirect product which is of special interest. This is the case in which $M \subseteq Z(H)$, $M\theta \subseteq Z(K)$, and ψ maps K onto the identity element of Aut H. Under these conditions, (5.3) and (5.4) are always satisfied, so the partial semidirect product of H by K with respect to $\{M, \theta, \psi\}$ always exists. Hence we have the following result:

Theorem 5.3

Let H, K, M be groups with $M \subseteq Z(H)$ and suppose there is an isomorphism θ of M into $Z(K)$. Then if we identify M with its image $M\theta$, there exists a group G of the form $G = HK$ with $M = H \cap K \subseteq Z(G)$ such that H centralizes K.

Any group G satisfying the conditions of the theorem is said to be the *central* product of H and K (with respect to M). If $M = 1$, the central product reduces, of course, to a direct product.

6. AUTOMORPHISMS AS LINEAR TRANSFORMATIONS

Let H be a subgroup of G and set $N = N_G(H)$ and $C = C_G(H)$. For each x in N, the mapping $(h)\phi_x = x^{-1}hx$, $h \in H$, is an automorphism of H, the automorphism of H induced by conjugation by x. Furthermore, it is immediate that $\phi_x \phi_y = \phi_{xy}$ for x, y in N. Hence the mapping α of N into Aut H given by $(x)\alpha = \phi_x$ is a homomorphism. Now x is in the kernel of α if and only if $(h)\phi_x = h$ for all h in H; hence, if and only if $x \in C$. We see then that N/C is isomorphic in a natural way to a subgroup of Aut H.

Of particular importance in what is to follow is the special case that H is an elementary abelian p-group for some prime p. In this case H can be regarded as a vector space over the field Z_p with p elements by Theorem

1.3.2. When this is done, the elements of Aut H act on H as linear transformations. Indeed, we have

Theorem 6.1

If the elementary abelian p-group H is regarded as a vector space over Z_p, then Aut H is isomorphic to the group of nonsingular linear transformations of H.

Proof

The elements of Aut H, by definition, preserve the additive structure of H. That they also preserve scalar multiplication follows from the multiplicative relation $(x^a)\phi = (x\phi)^a$, which holds for any ϕ in Aut H and any integer a and which in additive notation becomes $(ax)\phi = a(x\phi)$. Thus Aut H is isomorphic to a group of nonsingular linear transformations of H. Since any nonsingular linear transformation on H is certainly an automorphism of the additive group of H, the theorem follows.

The preceding argument applies as well to endomorphisms as to automorphisms of H, so that when H is regarded as a vector space over Z_p, any ring of endomorphisms of H becomes a ring of linear transformations.

Theorem 6.1 allows us to rephrase many group-theoretic problems as questions about linear transformations. We shall illustrate this idea in a moment by deriving a result about p-groups as a consequence of a property of p-groups of linear transformations. But first we introduce some convenient general notation.

If G is a group of linear transformations of a vector space V, we set $C_V(G) = \{v \in V \mid vx = v \text{ for all } x \text{ in } G\}$. We speak of $C_V(G)$ as the *centralizer* of G on V. Clearly, $C_V(G)$ is a subspace of V. Similarly, if G is any group and H, K are subgroups of G, we write $C_H(K) = \{h \in H \mid h^k = h\}$ for all k in K and speak of the centralizer of K in H. Clearly $C_H(K)$ is a subgroup.

In the particular case that H is an elementary abelian p-group and $K \subseteq N_G(H)$, we know that $\bar{K} = K/C$ is isomorphic to a group of linear transformations of H, regarded as a vector space over Z_p, where $C = C_K(H)$. Thus, on the one hand, we can speak of the centralizer of the group K on H; and, on the other hand, of the centralizer of the group of linear transformations $\bar{K}$ on H. Moreover, it follows directly from the definitions that

$$C_H(K) = C_H(\bar{K}).$$

This notational device will be extremely useful in passing between the group-theoretic and linear transformation points of view.

Our result on p-groups of linear transformations requires the following simple lemma:

Lemma 6.2

If G is a group of linear transformations acting on a vector space V over a field F and H is a normal subgroup of G, then $C_V(H)$ is G-invariant.

Proof

Set $W = C_V(H)$ and let $w \in W$, $h \in H$, and $x \in G$. As $H \lhd G$, we have $h^{x^{-1}} \in H$ and so $(w)h^{x^{-1}} = w$. Thus $(w)xhx^{-1} = w$ and consequently h fixes $(w)x$ for all h in H. Hence $(w)x \in W$ and the lemma follows.

Lemma 6.3

Let G be a p-group of linear transformations acting on a vector space V over a field F of characteristic p. Then some nonzero vector of V is fixed by every element of G.

Proof

We proceed by induction on $|G|$. Let M be a maximal subgroup of G. Then we have $M \lhd G$ and $|G : M| = p$. Setting $W = C_V(M)$, it follows by induction that $W \neq 0$. Furthermore, W is G-invariant by the preceding lemma.

Choosing y in $G - M$, we have $y^p \in M$ and so the order of y on W is 1 or p. Hence the minimal polynomial of y on W divides X^{p-1}. But $X^p - 1 = (X - 1)^p$ as F is of characteristic p and so 1 is the unique characteristic root of y on W. Hence there exists a nonzero vector w_1 in W which is fixed by y. Since w_1 is fixed by $\langle M, y \rangle = G$, the lemma is proved.

On the basis of this result, we now prove

Theorem 6.4

If K is a nontrivial normal subgroup of the p-group G, then $K \cap Z(G) \neq 1$.

Proof

Since $Z(K) \neq 1$, so also $H = \Omega_1(Z(K)) \neq 1$. Now H char $Z(K)$ char $K \lhd P$ and so $H \lhd G$. Furthermore, H is elementary abelian. But by definition $H \cap Z(G) = C_H(G)$ and consequently $H \cap Z(G) = C_H(\bar{G})$, where $\bar{G} = G/C$ and $C = C_G(H)$. Since $\bar{G}$ is a p-group of linear transformations of H regarded as a vector space over Z_p, $C_H(\bar{G})$ is nontrivial by the preceding lemma. Thus $1 \neq H \cap Z(G) \subseteq K \cap Z(G)$, as asserted.

Since every nilpotent group is the direct product of its Sylow subgroups, we obtain at once as a corollary:

Corollary 6.5

If K is a nontrivial normal subgroup of a nilpotent group G, then $K \cap Z(G) \neq 1$.

Once again let H be an elementary abelian p-subgroup of G and let K be a subgroup of $N_G(H)$. For x in K, consider the mapping ψ_x of H into H defined by $(h)\psi_x = [h, x] = h^{-1}h^x$ for all h in H. Since H is abelian, it is immediate that $(hh')\psi_x = (h)\psi_x(h')\psi_x$, h, h' in H. Thus ψ_x is an endomorphism of H and so is a linear transformation of H regarded as a vector space over Z_p. In fact, we see that $\psi_x = \phi_x - 1$, where ϕ_x denotes the linear transformation induced by conjugation of H by the element x and 1 denotes the identity transformation of H.

Inductively it follows that the mappings $(h)\psi_x^{(n)} = [\underbrace{h, x, x, \ldots, x}_{n}]$, h in H,

are endomorphisms of H and, as a linear transformation of H,

$$\psi_x^{(n)} = (\phi_x - 1)^n.$$

This dual interpretation of the higher commutators is especially important when the element x is a p-element, for then $|\phi_x| = p^m$ as a linear transformation and so ϕ_x satisfies the polynomial $X^{p^m} - 1 = (X - 1)^{p^m}$. Hence the minimal polynomial of ϕ_x on H is $(X - 1)^r$ for some r. Clearly r is the least integer such that $(h)(\phi_x - 1)^r = 0$ for all h in H; equivalently it is the least integer such that $[\underbrace{h, x, x, \ldots, x}_{r}] = 1$ for all h in H. We have thus proved:

Theorem 6.6

Let H be an elementary abelian p-subgroup of G and let x be a p-element of $N_G(H)$. If ϕ_x denotes the linear transformation of H regarded as vector space over Z_p, then the minimal polynomial of ϕ_x is $(X - 1)^r$ for some r and r is the least integer such that

$$[\underbrace{h, x, x, \ldots, x}_{r}] = 1 \qquad \text{for all } h \text{ in } H.$$

We have seen above that it is useful to have an enlarged concept of centralizer. The same will be true for the concept of commutator which we shall now extend to $[h, \phi]$, where h is an element of the group H and ϕ is an automorphism of H. Indeed, let H be a group and A a subgroup of Aut H. Then we can form the semidirect product $G = HA$ of H by A and with appropriate identifications the image h^ϕ of h under ϕ is represented in G by the element $\phi^{-1}h\phi$, $h \in H$, $\phi \in A$. Hence in G the commutator $[h, \phi]$

is the same element of H as $h^{-1}h^\phi$. Thus it is natural to define $h^{-1}h^\phi$ directly to be the commutator of h and ϕ (without passing to the semidirect product G) and to denote it by $[h, \phi]$. Similarly, we write $[H, A]$ for the subgroup of H generated by all $h^{-1}h^\phi$ with h in H, ϕ in A. This is the same subgroup of H designated by this symbol in $G = HA$. Since $[H, A] \lhd \langle H, A \rangle = G$ by Theorem 2.1(iii), we see that $[H, A]$ is a normal subgroup of H invariant under the group of automorphisms A. Thus A can be considered as a group of automorphisms of $[H, A]$ and so the subgroup $[[H, A], A]$ of $[H, A]$ is defined. As usual, we write this group as $[H, A, A]$ and introduce corresponding notation for higher commutators.

We also use the notation $C_H(A)$ for the subgroup of H left elementwise fixed by the elements of A. Clearly $C_H(A)$ is A-invariant. Furthermore, this use of the centralizer notation is consistent with that introduced before.

7. TRANSITIVE AND DOUBLY TRANSITIVE PERMUTATION GROUPS

A permutation group G acting on a set S is said to be *transitive* on S provided for s, s' in S, there exists an x in G such that $(s)x = s'$ and is said to be *doubly transitive* on S provided for each set of pairs $\{s_1, s_2\}$ and $\{s_1', s_2'\}$ with $s_i, s_i' \in S$, $1 \leqslant i \leqslant 2$, and $s_1 \neq s_2$, $s_1' \neq s_2'$, there exists an element x in G such that $(s_i)x = s_i'$, $1 \leqslant i \leqslant 2$. Triple and, more generally, m-fold transitivity is defined similarly. The integer $|S|$ is called the *degree* of G.

In any permutation group G acting on a set S, the subset G leaving any subset T of S invariant (either as a set or elementwise) is clearly a subgroup of G.

Let H be a subgroup of G and let Hx_i, $x_i \in G$, $1 \leqslant i \leqslant n$, be a complete set of cosets of H in G. Denote the set of these cosets by S. Then for x in G, the mapping π_x defined by

$$(Hx_i)\pi_x = H(x_i x), 1 \leqslant i \leqslant n,$$

is a permutation of S since $H(x_i x) \in S$ and $H(x_i x) \neq H(x_j x)$ if $i \neq j$. Furthermore, it is immediate that $\pi_x \pi_y = \pi_{xy}$ for x, y in G. Hence the mapping π_H of x to π_x is a homomorphism of G into the symmetric group S_n on the set S. The kernel K of π_H is the set of x in G fixing each Hx_i. Equivalently $x \in K$ if and only if $x \in x_i^{-1}Hx_i$ for all i, $1 \leqslant i \leqslant n$. Thus

$$K = \bigcap_{i=1}^{n} H^{x_i}.$$

We have that G/K, the image of π_H, is isomorphic to a group of permutations of S. Moreover, G/K acts transitively on S, for if Hx_i, Hx_j are two elements of S and we set $x = x_i^{-1}x_j$, then π_x transforms Hx_i into Hx_j. If we assume, as we may, that $x_1 = 1$, we verify directly that $(H)\pi_H$ is the subgroup fixing the letter Hx_1 and more generally that $(H^{x_i})\pi_H$ is the subgroup fixing the letter Hx_i of S.

We call π_H the *transitive permutation representation* of G on the right cosets of H. Clearly π_H is determined entirely by H and is independent of the choice of the coset representatives x_i of H in G.

More generally, any homomorphism π of G into the symmetric group on a set S is called a *permutation representation* of G on S. The integer $|S|$ is called the degree of π. We say π is (doubly) transitive if $G\pi$ acts (doubly) transitively on S. If θ is a one-to-one mapping of S onto a set S', then obviously the composition $\pi' = \theta^{-1}\pi\theta$ gives a representation of G on S'. Clearly the action of $G\pi'$ on S' is determined from that of $G\pi$ on S (together with θ) and vice versa. Under these circumstances we shall say that π and π' are *equivalent* or *isomorphic* permutation representation of G.

One has the following basic result:

Theorem 7.1

Every transitive permutation representation of G is equivalent to one on the right cosets of a subgroup of G.

Proof

Let π be a transitive permutation representation of G on S, where we identify S with $\{1, 2, \ldots, n\}$. As above, we denote the image of x by π_x. Let H be the subgroup of G fixing the letter 1. We shall argue that π and π_H are equivalent.

Since π is transitive, there exist elements x_i in G such that $(1)\pi_{x_i} = i$, $1 \leqslant i \leqslant n$. Then as π is a homomorphism, $(1)\pi_{hx_i} = i$ for every h in H. Conversely if $(1)\pi_x = i$, then $(1)\pi_{xx_i^{-1}} = 1$ and so $x \in Hx_i$. Thus Hx_i is the complete set of elements transforming 1 into i. In particular, $Hx_i \neq Hx_j$ if $i \neq j$. Moreover, since an element of G transforms 1 into i for some i, every element of G lies in Hx_i for some i, $1 \leqslant i \leqslant n$. Thus the set $S' = \{Hx_i \mid 1 \leqslant i \leqslant n\}$ is a complete set of coset representatives of H in G.

Now set $(i)\theta = Hx_i$, $1 \leqslant i \leqslant n$, and $\pi' = \theta^{-1}\pi\theta$. Then π' is a permutation representation of G on S' which is equivalent to π. Furthermore, let $x \in G$ and $i \in S$, and suppose $H(x_i x) = Hx_j$, in which case $(1)\pi_{x_i x} = j$ and consequently $(i)\pi_x = j$. Applying θ, we obtain $(Hx_i)\pi'_x = Hx_j = H(x_i x)$. Thus $\pi' = \pi_H$ and the theorem is proved.

The case $H = 1$ is of particular importance. Certainly the kernel of π_H is 1 in this case and so $\rho = \pi_H$ is an isomorphism of G into the symmetric group of degree $|G|$, which is precisely the contents of Cayley's theorem (1.2.16). We refer to this representation ρ as the (right) *regular* representation of G.

The following property of the regular representation follows at once from its definition:

Theorem 7.2

In the regular representation of G only the identity element fixes more than one letter.

A transitive permutation group G is said to be *primitive* if the corresponding subgroup H of G is a maximal subgroup.

Our next result gives simple, but important, criteria for a transitive permutation group to be doubly transitive.

Theorem 7.3

Let G be a transitive permutation group acting on a set S and let H be the subgroup of G fixing a letter. Then we have

  (i) *G is doubly transitive if and only if H acts transitively on the remaining letters.*

  (ii) *G is doubly transitive if and only if*

$$G = HTH,$$

  where T is a subgroup of G of order 2 not contained in H.

  (iii) *If G is doubly transitive and $|G : H| = n$, then*

$$|G| = d(n - 1)n,$$

  where d is the order of the subgroup fixing two letters. Furthermore, H is a maximal subgroup of G and G is a primitive group.

Proof

Let $S = \{1, 2, \ldots, n\}$ and assume H fixes 1. Suppose H acts transitively on $\{2, \ldots, n\}$. Let $\{i, j\}$, $\{i', j'\}$ be two pairs from S with $i \neq j$, $i' \neq j'$. Then $(i)x = i'$ for some x in G. Set $k = (j)x$. Then $k \neq i'$ as $i \neq j$. Now the subgroup fixing i' is conjugate to H and hence by our assumptions there exists an element y of G fixing i' and transforming k into j' (as k and j are distinct from i'). The element $z = xy$ then transforms i into i' and j into j'. So G is doubly transitive. Moreover, if M denotes the subgroup of H fixing 2, it follows from Theorem 7.1 that $|H : M| = n - 1$ and for the same reason that $|G : H| = n$. Hence $|G| = d(n - 1)n$, where $d = |M|$. On the

other hand, the converse of (i) is clear. Hence (i) and the first assertion of
(iii) hold.

To prove (ii), choose x_i in G such that $(1)x_i = i$, $1 \leqslant i \leqslant n$, so that the
Hx_i are a complete set of cosets of H in G and our permutation representation of G is equivalent to that of G on the cosets of H. Then by (i), G
is doubly transitive if and only if there exist elements h_i in H, $2 \leqslant i \leqslant n$,
with $h_2 = 1$ such that $Hx_2 h_i = Hx_i$. But the cosets Hx_i, $2 \leqslant i \leqslant n$, contain
every element of G not in H. Thus G is doubly transitive if and only
if $G - H = \bigcup_{i=2}^{n} Hx_2 h_i$ for suitable h_i in H or equivalently if and only if
$G - H = Hx_2 H$; that is, $G = H \cup Hx_2 H$. Clearly this argument applies
equally well for any x_j, $2 \leqslant j \leqslant n$. Thus G is doubly transitive if and only if
$G = H \cup HxH$ for any element x of $G - H$. In particular, if this holds, any
subgroup of G containing H properly necessarily contains x and so is G.
Thus H is a maximal subgroup of G, whence G is a primitive group and
the final assertion of (iii) is also proved.

Moreover, if $G = HTH$ with $T = \langle t \rangle$ of order 2, and $t \notin H$, then certainly
$G = H \cup HtH$, so G is doubly transitive by the preceding arguments.
Conversely if G is doubly transitive, it has even order by (iii) and so
contains an element u of order 2. Since u does not fix all the letters, some
conjugate t of u does not fix 1 and so $t \notin H$. Hence $G = H \cup HtH$. Setting
$T = \langle t \rangle$, we conclude that $G = HTH$, proving (ii).

The following general property of transitive and doubly transitive groups
is useful as well as interesting.

Theorem 7.4

*Let G be a transitive permutation group acting on a set S and let $\alpha(x)$ denote
the number of letters of S fixed by the element x of G. Then we have*

(i) $\sum_{x \in G} \alpha(x) = |G|$.

(ii) G *is doubly transitive if and only if*

$$\sum_{x \in G} \alpha(x)^2 = 2|G|.$$

Proof

Let $S = \{1, 2, \ldots, n\}$ and denote by $\beta(i)$ the number of elements of G
fixing i, $1 \leqslant i \leqslant n$. Clearly we have

(7.1) $$\sum_{x \in G} \alpha(x) = \sum_{i=1}^{n} \beta(i).$$

But $\beta(i)$ is simply the order of the subgroup H_i fixing i. As G is transitive, we have $|H_i| = |H_1|$ for all i and $|G| = n|H_1|$. Thus $\sum\limits_{i=1}^{n} \beta(i) = \sum\limits_{i=1}^{n} |H_i| = n|H_1| = |G|$ and now (i) follows from (7.1). We note that this argument applies equally well if G does not act faithfully on S, but instead some nontrivial normal subgroup of G fixes every element of S.

Consider the action of H_1 on S. We can clearly decompose S into the disjoint union of subsets $S_1, S_2, \ldots, S_t$ with $S_1 = \{1\}$ on each of which H_1 acts transitively (but not necessarily faithfully). Observe, first of all, that by Theorem 7.3(i) G is doubly transitive if and only if H_1 acts transitively on $S - \{1\}$ and hence if and only if $t = 2$. Now let $\alpha_i(x)$ denote the number of letters of S_i fixed by x in H_1, $1 \leq i \leq t$; then obviously $\alpha(x) = \sum\limits_{i=1}^{t} \alpha_i(x)$. On the other hand, by (i), $\sum\limits_{x \in H_1} \alpha_i(x) = |H_1|$ for each i, whence $\sum\limits_{x \in H_1} \alpha(x) = t|H_1|$. Since G is transitive, this holds for each H_i and so

$$(7.2) \qquad \sum_{x \in H_i} \alpha(x) = t|H_i| \qquad 1 \leq i \leq n.$$

Summing (7.2) over i, we get

$$(7.3) \qquad \sum_{i=1}^{n} \sum_{x \in H_i} \alpha(x) = \sum_{i=1}^{n} t|H_i| = tn|H_1| = t|G|.$$

But on the left we have counted $\alpha(x)$ once for every H_i which contains x. However, x fixes $\alpha(x)$ letters and so is contained in exactly $\alpha(x)$ distinct H_i's. This means that each x of the left side of (7.3) gives a contribution of $\alpha(x)^2$ to the sum. On the other hand, any element x of G not in one of the H_i's moves all the letters of S and so $\alpha(x) = 0$ for any such x. Thus the sum in (7.3) is unaffected if taken over all elements of G, and now (ii) follows.

The regular representation of a group G has the property that only the identity element fixes more than one letter. In this case, of course, the subgroup fixing a letter is the identity. The class of transitive permutation groups in which only the identity fixes more than one letter, but the subgroup fixing a letter is nontrivial, is of fundamental importance in the theory of finite groups, and several basic problems that we shall later investigate stem from this class of groups. Such a permutation group G will be called a *Frobenius* group, after the person who first studied them.

Frobenius discovered a basic property of this class of groups which we shall establish in Chapter 4 with the aid of some results involving group characters. We state it here without proof and then go on to discuss a few elementary properties of Frobenius groups.

Theorem 7.5 (Frobenius)

Let G be a Frobenius group and let H be the subgroup fixing a letter. Then the subset of G consisting of the identity together with those elements which fix no letters forms a normal subgroup K of G of order $|G:H|$.

We shall refer to this normal subgroup K as the *Frobenius kernel* of G. Moreover, the subgroup fixing a letter will be called a *Frobenius complement*.

As an immediate consequence of Frobenius' theorem we have:

Theorem 7.6

Let G be a Frobenius group with complement H and kernel K. Then
  (i) *$G = HK$ with $H \cap K = 1$, so that G is the semidirect product of K by H.*
  (ii) *$|H|$ divides $|K| - 1$.*
  (iii) *Every element of $H^{\#}$ induces by conjugation an automorphism of K which fixes only the identity element of K.*
  (iv) *$C_G(y) \subseteq K$ for every y in $K^{\#}$.*

Proof

Since the elements of $K^{\#}$ fix no letters, $H \cap K = 1$. But $|K| = |G:H|$ by Frobenius' theorem and consequently $|G| = |HK|$. Thus $G = HK$ and (i) holds.

Now as G is transitive and H is the subgroup fixing a letter, our representation is equivalent to that on the cosets of H. In the present case we can take the elements of K themselves as coset representatives of H in G. Suppose then that $k^h = k$ for some h in $H^{\#}$ and k in $K^{\#}$. Then it is immediate that h fixes the coset Hk as well as the coset H. But by definition of a Frobenius group, only the identity fixes more than one letter. Thus $k^h \neq k$ for any h in $H^{\#}$ and k in $K^{\#}$. In particular, (iii) holds. Moreover, for a fixed $k \neq 1$, the set $\Gamma_k = \{k^h \mid h \in H\}$ must consist of $m = |H|$ distinct elements of K. But clearly for k, k' in $K^{\#}$, we have either $\Gamma_k = \Gamma_{k'}$ or $\Gamma_k \cap \Gamma_{k'} = \emptyset$, the empty set. Hence $|K^{\#}|$ is a multiple of m and (ii) follows.

Finally, by (iii), no element of $K^{\#}$ centralizes any element of a conjugate of $H^{\#}$. But the conjugates of H are simply the subgroups fixing a letter, and consequently by Theorem 7.5 K consists precisely of the elements of G which lie in no conjugate of $H^{\#}$. We conclude that $C_G(y) \subseteq K$ for y in $K^{\#}$, proving (iv).

Condition (iii) of the theorem suggests the importance of studying groups of automorphisms with this special property. We thus are led to make the following definition:

A nontrivial group of automorphisms A of a group G is said to be a *regular* group of automorphisms provided each element of $A^{\#}$ leaves only the identity element G fixed.

If A is a regular group of automorphisms of a group G, we leave to the reader the fact that the semidirect product GA of G by A is a Frobenius group with kernel G and complement A.

Later we shall derive fairly complete results concerning the structure of both G and A; equivalently, of both the kernel and complement of a Frobenius group.

Finally we give a simple condition for a group G to be a Frobenius group with complement H which is independent of Frobenius' theorem.

Theorem 7.7

Let H be a nontrivial subgroup of G. Then G is a Frobenius group with complement H if and only if H is disjoint from its conjugates and is its own normalizer in G.

Proof

Let Hx_i, $x_i \in G$, $x_1 = 1$, $1 \leqslant i \leqslant n$, be a complete set of cosets of H in G. If some element of G fixes two cosets of H, then by transitivity some element of $H^{\#}$ fixes one of the cosets Hx_i with $i > 1$. Hence G is a Frobenius group with complement H if and only if no element of $H^{\#}$ fixes any Hx_i with $i > 1$. But for h in $H^{\#}$, $Hx_i = Hx_i h$ if and only if $x_i h x_i^{-1} \in H$ or equivalently, $h \in H \cap H^{x_i}$. Thus G and H have the given properties if and only if

$$(7.4) \qquad\qquad H \cap H^{x_i} = 1 \qquad 2 \leq i \leq n.$$

We argue that (7.4) is equivalent to the two conditions of the theorem. Indeed, assume (7.4). If $N_G(H) \supset H$, we can take x_2 in $N_G(H)$ to obtain $H \cap H^{x_2} = H$, a contradiction; so $N_G(H) = H$. Furthermore, if $x \in G - H$, then $x \in Hx_i$ for some $i > 1$, whence $H \cap H^x = H \cap H^{x_i} = 1$. Conversely, if $N_G(H) = H$ and H is disjoint from its distinct conjugates, then $H \cap H^x = 1$ for any x in $G - H$ and so (7.4) holds.

8. THE TWO-DIMENSIONAL LINEAR AND PROJECTIVE GROUPS

The group $GL(2, q)$ of all 2×2 nonsingular matrices with entries in the finite field $GF(q)$ of q elements together with certain closely related groups will play an important role at various points throughout the book. As a result, we shall require a number of properties of these groups, which we shall establish in this section.

$GL(2, q)$ is known as the *general* linear group (in dimension 2); its subgroup consisting of matrices of determinant 1 is called the *special* linear group and is denoted by $SL(2, q)$. The center of $GL(2, q)$ consists of the scalar matrices and the corresponding factor group $PGL(2, q)$ is called the *projective* linear group. Finally, the image $PSL(2, q)$ of $SL(2, q)$ in $PGL(2, q)$ is called the *projective special* linear group. For simplicity of notation we shall usually denote this last group by $L_2(q)$. It is properties of $SL(2, q)$ and $L_2(q)$ in which we are primarily interested.

First of all, we have

Theorem 8.1

The orders of $GL(2, q)$, $SL(2, q)$, $PGL(2, q)$ and $L_2(q)$ are, respectively, $(q^2 - 1)(q^2 - q)$, $(q^2 - 1)q$, $(q^2 - 1)q$, and $\varepsilon(q^2 - 1)q$, where $\varepsilon = 1$ if q is even and $\varepsilon = \frac{1}{2}$ if q is odd.

Proof

We regard $G = GL(2, q)$ as a group of linear transformations of a vector space V of dimension 2 over $GF(q)$. If v_1, v_2 is a basis of V, an element x of G is uniquely determined by its effect on this basis and, moreover, $v_1 x$, $v_2 x$ must also be a basis of V as x is nonsingular. Thus $v_1 x$ can be any one of the $q^2 - 1$ nonzero vectors in V, while $v_2 x$ can then be any one of the $q^2 - q$ vectors in V which are not a multiple of $v_1 x$. Hence $|G| = (q^2 - 1)(q^2 - q)$.

Since G contains elements of arbitrary nonzero determinant, $H = SL(2, q)$ has index $q - 1$ in G, so $|H| = (q^2 - 1)q$. Furthermore, the center $Z(G)$ consists of the scalar matrices and so has order $q - 1$. Hence $PGL(2, q) = G/Z(G)$ also has order $(q^2 - 1)q$. Finally, the only scalar matrices of determinant 1 are $\pm I$, where I is the identity matrix; and these are identical if and only if $q = 2^n$. Since $H/Z(G) \cap H = L_2(q)$, it follows that $L_2(q)$ has the given order.

The group $PGL(2, q)$ can be identified in a natural way with the group of projective transformations

$$(8.1) \qquad \alpha : z' = \frac{az + b}{cz + d} \qquad a, b, c, d \in GF(q), \ ad - bc \neq 0,$$

of the projective line $\mathscr{L}$ of $q + 1$ points coordinatized by the elements of $GF(q)$ and the symbol ∞. In this form the element α lies in $L_2(q)$ precisely when $ad - bc$ is a square in $GF(q)$. Since each element of $PGL(2, q)$ thus induces permutations of the elements of $\mathscr{L}$ as a set, $PGL(2, q)$, and hence also $L_2(q)$, is represented on $\mathscr{L}$ as a permutation group of degree $q + 1$. Concerning this representation, we have

Theorem 8.2

$L_2(q)$ is doubly transitive on $\mathscr{L}$ and only the identity fixes three letters. Moreover,

   (i) For $q > 3$, the subgroup N fixing a letter is a Frobenius group with cyclic complement H of order $\varepsilon(q - 1)$ and elementary abelian kernel K of order q which is disjoint from its conjugates.

   (ii) H is the subgroup fixing two letters and H is inverted by an element of order 2 in $L_2(q)$.

Proof

Let N be the subgroup of $L_2(q)$ fixing ∞. Since α takes ∞ into a/c, α fixes ∞ if and only if $c = 0$. Thus N consists of the affine transformations $z' = az + b$ with $a \neq 0$ a square in $GF(q)$. Clearly N acts transitively on the points of $\mathscr{L}$ other than ∞ and so $L_2(q)$ is doubly transitive on $\mathscr{L}$ by Theorem 7.3(i). Furthermore, the subgroup H of N fixing 0 and ∞ consists of the transformations $z' = az$. But no transformation of this form except $z' = z$ fixes any other letter. Hence only the identity fixes three letters.

Now $N = HK$, where K consists of the translations $z' = z + b$. Thus if $q = p^r$, K is an elementary abelian p-group of order p^r. Morever, no elements of $K^{\#}$ fixes any letter other than ∞. Since K^x fixes the letter $(\infty)x$ for x in $L_2(q)$, the assumption $K \cap K^x \neq 1$ thus implies that $(\infty)x = \infty$ and hence that $x \in N$, whence $K^x = K$. Therefore K is disjoint from its conjugates.

Furthermore, by the first paragraph of the proof, H is cyclic of order $q - 1$ if $p = 2$ and $\frac{1}{2}(q - 1)$ if p is odd. Now N acts transitively on $\mathscr{L} - \{\infty\}$ and only the identity fixes two letters of $\mathscr{L} - \{\infty\}$. But then if $H \neq 1$, or equivalently if $q > 3$, it follows from the definition that N is a Frobenius group with complement H and kernel K. Finally, the transformation $z' = 1/z$ has order 2, lies in $L_2(q)$, and conjugates $z' = az$ into its inverse $z' = (1/a)z$. Thus (i) and (ii) also hold.

The class of doubly transitive groups in which only the identity fixes three letters is a very important and interesting one, which we shall study in detail in Chapter 13. We call such a group a *Zassenhaus* group, after the person who began their systematic investigation. As in the case of Frobenius groups, we restrict the definition to those doubly transitive groups in which only the identity fixes three letters, but the subgroup fixing two letters is nontrivial. Thus in a Zassenhaus group, the subgroup fixing a letter is always a Frobenius group in its action on the remaining letters.

We next derive some properties of $SL(2, q)$.

Theorem 8.3

The following conditions hold:
(i) $SL(2, q)$ *contains cyclic subgroups of order* $q - 1$ *and* $q + 1$.
(ii) *An* S_2-*subgroup of* $SL(2, q)$ *is elementary abelian if* q *is even and is generalized quaternion if* q *is odd.*
(iii) $SL(2, p)$ *is nonsolvable,* p *a prime,* $p \geqslant 5$.

Proof

The matrices $\begin{pmatrix} \lambda & 0 \\ 0 & \lambda^{-1} \end{pmatrix}$, $\lambda \neq 0$ in $GF(q)$, form a group A isomorphic to the multiplicative group of $GF(q)$. Hence A is cyclic of order $q - 1$. Since the elements of A have determinant 1, $A \subseteq SL(2, q)$.

Now consider $GL(2, q)$ in its natural action on a two-dimensional vector space V over $GF(q)$. We can identify V with the additive group of $GF(q^2)$. But then if ω is a primitive element in $GF(q^2)$, right multiplication by ω effects a linear transformation of V of order $q^2 - 1$. This means that $GL(2, q)$ contains a cyclic subgroup L of order $q^2 - 1$. Consider the map $x \to \det x$ for x in L, which is a homomorphism of L into the multiplicative group of $GF(q)$ which has order $q - 1$. The kernel of this homomorphism is cyclic of order a multiple of $q + 1$ and so contains a cyclic subgroup B of order $q + 1$. Since $\det x = 1$ for x in B, $B \subseteq SL(2, q)$ and so (i) holds.

The set of matrices $P = \left\{ \begin{pmatrix} 1 & 0 \\ \lambda & 1 \end{pmatrix} \middle| \lambda \in GF(q) \right\}$ forms an elementary abelian subgroup of $SL(2, q)$ of order $q = p^r$. Since $|SL(2, q)| = q(q^2 - 1)$, P is an S_p-subgroup and so (ii) holds if q is even. Consider next the case $q \equiv 1 \pmod 4$ and let 2^a be the highest power of 2 dividing $q - 1$. In this case $q + 1$ is divisible by 2, but not 4, and so an S_2-subgroup of $SL(2, q)$ has order 2^{a+1}. Let α be an element of $GF(q)$ of order 2^a and set $x = \begin{pmatrix} \alpha & 0 \\ 0 & \alpha^{-1} \end{pmatrix}$ and $y = \begin{pmatrix} 0 & 1 \\ -1 & 0 \end{pmatrix}$. Then $x, y \in SL(2, q)$, $|x| = 2^a$, $|y| = 4$, $y^{-1}xy = x^{-1}$, and $y^2 = x^{2^{a-1}} = \begin{pmatrix} -1 & 0 \\ 0 & -1 \end{pmatrix}$, as can be directly checked. Thus $\langle x, y \rangle$ is generalized quaternion of order 2^{a+1} and is an S_2-subgroup of $SL(2, q)$.

To treat the case $q \equiv -1 \pmod 4$, we use the fact that $SL(2, q)$ is a subgroup of $SL(2, q^2)$, which is clear from the definition since $GF(q) \subseteq GF(q^2)$. Since $q^2 \equiv 1 \pmod 4$, it follows from the preceding case that an S_2-subgroup

S of $SL(2, q^2)$ is generalized quaternion. Now an S_2-subgroup T of $SL(2, q)$ is isomorphic to a subgroup of S. But one can easily check from the defining relations for S that its subgroups are either cyclic or generalized quaternion (compare Theorem 5.4.3). Thus T is either cyclic or generalized quaternion.

We argue that T is not cyclic, from which (ii) will follow. So assume $T = \langle z \rangle$ is cyclic. Then $|z| = 2^{b+1}$, where 2^b is the largest power of 2 dividing $q + 1$. To derive a contradiction, it will suffice to show that $|z|$ divides $q - 1$ or $q + 1$, whence $|z| \leq 2^b$. Now the characteristic polynomial $f(X)$ of z has degree 2 over $GF(q)$. Hence its characteristic roots β, β' lie in $GF(q^2)$. Since $\det z = 1$, we have $\beta' = \beta^{-1}$. Since $z^2 \neq 1$, $\beta^{-1} \neq \beta$ and so z is diagonalizable over $GF(q^2)$, which implies at once that $|z| = |\beta|$. If $\beta \in GF(q)$, then $|\beta|$ divides $q - 1$. In the contrary case, $f(X)$ must be irreducible over $GF(q)$ and so β^{-1} must be algebraically conjugate to β under the automorphism $\gamma \to \gamma^q$ of $GF(q^2)$. Thus $\beta^{-1} = \beta^q$, whence $|\beta|$ divides $q + 1$. In either case, we obtain the desired contradiction, thus completing the proof of (ii).

Suppose $SL(2, p)$ were solvable, $p \geq 5$. Then also $G = L_2(p)$ is solvable. Let H be a minimal normal subgroup of G, so that by Theorem 4.1(v), H is an elementary abelian t-group for some prime t. If $t = p$, we can identify H with the group P of translations $z' = z + b$, $b \in GF(p)$. But then $N_G(H) = N_G(P)$ is the subgroup of G of affine transformations, which is proper. Thus $t \neq p$.

Consider the case t odd. Since $|SL(2, p)| = p(p - 1)(p + 1)$ it follows from (i) that the S_t-subgroups of $SL(2, p)$ are cyclic. Hence the same is true of G and so H is cyclic, whence $|H| = t$. But then $|\text{Aut } H| = t - 1$ by Theorem 1.3.10(ii). However, $t < p$ as t divides $p \pm 1$ and t is odd. Therefore $|\text{Aut } H|$ is prime to p and consequently P centralizes H. In particular, H consists of affine transformations. But clearly the only such transformations which centralize P lie in P. Thus $t = 2$.

Now an S_2-subgroup of $SL(2, p)$ is generalized quaternion by (ii) and $S/Z(S)$ is an S_2-subgroup of G. It follows at once that $S/Z(S)$ is a dihedral group and hence contains no elementary abelian subgroup of order 8. Thus $|H| \leq 4$. Since H can be regarded as a vector space of dimension 1 or 2 over $GF(2)$, Theorem 8.1 implies that $|\text{Aut } H| = 1$ or 6 and so is prime to p. In either case P centralizes H, giving the same contradiction. Thus $SL(2, p)$ is nonsolvable, as asserted.

Actually the groups $L_2(q)$ are simple for all $q > 3$, as is not difficult to show with the aid of a few general, but elementary, results to be proved later, together with the easily established fact that $L_2(q)$ is generated by its p-elements for $q = p^r$. In Chapter 15 we shall prove this theorem for odd p, basing our argument on the following stronger result concerning the generation of $SL(2, p^r)$ by p-elements which we shall need in Chapter 3. The brilliant proof of this latter result which we shall now present appears without essential change in Dickson's book on linear groups; it fore-shadows a number of general counting techniques which have been successfully used in the study of groups. We note also that in the form stated, the theorem is false for $p = 2$, as two elements of order 2 always generate a dihedral group (see Theorem 9.1.1).

Theorem 8.4 (Dickson)

Let λ be a generator of $GF(p^r)$ over the prime field of order p, p odd, and set $L = \left\langle \begin{pmatrix} 1 & 0 \\ \lambda & 1 \end{pmatrix}, \begin{pmatrix} 1 & 1 \\ 0 & 1 \end{pmatrix} \right\rangle$. Then we have either

(i) $L = SL(2, p^r)$, or
(ii) $p^r = 9$, $|Z(L)| = 2$, $L/Z(L)$ is isomorphic to A_5,

and L contains a subgroup isomorphic to $SL(2, 3)$.

Remark   In the exceptional case, L is actually isomorphic to $SL(2, 5)$, but we shall not need this result. Since $SL(2, p) \subseteq SL(2, p^r)$, L contains a subgroup isomorphic to $SL(2, p)$ in all cases. It is this fact that we shall use in our primary application of Dickson's theorem (see Theorem 3.8.1).

Proof

Set $G = SL(2, p^r)$. Consider a conjugate L^x of L by an element x of G of the form $\begin{pmatrix} 1 & \gamma \\ 0 & 1 \end{pmatrix}$, $\gamma \in GF(p^r)$. It will suffice to show that either

(A) $L^x = SL(2, p^m)$ for some $m \le r$, or
(B) $p = 3$, $|Z(L^x)| = 2$, $L^x/Z(L^x)$ is isomorphic to A_5, and K^x contains a subgroup isomorphic to $SL(2, 3)$.

Indeed, assume first that case A holds. Then if

$$y = \begin{pmatrix} 1 - \gamma\lambda & -\gamma^2\lambda \\ \lambda & 1 + \gamma\lambda \end{pmatrix} = \begin{pmatrix} 1 & -\gamma \\ 0 & 1 \end{pmatrix} \begin{pmatrix} 1 & 0 \\ \lambda & 1 \end{pmatrix} \begin{pmatrix} 1 & \gamma \\ 0 & 1 \end{pmatrix},$$

$y \in L^x$, and consequently $\lambda \in GF(p^m)$. But $Z_p(\lambda) = GF(p^r)$ and so $r \le m$. Hence $r = m$ and $L = L^x = G$. Thus the theorem will follow in case A.

Now assume case B holds, whence $p = 3$, $|Z(L)| = 2$, and $L/Z(L)$ is isomorphic to A_5. The images of $y = \begin{pmatrix} 1 & 0 \\ \lambda & 1 \end{pmatrix}$ and $z = \begin{pmatrix} 1 & 1 \\ 0 & 1 \end{pmatrix}$ in A_5 are elements of order 3 which generate A_5. Hence by considering an automorphism of A_5, if necessary, we can assume without loss that these images are (123) and (345), respectively. Now the product $(123)(345)(123)^{-1}$ $(345) = (25)(34)$, and so has order 2. Since $\begin{pmatrix} -1 & 0 \\ 0 & -1 \end{pmatrix}$ is the unique element of order 2 in G, we conclude that

$$u = yzy^{-1}z = \begin{pmatrix} 1 - \lambda & 2 - \lambda \\ -\lambda^2 & 1 + \lambda - \lambda^2 \end{pmatrix}$$

is an element of L whose square is $\begin{pmatrix} -1 & 0 \\ 0 & -1 \end{pmatrix}$. But as we shall show in general in Lemma 8.5(iii) below in a moment, this implies that u has trace 0 and hence that $(1 - \lambda) + (1 + \lambda - \lambda^2) = 0$, whence $\lambda^2 = 2 = -1$ as $p = 3$. Thus $|Z_p(\lambda)| = 9$. Moreover, our assumption implies that L contains a subgroup isomorphic to $SL(2, 3)$. Hence the theorem will hold in case B as well.

We shall now determine a conjugate L^x of L so as to satisfy a suitable normalization condition. Let K be the subgroup of upper triangular matrices in G, so that $K = AQ$, where $Q = \left\{ \begin{pmatrix} 1 & \alpha \\ 0 & 1 \end{pmatrix} \middle| \alpha \in GF(p^r) \right\}$ and $A = \left\{ \begin{pmatrix} \beta & 0 \\ 0 & \beta^{-1} \end{pmatrix} \middle| \beta \in GF(p^r), \beta \neq 0 \right\}$ is cyclic of order $p^r - 1$. Since $G/Z(G)$ is $L_2(p^r)$, Theorem 8.2 implies that Q is disjoint from its conjugates and that $K/Z(G)$ is a Frobenius group with complement $A/Z(G)$. This latter fact implies at once that every subgroup of K of order dividing $p^r - 1$ lies in a conjugate of A by an element of Q.

Since $\begin{pmatrix} 1 & 1 \\ 0 & 1 \end{pmatrix} \in L \cap Q$ and Q is disjoint from its conjugates, $L \cap Q$ is an S_p-subgroup of L. For the same reason $N_L(L \cap Q) \subseteq K$, and so by the preceding paragraph $N_L(L \cap Q) = (L \cap A^z)(L \cap Q)$ for some z in Q. We now choose the element x to be z^{-1} and set $M = L^x$. Since Q is abelian, $M \cap Q$ is an S_p-subgroup of M and contains $\begin{pmatrix} 1 & 1 \\ 0 & 1 \end{pmatrix}$. Moreover, by our choice of x, we have

(8.2) $N_M(M \cap Q) = (M \cap A)(M \cap Q).$

Note also that L, and hence M, has more than one S_p-subgroup and is generated by its p-elements.

Now there may exist more than one element x in Q such that $M = L^x$ satisfies (8.2). Clearly for our purposes any such x is permissible. Hence to establish the theorem it will suffice to prove that if M is any subgroup of G

containing $\begin{pmatrix} 1 & 1 \\ 0 & 1 \end{pmatrix}$ which is generated by its p-elements, possesses more than

one S_p-subgroup, and satisfies (8.2), then for some conjugate M^* of M
by an element of Q, also satisfying (8.2), we have either $M^* = SL(2, p^m)$ for
some $m \le r$ or $p = 3$, $|Z(M^*)| = 2$, $M^*/Z(M^*)$ is isomorphic to A_5, and
M^* contains a subgroup isomorphic to $SL(2, 3)$. In fact, M^* will turn out to be
M except possibly in the case $p^m = 3$. We shall carry this out in a long sequence of
lemmas. Set $H = M \cap A$, $P = M \cap Q$, $N = N_M(P)$, $d = |H|$, and $p^m = |P|$. Thus

$H = \left\{ \begin{pmatrix} \beta & 0 \\ 0 & \beta^{-1} \end{pmatrix} \right\}$, where β ranges over the elements of the unique subgroup

D of the multiplicative group $GF(p^r)$ of order d. We also have $P = \left\{ \begin{pmatrix} 1 & \alpha \\ 0 & 1 \end{pmatrix} \right\}$,

where α ranges over a subgroup E of order p^m of the additive group of
$GF(p^r)$. We preserve this notation throughout.

We begin with some elementary facts concerning the elements of M.

Lemma 8.5

Let $x = \begin{pmatrix} a & b \\ c & d \end{pmatrix} \in M$, $a, b, c, d \in GF(p^r)$.

Then we have
(i) If $c = 0$, then $x \in N$.
(ii) If $|x| = p$, then $a + d = 2$.
(iii) If $x^2 = \begin{pmatrix} -1 & 0 \\ 0 & -1 \end{pmatrix}$, then either $a + d = 0$ or $b = c = 0$.

Proof

If $c = 0$, then $b = a^{-1}$ as $\det x = 1$. Hence $x \in K$ and so $x \in M \cap K$. But
$M \cap K$ normalizes $M \cap Q = P$, whence $M \cap K = N$, proving (i).

Next let $|x| = p$. Since the entries of x lie in a field of characteristic p,
each of its characteristic roots must be 1 and (ii) follows at once.

Finally $x^2 = \begin{pmatrix} a^2 + bc & b(a + d) \\ c(a + d) & d^2 + bc \end{pmatrix}$. But then if $x^2 = \begin{pmatrix} -1 & 0 \\ 0 & -1 \end{pmatrix}$, it is

immediate that either $b = c = 0$ or $a + d = 0$.

Lemma 8.6

For some integer $f \ge 1$, we have

$$|M| = dp^m(1 + fp^m).$$

Proof

Let $P_1, P_2, \ldots, P_s$ be the S_p-subgroups of M other than P. Then P induces
by conjugation a permutation of the P_i. Now each P_i is an S_p-subgroup of

$N_M(P_i)$. Moreover, $P \cap P_i = 1$ since Q is disjoint from its conjugates in G. It follows that no element of $P^{\#}$ fixes any P_i. Thus P permutes the P_i in cycles consisting of $p^m = |P|$ elements, and so the number of S_p-subgroups of M is of the form $1 + fp^m$. Since P is not the unique S_p-subgroup of M, $f \geqslant 1$.

Now the number of conjugates of P in M is $|M : N|$ by Theorem 1.2.3(iii) and $|M : N| = 1 + fp^m$ by Sylow's theorem. Since $|N| = dp^m$, the lemma follows.

Lemma 8.7

We have $d = \varepsilon(p^m - 1)$, where $\varepsilon = 1$ or 2.

Proof

Let h be the number of elements of order p in M. We compute h in two ways. First of all, as P has $1 + fp^m$ conjugates which are disjoint from each other, we get

$$h = (p^m - 1)(1 + fp^m).$$

On the other hand, we can estimate the number of elements of order p in each coset Ny of N in M with $y \in M - N$. Indeed, if $y = \begin{pmatrix} t & u \\ v & w \end{pmatrix}$,

$$(8.3) \quad Ny = \left\{ \begin{pmatrix} \beta & 0 \\ 0 & \beta^{-1} \end{pmatrix} \begin{pmatrix} 1 & \alpha \\ 0 & 1 \end{pmatrix} \begin{pmatrix} t & u \\ v & w \end{pmatrix} = \begin{pmatrix} \beta t + \beta \alpha v & \beta u + \beta \alpha w \\ \beta^{-1} v & \beta^{-1} w \end{pmatrix}, \beta \in D, \alpha \in E \right\}.$$

By Lemma 8.5(ii), if an element of Ny has order p, then

$$(8.4) \qquad\qquad \beta t + \beta \alpha v + \beta^{-1} w = 2.$$

Furthermore, $v \neq 0$ by Lemma 8.5(i) since $y \notin N$. Hence for each β in D, there is at most one value α in E satisfying (8.4), and so Ny contains at most d elements of order p. Since the number of cosets of N in $M - N$ is fp^m and since N contains exactly $p^m - 1$ elements of order p, it follows that

$$(8.5) \qquad\qquad h \leqslant p^m - 1 + dfp^m.$$

Comparing (8.5) with the above equality for h, we obtain

$$(8.6) \qquad\qquad d \geqslant p^m - 1.$$

But every element of H not in $Z(G)$ induces a regular automorphism of P, which means that the elements of $P^{\#}$ are permuted in orbits of size $|H : H \cap Z(G)|$ under the action of $H/H \cap Z(G)$. Hence either d or $d/2$ must divide $p^m - 1$ according as $|H \cap Z(G)| = 1$ or 2. Combined with (8.6), we obtain the conclusion of the lemma.

Since D is cyclic, it thus possesses a cyclic subgroup $B = \langle \gamma \rangle$ of order $p^m - 1$.

Lemma 8.8

We have m divides r and B, E are, respectively, the multiplicative and additive subgroups of $GF(p^m)$.

Proof

The field $Z_p(\gamma)$ contains p^m distinct roots of the polynomial $X^{p^m} - X$: namely, 0 and γ^i, $1 \leq i \leq p^m - 1$. Hence $Z_p(\gamma)$ is a splitting field of this polynomial and so $Z_p(\gamma) = GF(p^m)$. In particular, B is the multiplicative subgroup of $GF(p^m)$. Moreover, since $Z_p(\gamma) \subseteq GF(p^r)$, we also have $m \mid r$.

Finally we have

$$\begin{pmatrix} \beta & 0 \\ 0 & \beta^{-1} \end{pmatrix} \begin{pmatrix} 1 & 1 \\ 0 & 1 \end{pmatrix} \begin{pmatrix} \beta^{-1} & 0 \\ 0 & \beta \end{pmatrix} = \begin{pmatrix} 1 & \beta^2 \\ 0 & 1 \end{pmatrix}$$

for all β in D. But $\beta^2 \in B$ as $|D : B| \leq 2$. Hence the $d/2$ elements $\begin{pmatrix} 1 & \beta^2 \\ 0 & 1 \end{pmatrix}$ all lie in $SL(2, p^m)$. Moreover, the subgroup P_0 of P that they generate is H-invariant. But $P_0^{\#}$ is a union of orbits under the action of H and each such orbit contains $d/2 \geq \frac{1}{2}(p^m - 1)$ elements. Thus $|P_0| \geq \frac{1}{2}(p^m + 1)$. Since $|P_0|$ divides $|P| = p^m$, this forces $P_0 = P$ and so $E \subseteq GF(p^m)$. Since $|E| = p^m$, we conclude that E is the additive group of $GF(p^m)$.

We shall treat the cases $\varepsilon = 1$ and $\varepsilon = 2$ separately.

Lemma 8.9

If $\varepsilon = 1$ and $p^m > 3$, then $M = SL(2, p^m)$.

Proof

In this case $B = D$ and so H, P, N lie in $SL(2, p^m)$. Moreover, (8.5) becomes an equality and the argument preceding it shows that each coset of N in $M - N$ must contain exactly $d = p^m - 1$ elements of order p. In particular, if Ny is such a coset, we may assume that the element $y = \begin{pmatrix} t & u \\ v & w \end{pmatrix}$ has order p, in which case $t + w = 2$ by Lemma 8.5(ii). Now (8.4), which must be satisfied for an element of Ny of order p, reduces upon substituting $w = 2 - t$ to

$$(8.7) \qquad (\beta - \beta^{-1})t + \beta \alpha v = 2 - 2\beta^{-1}.$$

We know in the present case that to each β in D there is determined a unique element α of E satisfying (8.7). Taking $\beta = -1$, we obtain $-\alpha v = 4$.

Since p is odd, $4 \neq 0$, so $\alpha \neq 0$ and consequently $v \in GF(p^m)$. We note that this part of the argument applies for all values of p^m including $p^m = 3$.

Since $p^m > 3$ by assumption, $d > 2$ and so we can choose β in D so that $\beta - \beta^{-1} \neq 0$, in which case (8.7) implies that also $t \in GF(p^m)$. Since $w = 2 - t$, also $w \in GF(p^m)$. Moreover, $tw - uv = 1$ as $\det y = 1$ and $v \neq 0$ as $y \notin N$. Hence also $u \in GF(p^m)$. Thus $y \in SL(2, p^m)$. Since $N \subseteq SL(2, p^m)$ and y is arbitrary in $M - N$, we conclude that $M \subseteq SL(2, p^m)$. But now a comparison of orders forces the desired conclusion $M = SL(2, p^m)$.

If $\varepsilon = 1$ and $p^m = 3$, then $H = Z(G)$ and so every conjugate of M by an element of Q will satisfy (8.2). Hence to dispose of this case, it will suffice to prove

Lemma 8.10

If $\varepsilon = 1$ and $p^m = 3$, then a conjugate of M by an element of Q is equal to $SL(2, 3)$.

Proof

First of all, the argument of the preceding lemma shows that $v \in GF(3)$ and $v \neq 0$, so $v = \pm 1$. Hence by (8.3) every element of Ny has the entry of its second row, first column in $GF(3)$. Since Ny is an arbitrary coset of $M - N$, and since the corresponding entry is 0 for elements of N, we conclude that every element of M satisfies this same condition.

Now as $\det y = 1$ and $t + w = 2 = -1$, we can write $y = \begin{pmatrix} t & -v(1 + t + t^2) \\ v & -1 - t \end{pmatrix}$.

We set $z = \begin{pmatrix} v & 1 \\ 0 & v \end{pmatrix} y$, so that z is also a coset representative of Ny and we have

$$z = \begin{pmatrix} vt + v & 1 + t - t^2 \\ 1 & -vt - v \end{pmatrix}.$$

Setting $s = vt + v$, we obtain

$$(8.9) \qquad z = \begin{pmatrix} s & -1 - s^2 \\ 1 & -s \end{pmatrix} \qquad s \in GF(3^r).$$

Thus each coset of N in $M - N$ contains such an element z, which correspondingly depends on an element s of $GF(3^r)$.

If $x = \begin{pmatrix} 1 & s \\ 0 & 1 \end{pmatrix}$, a direct computation shows that $z^x = \begin{pmatrix} 0 & -1 \\ 1 & 0 \end{pmatrix}$. Since $x \in Q$, it is enough to prove the lemma for M^x. Since M^x satisfies the same conditions as M, we may assume without loss that $M = M^x$ and hence that the element $z_0 = \begin{pmatrix} 0 & -1 \\ 1 & 0 \end{pmatrix}$ lies in M.

Consider once again the element z representing an arbitrary coset of N in $M - N$. We have

$$(8.10) \qquad z_0 z = \begin{pmatrix} -1 & s \\ s & -1 - s^2 \end{pmatrix}.$$

But by the first paragraph of the proof, the entry s of the second row, first column of $z_0 z$ lie $GF(3)$. Thus each $s \in GF(3)$ and we conclude at once that $M = SL(2, 3)$.

We turn now to the case $\varepsilon = 2$. Since p is odd, d is divisible by 4 and so D contains an element δ of order 4. The element $a = \begin{pmatrix} \delta & 0 \\ 0 & \delta^{-1} \end{pmatrix}$ is thus an element of order 4 in H. In this case we shall count elements of order 4 in M in roughly the same fashion as we counted p-elements in the case $\varepsilon = 1$. Note that $\begin{pmatrix} -1 & 0 \\ 0 & -1 \end{pmatrix}$ is the unique element of order 2 in G, so an element of G has order 4 if and only if its square is $\begin{pmatrix} -1 & 0 \\ 0 & -1 \end{pmatrix}$. We first prove

Lemma 8.11

Assume $\varepsilon = 2$. Then we have
  (i) a is inverted by an element of M.
  (ii) The conjugate class of a in M contains $p^m(1 + fp^m)$ elements.
  (iii) f is odd.

Proof

It is immediate that $C_G(a) = A$, the set of diagonal matrices of determinant 1. Hence $C_M(a) = D$ and consequently the conjugate class of a contains $p^m(1 + fp^m)$ elements. Likewise the conjugate class of a^{-1} contains the same number of elements. If a and a^{-1} are in the same class, (i) and (ii) hold. In the contrary case, our argument shows that there are at least $2p^m(1 + fp^m)$ elements of order 4 in M. We shall show that this is not true.

Once again consider the coset Ny, $y \in M - N$. Since $\beta^{-1}v \neq 0$ for any element x of Ny, Lemma 8.5(iii) shows that $|x| = 4$ only if

$$(8.11) \qquad \beta t + \beta \alpha v + \beta^{-1} w = 0.$$

Moreover, for each β in D, there is at most one α in E for which (8.11) holds. Thus each coset of N in $M - N$ contains at most d elements of order 4. One verifies directly that N contains $2p^m$ elements of order 4. Hence if

k denotes the number of elements of order 4 in M, we have

(8.12) $k \leqslant 2p^m + d(1 + fp^m) = 2p^m + 2(p^m - 1)(1 + fp^m).$

But by assumption $k \geqslant 2p^m(1 + fp^m) = 2p^m + 2p^m(fp^m)$, which contradicts (8.12) and establishes (i) and (ii).

Finally if b is in the conjugate class of a, so is b^{-1} and $b^{-1} \neq b$. Hence $p^m(1 + fp^m)$ must be even. Since p is odd, this forces f to be odd, proving (iii).

Lemma 8.12

Assume $\varepsilon = 2$. Then either $f = 1$ or $f = 3$, $p^m = 3$, $|G| = 120$.

Proof

If the coset Ny contains an element of order 4, we can choose y to be of order 4, in which case $t + w = 0$ and (8.11) reduces to

(8.13) $(\beta - \beta^{-1})t + \beta\alpha v = 0.$

To exploit this relation, we need a preliminary fact: If Ny' is a second coset of N in $M - N$ with $y' = \begin{pmatrix} t' & u' \\ v' & -t' \end{pmatrix}$ of order 4, then $t'/v' \neq t/v$. Indeed,

$$yy' = \begin{pmatrix} t & u \\ v & -t \end{pmatrix}\begin{pmatrix} t' & u' \\ v' & -t' \end{pmatrix} = \begin{pmatrix} tt' + uv' & tu' - ut' \\ vt' - tv' & vu' - tt' \end{pmatrix}.$$

But $yy' \notin N$, since otherwise $y \in Ny'^{-1} = Ny'$. It follows that the entry $vt' - tv'$ of yy' is nonzero. Hence $t/v \neq t'/v'$, as asserted.

Observe next that $|y^{-1}| = 4$ and $y^{-1} \in Ny$. Hence a coset of N in $M - N$ contains either 0, 2, or $s > 2$ elements of order 4. Let I be the set of cosets containing exactly 2 elements of order 4 and J the set containing more than 2 elements. If $Ny \in J$, then there must be a solution α, β of (8.13) with $\beta \neq \pm 1$. For such a choice of α, β we obtain

(8.14) $\dfrac{t}{v} = \dfrac{-\beta\alpha}{\beta - \beta^{-1}} = \dfrac{-\beta^2\alpha}{\beta^2 - 1}.$

However, $\beta^2 \in B$, as $|D : B| = 2$ in this case. Hence both β^2 and α lie in $GF(p^m)$ and so the ratio t/v is an element of $GF(p^m)$. But by the preceding paragraph, the corresponding ratios for any two elements in different cosets of the set J are distinct. We conclude that

(8.15) $|J| \leqslant p^m.$

We already know that any coset of N in $M - N$ contains at most d elements of order 4. Moreover, the number of such cosets is fp^m, so we also have

(8.16) $|I| + |J| \leqslant fp^m.$

Since N contains $2p^m$ elements of order 4, it follows from these relations that

(8.17) $k \leqslant 2p^m + 2|I| + |J|d \leqslant 2p^m + 2fp^m + |J|(d - 2)$

$\leqslant 2p^m + 2fp^m + p^m(2p^m - 4).$

On the other hand, $k \geqslant p^m + fp^{2m}$ by Lemma 8.11(ii). Combined with (8.17), this leads to the inequality

(8.18) $p^m(2p^m - 3) \geqslant fp^m(p^m - 2).$

Since f is odd, the only solutions of (8.18) are $f = 1$ and $f = 3$, $p^m = 3$. In the latter case $d = 4$ and it follows from Lemma 8.6 that $|G| = 120$.

Lemma 8.13

The case $f = 1$ does not occur.

Proof

Assume $f = 1$. We shall show that M possesses a normal subgroup M_0 of index 2. Then all p-elements of M will lie in M_0 and so will generate a subgroup of M_0. But by assumption, M is generated by its p-elements, a contradiction.

First of all, one checks directly that the elements of G inverting $a = \begin{pmatrix} \delta & 0 \\ 0 & \delta^{-1} \end{pmatrix}$ are all of the form $\begin{pmatrix} 0 & -\sigma^{-1} \\ \sigma & 0 \end{pmatrix}$, $\sigma \in GF(p^r)$. But a is inverted by an element of M by Lemma 8.11(i) and so M contains an element $b = \begin{pmatrix} 0 & -\tau^{-1} \\ \tau & 0 \end{pmatrix}$, $\tau \in GF(p^r)$, $\tau \neq 0$. If $x = \begin{pmatrix} 1 & \alpha \\ 0 & 1 \end{pmatrix}$ is an arbitrary element of P, then

(8.19) $b^x = \begin{pmatrix} -\alpha\tau & -\alpha^2\tau - \tau^{-1} \\ \tau & \alpha\tau \end{pmatrix}.$

Now each b^x is an element of M of order 4 and is not in N as $\tau \neq 0$. Furthermore, these elements lie in distinct cosets. Indeed, suppose for some β in D, η in E, and x in P,

$\begin{pmatrix} \beta & \beta\eta \\ 0 & \beta^{-1} \end{pmatrix} b^x = \begin{pmatrix} -\beta\alpha\tau + \beta\eta\tau & * \\ \beta^{-1}\tau & \beta^{-1}\alpha\tau \end{pmatrix}$

were equal to $b^{x'}$ for some x' in P. Then $\beta^{-1}\tau = \tau$, so $\beta = 1$. Since $b^{x'}$

has trace 0, this in turn forces $\eta = 0$, whence $b^{x'} = b^x$. This proves the assertion.

On the other hand, the number of cosets of N in $M - N$ is $fp^m = p^m$. We conclude that each coset of N in $M - N$ contains exactly one of the elements b^x, which we may therefore take as coset representatives. In particular, each coset of N in $M - N$ contains an element of order 4.

Now if $x_1 \neq x_2$, then $b^{x_1} \notin Nb^{x_2} = N(b^{x_2})^{-1}$, so $b^{x_1}b^{x_2} \notin N$. Hence for some x_3 and suitable β in D, η in E, we have

$$(8.20) \qquad b^{x_1}b^{x_2} = \begin{pmatrix} \beta & \eta \\ 0 & \beta^{-1} \end{pmatrix} b^{x_3}.$$

Let $x_i = \begin{pmatrix} 1 & \alpha_i \\ 0 & 1 \end{pmatrix}$, $1 \leqslant i \leqslant 2$, so that $\alpha_1 \neq \alpha_2$. Then computing the entry of the second row, first column of each side of (8.20), we obtain the equation

$$(8.21) \qquad -\alpha_2\tau^2 + \alpha_1\tau^2 = \beta^{-1}\tau.$$

This yields $\tau = \beta^{-1}/\alpha_1 - \alpha_2$ and consequently $\tau^2 \in GF(p^m)$. Thus $|\tau|$ divides d and we conclude that $\tau \in D$.

Finally, a coset Nb^x consists of the dp^m elements

$$\begin{pmatrix} \beta & \beta\eta \\ 0 & \beta^{-1} \end{pmatrix} \begin{pmatrix} -\alpha\tau & -\alpha^2\tau - \tau^{-1} \\ \tau & \alpha\tau \end{pmatrix}$$

with $\beta \in D$ and $\eta, \alpha \in E$. Hence such an element lies in $SL(2, p^m)$ if and only if $\beta\tau \in B$. Since $\tau \in D$ and $|D : B| = 2$, it follows that exactly half the elements of each coset lie in $SL(2, p^m)$. Since also half the elements of N lie in $SL(2, p^m)$, we conclude that $M_0 = M \cap SL(2, p^m)$ consists of half the elements of M. Thus $|M : M_0| = 2$. Since $M - M_0$ consists of one right and one left coset, these must be identical and so $M_0 \lhd M$, and the lemma is proved.

The next lemma will thus complete the proof of Theorem 8.4.

Lemma 8.14

If $\varepsilon = 2$, then $p^m = 3$, $|Z(M)| = 2$, $M/Z(M)$ is isomorphic to A_5, and M contains $SL(2, 3)$.

Proof

By Lemmas 8.12 and 8.13 we have $f = p^m = 3$. In this case (8.18) becomes an inequality and hence so also do (8.15) and (8.16). Thus $|J| = 3$ and

$|I| = 6$. Moreover, for the same reason each element of J contains $d = 4$ elements of order 4. Since N contains $2p^m = 6$ elements of order 4, it follows that M contains exactly $6 + 2 \cdot 6 + 4 \cdot 3 = 30$ elements of order 4. Since $|C_G(a)| = d = 4$ and $|M| = 120$, these all lie in the conjugate class of a. Since an element of order 4 and its inverse map to the same element of order 2 in $\bar{M} = M/Z(G)$, we conclude that $\bar{M}$ contains exactly 15 elements of order 2 and they are all conjugate. Furthermore, the element $b = \begin{pmatrix} 0 & -\tau^{-1} \\ \tau & 0 \end{pmatrix}$ inverts a. Since $|a| = 4$, every odd power of b inverts a and so a is inverted by a 2-element of M. Hence without loss we may assume b is a 2-element, in which case $S = \langle a, b \rangle$ is a nonabelian 2-group. But an S_2-subgroup of M has order 8 as $|M| = 120$, whence $|b| = 4$, S is a quaternion group, and S is an S_2-subgroup of M. The image $\bar{S}$ of S in $\bar{M}$ is thus an S_2-subgroup of $\bar{M}$ and is abelian of type $(2, 2)$.

We claim next that $\bar{S}$ is disjoint from its conjugates in $\bar{M}$. Suppose $\bar{S} \cap \bar{T} \neq 1$ for some S_2-subgroup $\bar{T}$ of $\bar{M}$. Since $\bar{M}$ has only one class of elements of order 2, we may assume without loss that $\bar{a} \in \bar{S} \cap \bar{T}$, where $\bar{a}$ is the image of a in $\bar{S}$. Since $\bar{T}$ is abelian, $\bar{T}$ centralizes $\bar{a}$ and so the inverse image T of $\bar{T}$ in M consists of elements which either centralize or invert a. But S is the set of all such elements of M, whence $T = S$ and $\bar{T} = \bar{S}$, proving the assertion.

Since $\bar{M}$ contains exactly 15 elements of order 2, and since each S_2-subgroup of M contains 3 of them, it follows from the preceding paragraph that $\bar{M}$ contains precisely 5 S_2-subgroups. Since these are all conjugate, this yields that $|\bar{M} : N_{\bar{M}}(\bar{S})| = 5$. Since $|\bar{M}|$ is 60, we conclude that $\bar{R} = N_{\bar{M}}(\bar{S})$ has order 12.

We now consider the permutation representation π of $\bar{M}$ on the right cosets of $\bar{R}$, which maps $\bar{M}$ homomorphically into the symmetric group S_5. It will suffice to show that π is an isomorphism, for then $\bar{M}$ will be isomorphic to a subgroup of order 60. Since the only such subgroup of S_5 is A_5, we shall then have $\bar{M}$ isomorphic to A_5. This in turn will imply that $Z(G) = Z(M)$, and this will prove all but the final assertion of the lemma.

Now the kernel $\bar{U}$ of π is a subgroup of $\bar{R}$ and is normal in $\bar{M}$. Since $\bar{S}$ contains all elements of order 2 in $\bar{R}$, we have $\bar{S} \cap \bar{U} \lhd \bar{M}$. Since $\bar{S}$ is disjoint from its conjugates, we have either $\bar{S} \cap \bar{U} = \bar{S}$ or $\bar{1}$. However, in the first case $\bar{M}$ would contain only 3 elements of order 2. Thus $\bar{S} \cap \bar{U} = \bar{1}$ and so $|\bar{U}| = 1$ or 3. But in the latter case, the 3-elements of $\bar{M}$ generate a proper subgroup and hence the same is true of the 3-elements of M, contrary to assumption. Therefore $\bar{U} = \bar{1}$ and π is an isomorphism.

Finally, since the the S_2-subgroup S of M is quaternion, one verifies directly that the inverse image of $\bar{R}$ in M is isomorphic to $SL(2, 3)$.

This completes the proof of Dickson's theorem.

EXERCISES

1. Prove Theorem 1.1.
2. Prove Theorem 1.2.
3. Prove Lemma 2.4.
4. Let H, K, L be subgroups of G. Show that any normal subgroup of G containing two of the groups $[H, K, L]$, $[K, L, H]$, and $[L, H, K]$ necessarily contains the third.
5. If every maximal proper subgroup of G is normal in G, show that G is nilpotent.
6. If for each prime p in $\pi(G)$, the set of p'-elements of G forms a normal subgroup, prove that G is nilpotent.
7. G is called *supersolvable* if G possesses a normal series with cyclic factors such that each term is normal in G. Prove
   (i) If G is supersolvable, G possesses a chief series whose factors have prime order.
   (ii) Show that the derived group of a supersolvable group is nilpotent.
8. Show that either of the following two conditions implies that G is nilpotent of class at most 2.
   (i) Any two conjugate elements of G commute.
   (ii) For x, y in G, $(xy)^i = [x, y]^{1/2 i(i-1)} x^i y^i$.
9. If G possesses a normal series with abelian factors, prove that G is solvable.
10. Let A be a subgroup of Aut G.
    (i) If A acts transitively on $G^\#$, show that G is an elementary abelian p-group for some prime p.
    (ii) If A acts doubly transitively on $G^\#$, show that either $p = 2$ or $|G| = 3$.
11. If G possesses a subgroup of index at most 4 and G is not of prime order, show that G is not simple.
12. Let H^{x_i} be the distinct conjugates of the subgroup H of G, $x_i \in G$, $1 \leqslant i \leqslant n$. For x in G, define $\theta(x)$ to be the permutation of this set of conjugates by the rule $H^{x_i}\theta(x) = H^{x_i x}$, $1 \leqslant i \leqslant n$. Prove
    (i) The mapping θ is a transitive permutation representation of G of degree n.

(ii) The representation θ is equivalent to the permutation representation on the right cosets of $N_G(H)$.

13. Let P be an S_p-subgroup of G and let π be the permutation representation of G on the right cosets of $N_G(P)$. Prove

   (i) $\pi(P)$ fixes exactly one letter.

   (ii) If $|P| = p$, then $\pi(x)$ is a product of one 1-cycle and a certain number of p cycles for any x in $P^\#$.

   (iii) If $|P| = p$ and $y \in N_G(P) - C_G(P)$, then $\pi(y)$ fixes at most r letters, where r denotes the number of orbits under the action of $\pi(P)$.

14. If a permutation group G contains an odd permutation, show that G possesses a normal subgroup of index 2.

15. Use Exercises 13 and 14 to prove that a group of order 264 is not simple.

16. Let G be a transitive permutation group of prime degree p and let P be an S_p-subgroup of G. Prove that $|P| = p$ and that $N_G(P)$ is a Frobenius group with kernel P.

17. If A is a regular group of automorphisms of G, prove that the semidirect product AG is a Frobenius group with kernel G and complement A.

18. Let G be the group of semilinear transformations $x' = ax^\sigma + b$, where $a, b \in GF(p^n)$, $a \neq 0$, and σ is an element of the Galois group of $GF(p^n)$. Prove

   (i) G is solvable of order $p^n(p^n - 1)n$.

   (ii) Let T be the translation subgroup of G consisting of all $x' = x + b$. If G acts triply transitively on $T^\#$, then $p^n = 4$.

   (iii) Let H be the affine subgroup of G consisting of all $x' = ax + b$. Then H is a Frobenius group with kernel T and cyclic complement A consisting of all $x' = ax$.

   (iv) If $B = \langle \beta \rangle$ is the subgroup generated by $x' = -x + 1$, then the set $ABA = H$. Moreover, every element of $H - A$ has a unique representation of the form $\alpha_1 \beta \alpha_2$ with $\alpha_1, \alpha_2 \in A$.

19. Let A, B be subgroups of G with $G = ABA$ and assume that every element of $G - A$ has a unique representation of the form $a_1 b a_2$ with $a_1, a_2 \in A$ and $b \in B$. Prove that G is a Frobenius group with complement A.

20. (i) Using the methods of semidirect products construct two groups G_1, G_2, each of order $7^3 \cdot 3$ with nonabelian commutator subgroups of order 7^3, such that G_1, but not G_2, is a Frobenius group.

   (ii) Show that $SL(3, 7)$ contains a subgroup is isomorphic to G_1.

21. (i) Determine the conjugate classes in $L_2(p)$.

   (ii) Determine the conjugate classes of p-elements in $SL(3, p)$.

22. Suppose that $G = [G, G]$, $|Z(G)| = 2$, and $G/Z(G)$ is isomorphic to $L_2(5)$ (equivalently, to A_5). Show that G is isomorphic to $SL(2, 5)$.

23. If $|L_2(q)|$ is divisible by 60, prove that $L_2(q)$ possesses a subgroup isomorphic to A_5.

24. Let P be an S_p-subgroup of G. Assume that $Z = \Omega_1(Z(P))$ has order p and that $N_P(B) \supset C_P(B)$ for any elementary abelian subgroup of B of order p^2 containing Z. Prove that if $Z^x \subseteq P - Z$ for some x in G, then $N_G(\langle Z^x, Z \rangle)$ involves $SL(2, p)$.

25. Give a direct proof without appeal to Dickson's theorem that $SL(2, p^n)$ is generated by all its p-elements.

CHAPTER 3

REPRESENTATIONS OF GROUPS

In this chapter we establish those results concerning representations of groups that we shall need, but which do not depend upon the methods of character theory. After introducing a large number of basic concepts of representation theory, we discuss in succession representations of abelian groups, conditions for complete reducibility, and the important theorem of Clifford. We then study G-homomorphisms and apply our results to obtain descriptions of irreducible G-modules, conditions for absolute irreducibility of representations, and to determine the structure of the group algebra of G over suitable fields. Some of these results are also applied to give a description of the irreducible representations of direct and central products of groups. Finally, we treat the basic topic of p-stable representations which will play a crucial role in the analysis of many later problems.

1. BASIC CONCEPTS

If π is a permutation representation of a group G on a set S, we can regard the elements of S as a basis of a vector space V over an arbitrary field F and can then consider the elements of $(G)\pi$ as linear transformations of V represented with respect to the given basis by the appropriate permutation matrices. Thus π induces a homomorphism of G into the group of nonsingular linear transformations of V/F or equivalently of nonsingular matrices with coefficients in F. Likewise, if H is an elementary abelian p-subgroup of the group G, we have seen that there is a homomorphism of $N_G(H)$ into the group of nonsingular linear transformations on H regarded as a vector space over Z_p. Clearly these are special cases of the general concept of a homomorphism of a group into the group of nonsingular linear transformations of a vector space V over a field F. In this chapter we shall study some of the properties of such homomorphisms.

If V is a vector space of dimension n over a field F, we denote by $GL(V, F)$ the group of all nonsingular linear transformations on V and by $GL(n, F)$ the group of all $n \times n$ matrices with coefficients in F. As usual, for each basis $(v) = \{v_1, v_2, \ldots, v_n\}$ of V/F, we associate to each T in $GL(V, F)$ the matrix $T_{(v)}$ of T with respect to the given basis. Then the mapping $\alpha_{(v)} : T \to T_{(v)}$ is an isomorphism of $GL(V, F)$ onto $GL(n, F)$.

A homomorphism ϕ of a group G into the group $GL(V, F)$ of nonsingular transformations of a vector space V over a field F is called a *representation* of G. V is called a *representation space* or *representation module* for G. We also say that ϕ is *represented* on V/F or that ϕ is a representation of G *over* F. The kernel K of ϕ is called the *kernel* of the representation. If ϕ is one-to-one, so that G is mapped isomorphically into $GL(V, F)$ and $K = 1$, we say that ϕ is a *faithful* representation. At the other extreme, we say that ϕ is *trivial* if $K = G$, in which case $(G)\phi$ consists only of the identity transformation of V. In general the dimension of V over F (denoted $\dim_F V$) is called the *degree* of ϕ. Representations of degree 1 are called *linear* representations. In this book we shall restrict ourselves entirely to finite-dimensional representations.

The representation ϕ above induces in a natural way a homomorphism ϕ^* of G/K into $GL(V, F)$, which is one-to-one. Thus every representation of G induces a faithful representation of G modulo the kernel of ϕ on the same vector space.

Now the image $(G)\phi$ of G under ϕ is a group of linear transformations of V and so we have the basic relations:

(1.1) $$(xy)\phi = (x\phi)(y\phi) \qquad \text{for } x, y \text{ in } G.$$

(1.2) $$(av + a'v')(x\phi) = a(v(x\phi)) + a'(v'(x\phi)) \qquad \text{for } a, a' \text{ in } F \text{ and } v, v' \text{ in } V.$$

By choosing a fixed basis (v) of V/F, the composition mapping $\phi\alpha_{(v)}$ is a homomorphism of G into $GL(n, F)$ which we refer to as a *matrix* representation of G. For x in G, we write for brevity $(x\phi)_{(v)}$ for the matrix $(x)\phi\alpha_{(v)}$. It may happen that for a particular basis (v) of V, the entries of the matrices $\phi\alpha_{(v)}$ all lie in a subfield L of F. If this is the case, we shall say that ϕ *can be written in L*.

Given any subfield K of F, ϕ can always be written in a subfield L of F which is finitely generated over K, for if (v) is any basis of V/F, then there are only a finite number of entries in the matrices $(x\phi)_{(v)}$ and the subfield they generate over K has the required properties.

If W is a subspace of V invariant under $(G)\phi$, then ϕ induces a homomorphism of G into $GL(W, F)$ which we call the *restriction* of ϕ to W and denote by $\phi|_H$. Such a representation is also said to be a *subrepresentation* of ϕ. At the same time if ψ denotes the natural homomorphism of V onto V/W, the composition $\phi\psi$ is a homomorphism of G into $GL(V/W, F)$, which we call the *factor* or *quotient* representation of G on V/W induced by ϕ.

There are two very important types of representations: the irreducible and indecomposable. A representation ϕ of G on V/F is called *irreducible* if 0 and V are the only $(G)\phi$-invariant subspaces of V. In the contrary case, we say that ϕ is *reducible*. We say that ϕ is *indecomposable* if it is not possible to write V as the direct sum of two nontrivial $(G)\phi$-invariant subspaces. In the contrary case, we say that ϕ is *decomposable*. Clearly irreducibility implies indecomposability, but the converse is not necessarily true. In fact, in Section 3 we shall give a sufficient condition for an indecomposable representation to be irreducible. This question is closely related to another important concept—that of complete reducibility. We say that a representation ϕ of G on V/F is *completely reducible* provided $V = V_1 \oplus V_2 \ldots \oplus V_r$, where V_i is a nonzero $(G)\phi$-invariant subspace of V and $\phi|_{V_i}$ is irreducible, $1 \leqslant i \leqslant r$.

We have seen in Chapter 2 the usefulness of the concept of equivalent or isomorphic permutation representations. This notion has a natural extension to general representations which is equally important and which we shall now describe. Let ϕ be a representation of G on V/F and let (v), (v') be two bases of V/F. Then for x in G, we have

(1.3) $(x\phi)_{(v')} = P^{-1}(x\phi)_{(v)}P,$

where P denotes the matrix of the change of basis from (v) to (v'). Thus a given representation of ϕ determines a number of matrix representations of G, which we obviously wish to consider as being equivalent.

A similar situation occurs if ϕ, ϕ' are representations of G on V, V' over

F, respectively, of the same dimension, (v), (v') are bases of V and V', P is the matrix of an isomorphism ψ of V on V' mapping the elements of (v) on the corresponding elements of (v'), and for each x in G we have

$$(1.4) \qquad (x\phi')_{(v')} = P^{-1}(x\phi)_{(v)}P.$$

Again we clearly wish to consider ϕ and ϕ' as equivalent representations.

Expressed in terms of linear transformations condition (1.4) reads $x\phi = \psi^{-1}(x\phi)\psi$; that is,

$$(1.5) \qquad u\psi(x\phi') = u(x\phi)\psi \qquad \text{for all } x \text{ in } G, u \text{ in } V.$$

Thus we shall say that two representations ϕ, ϕ' of G on vector spaces V and V' over F, respectively, are *equivalent* or *isomorphic* provided there exists an isomorphism ψ of V on V' for which (1.5) holds.

It follows immediately from the definition that this notion of equivalence is an equivalence relation on the category of all representations of a group G on vector spaces over a given field F. We should like also to illustrate this concept with a simple general example which we incorporate into a lemma:

Lemma 1.1

Let ϕ be a representation of G on V/F and let U and W be two $(G)\phi$-invariant subspaces of V such that $U \cap W = 0$. Let $\bar{\phi}$ be the quotient representation of G on $\bar{V} = V/W$ and let $\bar{U}$ be the image of U in $\bar{V}$. Then $\bar{U}$ is $(G)\bar{\phi}$-invariant and $\phi|_U$ is equivalent to $\bar{\phi}|_{\bar{U}}$.

Proof

Let ψ be the natural homomorphism of V onto $\bar{V} = V/W$. Then by definition of $\bar{\phi}$, we have for $\bar{v}$ in $\bar{V}$ and x in G,

$$(1.6) \qquad \bar{v}(x\bar{\phi}) = (v(x\phi))\psi,$$

where v is an element of V which maps on $\bar{v}$. Since $v(x\phi) \in U$ if $v \in U$, it follows at once from (1.6) that $\bar{U}$ is $(G)\bar{\phi}$-invariant.

Set $\phi_1 = \phi|_U$ and $\bar{\phi}_1 = \bar{\phi}|_{\bar{U}}$. Then for u in U, and x in G, (1.6) reduces to

$$(1.7) \qquad u\psi(x\bar{\phi}_1) = u(x\phi_1)\psi.$$

But ψ is an isomorphism of U onto $\bar{U}$ as $U \cap W = 0$. We conclude at once from the definition that the representations ϕ_1, $\bar{\phi}_1$ of G on U, $\bar{U}$, respectively, are equivalent.

Given a representation ϕ of G on V/F, it is very often convenient to make V into a right G-module (that is, a right FG-module) by setting

$$ux = u(x\phi) \qquad \text{for all } u \text{ in } V.$$

When this is done, each element of G becomes itself a linear transformation of V. Note that elements lying in the same coset of the kernel of ϕ determine the same linear transformation. Once V is made into a G-module, we can carry over to the language of modules the various concepts that have just been introduced. Thus a $(G)\phi$-invariant subspace of V becomes a G-submodule of V, V is an irreducible G-module if 0 and V are the only G-submodules of V, V is a faithful G-module if only the identity element of G determines the identity transformation on V, V and V' are isomorphic G-modules over F if and only if there exists an isomorphism ψ of V on V' which commutes with the elements of G; that is,

$$(1.8) \qquad u(\psi x) = u(x\psi) \qquad \text{for } x \text{ in } G, u \text{ in } V;$$

with similar interpretations of the remaining terms and concepts of representation theory.

Conversely, if V/F is a G-module, each element x of G determines a linear transformation T_x of V by setting $vT_x = vx$ for v in V; and the mapping ϕ given by $(x)\phi = T_x$ is easily seen to be a representation of G on V. Thus the notions of a representation of G and of a G-module (over a field) are equivalent and so can be used interchangeably. In a given context we shall use whichever of the two is the more convenient.

Statements concerning groups of linear transformations can invariably be rephrased as results about representations (equally well about modules). For example, Theorem 2.6.4 becomes the following statement:

Theorem 1.2

Every irreducible representation of a p-group on a vector space over a field of characteristic p is trivial. Equivalently a nontrivial p-group does not possess a faithful irreducible representation on a vector space over a field of characteristic p.

The argument can be extended to give the following generalization:

Theorem 1.3

If G possesses a faithful irreducible representation on a vector space over a field of characteristic p, then G has no nontrivial normal p-subgroups.

Proof

Let ϕ be a faithful irreducible representation of G on V/F, where F is of characteristic p and let P be a normal p-subgroup of G. By Lemma 2.6.3, $(P)\phi$ fixes some nonzero vector of V, so $W = C_V((P)\phi) \neq 0$. But W is $(G)\phi$-invariant by Lemma 2.6.2; and as ϕ is irreducible, the only possibility is $W = G$. Thus $(P)\phi$ acts trivially on G. Since ϕ is also faithful, this implies that $P = 1$, proving the theorem.

To motivate the next concept, that of extending the base field, consider a G-module V/F and set $m = |G|$. Then each element x of G determines a linear transformation T_x of V of order dividing m, so that T_x satisfies the polynomial $X^m - 1$. Thus for each x in G, the characteristic roots of T_x are mth roots of unity over F. These roots of unity can all be taken to lie in an extension field $F(\omega)$, where ω is a primitive mth root of unity. We shall speak of these as the characteristic roots of x on V. In many circumstances the analysis turns out to be considerably easier if the field F itself contains a primitive mth root of unity or is even algebraically closed. When F does not satisfy one or the other of these conditions it is necessary to replace V by a suitable vector space over an extension field L of F.

To describe this process, let V be a vector space over F, let L be an extension field of F, and form the tensor product $V_L = V \otimes_F L$, which is then a vector space over L. Indeed, if $(v) = \{v_i | 1 \leqslant i \leqslant n\}$ is a basis of V over F and $1 = 1_L$ denotes the unity element of L, then the elements $\{v_i \otimes 1 | 1 \leqslant i \leqslant n\}$ form a basis of V_L/L. We can identify the element $u = \sum_{i=1}^{n} a_i v_i$ of V, $a_i \in F$ with its image $\sum_{i=1}^{n} a_i(v_i \otimes 1)$ in V_L. When this is done, V becomes a subset of V_L and also each element of V_L then has a unique representation of the form $\sum_{i=1}^{n} b_i v_i$ with $b_i \in L$. Thus, in effect, in passing from V to V_L we are extending the field of operators from F to L. Note, however, that V is not a subspace of V_L (unless $F = L$), as V_L is a vector space over L.

If T is a linear transformation of V/F, then $T_{(v)}$ can be regarded as a matrix over L as well as over F and, in view of the preceding identification, as the matrix of a linear transformation T_L of V_L with respect to the basis (v) of V_L. If follows from this that the mapping $T \to T_L$ gives an isomorphism of $GL(V, F)$ into $GL(V_L, L)$. We note also that the characteristic and minimal polynomials of T_L on V_L are identical with those of T on V.

But now we see that if ϕ is a representation of V/F, the elements $(x\phi)_L$ for x in G are linear transformations of V_L and that the mapping ϕ_L of G into $GL(V_L, L)$ given by

$$(x)\phi_L = (x\phi)_L \qquad \text{for } x \text{ in } G$$

is a representation of G on V_L. Likewise if V/F is a G-module, then V_L/L is also a G-module.

If ϕ is irreducible, the representation ϕ_L above may or may not be irreducible. This leads to the important notion of an absolutely irreducible representation or G-module. A representation ϕ of G on V/F is said to be *absolutely irreducible* provided the extended representation ϕ_L of G on V_L/L is irreducible for every extension field L of F. Moreover, a field F with the property that every irreducible representation ϕ of G on a vector space V/F is absolutely irreducible is called a *splitting field* for G.

2. REPRESENTATIONS OF ABELIAN GROUPS

In this section we establish some basic properties of the representations of abelian groups. Our first result will follow as a corollary of a general necessary condition for a group to possess a faithful irreducible representation. We need the following lemma:

Lemma 2.1

Let V/F be an irreducible G-module. If an element z of $Z(G)$ has a characteristic root λ in F, then $vz = \lambda v$ for all v in V. In particular, if V is a faithful G-module, either $z = 1$ or $\lambda \neq 1$.

Proof

Let $W = \{w \in V \mid wz = \lambda w\}$, so that by assumption $W \neq 0$. Clearly W is a subspace of V. Moreover, if $x \in G$ and $w \in W$, we have

$$(wx)z = w(xz) = w(zx) = (wz)x = (\lambda w)x = \lambda(wx)$$

as $z \in Z(G)$. Thus $wx \in W$ and consequently W is G-invariant. But now the irreducibility of G on V forces $W = V$, whence $vz = \lambda v$ for all v in V. Furthermore, if G acts faithfully on V and $z \neq 1$, then z does not induce the identity linear transformation on V, so $\lambda \neq 1$.

We can now prove

Theorem 2.2

If G possesses a faithful irreducible representation, then $Z(G)$ is cyclic.

Proof

Suppose G has a faithful irreducible representation ϕ on V/F. We regard V as a G-module. Set $m = |G|$ and consider first the case that F contains a primitive mth root of unity, so that the characteristic roots of the elements of G lie in F. In particular, each z in $Z(G)$ has a characteristic root $\lambda(z)$ in F and hence by the preceding lemma z acts on V like the scalar transformation $\lambda(z)I$. As V is a faithful G-module, the preceding lemma also implies that the homomorphism: $z \to \lambda(z)$, is one-to-one. Thus $Z(G)$ is isomorphic to a subgroup of F. But it is well known that a finite subgroup of the multiplicative group of a field is cyclic. Hence $Z(G)$ is cyclic in this case.

For the general case, we set $L = F(\omega)$, where ω is a primitive mth root of unity and consider the extended G-module $V_L = V \otimes_F L$. Let W be a minimal nonzero G-submodule of V_L and let K be the kernel of the representation of G on W, so that $\bar{G} = G/K$ acts faithfully and irreducibly on W. Since L contains a primitive $|\bar{G}|$-th root of unity, it follows from the preceding case that $Z(\bar{G})$ is cyclic. But obviously the image of $Z(G)$ in $\bar{G}$ lies in $Z(\bar{G})$, and hence $Z(G)/Z(G) \cap K$ is cyclic. Thus to complete the proof it will suffice to show that $Z(G) \cap K = 1$.

Indeed, if $z \in Z(G) \cap K$, then z has 1 as a characteristic root on W and hence on V_L. But as z has the same characteristic polynomial on V as it does on V_L, 1 is a characteristic root of z on V. But then z must induce the identity transformation on V by the preceding lemma, Since V is a faithful G-module, this forces $z = 1$. Thus $Z(G) \cap K = 1$, as required.

As a corollary we have:

Theorem 2.3

If ϕ is an irreducible representation of an abelian group G with kernel K, then G/K is cyclic. In particular, a noncyclic abelian group does not possess a faithful irreducible representation.

Proof

By definition of K, ϕ induces a faithful irreducible representation of G/K. But $Z(G/K) = G/K$ as G is abelian and so G/K is cyclic by the theorem.

As an additional corollary, we have:

Theorem 2.4

Let G be an abelian group of order n and F a field which contains a primitive nth root of unity. Then every irreducible representation of G over F is linear.

Proof

Let V/F be an irreducible G-module and let K be the kernel of G on V, so that G/K is cyclic by Theorem 2.3. Choose x in G so that Kx generates G/K. As F contains a primitive nth root of unity, x possesses a nonzero characteristic vector v_1 in V. Since the elements of K induce the identity transformation on V, it follows that the subspace V_1 generated by v_1 is G-invariant. But now the irreducibility of G forces $V_1 = V$, whence $\dim_F V = 1$ and the representation of G on V is linear.

Finally as a partial converse of this result, we prove:

Theorem 2.5

If ϕ is a linear representation of G, then G/K is cyclic, where K is the kernel of ϕ. In particular, a noncyclic group does not possess a faithful representation of degree 1.

Proof

Suppose V/F is a G-module determined by the representation ϕ with $\dim_F V = 1$. Then if v is a basis element of V, we have $vx = \lambda(x)v$ with $\lambda(x) \in F$ for any x in G. It follows that the mapping $\alpha : x \to \lambda(x)$ is a homomorphism of G into the multiplicative group of F, whence G/K is cyclic, where K is the kernel of α. But clearly K is precisely the set of elements of G which induce the identity transformation on V and so K is also the kernel of ϕ.

3. COMPLETE REDUCIBILITY

We shall now establish a fundamental sufficient criterion for a representation to be completely reducible.

Theorem 3.1 (Maschke)

Let ϕ be a representation of G on V/F and assume that either F is of characteristic 0 or of characteristic relatively prime to $|G|$. Then ϕ is completely reducible.

Proof

The proof depends upon a certain "averaging" argument which we shall have several further occasions to employ. Set $n = |G|$ and $p = $ characteristic of F. We may assume that F contains the rational numbers if $p = 0$ and contains Z_p if $p \neq 0$. Since $(n, p) = 1$ by assumption if $p \neq 0$, it follows in either case that $1/n$ is a well-defined element of F. This means that for v in V, $(1/n)v$ is a well-specified element of V; and, moreover,

$$(3.1) \qquad n((1/n)v) = (1/n)(nv) = v.$$

We regard V as a G-module and let V_1 be a minimal nonzero G-submodule of V. Since G acts irreducibly on V_1, the theorem follows if $V_1 = V$, so we may assume $V_1 \subset V$. Let u_i, $1 \leqslant i \leqslant r$, be a basis of V_1, which we extend to a basis u_i, $1 \leqslant i \leqslant m$, of V. Setting W equal to the subspace spanned by the u_i, $r + 1 \leqslant i \leqslant m$, we have $V = V_1 \oplus W$ and $W \neq 0$. Thus W is a complement of V_1 in V, but of course W need not be

G-invariant. Our aim will be to show that, in fact, a G-invariant complement of V_1 exists.

For v in V, we can write $v = v_1 + w$ uniquely, where $v_1 \in V_1$ and $w \in W$. We set $v\theta = w$, so that θ is the projection map of V on W. Since $w\theta = w$ for w in W, we have $\theta^2 = \theta$, so that θ is idempotent. Furthermore, θ is clearly a linear map and also $v - v\theta = v_1 \in V_1$. We now define for v in V,

$$(3.2) \qquad v\psi = 1/n \sum_{x \in G} ((vx)\theta)x^{-1}.$$

Since $1/n$ is a well-determined element of F, ψ is a well-defined map of V into V. Since θ is linear and V is a G-module, it is immediate that ψ is a linear transformation.

We argue first that $V_2 = (V)\psi$ is G-invariant. Indeed, for y in G, set $z = y^{-1}x$. Then

$$(3.3) \qquad (v\psi)y = 1/n \sum_{x \in G} (vx\theta x^{-1})y = 1/n \sum_{x \in G} v(yz)\theta z^{-1}.$$

Since z ranges over G as x does, (3.3) and (3.2) yield

$$(3.4) \qquad (v\psi)y = 1/n \sum_{z \in G} (vy)z\theta z^{-1} = (vy)\psi \in V_2,$$

which implies that V_2 is G-invariant.

We shall now show that $V = V_1 \oplus V_2$. First of all, if $v \in V$, write $v = v_1 + v_2$, where $v_2 = v\psi$, and $v_1 = v - v_2$. Then $v_2 \in V_2$ by definition of V_2. On the other hand, as $vxx^{-1} = v$, we can write

$$(3.5) \qquad v_1 = v - v\psi = 1/n \sum_{x \in G} (vx - vx\theta)x^{-1}.$$

But $vx - vx\theta \in V_1$ for each x in G and now (3.5) yields that $v_1 \in V_1$. Thus $V = V_1 + V_2$ and so it remains to show that $V_1 \cap V_2 = 0$.

To establish this, we derive two preliminary results: $v_1\psi = 0$ for all v_1 in V_1 and $\psi^2 = \psi$. Indeed, if $v_1 \in V_1$, then so does v_1x for x in G and consequently $(v_1x)\theta = 0$ for all x in G. Clearly this implies that $v_1\psi = 0$. Furthermore, as we have shown in the preceding paragraph, $v - v\psi \in V_1$ for all v in V_2 and hence $(v - v\psi)\psi = 0$. This yields $v\psi = v\psi^2$ as ψ is linear, whence also $\psi^2 = \psi$.

But now if $v \in V_1 \cap V_2$, then, on the one hand, we have $v\psi = 0$; and on the other, $v = u\psi$ for some u in V as $V_2 = (V)\psi$. Thus

$$0 = v\psi = u\psi^2 = u\psi = v,$$

whence $V_1 \cap V_2 = 0$, giving the desired conclusion $V = V_1 \oplus V_2$.

Since V_2 is a G-module of lower dimension then V, it follows now by induction on $\dim_F V$ that V_2 is the direct sum of irreducible G-submodules. Hence the same is true of V and we conclude that the given representation ϕ of G is completely reducible.

Remark With respect to the basis $(u) = \{u_i \mid 1 \leqslant i \leqslant m\}$ of $V = V_1 \oplus W$, the matrix $x_{(u)}$ of the transformation of V determined by x has the form

$$(3.6) \qquad\qquad x_{(u)} \quad \begin{pmatrix} A(x) & 0 \\ C(x) & B(x) \end{pmatrix},$$

where $A(x)$ is $r \times r$ and $B(x)$ is $(m - r) \times (m - r)$. If $\bar{V}$ denotes the factor module V/V_1 and $\bar{u}_i$ the image of u_i in $\bar{V}$, $r + 1 \leqslant i \leqslant m$, then $(\bar{u}) = \{\bar{u}_i \mid r + 1 \leqslant i \leqslant m\}$ is a basis of $\bar{V}$ and relative to this basis the matrix of the transformation determined by x is $x_{(\bar{u})} = B(x)$. On the other hand, since $V = V_1 \oplus V_2$ and V_2 is G-invariant, V_2 and $\bar{V}$ are isomorphic G-modules by Lemma 1.1. This means that with respect to a suitable basis of V_2, the matrix of x on V_2 is $B(x)$. Combining this basis with the given basis of V_1, we obtain a basis (v) of V and the matrix of x relative to (v) is

$$(3.7) \qquad\qquad x_{(v)} = \begin{pmatrix} A(x) & 0 \\ 0 & B(x) \end{pmatrix}.$$

Thus in terms of matrices the preceding argument proves the existence of an $m \times m$ nonsingular matrix P of the form

$$(3.8) \qquad\qquad P = \begin{pmatrix} I_r & 0 \\ Q & I_{m-r} \end{pmatrix},$$

where Q is a suitable $(m - r) \times r$ matrix over F, with the property that for all x in G,

$$(3.9) \qquad\qquad P^{-1}\begin{pmatrix} A(x) & 0 \\ C(x) & B(x) \end{pmatrix}P = \begin{pmatrix} A(x) & 0 \\ 0 & B(x) \end{pmatrix}.$$

An alternative proof of this result under the specified hypotheses on F and $|G|$ can be given directly in terms of matrices.

Theorem 3.1 applies, in particular, to the case that V is an elementary abelian p-group and G is a group of automorphisms of V of order n with $(n, p) = 1$. In actuality the proof does not require V to be elementary; in fact, the argument holds equally well for any abelian p-group V (written additively) which possesses a G-invariant direct summand V_1. The only change required for the proof is to replace the term "linear" by "homomorphism" throughout. Even though V is no longer a vector space over Z_p, $(1/n)v$ is still a well-defined element of V satisfying (3.1). Indeed, as

$(p, n) = 1$, there exists an integer a (depending upon $|v|$) such that $an \equiv 1$ (mod p) and we define $(1/n)v$ to be av. Moreover, the endomorphisms of an abelian group form a ring, and consequently the mapping ψ above is a well-defined endomorphism of V. Hence as a corollary of the proof, we have

Theorem 3.2

Let G be a p'-group of automorphisms of an abelian p-group V and suppose V_1 is a G-invariant direct factor of V. Then $G = V_1 \times V_2$, where V_2 is also G-invariant.

We should like now to give a simple, but extremely important, group-theoretic application of Theorems 2.3 and 3.1 to illustrate some of the ideas so far developed.

Theorem 3.3

Let P be an elementary abelian p-group and let Q be a noncyclic abelian q-subgroup of Aut P, q a prime distinct from p. Then

$$P = \prod_{x \in Q^{\#}} C_P(x).$$

In particular, P is generated by its subgroups $C_P(x)$ with x in $Q^{\#}$.

Proof

We consider P to be a vector space over Z_p and then we regard P as a Q-module. As $p \neq q$, Theorem 3.1 gives that P is a completely reducible Q-module. Hence

$$P = P_1 \oplus P_2 \oplus \cdots \oplus P_n,$$

where P_i is an irreducible Q-submodule of P, $1 \leqslant i \leqslant n$. Since Q is abelian, Theorem 2.3 implies that Q/Q_i is cyclic, where Q_i denotes the kernel of the representation of Q on P_i. But as Q is noncyclic, this forces $Q_i \neq 1$, $1 \leqslant i \leqslant n$. Choosing x_i in $Q_i^{\#}$, we have $P_i \subseteq C_P(x_i)$, whence

$$P = \sum_{i=1}^{n} C_P(x_i) \subseteq \sum_{x \in Q^{\#}} C_P(x).$$

Reverting to multiplicative notation, the theorem follows.

As a further corollary, we have

Theorem 3.4

Let ϕ be a representation of G on V/F and assume that either F is of characteristic 0 or characteristic prime to $|G|$. Suppose

$$V = V_1 \supset V_2 \supset \cdots \supset V_{n+1} = 0$$

is a sequence of $(G)\phi$-invariant subspaces such that $(G)\phi$ acts trivially on each V_i/V_{i+1}. Then ϕ is the trivial representation on V.

Proof

By Theorem 3.1, $V = V_n \oplus W$, where W is $(G)\phi$-invariant. By Lemma 1.1, $\phi|_W$ is equivalent to the quotient representation $\bar{\phi}$ of G on V/V_n. But then by induction on $\dim_F V$ we have that $\phi|_W$ is trivial. Since $\phi|_{V_n}$ is also trivial, the theorem follows.

4. CLIFFORD'S THEOREM

If G is represented irreducibly on V/F and H is a normal subgroup of G, it is important to know how the space V decomposes under the action of H. This question is answered in the following fundamental theorem:

Theorem 4.1 (Clifford)

Let V/F be an irreducible G-module and let H be a normal subgroup of G. Then V is the direct sum of H-invariant subspaces V_i, $1 \leqslant i \leqslant r$, which satisfy the following conditions:

(i) *$V_i = X_{i1} \oplus X_{i2} \oplus \cdots \oplus X_{it}$, where each X_{ij} is an irreducible H-submodule, $1 \leqslant i \leqslant r$, t is independent of i, and $X_{ij}, X_{i'j'}$ are isomorphic H-submodules if and only if $i = i'$.*

(ii) *For any H-submodule U of V, we have $U = U_1 \oplus U_2 \oplus \cdots \oplus U_r$, where $U_i = U \cap V_i$, $1 \leqslant i \leqslant r$. In particular, any irreducible H-submodule of V lies in one of the V_i.*

(iii) *For x in G, the mapping $(x)\pi : V_i \to V_i x$, $1 \leqslant i \leqslant r$, is a permutation of the set $S = \{V_1, V_2, \ldots, V_r\}$ and π induces a transitive permutation representation of G on S. Furthermore, $HC_G(H)$ is contained in the kernel of π.*

Proof

First of all, consider any H-submodule W of V. For x in G, set $W^x = \{wx \mid w \in W\}$. Clearly W is a subspace of V. Moreover, if $wx \in W^x$, $w \in W$, and if $h \in H$, we have $(wx)h = (wh^{x^{-1}})x = w_1 x \in W^x$ as $h^{x^{-1}} \in H$ by the normality of H. Thus W^x is also an H-submodule of V. However, W and W^x need not be isomorphic H-modules. On the other hand, the mapping $U \to U^x$ sets up a one-to-one correspondence between the H-submodules of W and those of W^x, as follows easily from the fact that $(W^x)^{x^{-1}} = W$. In particular, W^x is irreducible if and only if W is. Moreover, if Y is an H-submodule of V isomorphic to W under an H-isomorphism θ, one verifies at once that W^x and Y^x are isomorphic H-modules with respect to the H-isomorphism $x^{-1}\theta x$.

Now let $W = W_1 \oplus W_2 \oplus \cdots \oplus W_s$ be a direct sum of irreducible H-submodules W_i of V, $1 \leqslant i \leqslant s$, where s is chosen to be maximal. Suppose $W_i^x \nsubseteq W$ for some i and some x in G. Then $W \cap W_i^x$ is a proper H-submodule of W_i^x. But W_i^x is irreducible and hence $W \cap W_i^x = 0$. Thus $W + W_i^x = W \oplus W_i^x$ and we see that our maximal choice of s is contradicted. Thus $W_i^x \subseteq W$ for all i and x, whence W is G-invariant. Since V is an irreducible G-module, we conclude that $W = V$. Hence V is the direct sum of irreducible H-submodules.

We now relabel the W_i as X_{ij} in such a way that X_{ij} and $X_{i'j'}$ are isomorphic H-modules if and only if $i = i'$, and we set $V_i = X_{i1} \oplus X_{i2} \oplus \cdots \oplus X_{it_i}$, $1 \leqslant i \leqslant r$. By the preceding argument, $V = V_1 \oplus V_2 \oplus \cdots \oplus V_r$. However, note that we do not yet know that t_i is independent of i.

Next let U be any H-submodule of V. By the irreducibility of the W_j, the assumption that some $W_{j_1} \nsubseteq U$ implies that $U \cap W_{j_1} = 0$ and hence that $U + W_{j_1} = U \oplus W_{j_1}$. Repeating this argument as many times as possible, we find that there exist j_k, $1 \leqslant k \leqslant e$, such that

$$V^* = U \oplus W_{j_1} \oplus W_{j_2} \oplus \cdots \oplus W_{j_e}$$

is a direct sum and that $W_j \subseteq V^*$ for all j, $1 \leqslant j \leqslant s$. But as V is the direct sum of the W_j, this forces $V = V^*$. Setting V' equal to the direct sum of the W_j, $1 \leqslant k \leqslant e$, and V'' to the direct sum of the remaining W_j, we thus obtain

$$V = U \oplus V' \qquad \text{and} \qquad V = V'' \oplus V'.$$

But then by Lemma 1.1 both U and V'' are isomorphic to V/V' as H-modules and consequently U is isomorphic to V'' as an H-module. It follows that any H-submodule U of V is itself the direct sum of irreducible H-submodules. If (ii) holds for each of these irreducible submodules, then it will follow at once for U. Thus it suffices to prove (ii) when U is an irreducible H-submodule.

Set $W_m' = W_1 \oplus W_2 \oplus \cdots \oplus W_m$ and choose m maximal so that $U \nsubseteq W_m'$. Clearly $1 \leqslant m < s$ as $W_s' = V$. Furthermore, $U \subseteq W_{m+1}' = W_m' \oplus W_{m+1}$. Since U is irreducible, $U \cap W_m' = 0$, so $W_m' + U = W_m' \oplus U \subseteq W_m' \oplus W_{m+1}$. But then U is isomorphic to a nontrivial irreducible H-submodule of W_{m+1}'/W_m', which in turn is isomorphic to W_{m+1}. We conclude that U and W_{m+1} are isomorphic H-modules. Suppose $W_{m+1} \subseteq V_i$. We shall argue that $U \subseteq V_i$ and this will establish (ii).

If $U \not\subseteq V_i$, then U maps isomorphically onto an irreducible submodule of V/V_i. But V/V_i is isomorphic to the direct sum of those W_j's which are not isomorphic to W_{m+1} and hence which are not isomorphic to U. On the other hand, the argument of the preceding paragraph can be repeated in V/V_i for the image of U to yield that this image, and hence U itself, is isomorphic to one of these remaining W_j's, a contradiction. Thus $U \subseteq V_i$ and (ii) holds.

Now let $x \in G$. We have shown that X_{ij}^x is an irreducible H-submodule and hence by (ii) is isomorphic to $X_{i'j'}$ for suitable i', j'. We also know that X_{ij}^x and X_{ik}^x are isomorphic H-modules for all j, k, $1 \leqslant j, k \leqslant t_i$. Hence i' depends only upon i and not upon the choice of j. It follows therefore that $V_i^x \subseteq V_{i'}$. Furthermore, as V is an irreducible G-module, we must have $V = \langle V_i^x \mid x \in G \rangle$ for all i, $1 \leqslant i \leqslant r$. This means that for each choice of i, i', $1 \leqslant i, i' \leqslant r$, there exists an element $x_{ii'}$ in G such that $V_i^{x_{ii'}} \subseteq V_{i'}$. In particular, $\dim_F V_i \leqslant \dim_F V_{i'}$ for all i, i', whence $\dim_F V_{i'} = \dim_F V_{i'}$ for all i, i'. But for any i and any x in G, V_i^x has the same dimension as V_i and $V_i^x \subseteq V_{i'}$ for some i'. It follows therefore that $V_i^x = V_{i'}$. We have thus shown that the mapping $(x)\pi: V_i \to V_i^x = V_i x$ is a permutation of the set $S = \{V_1, V_2, \ldots, V_r\}$. Since $V_i^{xy} = (V_i^x)^y$ for x, y in G, it is immediate that π is a homomorphism and so is a permutation representation of G on S. Furthermore, as the elements $x_{1i'}$, $1 \leqslant i \leqslant r$, map V_1 into $V_{i'}$, π is transitive. In addition, X_{1j} and $X_{1j}^{x_{1i'}}$ have the same dimension for all j, $1 \leqslant j \leqslant t_1$. Since V_1 and $V_{i'}$ also have the same dimension, we must have $t_1 = t_{i'}$ for all i'. Hence t_i is determined independently of i.

Thus to complete the proof of the theorem, it remains only to show that $HC_G(H)$ is contained in the kernel of π. Since each V_i is an H-module, obviously H is contained in the kernel of π. Hence we need only show that $C_G(H)$ is, or equivalently that $V_i^x = V_i$ for all i, $1 \leqslant i \leqslant r$, and all x in $C_G(H)$. By the preceding argument, this will follow if we can prove that X_{ij} and X_{ij}^x are isomorphic H-modules whenever $x \in C_G(H)$. Let ψ_x denote the isomorphism of X_{ij} on X_{ij}^x given by $v\psi_x = vx$ for v in X_{ij}. Since $hx = xh$ for all h in H, we have

$$v\psi_x h = vh\psi_x$$

for v in X_{ij}, h in H, and x in $C_G(H)$; and now it follows at once from the definition that X_{ij} and X_{ij}^x are isomorphic H-modules for all x in $C_G(H)$. Thus all parts of the theorem are proved.

The subspaces $V_i, 1 \leqslant i \leqslant r$, are often referred to as the *Wedderburn components* of V with respect to H.

The argument which established the second statement of (ii) can easily be adapted to yield the following corollary:

Corollary 4.2

Let H be a group and let V/F be an H-module. If V is the direct sum of isomorphic irreducible H-submodules X_i, $1 \leqslant i \leqslant t$, then any irreducible H-submodule of V is isomorphic to X_1.

There is a case of some importance in which we can assert a little more:

Theorem 4.3

Let $G = HA$ be a Frobenius group whose kernel H is an elementary abelian q-group for some prime q and whose complement A is cyclic. Assume that G is faithfully and irreducibly represented on V/F, where F contains a primitive qth root of unity. Then the number of Wedderburn components of V with respect to H is exactly $|A|$.

Proof

By Theorem 2.7.6(iii) and the remark following it, the condition that G be a Frobenius group is equivalent to the fact that $C_H(u) = 1$ for every u in $A^{\#}$.

Let V_i, $1 \leqslant i \leqslant r$, be the Wedderburn components of V with respect to H and assume by way of contradiction that $r < |A|$. Since H leaves each V_i invariant, Clifford's theorem implies that A permutes the V_i transitively. Since the number of V_i is less than $|A|$, the subgroup A_1 of A fixing V_1 is thus nontrivial. Set $G_1 = HA_1$ and let N_1 be the kernel of the representation of G_1 on V_1. If x_i, $1 \leqslant i \leqslant r$, are elements of A such that $V_1 x_i = V_i$, then clearly $N_1^{x_i}$ is the kernel of the representation of $G_1^{x_i}$ on V_i. Since A is abelian, $A_1 \cap N_1 \subseteq N_1^{x_i}$ for all i. But as the representation of G on V is faithful, it follows that $A_1 \cap N_1 = 1$. The same is true for any conjugate of A_1 in G_1. However, as G is a Frobenius group, any element of G_1 not in a conjugate of A_1 lies in H. Hence $N_1 \subseteq H$. Since $H^{x_i} = H$, we conclude similarly that $N_1 \subset H$.

Now set $\bar{G}_1 = G_1/N_1 = \bar{H}\bar{A}_1$, so that $\bar{G}_1$ is faithfully represented on V_1 and V_1 is the direct sum of isomorphic H-submodules X_i, $1 \leqslant i \leqslant t$. Since $\bar{H}$ is abelian and F contains a primitive qth root of unity, Theorems 2.3 and 2.4 imply that $\bar{H} = \langle \bar{y} \rangle$ is cyclic that $\bar{y}$ acts on each X_i, which has dimension 1 over F, like a scalar transformation. Since the X_i are isomorphic Q-modules, $\bar{y}$ thus acts on V like a scalar transformation and so $\bar{y}$ commutes with the action of $\bar{A}_1$ on V_1. Since the representation of $\bar{G}_1$ on V_1 is faithful, we conclude that $\bar{H} \subseteq Z(\bar{G}_1)$.

Thus $\bar{A}_1$ centralizes $\bar{H} = H/N_1$ and consequently any element u of $A_1^{\#}$ has 1 as a characteristic root on H regarded as a vector space over Z_q. Hence $C_H(u) \neq 1$, contrary to the fact that G is a Frobenius group.

We conclude with a simple application of this last result which will be useful in the study of regular groups of automorphisms.

Theorem 4.4

Let $G = QP$, where Q is an elementary abelian normal q-subgroup of G and $|P| = p$, where p and q are distinct prime. Assume further that $C_G(Q) = Q$ and that Q is a minimal normal subgroup of G. Then if V/F is a faithful G-module in which F is not of characteristic q or p, we have $C_V(P) \neq 0$.

Proof

If $P = \langle x \rangle$, we need only show that 1 is a characteristic root of x on V. Hence it will be enough to prove this in V_L, where L is any extension field of F. Since such a V_L will also be a faithful G-module, it will thus suffice to consider the case that F contains a primitive qth root of unity.

Now V is a completely reducible G-module by Theorem 3.1 as F is not of characteristic q or p. Since Q is faithfully represented on V, there must therefore exist some irreducible G-submodule U of V on which Q acts nontrivially. Let K be the kernel of the representation of G on U. Since $K \cap Q \lhd G$ and Q is a minimal normal subgroup of G, we must have $K \cap Q = 1$, which implies that K is a p-group. But then if $K \neq 1$, $K = P$ is a normal S_p-subgroup of G as $|P| = p$. However, in this case $[Q, P] \subseteq Q \cap P = 1$ by Theorem 2.2.1(vi). Hence P centralizes Q and so $C_G(Q) = G$, contrary to hypothesis. Thus $K = 1$ and U is a faithful G-module. If $U \subset V$, then x has 1 as a characteristic root on U by induction on $\dim_F V$ and the theorem follows. Thus we may assume G acts irreducibly on V.

Now $C_Q(x) = 1$; otherwise x would centralize Q as Q is a minimal normal subgroup of G. Hence each element of $P^{\#}$ induces by conjugation an automorphism of Q which fixes only the identity element. Thus G is a Frobenius group with kernel Q and complement P. Hence by the preceding theorem, V has $p = |P|$ Wedderburn components V_i, $1 \leqslant i \leqslant p$, with respect to Q.

But then if v_1 is a nonzero vector of V_1, the vectors $v_1 x^{i-1}$ lie in V_i, $1 \leqslant i \leqslant p$, and so are linearly independent as V is the direct sum of the V_i. Thus the vector

$$v = v_1 + v_1 x + \cdots + v_1 x^{p-1} \neq 0.$$

On the other hand, it is immediate that $vx = v$ as $x^p = 1$. Hence 1 is a characteristic root of x on V and the theorem is proved.

5. *G*-HOMOMORPHISMS

If V/F and W/F are isomorphic G-modules, then by definition there exists an isomorphism ψ of V on W such that

$$(5.1) \qquad v(\psi x) = v(x\psi)$$

for all v in V and x in G. More generally if ψ is simply a homomorphism of V into W (that is, a linear transformation of V/F into W/F) which satisfies (5.1), we shall call ψ a *G-homomorphism*. The set of all G-homomorphisms of V into W will be denoted by $\mathrm{Hom}_G (V, W)$.

A number of questions about representations and modules are intimately related to the study of $\mathrm{Hom}_G (V, W)$ for various modules V and W. For example, its study will enable us to give a precise description of the irreducible H-submodules of the Wedderburn components V_i of Clifford's theorem (Theorem 4.1) and, in particular, to determine the number of such irreducible submodules in the case that F is finite. Furthermore, it will enable us to decide questions about absolute irreducibility. Finally, using it we shall be able to determine the structure of the group algebra of G over F and the number of irreducible representations of G over F for suitable fields F.

The set $\mathrm{Hom}(V, W)$ of all linear transformations of V into W itself forms a vector space over F provided we define $\phi + \psi$ and $a\phi$ for ϕ, ψ in $\mathrm{Hom}(V, W)$ and $a \in F$ by the rules

$$(5.2) \qquad v(\phi + \psi) = v\phi + v\psi \qquad \text{and} \qquad v(a\phi) = (av)\phi$$

for all v in V, as can be verified directly. If ϕ and ψ are in $\mathrm{Hom}_G (V, W)$, it also follows immediately from these definitions and from the fact that V/F and W/F are G-modules that $\phi + \psi$ and $a\phi$ are in $\mathrm{Hom}_G (V, W)$. Hence $\mathrm{Hom}_G (V, W)$ is a subspace of $\mathrm{Hom}(V, W)$ and, in particular, has finite dimension over F.

The particular case $V = W$ is of special interest, for then if $\phi, \psi \in \mathrm{Hom}_G (V, V)$, one also verifies that the mapping $\phi\psi$ given by

$$(5.3) \qquad v(\phi\psi) = (v\phi)\psi$$

for all v in V is a G-homomorphism, and with respect to this product operation together with the operations of addition and scalar multiplication $\mathrm{Hom}_G (V, V)$ forms an associative algebra over F. As is customary, we regard F as a subfield of $\mathrm{Hom}_G (V, V)$ by identifying the element a of F with the scalar linear transformation aI of V on itself.

We leave the verification of these results as an exercise, but summarize them here in the following theorem:

Theorem 5.1

If V/F and W/F are G-modules, then $\mathrm{Hom}_G (V, W)$ is a subspace of Hom (V, W) and $\mathrm{Hom}_G (V, V)$ is a finite-dimensional algebra over F.

We recall that a *division algebra* D is a ring in which the nonzero elements form a group under multiplication—that is, possess multiplicative inverses in D.

We first prove

Theorem 5.2

If V/F is an irreducible G-module, then $\mathrm{Hom}_G (V, V)$ is a division algebra with F in its center. In particular, every nonzero element of $\mathrm{Hom}_G (V, V)$ is a G-isomorphism.

Proof

Set $D = \mathrm{Hom}_G (V, V)$ and suppose $\psi \in D$, $\psi \neq 0$. Since $\psi x = x\psi$ for all x in G, the image $W = (V)\psi$ of V under ψ is a G-submodule of V and $W \neq 0$ as $\psi \neq 0$. Since V is an irreducible G-module, this forces $V = W$, whence ψ is an epimorphism and consequently is a nonsingular linear transformation of V. Thus, in fact, ψ is a G-isomorphism. Moreover, the linear transformation ψ^{-1} exists and it is immediate that it commutes with all x in G. Hence $\psi^{-1} \in D$ and so D is a division algebra. Since the transformations $(aI)\psi$ and $\psi(aI)$ are each equal to the transformation $a\psi$ for all a in F and all ψ in Hom (V, V), we also see that F is in the center of D.

Our next result is known as Schur's lemma:

Theorem 5.3 (Schur)

If V/F is an irreducible G-module, where F is algebraically closed, then

$$\mathrm{Hom}_G (V, V) = F.$$

In particular, every element of $\mathrm{Hom}_G (V, V)$ determines a scalar linear transformation of V.

Proof

Let $\psi \in D = \mathrm{Hom}_G (V, V)$. Then as D is finite-dimensional over F, the elements, $I, \psi, \psi^2, \ldots$ are not all linearly independent over F, and so there exists a nontrivial monic polynomial $f(X)$ over F such that $f(\psi) = 0$. Since F is algebraically closed, we have $f(X) = (X - a_1)(X - a_2) \cdots (X - a_n)$ for suitable a_i in F, $1 \leqslant i \leqslant n = \deg f(X)$. But ψ commutes with the elements $a_i = a_i I$ of D and consequently

$$0 = f(\psi) = (\psi - a_1)(\psi - a_2) \cdots (\psi - a_n).$$

On the other hand, D is a division algebra by the preceding theorem, whence $\psi - a_j = 0$ for some j. Thus $D = F$ and the theorem is proved.

The following theorem gives a description of Hom for the direct sum of isomorphic irreducible G-modules:

Theorem 5.4

Let V be the direct sum of the isomorphic G-modules V_i/F, $1 \le i \le t$. Then we have

(i) $\mathrm{Hom}_G(V_1, V_1)$ *and* $\mathrm{Hom}_G(V_i, V_j)$ *are G-isomorphic for all i, j.*

(ii) $\mathrm{Hom}_G(V_i, V)$ *and*
$\mathrm{Hom}_G(V_i, V_1) \oplus \mathrm{Hom}_G(V_i, V_2) \oplus \cdots \oplus \mathrm{Hom}_G(V_i, V_t)$ *are G-isomorphic for all i.*

(iii) *If* $\mathrm{Hom}_G(V_1, V_1) = F$, *then* $\mathrm{Hom}_G(V, V)$ *is isomorphic to the algebra of all $t \times t$ matrices over F.*

Proof

Set $D_{ij} = \mathrm{Hom}_G(V_i, V_j)$, $1 \le i, j \le t$, and $D = \mathrm{Hom}_G(V, V)$. Let ψ_i be a fixed G-isomorphism of V_1 on V_i, $1 \le i \le t$. Then it is immediate that for $\theta \in D_{11}$ the mapping $\theta \to \psi_i^{-1} \theta \psi_j$ is a G-isomorphism of D_{11} on D_{ij}, so (i) holds.

Let ρ_i be the injection map of V_i into V and let π_i be the projection map of V onto V_i, $1 \le i \le t$. Clearly $\rho_i \in \mathrm{Hom}_G(V_i, V)$ and $\pi_i \in \mathrm{Hom}_G(V, V_i)$, and, moreover, the following relations hold:

(5.4) $$\rho_i \pi_i = 1_i,$$

(5.5) $$\rho_i \pi_j = 0_i, \qquad i \ne j,$$

(5.6) $$\sum_{i=1}^{t} \pi_i \rho_i = 1,$$

where 1_i, 0_i are the identity and zero element of D_{ii} and 1 is the identity element of D.

Using these, we next prove (ii) for $i = 1$. Set $D_1 = \mathrm{Hom}_G(V_1, V)$ and for ϕ in D_1 define α by the rule

(5.7) $$\phi \alpha = (\phi \pi_1, \phi \pi_2, \ldots, \phi \pi_t).$$

Since $\phi \pi_i \in D_{1i}$, it is immediate that α is a G-homomorphism of D_1 into $D_{11} \times D_{12} \times \cdots \times D_{1t} = D_1^*$. Furthermore, (5.6) shows that each

$\phi\pi_i = 0_i$ only if $\phi = 0$, so α is one-to-one. On the other hand, if $\phi^* = (\phi_1, \phi_2, \ldots, \phi_t) \in D_1^*$, then the element $\phi = \sum_{i=1}^{t} \phi_i \rho_i \in D_1$ and (5.4) and (5.5) imply that $\phi\pi_i = \phi_i$, whence $\phi\alpha = \phi^*$. Thus α is a G-isomorphism of D_1 on D_1^* proving (ii).

Now assume $D_{11} = F$, in which case $D_{ij} = F$ for all $i, j, 1 \leqslant i, j \leqslant t$. Let E denote the ring of all $t \times t$ matrices over F. We define a mapping β of D into E by the rule

$$(5.8) \qquad\qquad \phi\beta = (\rho_i \phi\pi_j)$$

for ϕ in D. The element $\phi_{ij} = \rho_i\phi\pi_j \in \mathrm{Hom}_G(V_i, V_j)$ and so lies in F. Thus $\phi\beta$ is, in fact, a $t \times t$ matrix over F.

Since ρ_i and π_j are linear transformations, it follows for ϕ, ψ in D and a in F that

$$(5.9) \qquad \phi_{ij} + \psi_{ij} = (\phi + \psi)_{ij} \qquad \text{and} \qquad (a\phi)_{ij} = a\phi_{ij},$$

which together imply that β is a homomorphism of the vector space structure of D into that of E. Furthermore, we have, using (5.6), that

$$(5.10)$$
$$(\phi\psi)_{ij} = \rho_i\phi\psi\pi_j = \rho_i\phi\left(\sum_{k=1}^{t} \pi_k\rho_k\right)\psi\pi_j = \sum_{k=1}^{t}(\rho_i\,\phi\pi_k)(\rho_k\psi\pi_j) = \sum_{k=1}^{t}\phi_{ik}\psi_{kj}.$$

But now (5.10) yields that $(\phi\psi)\beta = (\phi\beta)(\psi\beta)$. Hence β is an algebra homomorphism of D into E.

Now let (a_{ij}) be an arbitrary element of E with $a_{ij} \in F$ and set

$$(5.11) \qquad\qquad \phi = \sum_{h,k=1}^{t} \pi_h a_{hk}\rho_k.$$

Using (5.4) and (5.5), we see at once that $\phi_{ij} = \rho_i\phi\pi_j = a_{ij}$, whence $\phi\beta = (a_{ij})$ and so β is an epimorphism.

Suppose finally that $\phi\beta = 0$ for ϕ in D. By (5.6), we have

$$(5.12) \qquad \phi = \left(\sum_{i=1}^{t} \pi_i\rho_i\right)\phi\left(\sum_{j=1}^{t} \pi_j\rho_j\right) = \sum_{i,j=1}^{t} \pi_i(\rho_i\phi\pi_j)\rho_j = 0$$

since $\phi_{ij} = \rho_i\phi\pi_j = 0$ for all i, j by our assumption $\phi\beta = 0$. Thus ϕ is one-to-one and we conclude that ϕ is an algebra isomorphism of D on E.

In applying part (ii) of Theorem 5.4, it is convenient to identify $\mathrm{Hom}_G(V_i, V_i)$ with its image in $\mathrm{Hom}_G(V_i, V)$ under the injection map ρ_i. When this is done, (ii) becomes an equality rather than an isomorphism and we obtain the following corollary:

Theorem 5.5

Let V be the direct sum of isomorphic irreducible G-modules V_i/F, $1 \leqslant i \leqslant t$, and assume that $\text{Hom}_G(V_1, V_1) = F$. Let ψ_i be a fixed G-isomorphism of V_1 into V_i, $1 \leqslant i \leqslant t$. Then any irreducible G-submodule W of V is of form $(V_1)\phi$, where

$$\phi = \sum_{i=1}^{t} a_i \psi_i,$$

and the elements a_i are suitable elements of F, uniquely determined by W up to a nonzero scalar multiple. In particular, the hypothesis is satisfied if F is algebraically closed.

Proof

By Corollary 4.2 there exists a G-isomorphism ϕ of V_1 onto W. Since $W \subseteq V$, $\phi \in \text{Hom}_G(V_1, V)$ and consequently by our identification and Theorem 5.4(ii), $\phi = \sum_{i=1}^{t} \phi_i$, where $\phi_i \in \text{Hom}_G(V_1, V_i)$. But then $a_i = \phi_i \psi_i^{-1} \in \text{Hom}_G(V_1, V_1) = F$. Hence $\phi_i = a_i \phi_i$ and $\phi = \sum_{i=1}^{t} a_i \psi_i$. Furthermore, if θ is any other G-isomorphism of V_1 into W, then $\theta\phi^{-1} \in \text{Hom}_G(V_1, V_1)$, whence $\theta\phi^{-1} = a \in F$. Thus $\theta = a\phi$ and we see that the a_i are uniquely determined by W up to a nonzero multiple. The final assertion of the theorem follows at once from Schur's lemma.

If V/F is an irreducible G-module over a finite field F, then $D = \text{Hom}_G(V, V)$ is a finite division ring with F in its center. In particular, D is a vector space over F, and consequently $|D| = p^e$ for some e, where p is the characteristic of F. (Actually D is a field by Wedderburn's well-known theorem, but we do not require this result.) With this preliminary observation, we can now prove the following result of J. A. Green:

Theorem 5.6

Let V be the direct sum of the isomorphic irreducible G-modules V_i/F, $1 \leqslant i \leqslant t$, where F is a finite field. Then the number of distinct irreducible G-submodules of V is exactly $(q^t - 1)/(q - 1)$, where $q = |\text{Hom}_G(V_1, V_1)|$.

Proof

Set $D = \text{Hom}_G(V_1, V_1)$ and $q = |D|$. If W is any irreducible G-submodule of V, we can repeat the proof of the preceding theorem verbatim with D in place of F to obtain that $W = (V_1)\phi$, where $\phi = \sum_{i=1}^{t} a_i \psi_i$, ψ_i are fixed G-isomorphisms of V_1 onto V_i and $a_i \in D$, with a_i uniquely determined up to a nonzero element of D. On the other hand, for any choice of a_i, $1 \leqslant i \leqslant t$, not all 0, and corresponding element ϕ, $(V_1)\phi$ is an irreducible G-submodule of V. We conclude at once from this that the number of distinct irreducible G-submodules of V is precisely $(q^t - 1)/(q - 1)$.

The structure of $\text{Hom}_G(V, V)$ also provides a simple criterion for the absolute irreducibility of the irreducible G-module V/F.

Theorem 5.7

Let V/F be an irreducible G-module and assume that the characteristic of F is either 0 or relatively prime to $|G|$. Then V is absolutely irreducible if and only if

$$F = \text{Hom}_G(V, V).$$

In particular, V is absolutely irreducible if F is algebraically closed.

Proof

Again the proof utilizes a simple averaging argument. Let L be an arbitrary extension field of F and set $D_L = \text{Hom}_G(V_L, V_L)$, $D = \text{Hom}_G(V, V)$, and $n = |G|$. Also put $E_L = \text{Hom}(V_L, V_L)$ and $E = \text{Hom}(V, V)$. Let $m = \dim_F V$, so that $m^2 = \dim_F E = \dim_L E_L$. We first derive a particular representation of the elements of D_L. If $\theta \in E_L$, set

$$(5.13) \qquad \theta\psi = 1/n \sum_{x \in G} x^{-1}\theta x.$$

Then ψ is a mapping from E_L into E_L, and as θ and each x in G is linear, ψ is a linear transformation. Furthermore, if $y \in G$ and we set $z = xy$, we have

$$(5.14) \qquad y^{-1}\theta\psi y = 1/n \sum_{x \in G} y^{-1}x^{-1}\theta xy = 1/n \sum_{z \in G} z^{-1}\theta z = \theta\psi,$$

using the fact that z runs over G as x does. Thus $\theta\psi$ commutes with each y in G and so $\theta\psi \in D_L$. It follows that $(E_L)\psi \subseteq D_L$.

We argue next that $(E_L)\psi = D_L$. Indeed, if $\phi \in D_L$, then

$$(5.15) \qquad \phi\psi = 1/n \sum_{x \in G} x^{-1}\phi x = 1/n \sum_{x \in G} \phi = 1/n(n\phi) = \phi,$$

as ϕ commutes with each x in G. Hence ψ is the identity on D_L and so $(E_L)\psi = D_L$, as asserted.

Now let $(v) = \{v_i \mid 1 \leqslant i \leqslant m\}$ be a basis of V/F so that (v) can also be considered as a basis of V_L/L. Let θ_{ij} be the linear transformations of E given by

$$(5.16) \quad (v_k)\theta_{ij} = 0 \quad \text{if} \quad k \neq i \qquad \text{and} \qquad (v_i)\theta_{ij} = v_j \quad 1 \leq i, j, k \leq m.$$

These m^2 transformations clearly form a basis for E_L/L as well as for E/F. But then the elements $\theta_{ij}\psi$, $1 \leqslant i, j \leqslant n$, span D_L/L. Since the mapping ψ is defined, in particular, if $L = F$, the $\theta_{ij}\psi$ also span D/F.

On the basis of the preceding discussion, we shall now show that $D_L = L$ if $D = F$. Indeed, suppose $D = F$, but that D_L contains an element θ which is not a scalar transformation of V_L. By the preceding paragraph

$$(5.17) \qquad \theta = \sum_{i,j=1}^{m} a_{ij}(\theta_{ij}\psi) \qquad \text{with } a_{ij} \in L, \, 1 \leqslant i, j \leqslant m.$$

If each $\theta_{ij}\psi$ were a scalar transformation $b_{ij}I$ with $b_{ij} \in L$, then we would have $\theta = bI$, where $b = \sum_{i,j=1}^{m} a_{ij}b_{ij}$, contrary to our choice of θ. Hence $\theta_{ij}\psi$ is not a scalar transformation for some i and j. But $\theta_{ij}\psi \in D = F$, a contradiction.

With this information, we can now establish the theorem. Suppose V_L is not an irreducible G-module for some extension field L of F. Since L has the same characteristic as F, V_L is a completely reducible G-module by Theorem 3.1, whence $V_L = U \oplus W$ for suitable nonzero G-submodules U and W. But then if θ denotes the element of E_L which is the identity on U and the zero transformation on W, it is immediate that $x\theta = \theta x$ for all x in G, so that $\theta \in D_L$. Since 0 and 1 are each characteristic roots of θ on V_L, θ is not a scalar transformation. Hence $D_L \neq L$ and consequently $D \neq F$. We have thus shown that if $D = F$, then V_L must be an irreducible G-module for every extension field L of F and so that V is absolutely irreducible. Since $D = F$ when F is algebraically closed by Schur's lemma, the final assertion of the theorem holds.

Suppose finally that $D \neq F$ and choose θ in $D - F$. Take as L an extension field of F containing a characteristic root λ of θ and let W be the subspace of V_L consisting of all characteristic vectors of θ belonging to λ. If $W = V_L$, then θ is the scalar transformation λI on V_L and, in particular, $v_i\theta = \lambda v_i$, $1 \leqslant i \leqslant n$. Since the v_i form a basis of V/F and θ is a linear transformation of V, it follows that $\lambda \in F$ and that $\theta = \lambda \in F$, contrary to our choice of θ. Thus $0 \subset W \subset V_L$. On the other hand, it is immediate that W is a G-submodule of V_L. We conclude that V_L is not an irreducible G-module and hence that V is not absolutely irreducible.

In particular, the theorem asserts that any algebraically closed field of characteristic 0 or characteristic prime to $|G|$ is a splitting field for G. Moreover, the argument of the final paragraph of the proof was independent of the hypotheses on F. Hence as a corollary, we have

Corollary 5.8

If F is a splitting field for G, then $\mathrm{Hom}_G(V, V) = F$ for every irreducible G-module V/F.

The following easy result is also useful:

Theorem 5.9

If F is a splitting field for G and if every irreducible representation of G over F can be written in the subfield L of F, then L is a splitting field for G.

Proof

Let ϕ be an irreducible representation of G on V/F which is written in L and assume that for some extension field K of L, the extended representation ϕ_K of ϕ on V_K is not irreducible. Since any representation of G over K can be written in a subfield of K that is finitely generated over L, we can assume without loss that K is finitely generated over L. But then one can readily construct a finitely generated extension F^* of F which possesses a subfield K^* isomorphic to K under an isomorphism α which is the identity transformation on L. Applying α to the matrices representing ϕ_K, we obtain a representation ϕ_{K^*} on the vector space $V_{K^*} = V \otimes_L K^*$ which is reducible and which is also an extension of the given representation ϕ. But then the corresponding extension ϕ_{F^*} of ϕ_{K^*}, and hence of ϕ, on V_{F^*} is reducible. Since $F \subseteq F^*$, this contradicts the fact that F is a splitting field of G.

6. IRREDUCIBLE REPRESENTATIONS AND GROUP ALGEBRAS

We shall now develop some deeper properties of the representations of finite groups, which depend upon certain structure theorems for simple and semisimple finite-dimensional algebras.

To motivate the discussion, we denote by $A(V, F)$ the algebra of all linear transformations of the vector space V/F. Suppose now that V/F is a faithful G-module, so that we can regard G itself as a group of linear transformations of V/F. Thus $G \subseteq A(V, F)$. We can then consider the smallest subalgebra $E(G)$ of $A(V, F)$ containing G. Clearly $E(G)$ consists simply of the set of all transformations of the form $\sum_{i=1}^{n} a_i x_i$ with $x_i \in G$ and $a_i \in F$, $1 \leqslant i \leqslant n$. We call $E(G)$ the *enveloping algebra* of G (with respect to the faithful G-module V). We see then that our representation of G

induces in a natural way a representation of a suitable finite-dimensional algebra over F.

To extend this idea to arbitrary G-modules, it is best to introduce first the notion of the *group algebra* $A(G, F)$ of G over the field F. Let $x_i, 1 \leqslant i \leqslant m$, be the distinct elements of G. Then by definition $A(G, F)$ consists of all formal linear combinations $x = \sum_{i=1}^{m} a_i x_i$ with a_i in F, $1 \leqslant i \leqslant m$. Addition and scalar multiplication in $A(G, F)$ are defined component-wise in the obvious way. Furthermore, multiplication of two elements x and $y = \sum_{i=1}^{m} b_i x_i$, $b_i \in F$, $1 \leqslant i \leqslant m$, of $A(G, F)$ is defined by the rule

$$(6.1) \qquad\qquad xy = \sum_{i,j=1}^{m} a_i b_j (x_i x_j),$$

the sum on the right being expressible in the form $\sum_{k=1}^{m} c_k x_k$, $c_i \in F$, $1 \leqslant i \leqslant m$.

It is an easy exercise that under these operations $A(G, F)$ is, in fact, an algebra over F with basis $x_i, 1 \leqslant i \leqslant m$. Since $m = |G|$, we note, in particular, that

$$(6.2) \qquad\qquad \dim_F A(G, F) = |G|.$$

Furthermore, if we identify the identity element of G with the unity element of F, we can regard F as a subset of $A(G, F)$.

Now if V/F is any G-module, the operation of G on V induces an operation of $A = A(G, F)$ on V by the rule

$$(6.3) \qquad\qquad v\left(\sum_{i=1}^{m} a_i x_i \right) = \sum_{i=1}^{m} a_i (v x_i)$$

for v in V. In this way V/F becomes an A-module. Furthermore, we can consider the *kernel B* of A, which by definition is

$$(6.4) \qquad\qquad B = \{ x \in A \mid vx = 0 \quad \text{for all } v \text{ in } V \}.$$

It is immediate that B is closed under addition, scalar multiplication, and multiplication on the right and left by arbitrary elements of A. Thus B is a two-sided ideal of A and so we can consider the factor algebra A/B. Just as in the case of G, we can make V/F into an A/B-module. When we do this, V becomes a faithful A/B-module and so A/B can be regarded as an algebra of linear transformations of V.

On the other hand, we can consider the kernel K of G on V, so that V/F is also a faithful G/K-module. But then we also have the enveloping algebra $E = E(G/K)$ acting on V. There is a natural homomorphism ψ of A onto E given by

$$(6.5) \qquad \left(\sum_{i=1}^{m} a_i x_i\right)\psi = \sum_{i=1}^{m} a_i(Kx_i);$$

and it is a direct consequence of the various definitions that the kernel of ψ is precisely B. Thus A/B and E are isomorphic.

Furthermore, we note the obvious but important fact, that any G-submodule of V is also an A-submodule and conversely. In particular, V is an irreducible G-module if and only if it is an irreducible A-module. In addition, we see that any G-homomorphism ϕ of V into V extends by linearity to an A-homomorphism ϕ^*—that is, a linear transformation of V such that $(vx)\phi^* = (v\phi^*)x$ for all v in V and x in A. Since conversely any A-homomorphism of V, when restricted to G, is a G-homomorphism, it follows directly that

$$(6.6) \qquad \operatorname{Hom}_G(V, V) = \operatorname{Hom}_A(V, V) = \operatorname{Hom}_E(V, V),$$

where $A = A(G, F)$ and $E = E(G/K)$, K the kernel of G on V.

The preceding discussion shows that there is a direct relation between the representation theory of G and that of its group algebra. To examine this relationship, we shall establish some general results concerning the representations and structure of arbitrary algebras. By an algebra A/F we shall mean an associative algebra of finite dimension over F. We regard F as embedded in A, so that, in particular, A has a unity element 1. We also use 0 for both the zero element and 0-ideal of A.

A representation of A/F is by definition an algebra homomorphism of A into the algebra $A(V, F)$ of linear transformations of the vector space V/F. The various concepts that were introduced in Section 1 concerning representations of groups and group modules carry over with obvious modifications to algebras and we shall use them whenever it is appropriate.

If V/F is a (right) A-module for the algebra A/F, we introduce the concept of the (right) *annihilator* $N(U)$ of the A-submodule U of V:

$$N(U) = \{x \in A,\ Ux = 0\}.$$

If $x, y \in N(U)$ and $a \in A$, we have

$$U(x + y) \subseteq Ux + Uy = 0 \quad U(xa) = (Ux)a = 0 \quad U(ax) = (Ua)x \subseteq Ux = 0.$$

Thus $x + y$, xa, and ax are all in $N(U)$ and so $N(U)$ is a two-sided ideal of A. Similarly, we can define the left annihilator of left A-modules.

The ideal structure of A/F will be very important to us. It is an immediate consequence of the definition that every ideal of A (left, right, or two-sided), being closed under addition and multiplication by elements of F, is a sub-space of A as a vector space over F. Since A is finite-dimensional over F, A thus satisfies both the ascending and descending chain conditions for left, right, or two-sided ideals.

If X and Y are subsets of A, we denote by XY the set of all finite sums $\sum_{i=1}^{n} x_i y_i$ with $x_i \in X$ and $y_i \in Y$, $1 \le i \le n$. If Y is a right ideal of A, it is immediate that XY is as well, with a similar conclusion holding if X is a left ideal. In particular, for any ideal R of A, there is defined an ideal $R^2 = RR$. Inductively, we can define the ideals $R^i = R^{i-1}R$ for all i with $R^1 = R$ and $R^0 = A$. Each R^i is then a right, left, or two-sided ideal according as R itself is; moreover, $R^{i+1} \subseteq R^i$ for all i and, because of linearity, $R^i R^j = R^{i+j}$ for all i, j.

The algebra A/F can be regarded in a natural way as a right A-module with the operation π_x, $x \in A$, of x on A given by

$$(6.7) \qquad\qquad a\pi_x = ax$$

for all a in A. The corresponding representation of A is called the right *regular representation of A*. Similarly, A possesses a left regular representation.

As a right A-module, only the vector-space structure of A is considered (together, of course, with the operation of A on this vector space). Thus for example, when considering $\mathrm{Hom}_A (A, A)$, it is to be understood that the terms in parentheses refer to A as a module, while the subscript refers to A as an algebra. Furthermore, we note that the submodules of A as an A-module are precisely the right ideals of A. In particular, then, the notion of the (right) annihilator $N(R)$ of a right ideal R of A is well-defined and is a two-sided ideal of A. Similar remarks hold for A as a left-module.

In the case that $A = A(G, F)$ for some group G, it follows at once from the definitions that the (right) regular representation of A is induced from that of G by extending the operations from G to A by linearity.

Finally, there are three concepts from group theory that it will be useful to carry over to algebras. First, the *center* $Z(A) = \{x \in A \mid xa = ax$ for all a in $A\}$. Clearly the center of A contains F and is a subalgebra of A.

Second, we have the notion of the internal and external direct product of algebras over the same field F. Theorem 1.2.12 holds without change for algebras provided the term "normal subgroup" is replaced by "two-sided ideal." Thus, for example, A/F is the internal direct sum of the two-sided ideals A_1, A_2 provided the vector space A is the direct sum of A_1 and A_2 and also all products $x_1 x_2 = 0$, $x_1 \in A_1$, $x_2 \in A_2$; equivalently, $A_1 A_2 = 0$. When this is the case, we shall write $A = A_1 \oplus A_2$, with similar notation for the direct sum of any number of ideals.

Third, because of the analogy between normal subgroup and two-sided ideal, we call an algebra A *simple* provided 0 and A are its only two-sided ideals.

Theorems 5.2 and 5.3 extend without change to algebras. Thus we have

Theorem 6.1

   Let V/F be an irreducible A-module for the algebra A/F. Then we have
   (i) *$\mathrm{Hom}_A(V, V)$ is a division algebra with F in its center.*
   (ii) *If F is algebraically closed, then $\mathrm{Hom}_A(V, V) = F$.*

Our first major result, which is a particular case of the Jacobson density theorem, gives the structure of algebras which possess a faithful irreducible representation.

Theorem 6.2

   Let A/F be faithfully and irreducibly represented on V/F. If $\mathrm{Hom}_A(V, V) = F$, then A is isomorphic to the algebra $A(V, F)$ of all linear transformations on V.

Proof

   Because of the faithful action of A on V, we can regard A as an algebra of linear transformations on V. Thus $A \subseteq A(V, F)$ and we must prove that equality holds.

   Let W be any proper subspace of V and u any element of $V - W$. Suppose, under these conditions, we can always find an element x of A such that

(6.8) $Wx = 0$ and $ux \neq 0$.

Then $uxA = \{uxz \mid z \in A\} \neq 0$. But uxA is clearly an A-invariant subspace of V and so $uxA = V$ by the irreducibility of A on V. This means that for any vector v in V, there exists an element a in A such that $uxa = v$. Setting $y = xa$, we then have

(6.9) $Wy = 0$ and $uy = v$.

   Now let v_i, $1 \leqslant i \leqslant n$, be a basis of V/F and let w_i, $1 \leqslant i \leqslant n$, be arbitrary vectors of V. Setting $W_i = \langle v_j \mid 1 \leqslant j \leqslant n, j \neq i \rangle$, we have that $v_i \in V - W_i$,

$1 \leqslant i \leqslant n$. Hence by (6.9) with W_i, v_i, w_i in the roles of W, u, v, respectively, there exists y_i in A such that

$$(6.10) \qquad W_i y_i = 0 \qquad \text{and} \qquad v_i y_i = w_i \quad 1 \leq i \leq n.$$

Setting $y = y_1 + y_2 + \cdots + y_n$, it follows from (6.10) that $v_i y = v_i y_1 + v_i y_2 + \cdots + v_i y_n = v_i y_i = w_i$, $1 \leqslant i \leqslant n$. Thus every linear transformation of V can be realized in A. Hence to prove that $A = A(V, F)$, we see that it will suffice to establish (6.8).

We proceed to do this by induction on $\dim_F W$. First of all, if $W = 0$, we can take $x = 1$. Assume then that $W \neq 0$ and write $W = U + wF$, where $\dim_F U = \dim_F W - 1$ and $w \in W - U$. Then (6.8) holds by induction for U in place of W. This means that if $N(U)$ is the annihilator of U in A, any element of $V - U$ can be moved to an arbitrary element of V by a suitable element of $N(U)$. In particular, if $v \in V$ and $vN(U) = 0$, then, in fact, $v \in U$. Since $w \notin U$, we have $wN(U) \neq 0$. But $wN(U)$ is an A-submodule of V as $N(U)$ is a right ideal and consequently

$$(6.11) \qquad\qquad wN(U) = V$$

by the irreducibility of A on V.

Now let $u \in V - W$ and suppose, by way of contradiction, that $ux = 0$ whenever $Wx = 0$, $x \in A$. We define a mapping T of V into V by the rule: for v in V, $vT = uy$, where $y \in N(U)$ is determined from (6.11) by the condition $wy = v$. Although y is not uniquely determined, T is well defined. Indeed, if also $wz = v$, $z \in N(U)$, then $0 = w(y - z)$, whence $W(y - z) = U(y - z) + w(y - z) = 0$. By our present assumption this implies that $u(y - z) = 0$ and so $vT = uy = uz$. Clearly $(v_1 + v_2)T = v_1 T + v_2 T$ and $(\lambda v)T = \lambda(vT)$ for $\lambda \in F$. Furthermore, if $v = wy$ and $x \in A$, then $vx = w(yx)$. Since yx is in the right ideal $N(U)$, we thus have

$$(vx)T = u(yx) = (uy)x = (vT)x.$$

We conclude that $T \in \operatorname{Hom}_A(V, V)$.

Hence by the hypothesis of the theorem $T = \lambda I$ for some λ in F. In other words, for y in $N(U)$, $uy = (wy)T = (\lambda w)y$, whence $(u - \lambda w)y = 0$. Thus $(u - \lambda w)N(U) = 0$. But as we have argued above, this forces $u - \lambda w$ to lie in U, whence $u \in U + wF = W$, contrary to the fact that $u \in V - W$. Thus (6.8) holds and the theorem is proved.

Theorem 6.2 has two corollaries, the first giving an important property of a faithful irreducible representation of a group.

Theorem 6.3

Let F be a splitting field of G of characteristic 0 or characteristic prime to $|G|$. If G is faithfully and irreducibly represented on V/F, then $E(G)$ is isomorphic to $A(V, F)$.

Proof

We regard G as a group of linear transformations of V. Since G acts irreducibly on V, so does $E(G)$. Now, by Theorem 5.7, we have $\mathrm{Hom}_G(V, V) = F$ and consequently $\mathrm{Hom}_{E(G)}(V, V) = F$ by (6.6). Hence $E(G)$ in its action on V satisfies all the conditions of Theorem 6.2 and we conclude that $E(G) = A(V, F)$.

We can also obtain Wedderburn's basic result on the structure of simple rings:

Theorem 6.4 (Wedderburn)

Let A/F be a simple algebra, where F is algebraically closed. Then A is isomorphic to the algebra F_n of all $n \times n$ matrices over F for some integer n.

Proof

Let V be a minimal right ideal of A. Then V is a right A-module and any submodule of V is a right ideal of A. Hence by the minimality of V, we have that V is an irreducible A-module. Since $N(V)$ is a two-sided ideal of A and $1 \notin N(V)$, we have $N(V) = 0$ by the simplicity of A or, equivalently, A acts faithfully on V. Since F is algebraically closed, we also have $\mathrm{Hom}_A(V, V) = F$ by Theorem 6.1. We conclude therefore from Theorem 6.2 that $A = A(V, F)$. Since $A(V, F)$ is isomorphic to F_n, where $n = \dim_F V$, the theorem follows.

A second, more classical, proof of Wedderburn's theorem will be available to us once we establish that every right ideal R of a simple algebra A consists of all multiples of an *idempotent* e (that is, a nonzero element e of R such that $e^2 = e$) (see Theorems 6.10 and 6.11 below). Indeed, on the basis of this result it is not difficult to show that as a vector space A is the direct sum of minimal right ideals V_i, $1 \leqslant i \leqslant m$, which are isomorphic as A-modules. But then Theorem 5.4(iii), which extends directly to algebras, will yield that $\mathrm{Hom}_A(A, A) = F_m$. On the other hand, it is also not difficult to show, using the simplicity of A, that $\mathrm{Hom}_A(A, A)$ is isomorphic to A. Thus A itself is isomorphic to F_m. It is trivial to check that F_m and F_n are not isomorphic for $n \neq m$. Hence the integer n of Theorem 6.4 and the integer m must be identical. We shall include the various parts of this proof among the exercises.

An element x of A is called *nilpotent* if $x^n = 0$ for some integer n. An ideal R of A (right, left, or two-sided) is called *nilpotent* if $R^n = 0$ for some integer n. Clearly then, every element of R is nilpotent. For finite-dimensional algebras, the converse is also true, although we shall not need this fact.

We say that A/F is *semisimple* provided 0 is the only nilpotent two-sided ideal of A. Clearly a simple ring is semisimple.

The importance for us of the concept of semisimplicity rests upon the fact that the group algebra $A(G, F)$ is semisimple whenever F has characteristic 0 or characteristic prime to $|G|$.

The proof of this result depends upon properties of the *trace* of a matrix. We therefore first list without proof the standard elementary facts concerning traces (some of which will not be needed until the next chapter). First of all, if $Y = (y_{ij}) \in F_n$, then, by definition,

$$\operatorname{tr} Y = \sum_{i=1}^{n} y_{ii}.$$

We have

Lemma 6.5

    Let $X, Y \in F_n$, let $Z \in F_m$, and let $\lambda, u \in F$. Then
      (i) $\operatorname{tr} X$ *is the sum of the characteristic roots of X.*
     (ii) *If X is nilpotent,* $\operatorname{tr} X = 0$.
    (iii) $\operatorname{tr} XY = \operatorname{tr} YX$.
    (iv) $\operatorname{tr} (\lambda X + \mu Y) = \lambda \operatorname{tr} X + \mu \operatorname{tr} Y$
     (v) *If X and Y are similar matrices, then* $\operatorname{tr} X = \operatorname{tr} Y$.
    (vi) $\operatorname{tr} (X \otimes Z) = (\operatorname{tr} X)(\operatorname{tr} Z)$
   (vii) $\operatorname{tr} (X^t) = \operatorname{tr} X$, *where X^t is the transpose of X.*

Because of (v), we can define the trace of a linear transformation T of a vector space V/F by setting $\operatorname{tr} T = \operatorname{tr} (T_v)$ for any basis (v) of V/F. Since the matrices of T with respect to any two bases of V are similar, $\operatorname{tr} T$ is independent of the choice of (v).

If $A = A(G, F)$, then for each x in A, right multiplication π_x of A by x is a linear transformation of A/F and so has a trace. For the elements of G, we have

Lemma 6.6

    If $x \in G$, then $\operatorname{tr} \pi_x = \begin{cases} 0 & \text{if } x \neq 1 \\ |G| & \text{if } x = 1. \end{cases}$

Proof

    We know that $\dim_F A = n$, where $n = |G|$. Obviously then the trace of the identity matrix is n and consequently $\operatorname{tr} \pi_1 = n$. Furthermore, the elements x_i, $1 \leqslant i \leqslant n$, of G form a basis of A and, for any x in G, $x_i \pi_x = x_i x = x_j$ for some j. Thus the matrix of π_x with respect to this basis is a permutation matrix. Moreover, if $x \neq 1$, $x_i x$ is never x_i and so the diagonal entries of this matrix are all 0. Hence tr $\pi_x = 0$ if $x \neq 1$.

We can now prove

Theorem 6.7

For any group G, $A(G, F)$ is semisimple if and only if F has characteristic 0 or characteristic prime to $|G|$.

Proof

Let p be the characteristic of F, let $n = |G|$. Let $x_1 = 1, x_2, \ldots, x_n$ be the elements of G and set $A = A(G, F)$. Consider first the case that either $p = 0$ or $(p, n) = 1$ and assume by way of contraction that A contains a nonzero nilpotent ideal R. Let $z = \sum_{i=1}^{n} \mu_i x_i \in R$, $\mu_i \in F$, $1 \leqslant i \leqslant n$, with $z \neq 0$. Then some $\mu_j \neq 0$ and, as R is an ideal, also $y = \mu_j^{-1} z x_j^{-1} \in R$. But for y we have

$$(6.12) \qquad y = \sum_{i=1}^{n} \lambda_i x_i \qquad \text{with} \qquad \lambda_1 = 1 \quad \text{and} \quad \lambda_i \in F, 1 \leqslant i \leqslant n.$$

We compute tr π_y. First of all, by the definition of π_x, for x in A, we have

$$(6.13) \qquad\qquad\qquad \pi_y = \sum_{i=1}^{n} \lambda_i \pi_{x_i},$$

whence

$$(6.14) \qquad\qquad\qquad \text{tr } \pi_y = \sum_{i=1}^{n} \lambda_i \text{ tr } \pi_{x_i}$$

by Lemma 6.5(iv). But tr $\pi_{x_1} = n$ and tr $\pi_{x_i} = 0$ for $i > 1$ by Lemma 6.6. Hence (6.14) reduces to tr $\pi_y = n$. On the other hand, y is nilpotent as $y \in R$ and R is nilpotent, which implies that π_y is a nilpotent linear transformation of A/F. But then tr $\pi_y = 0$ by Lemma 6.5(ii). This is a contradiction, since $n \neq 0$ in F by our assumption on p. Thus A is semisimple in this case.

Conversely, suppose $p \mid n$. Set $x = \sum_{i=1}^{n} x_i$. Since by definition of A the x_i are linearly independent over F, $x \neq 0$. Since $x_j x_i$ and $x_i x_j$ run over the elements of G as x_i does, it follows at once that $x_j x = x x_j = x$ for all j, $1 \leqslant j \leqslant n$. But then by linearity $ax = xa = x$ for all a in A. Thus $x \in Z(A)$

and $R = xA$ is a nonzero two-sided ideal of A consisting of the elements 0 and x.

On the other hand,

$$(6.15) \qquad x^2 = \left(\sum_{i=1}^{n} x_i \right) \left(\sum_{j=1}^{n} x_j \right) = \sum_{i,j=1}^{n} x_i x_j = n \sum_{k=1}^{n} x_k = nx,$$

since for each k there are clearly exactly n solutions (x_i, x_j) of the equation, $x_i x_j = x_k$; namely, the pairs $(x_i, x_i^{-1} x_k)$, $1 \leqslant i \leqslant n$. But $n = 0$ in F as $p \,|\, n$ and consequently $x^2 = 0$. It follows that $R^2 = 0$ and hence that R is a nonzero nilpotent two-sided ideal of A. We conclude that A is not semi-simple.

In the semisimple case (F algebraically closed), we can completely deter-mine the structure of $A(G, F)$ and in terms of it can describe all the irreducible representations of G over F. We shall obtain these results as a particular case of a general structure theorem for semisimple algebras.

To carry this out, we require a sharper characterization of semisimplicity, which depends upon some properties of the so-called *Jacobson radical* of an algebra:

Lemma 6.8

Let R be the intersection of all maximal right (left) ideals of the algebra A/F. Then we have

    (i) *R is the intersection of the annihilators of all irreducible right (left) A-modules. In particular, R is a two-sided ideal of A.*

    (ii) *If B is a two-sided ideal of A, then $(R + B)/B$ is contained in the intersection of the maximal right ideals of A/B.*

Proof

Let N be the intersection of the annihilators of all irreducible right A-modules. Since each of these annihilators is a two-sided ideal of A, so also is N. Hence (i) will follow once we show that $R = N$.

Let M be a maximal right ideal of A. Regarding A as a right A-module and M as a submodule, we can consider the factor A-module $V = A/M$. If W is an A-submodule of V, the inverse image of W in A is an A-sub-module and hence is a right ideal of A. But by the maximality of M, this ideal is either M or A. Hence $W = 0$ or V and we conclude that V is an irreducible A-module. But then if $x \in N$, $x \in N(V)$ and so $Vx = 0$. By definition of the operation of A on V, this is equivalent to the relation $Ax \subseteq M$. In particular, $x = 1 \cdot x \in M$. Since M and x are arbitrary, it follows at once that $N \subseteq R$.

On the other hand, suppose $y \in A - N$. Then by definition of N, there exists an irreducible right A-module V/F such that $Vy \neq 0$. Choose v in V so that $vy \neq 0$. Then $vA = \{vx \mid x \in A\}$ is a nonzero submodule of V, so $vA = V$ by the irreducibility of V. Consider the mapping θ of A into V defined by $x\theta = vx$ for x in A. It is immediate that θ is an A-homomorphism. Let M be the kernel of θ, that is, $M = \{z \in A \mid vz = 0\}$. Then clearly M is a right ideal of A. Furthermore, if S is a right-ideal of A containing M, we see that $S\theta$ is a submodule of V, whence $S\theta = 0$ or V. If $S\theta = 0$, then $S = M$. If $S\theta = V$, then for any x in V, there is an element z in S such that $vx = vz$, whence $x - z \in M$. Since $M \subseteq S$, $x \in S$ and so $S = A$. Hence M is a maximal ideal of A. But $y \notin M$ as $vy = 0$. Thus $y \notin R$. It follows that $R \subseteq N$ and we conclude that $R = N$.

To prove (ii), set $\bar{A} = A/B$ and let $\bar{R}$, $\bar{N}$ have analogous meanings as R, N. Then $\bar{R} = \bar{N}$ by (i) and so we need only show that $(N + B)/B \subseteq \bar{N}$. But if V/F is an irreducible $\bar{A}$-module, we can regard it as an irreducible A-module on which B acts trivially. Then $Vy = 0$ for any y in N by definition of N. Equivalently $V\bar{y} = 0$, where $\bar{y}$ is the image in $\bar{A}$. Thus $\bar{y} \in \bar{N}$ and so $(N + B)/B \subseteq \bar{N}$, proving (ii).

With the aid of this result, we can now prove

Theorem 6.9

If A/F is semisimple, then A contains no nonzero nilpotent left or right ideals.

Proof

Let R be the intersection of all maximal right (left) ideals of A. We argue, on the one hand, that $R = 0$ and, on the other, that R contains all nilpotent right (left) ideals of A, which together will establish the theorem.

First of all, R is a two-sided ideal by Lemma 6.8. Now the descending chain of two-sided ideals R^i, $i > 1$, stabilizes at some point n, so that $R^n = R^{n+1} = \cdots$. We shall argue that $R^{2n} = 0$, which will force $R = 0$ by the semisimplicity of A.

Consider the left annihilator L of R^n which by definition is the set of x in A such that $xR^n = 0$. Then $LR^n = 0$ and also L is a two-sided ideal of A. If $L \supseteq R^n$, then $0 = R^n R^n = R^{2n}$; so we may assume that $R^n \not\subseteq L$. Set $\bar{A} = A/L$ and let $\bar{R}^n$ be the image of R^n in $\bar{A}$, so that $\bar{R}^n$ is nonzero by our assumption. Now if $\bar{x} \in \bar{A}$ and $\bar{x}\bar{R}^n = 0$, then $xR^n \subseteq L$, x a representative of $\bar{x}$ in $\bar{A}$. But then $xR^{2n} = 0$ and consequently $xR^n = 0$ as $R^n = R^{2n}$. By definition of L, this yields $x \in L$, whence $\bar{x} = 0$. We conclude, in particular, that if $\bar{M}$ is a minimal right ideal of $\bar{A}$ contained in $\bar{R}^n$ then $\bar{M}\bar{R}^n \neq \bar{0}$. On the other hand, as $R^n \subseteq R$, R^n is contained in the intersection of the maximal right ideals of $\bar{A}$ by the preceding lemma. But then by the same lemma, applied to $\bar{A}$, $\bar{R}^n$ must be contained in the annihilator of $\bar{M}$, whence $\bar{M}\bar{R}^n = \bar{0}$, a contradiction. Thus $R = 0$, as asserted.

Finally, let B be a nilpotent right ideal of A. We shall argue that $B \subseteq N(V)$ for any irreducible right A-module V, whence $B \subseteq R$. Suppose, by way of contradiction, that $VB \neq 0$. Then $uB \neq 0$ for some $u \neq 0$ in V. Since uB is an A-submodule of V, it follows that $uB = V$. In particular, there exists y in B such that

$$(6.16) \qquad\qquad uy = -u.$$

On the other hand, $y^k = 0$ for some k as B is nilpotent. Hence $(1 + y)^{-1} = 1 - y + y^2 - \cdots \pm y^{k-1} \in A$. Setting $z = -y(1 + y)^{-1}$, we see that $z \in A$ and that

$$(6.17) \qquad\qquad y + z + yz = 0.$$

Now combining (6.16) and (6.17), we have $0 = u0 = u(y + z + yz) = -u + uz - uz = -u$, contrary to the fact that $u \neq 0$.

Similarly, every nilpotent left ideal of A is 0.

This property of semisimple algebras enables us to establish the following basic fact:

Theorem 6.10

Let A/F be a semisimple algebra and B a right ideal of A. Then we have
(i) There exists an idempotent e in B such that $x = ex$ for all x in B.
(ii) If B is a two-sided ideal, then $e \in Z(A)$.

Proof

Let M be a minimal right ideal of A contained in B. Since A is semisimple, $M^2 \neq 0$ by Theorem 6.9. Hence there exists u in M such that $uM \neq 0$. Since uM is also a right ideal of A, the minimality of M implies that $uM = M$. Hence $ue = u$ for some $e \neq 0$ in M, whence

$$(6.18) \qquad\qquad u(e^2 - e) = 0.$$

On the other hand, the annihilator $N_M(u)$ of u in M, defined by

$$N_M(u) = \{y \in M \,|\, uy = 0\},$$

is also a right ideal of A contained in M. However, $N_M(u) \subset M$ as $uM \neq 0$. Hence $N_M(u) = 0$ by the minimality of M. But $e^2 - e \in N_M(u)$ by (6.18). Thus $e^2 = e$ and we conclude that M, and therefore also B, contains an idempotent.

For each idempotent $e \neq 0$ of B, we consider the annihilator $N_B(e)$ of e in B and among all such idempotents, we choose e so that $N = N_B(e)$ is minimal. This is possible as each $N_B(e)$ is a right ideal of A. We shall show that (i) holds for such a choice of e. It will suffice to establish that $N = 0$, for then we shall have $e(x - ex) = ex - ex = 0$ for any x in B, whence $x - ex \in N = 0$ and the desired conclusion $x = ex$ will follow.

Suppose then that $N \neq 0$. By the first paragraph of the proof, N possesses an idempotent f. Set $g = e + f - fe$. Then $e^2 = e$, $f^2 = f$, and $ef = 0$. A direct calculation now yields

$$(6.19) \qquad\qquad g^2 = g \qquad eg = e \qquad gf = f.$$

In particular, g is a nonzero idempotent of B. Furthermore, if $x \in N_B(g)$, then $gx = 0$, whence $ex = (eg)x = 0$ and so $x \in N$. Thus $N_B(g) \subseteq N$. On the other hand, $f \in N$, but $f \notin N_B(g)$ inasmuch as $gf = f \neq 0$. Hence $N_B(g) \subset N = N_B(e)$, contrary to our choice of e. Thus $N = 0$ and (i) is proved.

Suppose now that B is two-sided. Then $L = \{x - xe \mid x \in B\}$ is a left ideal of A. Moreover, $Le = 0$. Hence $L^2 \subseteq LB = LeB = 0$ as $B = eB$. Since A contains no nilpotent left ideals by Theorem 6.9, this yields $L = 0$, whence also $x = xe$ for all x in B. But now for y in A, ye and ey are each in B, whence $ye = e(ye)$ and $ey = (ey)e$. Thus $ye = ey$ for all y in A and so $e \in Z(A)$, proving (ii).

We can now easily establish our desired structure theorem:

Theorem 6.11 (Wedderburn)
A semisimple algebra A/F is the direct sum of its minimal two-sided ideals, each of which is a simple ring.

Proof
Let A_1 be a minimal two-sided ideal of A. By the preceding theorem, $A_1 = Ae$ for some idempotent e in $Z(A)$. Set $B = (1 - e)A$. Since $e \in Z(A)$, it follows at once that B is also a two-sided ideal of A. Now $A_1 B \subseteq Ae(1 - e)A = 0$. Furthermore, if $x \in A$, we have $x = ex + (1 - e)x$, so $x \in A_1 + B$. Thus $A = A_1 \oplus B$ is the direct sum of its subalgebras A_1 and B. Clearly any ideal of B is an ideal of A inasmuch as $A_1 B = 0$. As A is semisimple, B thus contains no nilpotent two-sided ideals and so is also semisimple. Since $\dim_F B < \dim_F A$, B is the direct sum of its minimal two-sided ideals A_i, $2 \leq i \leq n$. Hence

$$(6.20) \qquad\qquad A = A_1 \oplus A_2 \oplus \cdots \oplus A_n.$$

As in the preceding paragraph, any two-sided ideal R_i of A_i is a two-sided ideal of A. Hence $R_i = 0$ or A_i by the minimality of A_i and so each A_i is a simple ring. Thus to complete the proof, it remains only to show that the A_i, $1 \leqslant i \leqslant n$, include all the minimal two-sided ideals of A. Let R be a minimal two-sided ideal of A. By (6.20), we have

$$AR = A_1 R \oplus A_2 R \oplus \cdots \oplus A_n R.$$

Furthermore, $A_i R$ is an ideal of A and is contained in $A_i \cap R$. Hence either $A_i R = 0$ or A_i. However, if $A_i R = 0$ for all i, $1 \leqslant i \leqslant n$, then $AR = 0$, whence $R^2 = 0$, contrary to the semisimplicity of A. Thus $A_i R = A_i$ for some i. But then $A_i \subseteq R$ and now the minimality of R yields $R = A_i$, as required.

Combined with Theorem 6.4, we obtain as a corollary

Theorem 6.12

A semisimple algebra A/F with F algebraically closed is isomorphic to

$$F_{n_1} \oplus F_{n_2} \oplus \cdots \oplus F_{n_r}$$

for suitable integers r and n_i, $1 \leqslant i \leqslant r$.

The minimal right ideals of an algebra A/F are all irreducible A-submodules and so determine irreducible representations of A. In the semisimple case, we can show conversely that every irreducible representation of A arises in this way.

Theorem 6.13

If A/F is semisimple, then every irreducible representation of A is equivalent to one determined by a minimal right ideal of A.

Proof

Let V/F be the representation space of an irreducible representation of A. We regard V as an A-module. We let $v \in V$, $v \neq 0$. Since $v1 = v$, it follows as in the proof of Lemma 6.8 that $vA = V$ and that the mapping $x\theta = vx$ for x in A is an A-homomorphism of A onto V whose kernel M is a maximal right ideal of A. But then θ induces an A-isomorphism of the factor A-module A/M and the A-module V. Hence it will suffice to show that A/M is A-isomorphic to the module determined by some minimal right ideal of A.

Since A is semisimple, M contains an idempotent e such that $ex = x$ for all x in M by Theorem 6.10(i). Set $B = (1 - e)A$. Then $y = ey + (1 - e)y \in M + B$ for any y in A. On the other hand, if $y \in M \cap B$, $y = ey$ and $y = (1 - e)z$, $z \in A$. But then $ey = e(1 - e)z = 0$, so $y = 0$. Thus $A = M \oplus B$. But by Lemma 1.1, extended to algebras, the A-modules A/M and B are

A-isomorphic. Since A/M is irreducible, so also is B and consequently B is a minimal right ideal of A, proving the theorem.

With this information we can now determine all the irreducible representations of a group G over an algebraically closed field F of characteristic 0 or prime to $|G|$. If ϕ is any representation of G over F, with representation space V/F, we know by Theorem 3.1 that ϕ is completely reducible; that is, V is the direct sum of $(G)\phi$-invariant subspaces on each of which $(G)\phi$ acts irreducibly. Thus we can write ϕ as the *sum* of certain irreducible representations of G, which we call the *constituents* of ϕ. It is convenient to identify equivalent constituents. When we do this, we can then write

$$\phi = m_1\phi_1 + m_2\phi_2 + \cdots + m_h\phi_h,$$

where the ϕ_i are the distinct inequivalent constituents of ϕ and m_i is the number of constituents of ϕ equivalent to ϕ_i, $1 \le i \le h$. We call m_i the *multiplicity* of ϕ_i in ϕ. It is an immediate consequence of the definition that

$$(6.21) \qquad \deg \phi = m_1 \deg \phi_1 + \cdots + m_h \deg \phi_h.$$

Our main result is as follows:

Theorem 6.14

Let G be a group and F an algebraically closed field of characteristic 0 or prime to $|G|$. Then the following holds:

(i) *$A = A(G, F)$ is isomorphic to $F_{n_1} \oplus F_{n_2} \oplus \cdots \oplus F_{n_r}$ for suitable integers r and n_i, $1 \le i \le r$.*

(ii) *The irreducible representations of A and G determined by minimal right ideals of F_{n_i} and F_{n_j} are equivalent if and only if $i = j$. Furthermore, if ϕ_i denotes such a representation determined by F_{n_i}, then $\deg \phi_i = n_i$, $1 \le i \le r$.*

(iii) *Every irreducible representation of G over F is equivalent to some ϕ_i, $1 \le i \le r$.*

(iv) *If π denotes the regular representation of A, then*

$$\pi = n_1\phi_1 + n_2\phi_2 + \cdots + n_r\phi_r.$$

(v) *$|G| = n_1^2 + n_2^2 + \cdots + n_r^2$.*

(vi) *The integer r is equal to both the number of conjugate classes of G and the dimension of $Z(A)$ over F.*

Proof

Since A is semisimple by Theorem 6.7, (i) follows from Theorem 6.12, as F is algebraically closed. We may identify A with $F_{n_1} \oplus F_{n_2} \oplus \cdots \oplus F_{n_r}$, in which case $A_i = F_{n_i}$, $1 \le i \le r$, are all the minimal two-sided ideals of A.

If B is a minimal right ideal of A, $BA_i = B$ or 0 for each i. Since $BA \neq 0$, we must have $BA_i = B$ for some i, whence $B \subseteq A_i$. Thus every minimal right ideal of A is contained in one of the A_i. Therefore by the preceding theorem every irreducible representation of A, and hence also of G, is equivalent to one determined by a minimal right ideal of one of the A_i. Thus (iii) will follow from (ii).

Now for x in A we can write x uniquely in the form $x = \sum\limits_{i=1}^{r} x_i, x_i \in A_i$. But then if π denotes the regular representation of A and if we set $(x)\pi_i = (x_i)\pi$ for x in A, we see at once that each π_i is a representation of A and that

$$(6.22) \qquad \pi = \pi_1 + \pi_2 + \cdots + \pi_r.$$

But for $i \neq j$, $(x_i)\pi_j$ is the zero transformation of A, while $(x_i)\pi_i$ is not, for all $x_i \neq 0$ in A_i. We conclude at once from the definition that π_i and π_j are inequivalent for $i \neq j$. This also shows that the action of $(A)\pi_i$ on A_i is the same as the action of $(A_i)\pi_i$ on A_i; consequently π_i can be identified with the regular representation of A_i.

We shall argue that $\pi_i = n_i \phi_i$, where ϕ_i is an irreducible representation of A_i, that $\deg \phi_i = n_i$, and that the representation of A_i determined by any of its right ideals is equivalent to $\phi_i, 1 \leq i \leq r$. Since π_i and π_j are inequivalent for $i \neq j$, this will clearly imply that ϕ_i and ϕ_j are inequivalent for $i \neq j$. Thus (ii) will follow. Furthermore, in view of (6.22), (iv) will also follow.

These assertions are properties of F_{n_i}, so for simplicity we drop the subscript i. Let e_{ij} be the matrix with 1 in the $\{i, j\}$th place and 0 elsewhere, and let U_i be the subspace spanned by $e_{i1}, e_{i2}, \ldots, e_{in}$. Thus U_i consists of the matrices whose ith row is arbitrary, but all other entries are 0. One verifies directly that $\dim_F U_i = n$, that

$$(6.23) \qquad F_n = U_1 \oplus U_2 \oplus \cdots \oplus U_n,$$

and that each U_i is a minimal right ideal of F_n. If P_{ij} denotes the permutation matrix in F_n which interchanges rows i and j, then $U_j = P_{ij}U_i$. Furthermore, for any matrix X of F_n, $P_{ij}X$ has the same effect on U_j as X has on U_i, which shows that the U_i determine equivalent irreducible representations of degree n. Denoting one of these by ϕ, it follows from (6.23) that the regular representation of F_n is equal to $n\phi$. Finally, since F_n is the direct sum of isomorphic irreducible F_n-modules, every irreducible submodule of F_n, and so every minimal right ideal of F_n, is isomorphic to

U_1 (compare Corollary 4.2). (Actually in the present case it is easy to see that the U_i are the only minimal right ideals of F_n.) This completes the proof of (ii) and (iv).

It follows now from (ii) and (iv) together with (6.21) that $\deg \pi = \sum_{i=1}^{r} n_i^2$. On the other hand, $\deg \pi = \dim_F A$, which is $|G|$ by definition of the group algebra. Hence (v) also holds.

To prove (vi), observe first that if $x \in Z(A)$ and $x = \sum_{i=1}^{r} x_i$ with $x_i \in A_i$, then for a in A,

$$xa = ax = \sum_{i=1}^{r} ax_i = \sum_{i=1}^{r} x_i a.$$

But ax_i and $x_i a$ are in A_i and, as the decomposition of A is direct, we must have $ax_i = x_i a$, whence each $x_i \in Z(A)$. However, $A_i = F_{n_i}$ and hence $Z(A_i)$ consists precisely of the scalar matrices of A_i. Hence $\dim_F Z(A_i) = 1$, $1 \le i \le r$, and we conclude that $\dim_F Z(A) = r$.

Finally, let $K_j, 1 \le j \le s$, be the conjugate classes of G and let $y_{jk}, 1 \le k \le m_j = |K_j|$ be the element of K_j. Consider the s elements y_j of A defined by

$$(6.24) \qquad\qquad y_j = \sum_{k=1}^{m_j} y_{jk} \qquad 1 \le j \le s.$$

We shall argue that $y_1, y_2, \ldots, y_s$ is a basis of $Z(A)$ over F, which will prove that $s = \dim_F Z(A) = r$.

First of all, for x in G,

$$(6.25) \qquad\qquad x^{-1} y_j x = \sum_{k=1}^{m_j} x^{-1} y_{jk} x = y_j,$$

since $x^{-1} y_{jk} x$ runs over the elements of the conjugate class K_j as y_{jk} does. Thus y_j centralizes each element of G and so by linearity is in the center of A. Furthermore, the elements of G, as elements of A, are linearly independent over F. Since each element of G is a summand of exactly one y_j, it follows that the y_j are linearly independent over F.

Finally, let $z = \sum \lambda_{jk} y_{jk}$, $\lambda_{jk} \in F$, $1 \le j \le s$, $1 \le k \le m_j$, be an arbitrary element of $Z(A)$. Denote by x_{jk} an element of G such that $x_{jk}^{-1} y_{j1} x_{jk} = y_{jk}$. Then using the fact that $x_{jk}^{-1} z x_{jk} = z$ and also the linear independence of the y_{jk}, it follows at once that $\lambda_{jk} = \lambda_{j1}$, $1 \le k \le m_j$. Thus $z = \sum_{j=1}^{s} \lambda_{j1} y_j$ and we see that the y_j span $Z(A)$ over F. Hence the y_j are indeed a basis of $Z(A)$ over F and (vi) is proved.

As a corollary, we obtain the following theorem on the existence of splitting fields:

Theorem 6.15

Let G be a group, let K be either the field of rational numbers or the field Z_p with p prime to $|G|$, and let F be an algebraic closure of K. Then there exists a subfield L of F of finite degree over K such that
    (i) Every irreducible representation of G over F can be written in L.
    (ii) L is a splitting field for G.

Proof

In view of Theorem 5.9, it will suffice to prove (i). By Theorem 6.14, G has only a finite number r of inequivalent irreducible representations ϕ_i, $1 \leqslant i \leqslant r$. Let V_i, $1 \leqslant i \leqslant r$, be the corresponding representation spaces of degree m_i and let (v_i) be a basis of V_i. Then for each x in G, we have

$$(6.26) \qquad\qquad (x\phi_i)_{(v_i)} = (\alpha_{jk}^{(i)}(x)),$$

where $\alpha_{jk}^{(i)}(x)$ is a suitable element of F, $1 \leqslant j, k \leqslant m_i$, $1 \leqslant i \leqslant r$. We let L be the subfield of F obtained from K by adjoining all the elements $\alpha_{jk}^{(i)}(x)$, which are clearly finite in number. Since F is an algebraic closure of K, each of these elements is algebraic over K and consequently L is of finite degree over K.

Now obviously by our choice of L, each of the representations ϕ_i can be written in L, $1 \leqslant i \leqslant r$. But then it is immediate from the definition that any representation of G over F equivalent to one of the ϕ_i can be written in L. Since every irreducible representation of G is equivalent to one of the ϕ_i, (i) follows. Furthermore, as L is a subfield of F and F is algebraically closed, Theorems 5.7 and 5.9 now yield that L is a splitting field for G.

7. REPRESENTATIONS OF DIRECT AND CENTRAL PRODUCTS

On the basis of the results of Sections 5 and 6 we shall now determine the irreducible representations of the direct and central products of groups in terms of those of the individual factors.

If $G = H \times K$ and V/F, W/F are H- and K-modules, respectively, there is a natural way of turning $U = V \otimes_F W$ into a G-module. Indeed, let $(v) = \{v_i \mid 1 \leqslant i \leqslant m\}$ and $(w) = \{w_j \mid 1 \leqslant j \leqslant n\}$ be bases of V/F and W/F, respectively, and let $(u) = \{u_{ij} = v_i \otimes w_j \mid 1 \leqslant i \leqslant m, 1 \leqslant j \leqslant n\}$ be the corresponding basis of U. Then if $x = (h, k)$ is any element of G with $h \in H$, $k \in K$, we define

$$(7.1) \qquad u_{ij} x = (v_i h) \otimes (w_j k) \qquad \text{for all } i, j,$$

and extend the operation of x to all of U by linearity. Using the basic properties of tensor products together with the facts that V and W are H- and K-modules, one checks easily that U becomes a G-module under this definition.

We call U/F a *product module* and the corresponding representation a *product representation*.

Our principal result is the following:

Theorem 7.1

Let $G = H \times K$ and let F be a splitting field for both H and K. If V/F and W/F are irreducible H- and K-modules, respectively, then the product module $V \otimes_F W$ is an irreducible G-module. Conversely, every irreducible G-module over F is equivalent to a product module of this form.

Proof

We regard G as the internal direct product of H and K, so that each $x \in G$ can be uniquely written in the form $x = hk$, $h \in H$, $k \in K$, and $hk = kh$. We first establish the converse and let U/F be an irreducible G-module. Apply Clifford's theorem with respect to the normal subgroup H, letting $U_i, 1 \leqslant i \leqslant r$, be the corresponding Wedderburn components. Since $K \subseteq C_G(H)$, Theorem 4.1(iii) implies that both H and K, and hence also G, leaves each U_i invariant. But then $U = U_1$ by the irreducibility of U as a G-module.

Hence $U = V_1 \oplus V_2 \oplus \cdots \oplus V_n$, where the V_i are isomorphic irreducible H-modules. Let ψ_j be a fixed H-isomorphism of V_1 onto $V_j, 1 \leqslant j \leqslant n$. Now for each k in K, $V_j k = (V_1) \psi_j k$ is an irreducible H-submodule of U isomorphic to V_1. Furthermore, we have $\text{Hom}_H(V_i, V_i) = F$ by Corollary 5.8, as F is a splitting field of H. It follows therefore from Theorem 5.5 that

$$(7.2) \qquad \psi_j k = \sum_{s=1}^{n} a_{js}(k) \psi_s,$$

where $a_{js}(k)$ are suitable elements of F which are uniquely determined by j and the element k, up to a nonzero scalar multiple.

Next let $v_i, 1 \leqslant i \leqslant m$, be a basis of V_1. Then the elements $v_i \psi_j$, $1 \leqslant i \leqslant m, 1 \leqslant j \leqslant n$, form a basis of U. Hence the action of G on U is determined by its effect on the elements $v_i \psi_j$. Now let $x \in G$ and set $x = hk$,

h in H, k in K. Using (7.2) together with linearity and the fact that h commutes with each ψ_j, we deduce that

(7.3) $$(v_i\psi_j)x = (v_ih)(\psi_jk) \qquad \text{for all } i, j.$$

On the other hand, let W be the vector space over F with basis $(\psi) = \{\psi_j \mid 1 \leqslant j \leqslant n\}$. We make W into a K-module by using (7.2) to define the action of k in K on W. But then the tensor product $T = V_1 \otimes_F W$ is a product G-module and we have

(7.4) $$(v_i \otimes \psi_j)x = (v_ih) \otimes (\psi_jk)$$

for all i, j and all $x = hk$ in G by definition of the product module.

But now if θ denotes the linear transformation of U onto T which maps the basis elements $v_i\psi_j$ of U on the corresponding basis element $v_i \otimes \psi_j$, (7.3) and (7.4) imply that for all x in G, we have

(7.5) $$(v_i\psi_j)x\theta = (v_i\psi_j)\theta x \qquad \text{for all } i, j.$$

Hence by linearity θ is a G-isomorphism of U on T and so the G-modules U/F and T/F are equivalent.

Finally V_1 is an irreducible H-module. If W contained a proper K-submodule $W_1 \neq 0$, then $V_1 \otimes W_1$ would be a nontrivial proper G-submodule of T, whence T would not be an irreducible G-module. But then U, being G-isomorphic to T, would also not be irreducible, a contradiction. Thus W is an irreducible K-module and the converse is completely proved.

To establish the first statement, let $U = V \otimes_F W$ be the product G-module of the irreducible H- and K-modules V and W. Let $\dim_F V = m$ and $\dim_F W = n$, so that $\dim_F U = mn$. Let U_1 be a nonzero G-submodule of U. Then by the converse part of the theorem, U_1 is equivalent to a product representation $V_1 \otimes_F W_1$, where V_1, W_1 are irreducible H- and K-modules, respectively. Let $m_1 = \dim_F V_1$ and $n_1 = \dim_F W_1$, so that $\dim_F U_1 = m_1n_1$. It will suffice to show that $m_1 \geqslant m$ and $n_1 \geqslant n$, for then $\dim_F U_1 \geqslant \dim_F U$, forcing $U_1 = U$, and the irreducibility of U will follow. By symmetry, we need only show that $n_1 \geqslant n$.

As U_1 is equivalent to $V_1 \otimes_F W_1$, it possesses an irreducible K-submodule T which is isomorphic to W_1, and we have $\dim_F T = n_1$. Now let $(v) = \{v_i \mid 1 \leqslant i \leqslant m\}$ be a basis for V. Since $T \subseteq U = V \otimes_F W$, we can express any element $u \neq 0$ of T in the form

(7.6) $$u = \sum_{j=1}^{r} v_{i_j} \otimes w_j,$$

where $i_j \neq i_{j'}$, if $j \neq j'$, and each w_j is a nonzero element of W. But now by definition of the action of G on U, we have for k in K,

$$(7.7) \qquad\qquad uk = \sum_{j=1}^{r} v_{i_j} \otimes w_j k.$$

On the other hand, as K acts irreducibly on W, there exist elements k_s, $1 \leqslant s \leqslant n$, such that the n elements $w_1 k_s$ are linearly independent in W/F, where w_1 is as in (7.6) and (7.7). However, it follows at once now from (7.7) that the elements uk_s, $1 \leqslant s \leqslant n$, are linearly independent in T/F. Hence $n_1 \geqslant n$, and the theorem is proved.

Consider next the case that $G = HK$ is a central product. The discussion of Section 2.5, shows that G is, in fact, a homomorphic image of the direct product $G^* = H \times K$. But, in general, if G and G^* are groups with $G = G^*/N^*$ for some normal subgroup N^* of G^*, then any G-module U/F can be considered to be a G^*-module, in which the elements of N^* induce the identity transformation of U. Thus the category of all G-modules coincides with the category of all G^*-modules in which N^* is in the kernel. We thus have

Theorem 7.2

A central product $G = HK$ of H and K can be identified with G^*/N^*, where $G^* = H \times K$ and N^* is a suitable normal subgroup of G^*. Then any G-module over a field F is a G^*-module in which N^* is in the kernel, and conversely.

In view of this result, Theorem 7.1 provides equally well a description of the irreducible G-modules for a central product $G = HK$ over a splitting field F of H and K.

Theorems 7.1 and 7.2 are stated for the direct and central products of two factors. Clearly one can prove easily by induction corresponding results for the direct and central products of any finite number of groups.

8. p-STABLE REPRESENTATIONS

If V/F is a faithful irreducible G-module, where F is a field of characteristic p, we can ask whether any p-element of G has a *quadratic* minimal polynomial. The answer to this question turns out to be of fundamental importance in a variety of problems, especially in the study of simple groups. If $p = 2$, then obviously any element x of G of order 2 satisfies the polynomial $X^2 - 1 = (X - 1)^2$ of degree 2 and, as V is faithful, this must be its minimal polynomial. We see then that the question is meaningful only when p is *odd*.

If $G = SL(2, p)$ acting on a two-dimensional vector space V over Z_p, then every element of G has a quadratic characteristic polynomial and so a nontrivial p-element certainly has a quadratic minimal polynomial in this case. Thus there do exist groups G and faithful irreducible G-modules V over fields of characteristic p, p odd, in which a p-element of G does have a quadratic minimal polynomial.

In treating this question systematically, it is convenient to drop the assumption of irreducibility. However, we note that by Theorem 1.3 a group G possesses a faithful irreducible module V/F, F of characteristic p, only if G has no nontrivial normal p-subgroups. In generalizing the situation, we must preserve this basic condition. Furthermore, for the applications, it is enough to restrict oneself to finite fields. We are thus led to introduce the following concept:

Let G be a group with no nontrivial normal p-subgroups, p odd. A faithful representation ϕ of G on a vector space V over $GF(p^n)$ will be called *p-stable* provided no p-element of $(G)\phi$ has a quadratic minimal polynomial on V. Moreover, we say that G is *p-stable* if all such faithful representations of G are p-stable.

Our analysis of p-stability depends on the following result:

Theorem 8.1

Let G be a group of linear transformations acting faithfully and irreducibly on a vector space V over an algebraic closure F of Z_p and assume that G is generated by two p-elements which have a quadratic minimal polynomial on V. Then G contains a subgroup isomorphic to $SL(2, p)$.

Proof

Let x_1, x_2 be the two given generators of G. Set $C_V(x_i) = V_i$, $1 \leqslant i \leqslant 2$. Since x_i is a p-element and F is of characteristic p, the minimal polynomial of x_i must be $(X - 1)^2$ and consequently $V(x_i - 1)^2 = 0$; $1 \leqslant i \leqslant 2$, where 1 denotes the identity transformation of V. Setting $W_i = V(x_i - 1)$, it follows that $W_i(x_i - 1) = 0$, whence $W_i \subseteq V_i$, $1 \leqslant i \leqslant 2$, Thus $x_i - 1$ is a linear transformation of V into V_i whose kernel is precisely V_i. But $\dim_F V - \dim_F \ker (x_i - 1) = \dim_F V(x_i - 1)$, and it follows that $d \leqslant 2d_i$, where $d = \dim_F V$ and $d_i = \dim_F V_i$, $1 \leqslant i \leqslant 2$.

Suppose d_1 or d_2 exceeds $d/2$, in which case $W = V_1 \cap V_2 \neq 0$. But x_1 and x_2 each act trivially on W and so $G = \langle x_1, x_2 \rangle$ also does. Since G acts irreducibly on V, this forces $V = W$, contrary to the fact that G acts faithfully on V. Hence $d = 2m$ is even, $d_1 = d_2 = m$, and $W = 0$. In particular, we have

(8.1) $$V = V_1 \oplus V_2.$$

Now $x_1 - 1$ maps V_2 into V_1. Since $V_1 \cap V_2 = 0$ and V_1, V_2 have the same dimensions, it follows that $x_1 - 1$ is an isomorphism of V_2 on V_1. Similarly $x_2 - 1$ is an isomorphism of V_1 on V_2. Let v_i, $1 \leqslant i \leqslant m$, be a basis of V_2, and set $v_{m+i} = v_i(x_1 - 1)$, $1 \leqslant i \leqslant m$. Then the v_{m+i} form a basis of V_1 and the v_i, $1 \leqslant i \leqslant 2m$, form a basis of V. Relative to this basis, x_1 and x_2 are represented, respectively, by the matrices

(8.2) $$A_1 = \begin{pmatrix} I & I \\ 0 & I \end{pmatrix} \quad \text{and} \quad A_2 = \begin{pmatrix} I & 0 \\ R & I \end{pmatrix},$$

where R is the matrix of the isomorphism of V_1 on V_2 determined by $x_2 - 1$. Thus R is nonsingular.

Since F is algebraically closed, there exists a nonsingular $m \times m$ matrix Q such that

(8.3) $$S = Q^{-1}RQ$$

is in Jordan canonical form. Hence if we conjugate A_1, A_2 by the matrix

(8.4) $$D = \begin{pmatrix} Q & 0 \\ 0 & Q \end{pmatrix},$$

which corresponds to a suitable change of basis of V, the matrices of x_1, x_2 with respect to the new basis are

(8.5) $$B_1 = A_1 \quad \text{and} \quad B_2 = \begin{pmatrix} I & 0 \\ S & I \end{pmatrix}.$$

Since S is a nonsingular matrix in Jordan canonical form, its diagonal entries are nonzero and S is a lower triangular matrix. Let λ be the entry of S in the upper left corner. Finally, let P be the $2m \times 2m$ permutation matrix obtained by interchanging rows 2 and $m + 1$ of the identity matrix and conjugate B_1, B_2 by P. With respect to the corresponding new basis u_i, $1 \leqslant i \leqslant 2m$, of V the matrices C_1, C_2 of x_1, x_2 have the form

(8.6) $$C_1 = \begin{pmatrix} 1 & 1 & \\ 0 & 1 & 0 \\ * & & * \end{pmatrix} \quad \text{and} \quad C_2 = \begin{pmatrix} 1 & 0 & \\ \lambda & 1 & 0 \\ * & & * \end{pmatrix}.$$

But now we see that x_1, x_2 each leave invariant the subspace U of V spanned by u_1, u_2. Since $G = \langle x_1, x_2 \rangle$, G thus leaves U invariant and therefore $U = V$ by the irreducibility of G on V. Hence $\dim_F V = 2$ and G is isomorphic to the group generated by the matrices $\begin{pmatrix} 1 & 1 \\ 0 & 1 \end{pmatrix}$ and $\begin{pmatrix} 1 & 0 \\ \lambda & 1 \end{pmatrix}$. Since $Z_p(\lambda)$ is a finite field, we conclude therefore from Dickson's theorem that G contains a subgroup isomorphic to $SL(2, p)$.

To exploit Theorem 8.1, we need a result of independent interest which is a particular case of a general theorem of Baer. The present proof is due to Suzuki and depends upon an ordering technique first used by Thompson. As with Dickson's theorem of Chapter 2, it foreshadows some general group-theoretic methods.

Theorem 8.2

Let K be a conjugate class of p-elements of the group G. If every pair of elements of K generates a p-group, then K lies in a normal p-subgroup of G.

Proof

Since the product of two normal p-subgroups of a group G is a p-group, any group G possesses a unique maximal normal p-subgroup, which is customarily denoted by $O_p(G)$. We shall adopt this terminology, which will be more fully developed in Section 6.3.

We shall establish the theorem by induction on $|G|$. If H is a proper subgroup of G, $K \cap H$ is clearly a union of conjugate classes $K_1, K_2, \ldots, K_r$ of H. Since every pair of elements of K_i generates a p-group, each $K_i \subseteq O_p(H)$ by induction and so $K \cap H \subseteq O_p(H)$. Similarly, if $\bar{G}$ is a proper homomorphic image of G, the image $\bar{K}$ of K in $\bar{G}$ is the union of conjugate classes of p-elements of $\bar{G}$, each of which satisfies the hypothesis of the theorem. Hence $\bar{K} \subseteq O_p(\bar{G})$ by induction. In particular, if $O_p(G) \neq 1$, we can take $\bar{G} = G/O_p(G)$ and conclude that $\bar{K} \subseteq O_p(\bar{G})$. But the inverse image L of $O_p(\bar{G})$ in G is certainly a normal p-subgroup of G, whence $L \subseteq O_p(G)$. Since $K \subseteq L$, we have $K \subseteq O_p(G)$ and the theorem follows in this case. Hence without loss we may assume that $O_p(G) = 1$. Obviously we may also assume that $K \neq 1$.

We introduce two families of p-groups:

$$\mathscr{H} = \{H \mid H \neq 1, H \text{ is not an } S_p\text{-subgroup of } G, \text{ and } H = O_p(N_G(H))\}.$$
$$\mathscr{H}_0 = \{H \mid H \neq 1, O_p(N_G(H)) \text{ is not an } S_p\text{-subgroup of } N_G(H)\}.$$

If $H \in \mathscr{H}$, $H \subset P$ for some S_p-subgroup P of G and $P \cap N_G(H) \supset H$ by Theorem 1.2.11(ii). Hence H is not an S_p-subgroup of $N_G(H)$. Thus $\mathscr{H} \subseteq \mathscr{H}_0$.

For the proof we need two properties of the sets $\mathcal{H}$ and $\mathcal{H}_0$:

(A) If $H_0 \in \mathcal{H}_0$, then there exists an element H in $\mathcal{H}$ containing H_0 such that $N_G(H_0) \subseteq N_G(H)$.

(B) If $H \in \mathcal{H}$ and L is a subgroup of G containing $N_G(H)$, then $O_p(L) \subseteq H$.

To prove (A), choose $H \supseteq H_0$ of maximal order such that $N_0 = N_G(H_0) \subseteq N = N_G(H)$. Obviously $H \lhd N$, whence $H \subseteq H^* = O_p(N)$ and $N_0 \subseteq N_G(H^*)$. Maximality of H thus forces $H = H^*$, so $H = O_p(N)$. Suppose H were an S_p-subgroup of G. Then H would be an S_p-subgroup of $L = HN_0$ and L/H would be a p'-group, whence $N_0/H \cap N_0$ would be a p'-group by the third isomorphism theorem. Since $H \cap N_0 \lhd N_0$, this is possible only if $H \cap N_0 = O_p(N_0)$ and $O_p(N_0)$ is an S_p-subgroup of N_0, contrary to the fact that $H_0 \in \mathcal{H}_0$. Thus H is not an S_p-subgroup of G and consequently $H \in \mathcal{H}$, proving (A).

Next let $H \in \mathcal{H}$ and suppose that $L \supseteq N = N_G(H)$. By Sylow's theorem $O_p(L)$ is the intersection of all the S_p-subgroups of L. Hence to prove (B), it will suffice to show that H is the intersection of certain of the S_p-subgroups of L, for then the conclusion $O_p(L) \subseteq H$ will follow. Now as with L, $O_p(N)$ is the intersection of the S_p-subgroups of N, which we denote by P_i, $1 \leqslant i \leqslant n$. We also have $H = O_p(N)$ since $H \in \mathcal{H}$. Let Q_i be an S_p-subgroup of L containing P_i and set $D = \bigcap_{i=1}^{n} Q_i$. Clearly $H \subseteq D$ and

$$N_D(H) \subseteq \bigcap_{i=1}^{n} (Q_i \cap N) = \bigcap_{i=1}^{n} P_i = H.$$

But then $H = D$ by Theorem 1.2.11(ii) and so H is the intersection of the S_p-subgroups Q_i of L, $1 \leqslant i \leqslant n$, as required.

With the aid of these results we can now prove the theorem. First of all, there must exist an S_p-subgroup of G not containing the conjugate class K, otherwise K would lie in $O_p(G)$, the intersection of all S_p-subgroups of G. But $O_p(G) = 1$ by assumption, whence $K = 1$, which is not the case.

It will suffice to establish the following assertion:

(C) If P and Q are any two S_p-subgroups of G such that $K \cap P \cap Q \neq \varnothing$, then $K \cap P \subseteq Q$.

Indeed, suppose (C) holds and choose P to be an S_p-subgroup of G not containing K. Let $x \in K$, $x \notin P$. By Sylow's theorem we have $K \cap P \neq \varnothing$ and so there also exists an element y in $K \cap P$. By hypothesis $\langle x, y \rangle$ is a p-group and hence lies in an S_p-subgroup Q of G. Then $y \in K \cap P \cap Q$ and therefore $K \cap P \subseteq Q$ by (C). But again by Sylow's theorem $|K \cap P| = |K \cap Q|$, whence $K \cap P = Q$. However, $x \in K \cap Q$, while $x \notin K \cap P$, a contradiction.

Suppose then that (C) is false. We choose P, Q to violate (C) in such a way that $H = P \cap Q$ has maximal order. Clearly then $P \neq Q$, whence $H \subset P$ and $H \subset Q$. Set $N = N_G(H)$ and let R, S be S_p-subgroups of G such that $R \cap N, S \cap N$ are S_p-subgroups of N with $R \cap N \supseteq N_P(H)$ and $S \cap N \supseteq N_Q(H)$. Again by Theorem 1.2.11(ii) we have $N_P(H) \supset H$ and $N_Q(H) \supset H$, whence $P \cap R \supset H$ and $Q \cap S \supset H$. Furthermore, $K \cap P \cap R \neq \varnothing$ and $K \cap Q \cap S \neq \varnothing$ since each contains $K \cap P \cap Q = K \cap H$, which is nontrivial by assumption. Hence by our choice of P, Q, (C) holds for the pairs P, R and S, Q, whence $K \cap P \subseteq R$ and $K \cap S \subseteq Q$. But then (C) must be false for the pair R, S; otherwise $K \cap R \subseteq S$ and the conclusion $K \cap P \subseteq Q$ would follow. However, $R \cap S \supseteq O_p(N) \supseteq H$ as $R \cap N$ and $S \cap N$ are S_p-subgroups of N. Moreover, $K \cap R \cap S \supseteq K \cap H \neq \varnothing$. Since (C) is false for R, S, our maximal choice of P, Q thus forces $R \cap S = O_p(N) = H$. We conclude that $H \in \mathscr{H}$. Since $|R \cap S|$ is also maximal subject to (C) being false for R, S, we can replace P, Q by R, S, if necessary, and so we can also assume without loss that $P \cap N$, $Q \cap N$ are S_p-subgroups of N.

We have thus produced an element H of $\mathscr{H}$ and an S_p-subgroup P of G such that $K \cap H \neq \varnothing$, $K \cap P \nsubseteq H$, and $P \cap N_G(H)$ is an S_p-subgroup of $N_G(H)$. Among all such pairs (H, P), we now choose (H^*, P^*) so that $|P^* \cap N_G(H^*)|$ is maximal. To obtain a contradiction and thus establish (C), we need only prove:

(D) $$P^* \subseteq N_G(H^*).$$

Indeed, set $N^* = N_G(H^*)$ and suppose (D) holds. Since $H^* = O_p(N^*)$ and $O_p(G) = 1$, we have $N^* \subset G$. But then the theorem holds by induction for N^*. Since $P^* \subseteq N^*$ by (D), it follows that $K \cap P^* \subseteq H^*$, contrary to our choice of (H^*, P^*).

Suppose then that $P^* \nsubseteq N^*$, set $H_0 = \langle K \cap H^* \rangle$, and $N_0 = N_G(H_0)$. Clearly the elements of $K \cap H^*$ are permuted among themselves by conjugation by the elements of N_0 and so $H_0 \lhd N^*$. Thus $N^* \subseteq N_0$. Furthermore, as in the preceding paragraph, the theorem holds by induction for N^* and consequently $K \cap P^* \cap N^* = K \cap H^*$. This implies that also $N_{P^*}(P^* \cap N^*)$ permutes the elements of $K \cap H^*$ and hence normalizes H_0. Since $P^* \cap N^* \subset P^*$, it follows that $P^* \cap N_0 \supset P^* \cap N^*$. On the other hand, since $H^* \in \mathscr{H}$ and $N^* \subseteq N_0$, (B) implies that $O_p(N_0) \subseteq H^*$. Therefore, $O_p(N_0) \subseteq P^* \cap N^* \subset P^* \cap N_0$, whence $O_p(N_0)$ is not an S_p-subgroup of N_0. We conclude that $H_0 \in \mathscr{H}_0$.

Finally we apply (A). There thus exists an element H_1 of $\mathscr{H}$ with $H_0 \subseteq H_1$ such that $N_0 \subseteq N_1$, where $N_1 = N_G(H_1)$. Let P_1 be an S_p-subgroup of G

such that $P_1 \cap N_1$ is an S_p-subgroup of N_1. Then $|P_1 \cap N_1| \geqslant |P^* \cap N_0| >$ $|P^* \cap N^*|$ and $K \cap H_1 \supseteq K \cap H^* \neq \varnothing$. It follows therefore from our maximal choice of (H^*, P^*) that $K \cap P_1 \subseteq H_1$. On the other hand, since $N^* \subseteq N_1$, another application of (B) yields that $H_1 = O_p(N_1) \subseteq H^*$. Thus $K \cap P_1 \subseteq H^*$. Since $H^* \subseteq P^*$, it follows that $K \cap P_1 \subseteq K \cap P^*$. But $|K \cap P_1| = |K \cap P^*|$ and consequently $K \cap P^* = K \cap P_1 \subseteq H^*$, contrary to our choice of (H^*, P^*). This completes the proof of (D) and the theorem.

We can now establish our main result on p-stability.

Theorem 8.3

Let G be a group with no nontrivial normal p-subgroups, p odd. If G is not p-stable, then G involves $SL(2, p)$.

Proof

We must show that a homomorphic image of some subgroup of G is isomorphic to $SL(2, p)$. By assumption G possesses a faithful representation on a vector space V over $GF(p^n)$ for some n in which some p-element x of G has a quadratic minimal polynomial. We regard V as a vector space over an algebraic closure F of $GF(p^n)$ and V/F as a G-module.

If K denotes the conjugate class containing x, then obviously every element of K has a quadratic minimal polynomial on V. Furthermore, since G has no nontrivial normal p-subgroups, Theorem 8.2 implies that for some y in K, the group $H = \langle x, y \rangle$ is not a p-group.

Let $V = V_1 \supset V_2 \supset \cdots \supset V_{m+1} = 0$ be a sequence of H-invariant subspaces of V such that H acts irreducibly on each $\bar{V}_i = V_i/V_{i+1}$, $1 \leqslant i \leqslant m$, and let N_i be the kernel of the representation of H on V_i. We argue that $N_i \subset H$ for some i; so assume the contrary. Since H is not a p-group, it possesses a nontrivial p'-subgroup Q. Our assumption implies that Q induces the identity transformation on each $\bar{V}_i$. But then Q induces the identity on V by Theorem 3.4, contrary to the fact that V is a faithful G-module.

Thus $N_i \subset H$ for some i. For such a choice of i, set $\bar{H} = H/N_i$ and let $\bar{x}, \bar{y}$ be the images of x, y in $\bar{H}$, so that $\bar{H} = \langle \bar{x}, \bar{y} \rangle$. Clearly the minimal polynomial of $\bar{x}$ on $\bar{V}_i$ is $(X - 1)^2$ or $(X - 1)$. However, in the latter case $\bar{x}$ acts trivially on $\bar{V}_i$, whence $\bar{x} = 1$ and $\bar{H} = \langle \bar{y} \rangle$ is a p-group. Since $\bar{H}$ acts faithfully and irreducibly on $\bar{V}_i$, Theorem 1.2 then yields $\bar{H} = 1$, whence $N_i = H$, contrary to our choice of i. Thus $\bar{x}$ has a quadratic minimal polynomial on $\bar{V}_i$. Similarly, $\bar{y}$ does also.

Now $\bar{H}$ can be regarded as a group of linear transformations acting faithfully and irreducibly on $\bar{V}_i/F$ and F is an algebraic closure of Z_p. Thus the hypotheses of Theorem 8.1 are satisfied and we conclude that $\bar{H}$ contains a subgroup isomorphic to $SL(2, p)$. Hence G involves $SL(2, p)$ and the theorem is proved.

As a corollary we have the following basic result:

Theorem 8.4

Let G be a group with no nontrivial normal p-subgroups, p odd, which satisfies one of the following conditions:
  (a) *G is of odd order.*
  (b) *A Sylow 2-subgroup of G is abelian.*
  (c) *A Sylow 2-subgroup of G is dihedral.*
  (d) *G is isomorphic to $L_2(q)$.*
  (e) *G is solvable and either $p \geqslant 5$ or $p = 3$ and $SL(2, 3)$ is not involved in G.*
Then G is p-stable.

Proof

Let S be an S_2-subgroup of G. If G is not p-stable, then Theorems 8.3 and 2.8.3(ii) together imply that there exist subgroups Q, R of S with $Q \lhd R$ and R/Q a quaternion group. Obviously then S is nonabelian. Furthermore, one verifies directly from the definition that a dihedral 2-group involves only cyclic and dihedral groups, so also S is not dihedral. On the other hand, if G is isomorphic to $L_2(q)$, then an S_2-subgroup of G is either abelian or dihedral by Theorem 2.8.3(ii). Thus the theorem holds if G satisfies (a), (b), (c), or (d). Finally $SL(2, p)$ is nonsolvable by Theorem 2.8.3(iii) for $p \geqslant 5$. Since a solvable group involves no nonsolvable subgroups by Theorem 2.4.1(i), the theorem also follows if G satisfies (e)

EXERCISES

1. Let M be a G-module and let α be a G-automorphism of M. If N is a submodule of M, show that $N^\alpha = \{x^\alpha \mid x \in N\}$ is a submodule of M. Show also that the mapping $N \to N^\alpha$ is one-to-one on both the set of all submodules and the set of all irreducible submodules of M.

2. Let G be an abelian group of exponent n and ω a primitive complex nth root of unity. Prove that $Q(\omega)$ is a splitting field for G, where Q denotes the field of rational numbers.

3. Let G be a dihedral group of order $2n$. Construct a complete set of in-equivalent representations of G over the complex numbers.

4. Suppose V/F has dimension 2, where F is of characteristic p. If P is a non-trivial p-group of linear transformations of V, show that $|P| = p$ and that V is an indecomposable, but not irreducible, P-module.

5. Let V/F be an irreducible G-module. Prove
    (i) There exists an extension field L of F such that if W_L is a minimal G-submodule of V_L, then W_L is an absolutely irreducible G-module.
    (ii) If $W_L \cap V \neq 0$, then $W_L = V_L$.
    (iii) If G contains an element which possesses $\dim_F V$ distinct characteristic roots on V in F, then V is absolutely irreducible. [Use (ii).]

6. Prove Corollary 4.2.

7. Show that Theorem 4.4 also holds under the assumption that F has characteristic p. Moreover, prove in this case that any element of $P^{\#}$ has $(X - 1)^p$ as its minimal polynomial on V.

8. Let V/F, W/F be G-modules of dimension m and n, respectively. Prove
    (i) Hom (V, W) is a vector space over F of dimension mn.
    (ii) Hom (V, V) is an associative algebra over F.
    (iii) $\mathrm{Hom}_G (V, W)$ is a subspace of Hom (V, W) and $\mathrm{Hom}_G (V, V)$ is a subalgebra of Hom (V, V).

9. Let $A = A(G, F)$ be the group algebra of G over F, let V/F be an A-module, let $B = \{x \in A \mid vx = 0 \text{ for all } v \text{ in } V\}$, and let $K = \{y \in G \mid vy = v \text{ for all } v \text{ in } V\}$. Prove
    (i) B is a two-sided ideal of A.
    (ii) A/B is isomorphic to the enveloping algebra $E(G/K)$.

10. Prove Theorem 6.1.

11. Use Theorems 6.10 and 6.11 to give an alternative proof of Wedderburn's theorem (Theorem 6.4).

12. Let A/F be an algebra over F and let e_i, $1 \leqslant i \leqslant n$, be idempotents of $Z(A)$ such that $1 = e_1 + e_2 + \cdots + e_n$ and $e_i e_j = 0$ for $i \neq j$.
    (i) Show that $A = Ae_1 \oplus Ae_2 \oplus \cdots \oplus Ae_n$, where each Ae_i is an ideal of A.
    (ii) Prove that Ae_i is a simple algebra if and only if each e_i is *primitive*—that is, it is not possible to write $e_i = f_i + g_i$, where f_i, g_i are nonzero idempotents of $Z(A)$ such that $f_i g_i = 0$.
    (iii) If A/F is semisimple, show that 1 can be expressed uniquely as a sum of primitive idempotents of $Z(A)$.

13. For any algebra A/F, we denote the Jacobson radical of A by rad A. Thus rad A is the intersection of all maximal right ideals of A (compare Lemma 6.8). Prove
    (i) rad (rad A) = rad A.
    (ii) rad A is a two-sided ideal of A.

    (iii) If B is a two-sided ideal of A, then $B \cap \operatorname{rad} A = \operatorname{rad} B$.

    (iv) $\operatorname{rad}(A/\operatorname{rad} A) = 0$.

14. An element x of an algebra A/F is called *quasi-right-regular* if $x + xy + y = 0$ for some y in A. Prove

    (i) Every element of $\operatorname{rad} A$ is quasi-right-regular.

    (ii) Any right ideal of A consisting entirely of quasi-right-regular elements lies in $\operatorname{rad} A$.

15. Let $A = A(G, F)$ and $B = A(H, F)$, where $H \lhd G$ and the characteristic of F divides $|G|$. Show that $B \cap \operatorname{rad} A = \operatorname{rad} B$.

16. Let A be the algebra of all $n \times n$ lower triangular matrices over F. Determine $\operatorname{rad} A$.

17. Prove that $L_3(q)$ is p-stable if q is not a power of p.

18. Prove that A_n is p-stable for all odd p.

CHAPTER 4

CHARACTER THEORY

Group characters are a powerful tool for the study of finite groups. This long chapter includes all the results we need for our later applications. After introducing the basic concepts and developing the standard orthogonality relations, we present several classical applications, including the well-known theorems of Burnside and Frobenius. We then take up in detail the theory of induced characters with special emphasis on the case in which the subgroup is disjoint from its conjugates. In particular, we study the characters of Frobenius groups and of groups which contain Frobenius groups as subgroups. This investigation leads to the important notion of coherence which we study in Section 6, culminating in a criterion of Feit for coherence. In the final section we develop Brauer's fundamental characterization of characters, which we then use to obtain a result on irreducible characters of a group G whose degrees are divisible by suitable factors of $|G|$.

1. BASIC PROPERTIES

Throughout this chapter F will denote the field of complex numbers. Then for any group G, the irreducible representations of G over F are determined from the group algebra $A(G, F)$ in accordance with Theorem 3.6.14. In particular, G has only a finite number r of inequivalent irreducible representations over F, where r is the number of conjugate classes of G.

For any representation ϕ of G over F with representation space V/F, we define the *character* χ of ϕ by setting, for y in G,

$$\chi(y) = \text{tr}\,(y\phi).$$

Here $\text{tr}\,(y\phi)$ denotes the trace of the linear transformation $y\phi$ of V. Thus χ is a function from G to F. We refer to χ as a *character* of G.

We have already had occasion in Section 2.7 to consider a particular character in our study of permutation groups, for if π is the matrix representation determined by a permutation group G acting on a set S, then the function $\alpha(y)$, which denotes the number of elements of S fixed by y, is precisely the number of diagonal entries of the matrix y whose value is 1 and consequently $\alpha(y)$ is just the character of π. In particular, the character ρ_G of the regular representation of G is 0 for y in $G^\#$ and has value $|G|$ on 1.

The *principal* or *trivial* character of G is the character of the trivial representation of G, which by definition maps each element of G onto the 1 element of F. Obviously this representation is of degree 1. The standard notation for the principal character will be 1_G.

As a first basic result, we have

Theorem 1.1
(i) *Equivalent representations of G over F have the same character.*
(ii) *If χ is a character of G, then the value of χ is constant on all elements of a conjugate class of G.*

Proof
If ϕ and ψ are equivalent matrix representations, of degree d, then by formula (3.1.4) there exists a nonsingular $d \times d$ matrix P over F such that $y\psi = P^{-1}(y\phi)P$ for all y in G. Thus $y\psi$ and $y\phi$ are similar and so $\text{tr}\,(y\psi) = \text{tr}\,(y\phi)$ by Lemma 3.6.5(v). We conclude that ϕ and ψ have the same characters.

Similarly, if χ denotes the character of the matrix representation ϕ and x, y are conjugate in G, then $y = z^{-1}xz$ for some z in G, whence $y\phi = (z^{-1}xz)\phi = (z\phi)^{-1}(x\phi)(z\phi)$ as ϕ is a homomorphism. Thus $y\phi$ and $x\phi$ are similar matrices and so have the same traces. Hence $\chi(y) = \chi(x)$.

Because of (ii), we say that a character χ is a *class function* on G.

A second elementary property of characters is the following:

Theorem 1.2
If χ is a character of G, then $\chi(y)$ is a sum of $|G|$th roots of unity for any y in G. In particular, $\chi(y)$ is an algebraic integer.

Proof

We have $y^m = 1$, where $m = |G|$. Hence if ϕ is a matrix representation with character χ, then $(y\phi)^m$ is an $n \times n$ identity matrix where $n = \deg \phi$. But by Lemma 3.6.5(i), $\chi(y) = \text{tr} \,(y\phi)$ is the sum of the characteristic roots ε_i, $1 \leqslant i \leqslant n$, of $y\phi$. However, the characteristic roots of $(y\phi)^j$ are ε_i^j and consequently $\varepsilon_i^m = 1$, $1 \leqslant i \leqslant n$. Thus ε_i is a $|G|$th root of unity. Since ε_i satisfies the monic polynomial $X^m - 1$ with integer coefficients, it is an algebraic integer. Since the algebraic integers form a ring, it follows that $\chi(y)$ is an algebraic integer.

We also have the following basic result:

Theorem 1.3

Let χ be the character of a representation ϕ of G of degree n and let $y \in G$. Then

(i) $|\chi(y)| \leqslant n$.

(ii) $|\chi(y)| = n$ if and only if $y\phi$ is a scalar transformation.

(iii) $\chi(y) = n$ if and only if $y\phi$ is the identity transformation.

Proof

We know that $\chi(y) = \sum\limits_{i=1}^{n} \varepsilon_i$, where each ε_i is a root of unity and also a characteristic root of $y\phi$. Hence

$$(1.1) \qquad |\chi(y)| = \left| \sum_{i=1}^{n} \varepsilon_i \right| \leqslant \sum_{i=1}^{n} |\varepsilon_i| = n,$$

proving (i).

If $\varepsilon_i = \varepsilon$ for all i, then $\chi(y) = n\varepsilon$ and so $|\chi(y)| = n$. Conversely, if $|\chi(y)| = n$, then the complex number $\sum\limits_{i=1}^{n} \varepsilon_i$ must lie on the circle of radius n with center at the origin in the complex plane. Since each ε_i has unit length, it is clear geometrically that this is possible only if all ε_i are equal. Thus (ii) is reduced to showing that $y\phi$ is a scalar transformation whenever its characteristic roots are all equal.

If this common value is ε, then the characteristic polynomial of $y\phi$ is $(X - \varepsilon)^n$. On the other hand, $y\phi$ also satisfies the polynomial $X^m - 1$, where $m = |G|$. Since the latter has distinct roots, the greatest common divisor of it and $(X - \varepsilon)^n$ must be $X - \varepsilon$. Hence $y\phi$ satisfies the polynomial $X - \varepsilon$ and so $y\phi$ is, in fact, the scalar transformation εI.

Finally, if $\chi(y) = n$, then $|\chi(y)| = n$, so $y\phi = \varepsilon I$ by (ii), whence $\chi(y) = n\varepsilon$. But then $\varepsilon = 1$ and $y\phi$ is the identity. Thus (iii) also holds.

Theorem 1.4

Let χ be a character of G and set

$$H = \{y \in G \mid \chi(y) = \chi(1)\}.$$

Then H is a normal subgroup of G.

Proof

Let ϕ be a representation of G with character χ and let $n = \deg \phi$. Since $(1)\phi$ is the identity transformation tr $(1)\phi = \deg \phi$ and so $\chi(1) = n$. Thus $y \in H$ if and only if $\chi(y) = n$. Hence by the preceding theorem, $y \in H$ if and only if $y\phi$ is the identity. Thus H is precisely the kernel of ϕ and so is a normal subgroup of G.

If χ is the character of a representation ϕ of G, we define ker $\chi = $ ker ϕ and deg $\chi = \deg \phi$. Then ker $\chi = \{y \in G \mid \chi(y) = \chi(1)\}$ by Theorem 1.4. Moreover, we have

(1.2)   deg $\chi = \chi(1)$.

We also call χ *irreducible, reducible, faithful,* or *linear* according as ϕ is irreducible, reducible, faithful, or linear. Since equivalent representations have the same character, it follows, in particular, that the number of distinct irreducible characters of G is $k \leqslant r$. In Section 2 we shall show that $k = r$.

A linear character has degree 1 and is irreducible. Moreover, Theorems 3.2.4 and 3.2.5 show that an irreducible character χ of G is linear if and only if its kernel contains G'.

Suppose that for suitable integers m_i and representations ϕ_i of $G, 1 \leqslant i \leqslant h$, we have

(1.3) $\phi = m_1\phi_1 + m_2\phi_2 + \cdots + m_h\phi_h$.

Then if χ_i denotes the character of ϕ_i, we shall write

$$\chi = m_1\chi_1 + m_2\chi_2 + \cdots + m_h\chi_h.$$

In particular, any representation ϕ of G is completely reducible by Theorem 3.3.1 and so can be expressed in the form (1.3) with each ϕ_i irreducible. It follows therefore that every character of G can be expressed as a linear combination with nonnegative integer coefficients of the irreducible characters of G.

Conversely we note that for any representations ϕ_i of G and any nonnegative integers m_i, $1 \leqslant i \leqslant h$, we can always construct a representation ϕ of the form (1.3): namely, we consider the direct sum V of h vector spaces V_i/F, where each V_i is the direct sum of m_i copies of the representation space of ϕ_i, $1 \leqslant i \leqslant h$, and then define $y\phi$ on V in accordance with the action of $y\phi_i$ on V_i. This means that any linear combination of characters with nonnegative integer coefficients is itself a character of G.

There is also a natural definition for the product of two characters, related to that of the tensor product of two representations. Indeed, if ϕ_i are representations of G with representation spaces V_i/F, $1 \leqslant i \leqslant 2$, then the mapping $\phi_1 \otimes \phi_2$ defined by setting

$$(y)\phi_1 \otimes \phi_2 = (y\phi_1) \otimes (y\phi_2)$$

for y in G is immediately verified to be a representation of G with representation space $V_1 \otimes_F V_2$. In fact, it should be clear that this representation is nothing else but the restriction of the product representation $\phi_1 \otimes \phi_2$ of $G \times G$ on $V_1 \otimes_F V_2$ to the diagonal $\{(y, y) \,|\, y \in G\}$ of $G \times G$. Moreover, if ϕ_i is considered to be a matrix representation with respect to a suitable basis of V_i, $1 \leqslant i \leqslant 2$, then the matrix $(y)\phi_1 \otimes \phi_2$ will be the tensor product of the matrices $y\phi_1$ and $y\phi_2$. But then by Lemma 3.6.5(vi), we have

(1.4) $\mathrm{tr}\,((y)\phi_1 \otimes \phi_2) = (\mathrm{tr}\, y\phi_1)(\mathrm{tr}\, y\phi_2)$

for all y in G. Thus the character of $\phi_1 \otimes \phi_2$ is the product of the characters χ_i of ϕ_i, $1 \leqslant i \leqslant 2$. We shall denote this character by $\chi_1\chi_2$. It follows at once from (1.4) that $\chi_1\chi_2 = \chi_2\chi_1$.

Because of the associative and distributive properties of tensor products of vector spaces, which carry over to the representations of G, one can show directly that this definition of multiplication is associative and is distributive over addition.

It is convenient, as well as useful, to extend the definition of character to allow for negative integer coefficients, to obtain a ring structure for the set of all characters of G. To do this, we define a *generalized* character of G to be the difference of any two ordinary characters of G. We then extend the definitions of addition and multiplication to generalized characters in the obvious way. The set of all generalized characters becomes then a module over the integers under addition, while multiplication remains associative and distributive. Hence the set of all generalized characters of G forms a commutative ring, called the *character ring* of G which we denote by ch (G). Clearly the irreducible characters of G span ch (G) over the integers.

We extend the definition of degree to generalized characters by setting $\deg \chi = \deg \chi_1 - \deg \chi_2$ if $\chi = \chi_1 - \chi_2$ with χ_1, χ_2 ordinary characters of G. Then clearly (1.2) holds also for generalized characters and so $\deg \chi$

is independent of the particular representation of χ as a difference of two characters.

Occasionally we shall need to consider the larger ring of all complex-valued class functions on G, which we denote by cf (G). Since cf (G) contains functions taking the value 1 on any one conjugate class and 0 on the remaining $r - 1$ classes, it is clearly an r-dimensional vector space over F.

The ring ch (G) is endowed with a natural involution. Indeed, if ϕ is any matrix representation of G, there is defined the *contragredient* representation ϕ' of ϕ by the relation

$$(1.5) \qquad\qquad y\phi' = ((y\phi)^{-1})^t,$$

$y \in G$, where t denotes transpose. Since the operations of transpose and inverse are each anti-isomorphisms of the group of nonsingular matrices of F_n, ϕ' is a homomorphism and so is a representation of G. Clearly equivalent representations give rise to equivalent contragredient representations. If χ is the character of ϕ, we denote by χ' the character of ϕ'.

It follows at once from (1.5) that $(\phi')' = \phi$ and consequently $(\chi')' = \chi$. Thus the mapping $\chi \to \chi'$ is involutory. Furthermore, it is immediate that for any characters χ_1, χ_2 of G, we have

$$(\chi_1 + \chi_2)' = \chi_2' + \chi_2' \qquad \text{and} \qquad (\chi_1\chi_2)' = \chi_1'\chi_2'.$$

Hence if we extend $'$ to generalized characters, and hence to ch (G), we conclude that the resulting mapping is, in fact, an automorphism of ch (G) of order 2.

The following theorem lists the basic properties of this mapping. Here $\bar{\lambda}$ denotes the complex conjugate of the complex number λ of F.

Theorem 1.5

For any character χ of G, we have

    (i) $\chi'(y) = \overline{\chi(y)} = \chi(y^{-1})$ *for all y in G.*

    (ii) $\deg \chi' = \deg \chi$ *and* $\ker \chi' = \ker \chi$.

    (iii) χ' *is irreducible if and only if χ is irreducible.*

Proof

Let ϕ be a representation with character χ. By (1.5) and Lemma 3.6.5(vii), we have

$$(1.6) \qquad\qquad \chi'(y) = \operatorname{tr} y\phi' = \operatorname{tr} ((y\phi)^{-1})^t = \operatorname{tr} (y\phi)^{-1}.$$

On the other hand, by Theorem 1.2 and Lemma 3.6.5(i),

$$(1.7) \qquad\qquad \chi(y) = \operatorname{tr} y\phi = \varepsilon_1 + \varepsilon_2 + \cdots + \varepsilon_n,$$

where the ε_i are roots of unity and also are the characteristic roots of y, $1 \leqslant i \leqslant n$, and $n = \deg \phi$. But then the characteristic roots of $(y\phi)^{-1}$ are ε_i^{-1}, $1 \leqslant i \leqslant n$. However, as $\varepsilon_i^m = 1$ for some m, $|\varepsilon_i| = 1$ and so $\varepsilon_i^{-1} = \bar{\varepsilon}_i$. Hence,

$$(1.8) \qquad \operatorname{tr}(y\phi)^{-1} = \bar{\varepsilon}_1 + \bar{\varepsilon}_2 + \cdots + \bar{\varepsilon}_n = \overline{\varepsilon_1 + \varepsilon_2 + \cdots + \varepsilon_n} = \overline{\chi(y)}.$$

Furthermore, since ϕ is a homomorphism, $\chi(y^{-1}) = \operatorname{tr}(y^{-1}\phi) = \operatorname{tr}(y\phi)^{-1}$ and now (i) follows from (1.6) and (1.8).

It is immediate from definition (1.5) that $\deg \phi' = \deg \phi$. Hence $\deg \chi' = \deg \chi$. Furthermore, for y in G, $y\phi$ is a scalar matrix if and only if $((y\phi)^{-1})^t$ is. Hence χ' and χ have the same kernels, proving (ii).

Finally if the matrix $y\phi$ can be decomposed into blocks which are 0 off the diagonal, then so also can the matrix $(y\phi^{-1})^t$. This shows that χ' is irreducible if and only if χ is and thus establishes (iii).

The character χ' can be constructed in an alternative manner. If ϕ is a matrix representation of G having χ as its character, we can construct a new representation $\bar{\phi}$ of G by setting $y\bar{\phi}$ equal to the matrix whose entries are the complex conjugates of those $y\phi$. Since conjugation is an automorphism of F, it is trivial to verify that $\bar{\phi}$ is also a representation of G. If $\bar{\chi}$ denotes the character of $\bar{\phi}$, then $\bar{\chi}(y) = \overline{\chi(y)}$ for $y \in G$ and so $\bar{\chi} = \chi'$ by Theorem 1.5(i). (As we shall see in Section 2, the representations ϕ' and $\bar{\phi}$, having the same character, must be equivalent.)

The preceding construction is a particular case of a more general way of obtaining other characters of G from a given character χ. By Theorem 3.6.15 the representation ϕ is equivalent to one whose matrix entries lie in a subfield F_0 of F of finite degree over the rational subfield Q of F. Since equivalent representations have the same character, we may assume without loss that ϕ itself can be written in F_0. Since F_0 is contained in a subfield of F which is a finite normal extension of Q, we may suppose without loss that F_0 itself is normal over Q. Then for each σ in the Galois group $G(F_0, Q)$ of F_0 over Q, we construct a new representation ϕ^σ by setting, for y in G,

$$(1.9) \qquad\qquad\qquad y\phi^\sigma = (y\phi)^\sigma,$$

where $(y\phi)^\sigma$ is the matrix obtained from $y\phi$ by replacing each entry by its image under the automorphism σ. Since $(yz)\phi^\sigma = ((yz)\phi)^\sigma = ((y\phi)(z\phi))^\sigma = (y\phi)^\sigma(z\phi)^\sigma = (y\phi^\sigma)(z\phi^\sigma)$ for all y, z in G, we see that ϕ^σ is, in fact, a representation of G. We denote by χ^σ the character of ϕ^σ. Thus for all y in G

(1.10) $$\chi^\sigma(y) = (\chi(y))^\sigma.$$

The representation ϕ^σ and its character χ^σ are said to be *algebraic conjugates* of ϕ and χ.

It is clear that, as with χ', χ^σ and χ have the same degrees and the same kernels and that χ^σ is irreducible if and only if χ is.

By Theorem 1.5(i) the character χ is *real* (that is, real-valued) if and only if $\chi' = \chi$. Similarly χ is *rational* (that is, has values in Q) if and only if $\chi^\sigma = \chi$ for every element σ of $G(F_0, Q)$.

There is yet another, somewhat analogous, way of obtaining characters from χ. If α is an automorphism of G, define a new mapping ϕ^α by setting

(1.11) $$y\phi^\alpha = (y^\alpha)\phi \qquad y \in G.$$

Since $(yz)\phi^\alpha = ((yz)^\alpha)\phi = (y^\alpha z^\alpha)\phi = (y^\alpha)\phi(z^\alpha)\phi = (y\phi^\alpha)(z\phi^\alpha)$ for all y, z in G, we see that ϕ^α is a representation of G. Clearly ϕ^α has the same degree and kernel as ϕ and is irreducible if and only if ϕ is. We denote the character of ϕ^α by χ^α, so that

(1.12) $$\chi^\alpha(y) = \chi(y^\alpha) \qquad y \in G.$$

We call ϕ^α, χ^α the *conjugate* representation and character induced by the automorphism α.

2. THE ORTHOGONALITY RELATIONS

We now seek to derive various relations among the irreducible characters of G and to obtain some important consequences of these relations. Throughout we denote by ϕ_i a complete set of inequivalent representations of G and by χ_i the character of ϕ_i, $1 \leqslant i \leqslant r$, with χ_1 being the principal character 1_G of G. We also set $n_i = \deg \chi_i$, $1 \leqslant i \leqslant r$, and preserve this notation as well.

First of all, the results of Section 3.6, yield:

Theorem 2.1

The following relations hold:

(i) $\sum_{i=1}^{r} n_i^2 = |G|.$

(ii) $\sum_{i=1}^{r} n_i \chi_i(y) = \begin{cases} 0 & \text{if } y \in G^\# \\ |G| & \text{if } y = 1. \end{cases}$

(iii) $\sum_{y \in G} \chi_i(y) = \begin{cases} 0 & \text{if } i > 1 \\ |G| & \text{if } i = 1. \end{cases}$

Proof

First, (i) follows from Theorem 3.6.14(v) and the definition of the degree of a character. Furthermore, (ii) follows immediately from Theorem 3.6.14(iv) and Lemma 3.6.6 together with the additivity of the trace. Since $\chi_1(y) = 1$ for all y in G, (iii) clearly holds for $i = 1$.

Thus it remains to prove (iii) for $i > 1$. Let $u = \sum_{y \in G} y$ in the group algebra $A = A(G, F)$. Then

$$(2.1) \qquad \operatorname{tr}(u\phi_i) = \sum_{y \in G} \operatorname{tr}(y\phi_i) = \sum_{y \in G} \chi_i(y),$$

so we need only show that $\operatorname{tr}(u\phi_i) = 0$. By its definition, $u \in Z(A)$ and consequently $u\phi_i = \lambda I$ for some scalar λ and suitable identity transformation I. On the other hand, since ϕ_i is not a trivial representation, there exists x in G such that $x\phi_i$ is not I. But it is immediate that $xu = u$. Hence $u\phi_i = (xu)\phi_i = (x\phi_i)(u\phi_i)$. Since $u\phi_i = \lambda I$, this yields

$$(2.2) \qquad \lambda(I - x\phi_i) = 0.$$

Since $x\phi_i \neq I$ by assumption, we must have $\lambda = 0$, whence $u\phi_i = 0$ and so $\operatorname{tr}(u\phi_i) = 0$, as desired.

Since all the characters of an abelian group G are linear, Theorem 2.1(i) shows that the number of irreducible characters of such a group is $|G|$. Since the linear characters of an arbitrary group G correspond in one-to-one fashion to linear characters of G/G', it follows that $|G/G'|$ is the number of distinct linear characters of G.

On ch (G) we introduce an inner product by the formula

$$(2.3) \qquad (\theta, \chi) = \frac{1}{|G|} \sum_{y \in G} \theta(y)\chi'(y)$$

for θ, χ in ch (G). The ring properties of ch (G) together with the fact that the mapping $'$ is an automorphism of ch (G) imply that this inner product is bilinear. Furthermore, by Theorem 1.5(i), it can also be defined by the relation

$$(2.4) \qquad (\theta, \chi) = \frac{1}{|G|} \sum_{y \in G} \theta(y)\overline{\chi(y)}.$$

However, it is immediate from (2.4) that $(\chi, \theta) = \overline{(\theta, \chi)}$. We see then that this inner product is Hermitian symmetric and positive definite.

More generally we can use (2.4) as the definition of the inner product of any two complex-valued class functions θ, χ on G. Thus cf (G) is also endowed with the same Hermitian symmetric positive definite inner product.

As is customary, we say that θ and χ are *orthogonal* if $(\theta, \chi) = 0$ and we define the *norm* $\|\chi\|$ of χ to be

$$(2.5) \qquad \|\chi\| = \sqrt{(\chi, \chi)}.$$

The fundamental importance of this product rests on the fact that under it the irreducible characters of G are mutually orthogonal of length 1.

Theorem 2.2

The characters χ_i of G, $1 \leqslant i \leqslant r$, form a normal orthogonal basis of ch (G) over the integers:

$$(\chi_i, \chi_j) = \begin{cases} 0 & \text{if } i \neq j \\ 1 & \text{if } i = j. \end{cases}$$

We shall derive Theorem 2.2 while simultaneously establishing the following additional property of ch (G):

Theorem 2.3

If $\chi_i \chi_j = \sum_{k=1}^{r} m_{ijk} \chi_k$ with m_{ijk} nonnegative integers, so that m_{ij1} is the number of times the trivial character χ_1 appears as a constituent of $\chi_i \chi_j$, then

$$m_{ij1} = \begin{cases} 0 & \text{if } \chi_j \neq \chi_i' \\ 1 & \text{if } \chi_j = \chi_i'. \end{cases}$$

Proof

Let V_i/F be the representation space of ϕ_i, $1 \leqslant i \leqslant r$. Without loss we can assume

$$(2.6) \qquad \phi_i \otimes \phi_j = \sum_{k=1}^{r} m_{ijk} \phi_k.$$

Suppose that for some i and j, we have $m_{ij1} \neq 0$. For simplicity of notation, set $\phi = \phi_i$, $\psi = \phi_j$, $U = V_i$, $V = V_j$, and $W = U \otimes_F V$. Our assumption implies that there is a nonzero vector w in W such that

$$(2.7) \qquad w(y(\phi \otimes \psi)) = w$$

for all y in G. We can write

$$(2.8) \qquad w = \sum_{k=1}^{s} u_k \otimes v_k,$$

where the u_k are linearly independent over F and each $v_k \neq 0$. Let U_1 be the subspace of U spanned by the u_k. By (2.7) and (2.8) we have, for y in G,

$$(2.9) \qquad \sum_{k=1}^{s} u_k(y\phi) \otimes v_k(y\psi) = \sum_{k=1}^{s} u_k \otimes v_k.$$

Since the u_k are linearly independent and the $v_k \neq 0$, it follows directly from (2.9) and the definition of tensor product that each $u_k(y\phi) \in U_1$. Hence U_1 is invariant under $y\phi$ for all y in G and so $U_1 = U$ by the irreducibility of ϕ. Thus $(u) = \{u_k \,|\, 1 \leqslant k \leqslant s\}$ is a basis of U.

Similarly the subspace V_1 of V spanned by the v_k is invariant under ψ and so $V_1 = V$ by the irreducibility of ψ. Hence $\dim_F V \leqslant s = \dim_F U$. However, the argument is clearly symmetric in U and V, whence also $\dim_F V \geqslant \dim_F U$. Thus equality holds and consequently also $(v) = \{v_k \,|\, 1 \leqslant k \leqslant s\}$ is a basis of V.

Now for a given y in G, let

(2.10) $(y\phi)_{(u)} = (a_{kh})$ and $(y\psi)_{(v)} = (b_{kh})$.

Then

(2.11) $u_k(y\phi) = \sum_{h=1}^{s} a_{kh} u_h$ and $v_k(y\psi) = \sum_{h=1}^{s} b_{kh} v_h$.

Substituting (2.11) in (2.9) and expanding, we obtain the relations

(2.12) $\displaystyle\sum_{k=1} a_{kh} b_{kg} = \begin{cases} 0 & \text{if } g \neq h \\ 1 & \text{if } g = h. \end{cases}$

But (2.12) asserts simply that the matrix $y\psi_{(v)}$ is the inverse transpose of $y\phi_{(u)}$. Since this holds for all y in G, we conclude that $\psi_{(v)} = \phi'_{(u)}$ and hence that $\psi = \phi'$.

We have therefore shown that if $m_{ij1} \neq 0$, then necessarily $\chi_j = \chi'_i$. With the aid of this result, we can now argue that $(\chi_i, \chi_j) = 0$ if $i \neq j$. Indeed, we write

(2.13) $\displaystyle \chi_i \chi'_j = \sum_{k=1}^{r} t_{ijk} \chi_k$

for suitable nonnegative integers t_{ijk}. Since $\chi''_j = \chi_j \neq \chi_i$, it follows from the preceding result that $t_{ij1} = 0$. But then evaluating (2.13) for each y in G, and summing over G, we obtain

(2.14) $\displaystyle \sum_{y \in G} \chi_i(y) \chi'_j(y) = \sum_{k=2}^{r} t_{ijk} \left(\sum_{y \in G} \chi_k(y) \right)$

But $\sum_{y \in G} \chi_k(y) = 0$ by Theorem 2.1(iii) as $k > 1$. Hence the right side of (2.14) is 0 and the desired conclusion $(\chi_i, \chi_j) = 0$ follows from (2.3).

A formal calculation will now yield the remaining parts of our theorems. Multiplying the relation of Theorem 2.1(ii) for y in G^* by $\chi'_j(y)$ and summing over $G^\#$, we obtain

$$(2.15) \qquad\qquad 0 = \sum_{i=1}^{r} n_i \sum_{y \in G} \chi_j(y)\chi_j'(y).$$

Since $(\chi_i, \chi_j) = 0$ for $i \neq j$ and since $\chi_i(1)\chi_j'(1) = n_i n_j$, for all i, j including $i = j$, we can rewrite (2.15) as

$$(2.16) \qquad\qquad 0 = n_j \sum_{y \in G} \chi_j(y)\chi_j'(y) - \sum_{i=1}^{r} n_j n_i^2.$$

But then dividing by n_j and using Theorem 2.1(i), it follows that

$$(2.17) \qquad\qquad \sum_{y \in G} \chi_j(y)\chi_j'(y) = |G|.$$

Now (2.17) and (2.3) give $(\chi_j, \chi_j) = 1$, completing the proof of Theorem 2.2.

Suppose finally that $\chi_j = \chi_i'$. Evaluate the relation $\chi_i \chi_j' = \sum_{k=1}^{r} m_{ijk} \chi_k$ for each y in G and sum over G. Since $\sum_{y \in G} \chi_k(y) = 0$ or $|G|$ according as $k > 1$ or $k = 1$, this yields

$$(2.18) \qquad\qquad \sum_{y \in G} \chi_i(y)\chi_j'(y) = m_{ij1} |G|.$$

It follows at once that $m_{ij1} = (\chi_i, \chi_i)$. Thus $m_{ij1} = 1$ by the preceding paragraph and so Theorem 2.3 is also proved.

The orthogonality relations of Theorem 2.2 together with the linearity of the inner product give the following corollary:

Theorem 2.4

If $\chi = \sum_{i=1}^{r} a_i \chi_i$, a_i integers, then

(i) $(\chi, \chi_i) = a_i$, $1 \leq i \leq r$.

(ii) $\|\chi\|^2 = (\chi, \chi) = \sum_{i=1}^{r} a_i^2$.

In particular, then, (χ, χ_i) is the multiplicity of χ_i in χ. Moreover, χ is irreducible if and only if $(\chi, \chi) = 1$. In addition, these formulas extend by linearity to generalized characters.

As a further corollary we have

Theorem 2.5

Two representations of G have the same character if and only if they are equivalent.

Proof

By Theorem 1.1, equivalent representations have the same character. Conversely, let ϕ, ψ be two representations of G with the same character χ. Without loss we may assume $\phi = \sum_{i=1}^{r} a_i \phi_i$ and $\psi = \sum_{i=1}^{r} b_i \phi_i$, a_i, b_i integers. But then $\chi = \sum_{i=1}^{r} a_i \chi_i$ and $\chi = \sum_{i=1}^{r} b_i \chi_i$, whence $(\chi, \chi_i) = a_i = b_i$, $1 \leqslant i \leqslant r$, by the preceding theorem. Hence $\phi = \psi$ and the theorem is proved.

Still another corollary which extends Theorem 2.3 is

Theorem 2.6

The multiplicity of χ_k in $\chi_i \chi'_j$ is equal to the multiplicity of χ_i in $\chi_k \chi_j$.

Proof

This follows at once from the fact that each of these multiplicities is equal to

$$\frac{1}{|G|} \sum_{y \in G} \overline{\chi_i(y)} \chi_j(y) \chi_k(y).$$

The following properties of the character ρ_G of the regular representation of G are also useful:

Theorem 2.7

   (i) $(\rho_G, \rho_G) = |G|$.
   (ii) *If χ is a character of G which is 0 on all elements of $G^{\#}$, then χ is a multiple of ρ_G.*

Proof

Since ρ_G is 0 on $G^{\#}$ and has the value $|G|$ on 1, (i) follows at once from the definition of the inner product. As for (ii), set $d = \deg \chi$. Since χ is 0 on $G^{\#}$, (2.3) gives $(\chi, 1_G) = (1/|G|)d$. But $(\chi, 1_G)$ is an integer and hence $d = e|G|$ for some integer e. But then $\chi = e\rho_G$.

We note also that Theorem 2.2 implies that the χ_i, being normal orthogonal, are linearly independent over F and so form a basis over F of the ring cf (G) of all complex-valued class functions on G. Thus any element θ of cf (G) is of the form $\theta = \sum_{i=1}^{r} b_i \chi_i$ with b_i in F. As in Theorem 2.4, the orthogonality relations imply that $b_i = (\theta, \chi_i)$, $1 \leqslant i \leqslant r$. In particular, we see that a complex-valued class function is a generalized character of G if and only if (θ, χ_i) is an integer for each i, $1 \leqslant i \leqslant r$.

Since $\chi_1(y) = 1$ for all y in G, the relations of Theorem 2.1(iii) become in terms of our inner product simply $(\chi_i, \chi_1) = 0$ or 1 according as $i > 1$ or

$i = 1$. Thus Theorem 2.2 can be regarded as a generalization of this result. We should like also to establish certain orthogonality relations which generalize Theorem 2.1(i) and (ii). These are given by

Theorem 2.8

For any y, z in G, we have

$$\sum_{i=1}^{r} \chi_i(y)\overline{\chi_i(z)} = \begin{cases} 0 & \text{if } y, z \text{ are not conjugate in } G \\ |C_G(z)| & \text{if } y, z \text{ are conjugate in } G. \end{cases}$$

Proof

First of all, Theorem 2.2, together with (2.3), gives

$$(2.19) \qquad \sum_{y \in G} \chi_i(y)\chi'_j(y) = |G|\delta_{ij},$$

where $\delta_{ij} = 0$ or 1 according as $i \neq j$ or $i = j$. Let K_k be the distinct conjugate classes of G with $h_k = |K_k|$, $1 \leqslant k \leqslant r$ and let $y_k \in K_k$. Since characters are constant on the elements of each K_k, we can rewrite (2.19) as

$$(2.20) \qquad \sum_{k=1}^{r} h_k \chi_i(y_k)\chi'_j(y_k) = |G|\delta_{ij}.$$

Let X, Y be the $r \times r$ complex matrices whose (i,j)th entries are $\chi_i(y_j)$ and $h_i \chi'_j(y_i)$ respectively. Then (2.20) implies the matrix equation

$$(2.21) \qquad XY = |G|I,$$

where I is the $r \times r$ identity matrix. But now we see that X and Y are non-singular and that $Y^{-1} = (1/|G|)X$. Since $YY^{-1} = I$, it follows that also

$$(2.22) \qquad YX = |G|I.$$

Reverting to summations, this yields

$$(2.23) \qquad \sum_{i=1}^{r} h_j \chi'_i(y_j)\chi_i(y_k) = |G|\delta_{jk}.$$

But $|G|/h_j = |G|/|K_j| = |C_G(y_j)|$ by Theorem 1.2.3(i). Hence dividing by h_j and using Theorem 1.5(i), we conclude that

$$(2.24) \qquad \sum_{i=1}^{r} \overline{\chi_i(y_j)}\chi_i(y_k) = |C_G(y_j)|\delta_{jk}.$$

Since y_j, y_k are arbitrary elements of G, we can take $y_j = z$ and $y_k = y$ in (2.24) and the theorem follows.

Setting $y = z = 1$ in Theorem 2.8 gives Theorem 2.1(i), while setting $z = 1$ with $y \neq 1$ gives Theorem 2.1(ii).

By analogy with Theorem 2.5, we have the following corollary of Theorem 2.8:

Theorem 2.9

The elements y, z of G are conjugate in G if and only if

$$\chi_i(y) = \chi_i(z) \qquad 1 \leqslant i \leqslant r.$$

Proof

If y and z are conjugate, the conclusion is clear. Suppose conversely that $\chi_i(y) = \chi_i(z)$, $1 \leqslant i \leqslant r$, but that y and z are not conjugate. Then the first relation of Theorem 2.8 holds and, in this case, gives

$$(2.25) \qquad \sum_{i=1}^{r} \chi_i(y)\overline{\chi_i(y)} = 0.$$

But $\chi_i(y)\overline{\chi_i(y)}$ is a nonnegative real number for all i and has the value 1 for $i = 1$. Hence (2.25) is impossible and so y and z must be conjugate in G.

The orthogonality relations imply the basic fact that the degrees n_i of the irreducible characters χ_i of G divide $|G|$. The proof requires a preliminary result which we shall also need later.

Theorem 2.10

If K is a conjugate class of G and $y \in K$, then $|K|\chi_i(y)/n_i$ is an algebraic integer, $1 \leqslant i \leqslant r$.

Proof

We shall make use of our knowledge of $A = A(G, F)$. Let K_j, $1 \leqslant j \leqslant r$, be the conjugate classes of G with $K_j = \{y_{jk} \mid 1 \leqslant k \leqslant h_j\}$, $h_j = |K_j|$, and set

$$(2.26) \qquad y_j = \sum_{k=1}^{h_j} y_{jk} \qquad 1 \leqslant j \leqslant r.$$

Then $y_j \in A$ and the proof of Theorem 3.6.14(vi) shows that the y_j, $1 \leqslant j \leqslant r$, form a basis for $Z(A)$ over F. Since $Z(A)$ is a subalgebra of A, $y_i y_j \in Z(A)$ for all i, j. Hence we have

$$(2.27) \qquad y_i y_j = \sum_{k=1}^{r} \lambda_{ijk} y_k \qquad \lambda_{ijk} \in F.$$

The λ_{ijk} are, in fact, nonnegative integers. To see this, expand the product $y_i y_j$. We obtain the sum of all products $x_i x_j$ with $x_i \in K_i$ and $x_j \in K_j$. If $x_i x_j = x \in K_k$, then $x_i^u x_j^u = (x_i x_j)^u = x^u$ is also in K_k for u in G. This implies that λ_{ijk} is precisely the number of times the product of an element of K_i and an element of K_j is a given element x of K_k and thus proves the assertion.

Once again let V_i/F be the representation space of ϕ_i, $1 \leqslant i \leqslant r$. We regard each ϕ_i also as a representation of A. Then $(A)\phi_i$ is an irreducible algebra of linear transformations of V_i. Since F is algebraically closed, Theorems 3.6.1 and 3.6.2 imply that $(A)\phi_i$ is the full algebra $A(V_i, F)$ of such linear transformations. Since $(Z(A))\phi_i$, it follows that $(Z(A))\phi_i$ consists of scalar transformations of V_i, $1 \leqslant i \leqslant r$. In particular,

$$(2.28) \qquad y_j \phi_i = \omega_i(y_j)I_i \qquad 1 \leqslant i, j \leqslant r$$

for suitable $\omega_i(y_j)$ in F, where I_i is the identity transformation of V_i. Hence if we apply the representations $\phi_1, \phi_2, \ldots, \phi_r$ to (2.27), we obtain

$$(2.29) \qquad \omega_m(y_i)\omega_m(y_j) = \sum_{k=1}^{r} \lambda_{ijk}\,\omega_m(y_k) \qquad 1 \leqslant i, j, m \leqslant r.$$

Keeping m and i fixed, the resulting r linear relations in y_j, when written homogeneously, have as matrix of coefficients:

$$(2.30) \qquad \Delta_{mi} = \begin{pmatrix} \lambda_{i11} - \omega_m(y_i) & \lambda_{i12} & \cdots & \lambda_{i1r} \\ \lambda_{i21} & \lambda_{i22} - \omega_m(y_i) & \cdots & \lambda_{i2r} \\ \cdot & \cdot & & \cdot \\ \cdot & \cdot & & \cdot \\ \cdot & \cdot & & \cdot \\ \lambda_{ir1} & \lambda_{i2r} & \cdots & \lambda_{irr} - \omega_m(y_i) \end{pmatrix}$$

Since the y_j represent a nontrivial solution of the corresponding system of homogeneous linear equations, we must have

$$(2.31) \qquad \det \Delta_{mi} = 0 \qquad 1 \leqslant i, m \leqslant r.$$

Since each λ_{ijk} is an integer, the polynomial equation obtained from (2.30) and (2.31) for $\omega_m(y_i)$ has integer coefficients and its leading coefficient is ± 1. Hence each $\omega_m(y_i)$ satisfies a monic polynomial with integer coefficients and so is an algebraic integer.

We can now easily complete the proof. By (2.26), (2.28), and the fact that $\dim_F V_i = \deg \phi_i = n_i$, we have

$$(2.32) \qquad \sum_{k=1}^{h_i} \operatorname{tr}(y_{ik}\phi_m) = \operatorname{tr}(y_i\phi_m) = \operatorname{tr}(\omega_m(y_i)I_m) = \omega_m(y_i)n_m.$$

But χ_m is constant on the elements y_{ik}, so (2.32) reduces to

$$(2.33) \qquad h_i\chi_m(y_{ik}) = \omega_m(y_i)n_m$$

for all i, k, m.

Since $\omega_m(y_i)$ is an algebraic integer, we conclude that $h_i\chi_m(y_{ik})/n_m$ is as well. Since h_i is the order of the conjugate class of y_{ik} and y_{ik} is arbitrary in G, the theorem follows.

We now prove

Theorem 2.11

The degree n_i of χ_i divides $|G|$, $1 \leq i \leq r$.

Proof

Let K_j, y_{jk}, and h_j have the same meanings as in the preceding theorem. Now by Theorem 2.2, we have

$$(2.34) \qquad \sum_{y \in G} \chi_i(y)\overline{\chi_i(y)} = |G|.$$

Since χ_i is constant on the elements of each K_j, this reduces to

$$(2.35) \qquad \sum_{j=1}^{r} h_j \chi_i(y_{j1})\overline{\chi_i(y_{j1})} = |G|,$$

whence dividing by n_i we have

$$(2.36) \qquad \sum_{j=1}^{r} \frac{h_j \chi_i(y_{j1})}{n_i} \overline{\chi_i(y_{j1})} = |G|/n_i.$$

Now $\chi_i(y_{j1})$ is an algebraic integer by Theorem 1.2 and hence so is $\overline{\chi_i(y_{j1})}$. But then by the preceding theorem and the fact that the set of algebraic integers is a ring, it follows that the left side of (2.36) is an algebraic integer. Thus $|G|/n_i$ is both a rational number and an algebraic integer, which is possible only if it is an ordinary integer. Hence n_i must divide $|G|$, $1 \leq i \leq r$.

As we have seen in the proof of Theorem 2.10, the integers λ_{ijk} of (2.27) which determine the multiplication table of the center of $A(G, F)$ have an alternative interpretation in terms of the conjugate classes of G. We show now that they can also be expressed in terms of the irreducible characters of G, which together will yield the following result:

Theorem 2.12

Denote the conjugate classes of G by K_i and let y_i be an element of K_i, $1 \leq i \leq r$. Then if λ_{ijk} is the number of times a given element of K_k can be expressed as an ordered product of an element of K_i and an element of K_j, we have

$$\lambda_{ijk} = \frac{|K_i|\,|K_j|}{|G|} \sum_{m=1}^{r} \frac{\chi_m(y_i)\chi_m(y_j)\overline{\chi_m(y_k)}}{n_m}$$

for $1 \leq i, j, k \leq r$.

Proof

As in Theorem 2.10, set $h_i = |K_i|$, $1 \leqslant i \leqslant r$, and apply (2.29) and (2.33) to obtain

$$(2.37) \qquad h_i h_j \chi_m(y_i)\chi_m(y_j) = n_m \sum_{s=1}^{r} \lambda_{ijs} h_s \chi_m(y_s)$$

for all i, j, m. Now multiply (2.37) by $(1/n_m)\overline{\chi_m(y_k)}$ and sum over m. Reversing the order of summation on the right side and using Theorem 2.9, it follows that

$$(2.38) \qquad h_i h_j \sum_{m=1}^{r} \frac{\chi_m(y_i)\chi_m(y_j)\overline{\chi_m(y_k)}}{n_m} = \lambda_{ijk} h_k |C_G(y_k)|.$$

But $|G| = h_k |C_G(y_k)|$ by Theorem 1.2.3(i) and the desired expression for λ_{ijk} follows.

Finally, we should like to mention the *character table* of G. Denote once again by K_i the distinct conjugate classes of G, let $h_i = |K_i|$, and let $y_i \in K_i$, $1 \leqslant i \leqslant r$. Then the $r \times r$ complex matrix

$$(2.39) \qquad X = (\chi_i(y_j))$$

is called a *character table* of G. Clearly it is independent of the choice of the representatives y_j of K_j. Furthermore, any character table of G can be transformed into any other by a permutation of the rows and columns.

Set $Y = DX$, where $D = \text{diag}(h_1, h_2, \dots, h_r)$ and let b_{ij} be the $\{i, j\}$th entry of $Y\bar{Y}^t$, so that

$$(2.40) \qquad b_{ij} = \sum_{k=1}^{r} h_k^2 \chi_i(y_k)\overline{\chi_j(y_k)}.$$

Since χ_i is a class function, it follows from (2.40) together with the orthogonality relations that

$$(2.41) \qquad b_{ij} = \sum_{y \in G} \chi_i(y)\overline{\chi_j(y)} = \delta_{ij}|G|, \qquad 1 \leqslant i, j \leqslant r,$$

where $\delta_{ij} = 0$ if $i \neq j$ and $\delta_{ii} = 1$. Thus

$$(2.42) \qquad Y\bar{Y}^t = |G|I,$$

where I is the $r \times r$ unit matrix. In particular, Y, and hence X, is nonsingular.

A knowledge of the character table gives considerable information about G; on the other hand, it does not determine G up to isomorphism, as there exist nonisomorphic groups with identical character tables (see exercises).

3. SOME APPLICATIONS

We shall now present some basic applications of the preceding results which we shall need for our later work. We begin with Burnside's famous theorem on the solvability of groups of order $p^a q^b$, p, q primes, which we derive as a consequence of two lemmas of independent interest.

Lemma 3.1

Let χ be an irreducible character of G of degree n and let y be an element of G whose conjugate class has order relatively prime to n. Then either $\chi(y) = 0$ or $|\chi(y)| = n$.

Proof

Let K be the conjugate class of y and let $h = |K|$. By Theorems 1.2 and 2.10, both $\alpha = \chi(y)$ and $\beta = h\chi(y)/n$ are algebraic integers. Suppose $\alpha \neq 0$ and let

$$(3.1) \qquad f(X) = X^m + a_1 X^{m-1} + \cdots + a_m$$

be its irreducible polynomial, a_i integers, $1 \leqslant i \leqslant m$. Since h/n is a rational number, the irreducible polynomial for β is also of degree m and so must be

$$(3.2) \qquad g(X) = X^m + a_1 \frac{h}{n} X^{m-1} + \cdots + a_m \left(\frac{h}{n}\right)^m$$

as $g(\beta) = (h/n)^m f(\alpha) = 0$. Now the coefficients of $g(X)$ are also integers, since β is an algebraic integer. But $(h, n) = 1$ by hypothesis and consequently n^i divides a_i for all i, $1 \leqslant i \leqslant m$. Thus

$$(3.3) \qquad h(X) = X^m + \frac{a_1}{n} X^{m-1} + \cdots + \frac{a_m}{n^m}$$

also has integer coefficients. But $\gamma = \alpha/n$ satisfies $h(X)$ and so also is an algebraic integer. Furthermore, as with β, $h(X)$ is the irreducible polynomial for γ.

Now by Theorem 1.3(i), $|\gamma| = |\chi(y)|/n \leqslant 1$. However, the m roots $\gamma = \gamma_1, \gamma_2, \ldots, \gamma_m$ of $h(X)$ are algebraic conjugates of γ, since $h(X)$ is irreducible; and so $|\gamma_i| \leqslant 1$, $1 \leqslant i \leqslant m$. But the product of the γ_i is the constant term $b_m = a_m/n^m$ of $h(X)$. Since b_m is an integer, the only possibility is $b_m = \pm 1$ and $|\gamma_i| = 1$ for all i. We conclude that $|\chi(y)| = n$.

Lemma 3.2

Let G be a group of composite order in which the number of elements in some conjugate class is of prime power order. Then G is not simple.

Proof

Suppose, by way of contradiction, that G is simple. Let χ_i be the irreducible characters of G, let ϕ_i be irreducible representations of G with character χ_i, set $n_i = \deg \chi_i$, $1 \leqslant i \leqslant r$, and let χ_1 be the principal character of G. Since G is simple, ϕ_i is faithful for $i > 1$. Let $H_i = \{y \in G \,|\, (y)\phi_i$ is a scalar transformation$\}$, $2 \leqslant i \leqslant r$. Then it is immediate that $(H_i)\phi_i$ is an abelian normal subgroup of $(G)\phi_i$ and hence that H_i is an abelian normal subgroup of G. Since G is simple of composite order, this forces $H_i = 1$, $2 \leqslant i \leqslant r$. But now Theorem 1.3(ii) yields $|\chi_i(y)| \neq n_i$ for any y in $G^\#$, $2 \leqslant i \leqslant r$.

Now let y be an element of G whose conjugate class consists of $h = p^a$ elements. Then certainly $y \neq 1$. Now either p divides n_i or $(h, n_i) = 1$. Since $|\chi_i(y)| \neq n_i$ for $i > 1$, Lemma 3.1 implies in the latter case that $\chi_i(y) = 0$. Hence for $i > 1$, either p divides n_i or $\chi_i(y) = 0$. Since $n_1 = \chi_1(y) = 1$, it follows therefore from Theorem 2.1(ii) that

$$(3.4) \qquad\qquad 1 + \sum{}' n_i \chi_i(y) = 0,$$

where the summation runs over those indices $i > 1$ for which p divides n_i. Setting $n_i = m_i p$ and $\beta = \sum' m_i \chi_i(y)$, we get

$$(3.5) \qquad\qquad\qquad 1 + p\beta = 0.$$

But each $\chi_i(y)$, and hence also β, is an algebraic integer. Since $\beta = -1/p$ is also rational, it must be an ordinary integer, which is clearly impossible.

As a corollary of Lemma 3.2, we have our main result:

Theorem 3.3 (Burnside)

Every group of order $p^a q^b$, p and q primes, is solvable.

Proof

Let $|G| = p^a q^b$. We proceed by induction on $|G|$. Since any subgroup or homomorphic image of G satisfies the same conditions, the theorem follows at once by induction if G is not simple. So we may assume G is simple. Since the theorem is obvious if G has prime order, we may also assume G has composite order. Since every group of prime power order is solvable, it follows, in particular, that $p \neq q$.

Now let Q be an S_q-subgroup of G and let y be an element of $Z(Q)^{\#}$. If K denotes the conjugate class containing y, then by Theorem 1.2.3(i) $|K| = |G : C|$, where $C = C_G(y)$. But $Q \subseteq C$ as $y \in Z(Q)$ and consequently $|G : C| = p^d$ for some $d \leqslant a$. Furthermore, $d \neq 0$, since otherwise $C = G$ and $y \in Z(G)$, contrary to the simplicity of G. Thus K has prime power order and so G is not simple by the preceding lemma. This contradiction completes the proof.

When Theorem 2.7.4 is interpreted in the light of orthogonality relations, it yields the following result on transitive permutation groups.

Theorem 3.4

Let G be a transitive permutation group and let χ be the character of the corresponding permutation representation of G. Then

    (i) *The principal character 1_G of G is a constituent of χ of multiplicity 1.*

    (ii) *G is doubly transitive if and only if*

$$\chi = 1_G + \theta,$$

where θ is an irreducible character of G.

Proof

As we have noted in Section 1, $\chi(y)$ is just the number of letters fixed by the element y of G. Hence by Theorem 2.2 and the definition of the inner product, Theorem 2.7.4(i) is equivalent to the assertion $(\chi, 1_G) = 1$, whence 1_G is a constituent of χ of multiplicity 1.

Since χ is integral-valued, $\chi'(y) = \overline{\chi(y)} = \chi(y)$ for all y in G. Hence applying Theorem 2.2 again we see that Theorem 2.7.4(ii) is equivalent to the assertion: G is doubly transitive if and only if

$$(3.6) \qquad\qquad\qquad (\chi, \chi) = 2.$$

On the other hand, if $\chi = \sum_{i=1}^{r} a_i \chi_i$, where χ_i are the irreducible characters of G, $1 \leqslant i \leqslant r$, Theorem 2.4(i) implies that

$$(3.7) \qquad\qquad\qquad (\chi, \chi) = \sum_{i=1}^{r} a_i^2 .$$

But since the a_i are integers, obviously the only solution of (3.6) and (3.7) is $a_i = 1$ for two values of i and $a_i = 0$ for the remaining, so that χ is a sum of two irreducible characters. By (i) and Theorem 2.4(i), one of these is 1_G and so (ii) follows.

We shall need a slight extension of Theorem 2.4(i). If G is a permutation group on $S = \{1, 2, \ldots, n\}$, we can clearly decompose S uniquely into the disjoint union of subsets S_k, $1 \leqslant k \leqslant t$, so that two elements i, j of S are in the same S_k if and only if there exists a y in G such that $(i)y = j$. This condition implies that G acts transitively on each S_k. We call the S_k the *transitive constituents* of G. Expressed in other terms, the S_k are simply the orbits of the elements of S under the action of G.

Theorem 3.5

If χ is the character of a permutation representation of G, then $(\chi, 1_G)$ is the number of transitive constituents of $(G)\pi$.

Proof

Let S_k, $1 \leqslant k \leqslant t$, be the transitive constituents of $(G)\pi$ and let $\pi_k = \pi \mid S_k$, $1 \leqslant k \leqslant t$. Regarding π and each π_k as matrix representations, we have $\pi = \sum_{k=1}^{t} \pi_k$. Hence if χ_k is the character of π_k, we need only show that $(\chi_k, 1_G) = 1$, for then $(\chi, 1_G) = t$ will follow by linearity. Thus it suffices to prove the theorem in the case that $(G)\pi$ acts transitively on S.

Let K be the kernel of π, let $\tilde{\pi}$ be the quotient representation induced on $\tilde{G} = G/K$ and let $\tilde{\chi}$ be its character. Since $\tilde{G}$ is isomorphic to the permutation group $(\tilde{G})\tilde{\pi}$, we have $(\tilde{\chi}, 1_{\tilde{G}}) = 1$ by Theorem 3.4(i). Hence

$$(3.8) \qquad\qquad \sum_{\tilde{y} \in \tilde{G}} \tilde{\chi}(\tilde{y}) = |\tilde{G}|.$$

But clearly $\tilde{\chi}(\tilde{y}) = \chi(y)$ for any y in the coset $\tilde{y}$, since $\tilde{y}\tilde{\pi}$ and $y\pi$ fix the same number of letters of S. It follows therefore from (3.8) that

$$(3.9) \qquad\qquad \sum_{y \in G} \chi(y) = |\tilde{G}| \, |K| = |G|,$$

whence $(\chi, 1_G) = 1$, completing the proof.

We conclude with an important property of the characters of a group of odd order.

Theorem 3.6 *(Burnside)*

Let G be a group of odd order. Then we have
   (i) *If χ is a nonprincipal irreducible character of G, then χ is nonreal and $\chi' \neq \chi$.*
   (ii) *If y is a nonidentity element of G, then there exists an irreducible character χ of G such that $\chi(y)$ is nonreal.*

Proof

Let $y, z \in G$ and suppose $y^z = y^{-1}$. Then $y^{z^2} = (y^{-1})^z = (y^z)^{-1} = y$, so z^2 centralizes y. Since $|z|$ is odd, it follows that z centralizes y. But then $y = y^{-1}$, so $y^2 = 1$ and hence $y = 1$, as $|y|$ is also odd. Thus in a group of odd order, no nonidentity element is conjugate to its inverse. We need this preliminary result for the proof.

First of all, because of it, Theorems 1.5 and 2.8 yield

$$(3.10) \qquad 0 = \sum_i \chi_i(y)\overline{\chi_i(y^{-1})} = \sum_i \chi_i(y)^2,$$

where the χ_i are the irreducible characters of G and $\chi_1 = 1_G$. Since $\chi_1(y) = 1$, (3.10) implies that $\chi_i(y)$ is nonreal for some $i > 1$. Hence (ii) holds.

Next let χ be a real irreducible character of G with $\chi \neq 1_G$ and let $n = \deg \chi$. By Theorem 2.11 and 2.1(iii), n is odd and

$$(3.11) \qquad n + \sum_{y \in G^\#} \chi(y) = 0.$$

Denote the second term of (3.11) by α. Now $y \neq y^{-1}$ for y in $G^\#$. Moreover, $\chi(y^{-1}) = \overline{\chi(y)} = \chi(y)$ by Theorem 1.5 and the fact that χ is real. Hence we can write $\alpha = 2\beta$, where β is the sum of $\chi(y)$ over half the elements of $G^\#$, each pair (y, y^{-1}) contributing one term to the sum. Thus we have both $\beta = -n/2$ and β an algebraic integer. This forces β to be an ordinary integer, contrary to the oddness of n. Therefore any nonprincipal irreducible character χ of G is nonreal. Thus $\chi' \neq \chi$ and (i) also holds.

4. INDUCED CHARACTERS AND TRIVIAL INTERSECTION SETS

The relationship between the characters of a group G and those of its subgroups H is of fundamental importance for the study of the structure of G. In this section we shall develop the general facts concerning this relationship. We shall then specialize to the case in which the subgroup H is disjoint from its conjugates, where considerably more precise statements can be made than in general.

First of all, if H is a subgroup of G, a representation ϕ of G over F induces by restriction a representation $\phi|_H$ of H. If χ is the character of ϕ, we denote by $\chi|_H$ the character of $\phi|_H$ and call it the *restriction* of χ to H. By its definition $\chi|_H$ and χ take the same value on elements of H. Clearly the restriction map is linear and preserves products of characters. Thus it induces a natural homomorphism of ch (G) into ch (H).

What is not so obvious is that there is also induced in a natural way a map from ch (H) to ch (G). This depends upon the notion of *induced representations*. Let χ_i, $1 \leqslant i \leqslant m$, be a complete set of coset representatives of H in G. Let ψ be a matrix representation of H and let its degree be d. We extend the definition of ψ to all of G by setting y equal to the $d \times d$

0 matrix for all y in $G - H$. We now define a map ψ^* on G to F_{md} by the rule

(4.1) $y\psi^* = ((x_i y x_j^{-1})\psi)$ $y \in G$.

Thus $y\psi^*$ is an $m \times m$ matrix of blocks whose (i,j)th entry is the $d \times d$ matrix $(x_i y x_j^{-1})\psi$. We now prove

Theorem 4.1

   Let H be a subgroup of G and ψ a representation of H. Then the mapping ψ^* defined in (4.1) is a representation of G of degree $|G : H| \deg \psi$.

Proof

   Let $x, y \in G$ and consider the product $(x\psi^*)(y\psi^*)$. The (i,j)th block of this product is

(4.2) $B_{ij}(x, y) = \sum_{k=1}^{m} (x_i x x_k^{-1})\psi(x_k y x_j^{-1})\psi.$

Now for a given i, there is a unique coset Hx_t such that $x_i y \in Hx_t$ and hence such that $x_i y x_t^{-1} \in H$. But then if $k \ne t$, $(x_i x x_k^{-1})\psi$ is the 0 matrix. Thus (4.2) reduces to

(4.3) $B_{ij}(x, y) = (x_i x x_t^{-1})\psi(x_t y x_j^{-1})\psi.$

   On the other hand, $x_i x y x_j^{-1} \in H$ if and only if $x_i x x_t^{-1} \in Hx_j y^{-1} x_t^{-1}$. Since $x_i x x_t^{-1} \in H$, this will be the case if and only if $x_t y x_j^{-1} \in H$. Thus

(4.4) $B_{ij}(x, y) = \begin{cases} 0 & \text{if } x_i x y x_j^{-1} \notin H \\ (x_i x x_t^{-1})\psi(x_t y x_j^{-1})\psi & \text{if } x_i x y x_j^{-1} \in H. \end{cases}$

However, as ψ is a representation of H, it follows in the second case that $(x_i x x_t^{-1})\psi(x_t y x_j^{-1})\psi = (x_i x y x_j^{-1})\psi$. Together with (4.4), this yields

(4.5) $(xy)\psi^* = (B_{ij}(x, y)).$

Since $(B_{ij}(x, y)) = (x\psi^*)(y\psi^*)$, we conclude that $(xy)\psi^* = (x\psi^*)(y\psi^*)$.

   Finally, it is immediate that $(1)\psi^*$ is the identity matrix. Since $(x\psi^*)(x^{-1}\psi^*) = (xx^{-1})\psi^* = (1)\psi^*$, it follows that $x\psi^*$ is nonsingular. Thus ψ^* is a homomorphism of G into $GL(md, F)$ and so is a representation of G of the given degree.

   As an illustration, we have

Theorem 4.2

   Let H be a subgroup of G and let ψ be the trivial representation of H. Then ψ^* is the permutation representation on the right cosets of H. In particular, if $H \lhd G$, then ψ^* is the regular representation of G/H.

Proof

With the notation, as above, we have for y in G and a given x_i that $x_i y x_j^{-1} \in H$ if and only if $x_i y \in Hx_j$. Hence j is uniquely determined by x_i and y and so $(x_i y x_k^{-1})\psi = 1$ or 0 according as k is or is not j. We see then that $y\psi^*$ is simply the permutation matrix determined by the mapping $Hx_i \to Hx_i y = Hx_j$, thus proving the first assertion. If $H \lhd G$, the permutation representation of G on the right cosets of H has H in its kernel and induces the regular representation on G/H, as is trivially verified.

In general we call ψ^* the representation of G *induced* by the representation ψ of H. If ψ has character χ, we denote the character of ψ^* by χ^* and refer to it as the character of G induced by χ. If ψ is written in a finite normal extension F_0 of the rationals Q with $F_0 \subseteq F$, then so also is ψ^*. Moreover, if σ is an element of the Galois group $G(F_0, Q)$, it is clear from the definition that σ commutes with the induction map. Thus

$$(4.6) \qquad\qquad (\psi^*)^\sigma = (\psi^\sigma)^*.$$

Frequently we shall be considering various subgroups of G and various induced characters from one subgroup to another. In such situations χ^* will always denote the character induced on G by a character χ of a subgroup.

Theorem 4.3

Let H be a subgroup of G and χ a character of H. Set $\chi(y) = 0$ for y in $G - H$. Then we have

   (i) $\chi^*(y) = (1/|H|) \sum_{u \in G} \chi(uyu^{-1})$ for all y in G.

   (ii) $\chi^*(y) = 0$ if y does not lie in a conjugate of H.

   (iii) If $\ker \chi \lhd G$, then $\ker \chi \leqslant \ker \chi^*$.

   (iv) Equivalent representations of H induce the same character of G.

Proof

Let χ be the character of the representation ψ of H and let the notation be as in Theorem 4.1. Then

$$(4.7) \qquad \chi^*(y) = \operatorname{tr}(y\psi^*) = \sum_{i=1}^{m} \operatorname{tr}(x_i y x_i^{-1})\psi = \sum_{i=1}^{m} \chi(x_i y x_i^{-1}).$$

Now for z in H, $zx_i y x_i^{-1} z^{-1} \in H$ if and only if $x_i y x_i^{-1} \in H$. Since χ is constant on the conjugate classes of H and is 0 off of H, it follows that $\chi(zx_i y x_i^{-1} z^{-1}) = \chi(x_i y x_i^{-1})$ for all z in H. Hence we can write (4.7) as

$$(4.8) \qquad\qquad \chi^*(y) = \frac{1}{|H|} \sum_{i=1}^{m} \sum_{z \in H} \chi(zx_i y x_i^{-1} z^{-1}).$$

But since x_i is a complete set of coset representatives of H in G, $u = zx_i$ runs over G as z runs over H and i goes from 1 to m, thus proving (i).

If y does not lie in a conjugate of H, then $uyu^{-1} \notin H$ for all u in G, whence $\chi(uyu^{-1}) = 0$ and (ii) follows from (i). Moreover, if $y \in \ker \chi$ and $\ker \chi \lhd G$, then $uyu^{-1} \in \ker \chi$ for all u in G, so $\chi(uyu^{-1}) = \chi(1)$. But then $\chi^*(y) = (1/|H|)|G|\chi(1) = \deg \chi^*$. Thus $y \in \ker \chi^*$, proving (iii). Finally, if ψ_1 is a representation of H, equivalent to ψ, then it has the same character χ. But then, again by (i), the character χ_1^* of ψ_1^* is given by the same formula as χ^*, so $\chi_1^* = \chi^*$, proving (iv).

The induction map $\chi \to \chi^*$ extends to a map of $\mathrm{ch}\,(H)$ into $\mathrm{ch}\,(G)$. Theorem 4.3(i) implies that this map is linear. So Theorem 4.3(i) and (ii) holds also for generalized characters. In particular, if χ is a generalized character of degree 0, these results together with Theorem 4.1 show that χ^* also has degree 0.

If $H \subseteq K \subseteq G$, we can induce a character from H to K and then to G or directly from H to G. Our next theorem shows that the result is the same.

Theorem 4.4

Let H, K be subgroups of G with $H \subseteq K$. Let χ be a character of H and $\tilde{\chi}$ the character of K induced by χ. Then

$$\chi^* = (\tilde{\chi})^*.$$

Proof

Set $\chi(y) = 0$ for y in $G - H$. Then by Theorem 4.3(i),

$$(4.9) \qquad \tilde{\chi}(z) = \frac{1}{|H|} \sum_{v \in K} \chi(vzv^{-1}) \qquad z \in K.$$

Now let $\tilde{\chi}(x) = 0$ for $x \in G - K$. Then for y in G, we have

$$(4.10) \qquad \tilde{\chi}^*(y) = \frac{1}{|K|} \sum_{u \in G} (uyu^{-1}).$$

But if $z \notin K$, then certainly $vzv^{-1} \notin H \subseteq K$ for any v in K, so (4.9) holds also for z in $G - K$. Hence by (4.9) and (4.10), we obtain

$$(4.11) \qquad \tilde{\chi}^*(y) = \frac{1}{|K|}\frac{1}{|H|} \sum_{u \in G} \sum_{v \in K} \chi(uvyv^{-1}u^{-1}).$$

However, every element of G can be written exactly $|K|$ times in the form uv, $u \in G$, $v \in K$ and so (4.11) reduces to

(4.12) $$\tilde{\chi}^*(y) = \frac{1}{|H|} \sum_{w \in G} \chi(wyw^{-1}) = \chi^*(y),$$

proving the theorem.

If H is a subgroup of G, we have inner products in both ch (H) and ch (G). To distinguish these, we shall write $(\ ,\ )_H$ and $(\ ,\ )_G$ for the respective inner products. Now if $\chi \in$ ch (G) and $\theta \in$ ch (H), we can consider χ restricted to H and then compute $(\theta, \chi|_H)_H$, on the one hand, and can consider θ induced to G and then compute $(\theta^*, \chi)_G$, on the other. What relationship exists between these multiplicities? This is answered by the fundamental *Frobenius reciprocity theorem*:

Theorem 4.5 (Frobenius)

Let H be a subgroup of G, θ a generalized character of H and χ a generalized character of G. Then

$$(\theta, \chi|_H)_H = (\theta^*, \chi)_G.$$

Proof

By the definitions and the fact that χ' is a class function on G, we have

(4.13) $$(\theta^*, \chi)_G = \frac{1}{|G|} \sum_{y \in G} \theta^*(y) \chi'(y)$$

$$= \frac{1}{|G|} \frac{1}{|H|} \sum_{u,y \in G} \theta(uyu^{-1}) \chi'(y)$$

$$= \frac{1}{|G|} \frac{1}{|H|} \sum_{u,y \in G} \theta(uyu^{-1}) \chi'(uyu^{-1}),$$

where θ is defined to be 0 on $G - H$. Since uyu^{-1} runs over G for a fixed u as y does, we can write (4.13) as

(4.14) $$(\theta^*, \chi)_G = \frac{1}{|G|} \frac{1}{|H|} \sum_{u,y \in G} \theta(y) \chi'(y)$$

$$= \frac{1}{|H|} \sum_{y \in G} \theta(y) \chi'(y).$$

But $\theta(y) = 0$ if $y \in G - H$, while on H, $\chi'(y) = \chi'|_H(y) = (\chi|_H)'(y)$, so (4.14) reduces to

(4.15) $$(\theta^*, \chi)_G = \frac{1}{|H|} \sum_{y \in H} \theta(y)(\chi|_H)'(y) = (\theta, \chi|_H)_H,$$

proving the theorem.

There is an important special case in which stronger conclusions about the relation between χ and χ^* can be asserted. This is the case in which the subgroup H is the normalizer in G of a subset A of H which is disjoint from its conjugates in G (that is, $A \cap A^x = A$ or $A \cap A^x \subseteq \{1\}$) and the character χ is 0 on $H - A$. For example, Theorem 2.7.7 shows that these conditions hold if G is a Frobenius group with $H = A$ a Frobenius complement, in which case χ may be any character of H. The basic result is the following:

Theorem 4.6 (Brauer-Suzuki)

Let A be a subset of G which is disjoint from its conjugates. Set $N = N_G(A)$ and let χ, θ be generalized characters of N which are 0 on $N - A$. Then we have

(i) $\chi^*(y) = \chi(y)$ for y in $A^\#$.

(ii) If $\deg \chi = 0$, then $(\chi, \theta)_N = (\chi^*, \theta^*)_G$.

Proof

Set $\chi(y) = 0$ for y in $G - N$. Then for any y in $G^\#$, Theorem 4.3(i) gives

$$(4.16) \qquad \chi^*(y) = \frac{1}{|N|} \sum_{u \in G} \chi(uyu^{-1}).$$

Since $\chi(y) = 0$ by hypothesis if $y \in N - A$, we have $\chi(uyu^{-1}) = 0$ unless $uyu^{-1} \in A$. In particular, $\chi^*(y) = 0$ unless y lies in a conjugate of A. Furthermore, for y in $A^\#$, we see that either $\chi(uyu^{-1}) = 0$ or $y \in A \cap A^{u^{-1}}$. However, in the latter case, $A = A^{u^{-1}}$ and $u \in N$ as A is disjoint from its conjugates. But $\chi(uyu^{-1}) = \chi(y)$ for u in N as χ is a class function on N. Hence for y in $A^\#$,

$$(4.17) \qquad \chi^*(y) = \frac{1}{|N|} \sum_{u \in N} \chi(uyu^{-1}) = \frac{1}{|N|} |N| \chi(y) = \chi(y),$$

proving (i).

Now assume $\deg \chi = 0$, so that also $\deg \chi^* = 0$. By (2.4) we have

$$(4.18) \qquad (\chi^*, \theta^*)_G = \frac{1}{|G|} \sum_{y \in G} \chi^*(y) \overline{\theta^*(y)}.$$

But by the preceding paragraph, $\chi^*(y) = 0$ for y not in a conjugate of A, while $\chi^*(y) = \chi(y)$ and $\theta^*(y) = \theta(y)$ for y in a conjugate of $A^\#$. Furthermore, $A^\#$ has exactly $|G : N|$ conjugates and no two have an element in common. Since $\chi(1) = \chi^*(1) = 0$, (4.18) therefore reduces to

$$(4.19) \qquad (\chi^*, \theta^*)_G = \frac{1}{|N|} \sum_{y \in A} \chi(y) \overline{\theta(y)}.$$

Since $\chi(y) = 0$ for y in $N - A$ by assumption, this gives finally

$$(4.20) \qquad (\chi^*, \theta^*)_G = \frac{1}{|N|} \sum_{y \in N} \chi(y)\overline{\theta(y)} = (\chi, \theta)_N,$$

proving (ii).

For any group G we denote by $\mathrm{ch}_0 (G)$ the subset of generalized characters of G of degree 0. Clearly $\mathrm{ch}_0 (G)$ is a module over the integers. In effect, Theorem 4.6(ii) asserts that the induction map * is an *isometry* of the submodule of $\mathrm{ch}_0 (N)$ consisting of those elements that are 0 on $N - A$ into the module $\mathrm{ch}_0 (G)$; that is, * preserves inner products or equivalently preserves norms.

In the special case that A is a subgroup of N, denote by $\tilde{\psi}$ the element of $\mathrm{ch} (N)$ induced by the element ψ of $\mathrm{ch} (A)$. Then $\tilde{\psi}$ is 0 on $N - A$ by Theorem 4.3(ii) and $\tilde{\psi} \in \mathrm{ch}_0 (N)$ if $\deg \psi = 0$. When A is a subgroup, it is usually this induction map which is used to construct elements of $\mathrm{ch}_0 (N)$ which have their *support* on A—that is, are 0 on $N - A$.

5. FROBENIUS GROUPS

As our first application of the results on induced characters, we shall now establish the fundamental property of Frobenius groups which was stated without proof in Theorem 2.7.5. We repeat its statement here.

Theorem 5.1

If G is a Frobenius group with H the subgroup fixing a letter, then the identity together with the elements of G which fix no letters form a normal subgroup of G of order $|G : H|$.

Proof

Let G act on $S = \{1, 2, \ldots, n\}$, let H fix 1, and let $h = |H|$. Since G is transitive on S, $|G| = hn$ by Theorem 2.7.1. Furthermore, by Theorem 2.7.7, H is disjoint from its conjugates, $H = N_G(H)$, and $H \neq 1$. Hence Theorem 4.6 is applicable with H in the role of both A and N.

Let $\theta_i, 1 \leqslant i \leqslant t$, be the irreducible characters of H with $\theta_1 = 1_H$. Also let $d_i = \deg \theta_i, 1 \leqslant i \leqslant t$. Since $H \neq 1, t > 1$. We set

$$(5.1) \qquad \psi_i = d_i\theta_1 - \theta_i \qquad 2 \leqslant i \leqslant t,$$

so that $\deg \psi_i = 0$. Then by Theorem 4.6(ii) and the orthogonality relations, we have

(5.2)
$$(\psi_i^*, \psi_i^*)_G = (d_i\theta_1 - \theta_i, d_1\theta_1 - \theta_i)_H$$
$$= d_i^2(\theta_1, \theta_1)_H - 2d_1(\theta_1, \theta_i)_H + (\theta_i, \theta_i)_H$$
$$= d_i^2 + 1.$$

On the other hand, by the Frobenius reciprocity theorem and Theorem 2.4(i),

(5.3)
$$(\psi_i^*, 1_G)_G = (\psi_i, \theta_1)_H = d_i$$

inasmuch as $\theta_1 = 1_H$ is the restriction of 1_G to H. Thus 1_G is a constituent of ψ_i^* of multiplicity d_i. In view of Theorem 2.4(ii), it follows now from (5.2) that $\psi_i^* = d_i 1_G + \varepsilon_i \chi_i$, where χ_i is an irreducible character of G and $\varepsilon_i = \pm 1$. However, $\deg \psi_i^* = 0$ by Theorem 4.1 since $\deg \psi_i = 0$. This forces $\varepsilon_i = -1$ and consequently we have

(5.4)
$$\psi_i^* = d_i 1_G - \chi_i \quad \text{and} \quad \deg \chi_i = d_i \quad 2 \leqslant i \leqslant t.$$

With this information we shall now construct the required normal subgroup. We set $\chi_1 = 1_G$, $d_1 = 1$, and put

(5.5)
$$\chi = \sum_{i=1}^{t} d_i \chi_i.$$

By (5.4) and Theorem 2.1(i), we have $\chi(1) = \sum_{i=1}^{t} d_i^2 = |H|$. Furthermore, if $y \in G$ and y is not in a conjugate of H, then $\psi_i^*(y) = 0$ by Theorem 4.3(ii) and so $\chi_i(y) = d_i$ by (5.4), $2 \leqslant i \leqslant t$. But then also $\chi(y) = \sum_{i=1}^{t} d_i^2 = \chi(1)$. It follows therefore from Theorem 1.4 that the kernel K of χ contains every element of G not in a conjugate of H.

On the other hand, if $y \in H^*$, then $\psi_i^*(y) = \psi_i(y)$ by Theorem 4.6(i), whence $\chi_i(y) = \theta_i(y)$, $2 \leqslant i \leqslant t$, by (5.1) and (5.4). But then $\chi(y) = \sum_{i=1}^{t} d_i \chi_i(y) = 0$ by Theorem 2.1(ii). Hence $H \cap K = 1$ and $\chi(y) = 0$ if y lies in a conjugate of H. Thus K^* consists precisely of the elements contained in no conjugate of H. But the conjugates of H are the subgroups that fix a letter of S. We conclude that K^* consists of the elements of G which fix no letter of S. Finally we have

(5.6)
$$(\chi, 1_G) = \frac{1}{|G|} \sum_{y \in G} \chi(y).$$

Since $\chi(y) = 0$ unless $y \in K$, in which case $\chi(y) = |H|$, it follows from (5.6) that $(\chi, 1_G) = |K||H|/|G|$. But KH is a subgroup of G of order $|K||H|$ as

$K \lhd G$ and $K \cap H = 1$. Since $(\chi, 1_G)$ is an integer, this forces $|K| \, |H| = |G|$ and $KH = G$, so $|K| = |G : H|$ and the theorem is proved.

As a consequence, a Frobenius group has the properties listed in Theorem 2.7.6, since that result was proved on the basis of the validity of Theorem 2.7.5. A further fundamental property of Frobenius groups, proved by Thompson, is that the Frobenius kernel is necessarily nilpotent. We shall establish this basic result in Chapter 10.

In a Frobenius group G there exists a precise relationship between the irreducible characters of G and those of its kernel, which we should like now to establish. We shall base our argument on a general, very useful, lemma of Brauer.

Let G be a group and let $X = (\chi_i(y_j))$ be a character table of G, where χ_i, $1 \leqslant i \leqslant r$, are the irreducible characters of G and y_j, $1 \leqslant j \leqslant r$, are representatives of the r conjugate classes K_j of G. If α is an automorphism of G, then certainly α induces a permutation of the K_j and so induces a permutation of the columns of X. On the other hand, we have seen in Section 1 that with each character χ of G there is defined a character χ^α of G and that χ^α is irreducible whenever χ is. Hence α also induces a permutation of the rows of X. Moreover, by (1.12) $\chi^\alpha(y_j) = \chi(y_j^\alpha)$ and consequently the matrices obtained from X by these two permutations are identical. It is this crucial fact which enables us to prove:

Lemma 5.2 (Brauer)

Let A be a group of automorphisms of G. Then the number of orbits of A as a group of permutations of the irreducible characters of G is the same as that of A as a group of permutations of the conjugate classes of G.

Proof

We preserve the above notation. As shown in Section 2, the character table X of G is nonsingular. Moreover, by the preceding discussion, if X^α denotes the permutation induced on the rows or columns of X by the element α of A, then

$$(5.7) \qquad\qquad P(\alpha)X = X^\alpha = XQ(\alpha)$$

for suitable permutation matrices $P(\alpha)$ and $Q(\alpha)$. The nonsingularity of X implies that $P(\alpha)$ and $Q(\alpha)$ are uniquely determined by α.

Now clearly $X^{\alpha\beta} = (X^\alpha)^\beta$ for α, β in A. It follows therefore from (5.7) that

$$(5.8) \qquad P(\beta)P(\alpha) = P(\alpha\beta) \qquad \text{and} \qquad Q(\alpha)Q(\beta) = Q(\alpha\beta).$$

This in turn implies that the mappings π_1, π_2 of A given by $\alpha\pi_1 = P(\alpha)^t$ and $\alpha\pi_2 = Q(\alpha)$, $\alpha \in A$, are permutation representations of A. Let θ_i be the character of π_i, $1 \leqslant i \leqslant 2$. Since $X^{-1}P(\alpha)X = Q(\alpha)$ by (5.7), $P(\alpha)^t$ and $Q(\alpha)$ have the same traces for each α in A and consequently $\theta_1 = \theta_2$.

On the other hand, the number d_1 of orbits of A as a group of permutations of the irreducible characters of G is the same as the number as a group of permutations of the rows of X and consequently also is the same as the number of orbits of $(A)\pi_1$ in its action as a group of permutations. Similarly, the number d_2 of orbits of A as a group of permutations of the set of conjugate classes of G is the same as that of $(A)\pi_2$. Thus the desired conclusion $d_1 = d_2$ will follow, since $\theta_1 = \theta_2$, provided we show that the number of orbits of $(A)\pi_i$ as a group of permutations is $(\theta_i, 1_A)$, $1 \leqslant i \leqslant 2$. Since this number of orbits is the same as the number of transitive constituents of $(A)\pi_i$, the desired conclusion holds by Theorem 3.5 and the proof is complete.

We remark that obviously the lemma holds more generally for any non-singular matrix X and any group A which induces the same group of permutations of the rows and columns of X.

We can now prove

Theorem 5.3

Let G be a Frobenius group with kernel K and complement H. Then we have
  (i) If ψ is a nonprincipal irreducible character of K, then ψ^* is an irreducible character of G.
  (ii) If χ is an irreducible character of G whose kernel does not contain K, then $\chi = \psi^*$ for some irreducible character ψ of K.
  (iii) If χ and ψ are as in (ii), then for y in H

$$\chi|_H(y) = \begin{cases} 0 & \text{if } y \neq 1 \\ |H| \deg \psi & \text{if } y = 1. \end{cases}$$

Proof

Now H induces by conjugation a group of automorphisms of K and hence also a permutation of the irreducible characters of K. If ψ is an irreducible character of K, we denote its image under u in H by ψ^u. Thus $\psi^u(y) = \psi(y^u)$ for y in K. We shall now apply the preceding lemma to show that $\psi \neq \psi^u$ for all u in $H^\#$ provided $\psi \neq 1_K$.

Let K_j, $1 \leqslant j \leqslant t$, be the conjugate classes of $K^\#$. Suppose $K_j^u = K_j$ for some u in $H^\#$ and some j. Then if $y \in K_j$, there exists x in K such that $y^u = y^x$, whence ux^{-1} centralizes y. But then $ux^{-1} \in K$ by Theorem 2.7.6(iv) and so $u \in K$ as well as H, forcing $u = 1$, a contradiction. Hence $K_j^u \neq K_j$

for any j and any u in $H^\#$ and consequently the $t + 1$ conjugate classes of K are distributed into $(t/h) + 1$ orbits under the action of H, where $h = |H|$. It follows therefore from Lemma 5.2 that the $t + 1$ irreducible characters of K are also distributed into $(t/h) + 1$ orbits under the action of H. The t nonprincipal irreducible characters of K are thus distributed into t/h orbits under the action of H, which clearly implies that $\psi^u \neq \psi$ if $u \in H^\#$ and ψ is a nonprincipal irreducible character of K.

With this information, we can now establish the theorem. First of all, let ψ be a nonprincipal irreducible character of K. To prove that ψ^* is irreducible is equivalent to showing that $(\psi^*, \psi^*)_G = 1$. Since $\psi^*(y) = 0$ for y in $G - K$ by Theorem 4.3(ii), we have

$$(5.9) \qquad (\psi^*, \psi^*)_G = \frac{1}{|G|} \sum_{y \in K} \psi^*(y) \overline{\psi^*(y)} = \frac{|K|}{|G|} (\psi^*|_K, \psi^*|_K)_K.$$

On the other hand, by Theorem 4.3(i) we have for y in K

$$(5.10) \qquad \psi^*(y) = \frac{1}{|K|} \sum_{u \in G} \psi(u^{-1}yu),$$

since u^{-1} runs over G as u does. If $u \in G$, we can write $u = vx$ with v, x uniquely determined in H, K, respectively, since $G = HK$ and $H \cap K = 1$. But then $\psi(v^{-1}yv) = \psi(x^{-1}u^{-1}yux) = \psi(u^{-1}yu)$ as ψ is a class function on K and $K \lhd G$. Hence (5.10) reduces to

$$\psi^*(y) = \sum_{u \in H} \psi(u^{-1}yu) = \sum_{u \in H} \psi^u(y) \qquad y \in K,$$

and consequently

$$(5.11) \qquad \psi^*|_K = \sum_{u \in H} \psi^u.$$

Since $\psi^u \neq \psi^v$ for u, v in H and $u \neq v$ by the first part of the proof, the orthogonality relations in K and the irreducibility of each ψ^u imply that

$$(5.12) \qquad \left(\sum_{u \in H} \psi^u, \sum_{v \in H} \psi^v \right)_K = \sum_{u \in H} (\psi^u, \psi^u)_K = \sum_{u \in H} 1 = |H|.$$

But now (5.9), (5.11), and (5.12) together yield that $(\psi^*, \psi^*)_G = (|K|/|G|)|H| = 1$ and so ψ^* is irreducible. Thus (i) holds.

Since $|G:K| = |H|$, we note that $\deg \psi^* = |H| \deg \psi$ by Theorem 4.1. Furthermore, K is not in the kernel of ψ^*; for if it were, then $(\psi^*|_K, 1_K)_K = |H| \deg \psi$. But this inner product is 0 by (5.12) and the fact that no $\psi^u = 1_K$. We use these facts in proving (ii).

Set $t/h = m$, so that m is the number of orbits of nonprincipal irreducible characters of K under the action of H. Let ψ_i, $1 \leqslant i \leqslant m$, be representatives of each of these orbits and set $d_i = \deg \psi_i$. Then d_i is also the degree of ψ_i^u for each u in H and consequently we have by Theorem 1.6(i),

$$(5.13) \qquad |H| \sum_{i=1}^{m} d_i^2 = |K| - 1.$$

On the other hand, by (i) and the preceding paragraph, ψ_i^* is an irreducible character of G of degree $|H|d_i$ and does not have K in its kernel, $1 \leqslant i \leqslant m$. Moreover, these characters are distinct, for $\psi_i^u \neq \psi_j^v$ for u, v in H and $i \neq j$, so $\psi_i^*|_K$ and $\psi_j^*|_K$ have no common irreducible constituents, which implies that $\psi_i^* \neq \psi_j^*$ when $i \neq j$. Now by (5.13), the sum of the squares of the degrees of these m irreducible characters of G is $|H|(|K| - 1)$ $= |G| - |H|$. But the sum of the squares of the degrees of the irreducible characters χ_k, $1 \leqslant k \leqslant s$, of G having K in their kernels is the same as that for all irreducible characters of G/K and this latter sum is $|G/K| = |H|$ by Theorem 2.1(i). Hence the sum of the squares of the degrees of the ψ_i^* and χ_k is $|G|$, and so by another application of Theorem 2.1(i), these are all the irreducible characters of G. We conclude that the ψ_i^* are the only irreducible characters of G not having K in their kernel and this proves (ii).

Since $\psi^*(y) = 0$ for y in $G - K$ and $\deg \psi^* = |H| \deg \psi$, (iii) also holds.

In several important applications one encounters the following interesting situation: a group G and a nonnormal subgroup K of G disjoint from its conjugates in G such that $N = N_G(K)$ is a Frobenius group with kernel K. For example, the groups $L_2(q)$ satisfy these conditions with N the subgroup fixing a letter. Furthermore, they are always satisfied by an S_p-subgroup of a permutation group of prime degree p, as is easily verified.

These conditions on K are a very particular case of the general notion of *tamely embedded* subset as defined by Feit and Thompson.

Under this set of hypotheses, we are in a position to apply both Theorems 4.6 and 5.3. In discussing this situation, it will be convenient to denote by $I(K)$ the submodule of ch (N) generated by the characters of N induced from the nonprincipal irreducible characters of K. By Theorem 5.3, $I(K)$ has a basis consisting of the irreducible characters of N which do not have K in their kernel. Moreover, every element of $I(K)$ is 0 on $N - K$. We also set $I_0(K) = I(K) \cap \text{ch}_0(N)$ and denote by $C_d = C_d(K)$ the set of all nonprincipal irreducible characters of K of degree d. Furthermore, we let t be the number of orbits of the elements of C_d under the action of a Frobenius complement H in N.

We shall assume $t \geqslant 2$, for the ensuing discussion is not applicable in the contrary case. Let θ_i, $1 \leqslant i \leqslant t$, be representatives of the distinct orbits of C_d under H. Then by Theorem 5.3(i), the characters $\tilde{\theta}_i$ induced on N from the θ_i are distinct and irreducible, $1 \leqslant i \leqslant t$. Moreover, each $\tilde{\theta}_i$ has degree $d|N:K|$ and is 0 on $N - K$ by Theorems 4.1 and 4.3(ii). Set

$$(5.14) \qquad\qquad \zeta_{ij} = \tilde{\theta}_i - \tilde{\theta}_j, \qquad i \leqslant i, j \leqslant t.$$

Then $\deg \zeta_{ij} = 0$ and ζ_{ij} is 0 on $N - K$, so each $\zeta_{ij} \in I_0(K)$. Let $\psi_{ij} = \zeta_{ij}^*$, $1 \leqslant i, j \leqslant t$. Because of our assumptions, we can apply Theorem 4.6 and obtain

$$(5.15) \qquad (\psi_{ij}, \psi_{hk})_G = (\zeta_{ij}, \zeta_{hk})_N = (\tilde{\theta}_i - \tilde{\theta}_j, \tilde{\theta}_h - \tilde{\theta}_k)_N.$$

But each $\tilde{\theta}_i$ is an irreducible character of N and consequently $(\tilde{\theta}_r, \tilde{\theta}_s) = \delta_{rs}$, where $\delta_{rs} = 0$ or 1 according as $r \neq s$ or $r = s$. Hence expanding (5.15), we conclude that

$$(5.16) \qquad (\psi_{ij}, \psi_{hk})_G = \delta_{ih} - \delta_{jh} - \delta_{ik} + \delta_{jk} \qquad 1 \leqslant i, j, h, k \leqslant t.$$

We have thus constructed a set of t^2 generalized characters of G of degree 0 satisfying (5.16). These relations have an important implication:

Theorem 5.4 (Brauer-Suzuki)

Let ψ_{ij}, $1 \leqslant i, j \leqslant t$, $t \geqslant 2$, be elements of $\mathrm{ch}_0(G)$ which satisfy condition (5.16). Then there exists a sign $\varepsilon = \pm 1$ and uniquely determined distinct irreducible characters χ_i, $1 \leqslant i \leqslant t$, of G such that

$$\psi_{ij} = \varepsilon(\chi_i - \chi_j) \qquad 1 \leqslant i, j \leqslant t.$$

Moreover, ε is arbitrary if $t = 2$, while ε is uniquely determined if $t > 2$.

Proof

First of all, (5.16) implies that $(\psi_{ij}, \psi_{ij})_G = 0$ or 2 according as $i = j$ or $i \neq j$. But then by Theorem 2.4(ii), ψ_{ii} must be the 0 character and ψ_{ij} must have exactly two irreducible constituents, each of multiplicity ± 1. However, since $\psi_{ij}(1) = 0$, these occur with opposite multiplicities. Furthermore, (5.16) yields $(\psi_{ij}, \psi_{ji})_G = -2$ for $i \neq j$. By Theorem 2.4(i), this is possible only if the two irreducible constituents of ψ_{ji} are the same as those of ψ_{ij}, but occur with opposite signs. Thus $\psi_{ji} = -\psi_{ij}$. Now write

$$(5.17) \qquad\qquad \psi_{12} = \varepsilon(\chi_1 - \chi_2),$$

where χ_1, χ_2 are the corresponding irreducible characters of G and $\varepsilon = \pm 1$. By Theorem 2.4(i), χ_1, χ_2 are uniquely determined.

If $t = 2$, we can also write $\psi_{12} = (-\varepsilon)(\chi_2 - \chi_1)$. Since $\psi_{21} = -\psi_{12}$ and $\psi_{ii} = 0$, the theorem follows in this case. Hence we may assume that $t > 2$.

Again by (5.16), $(\psi_{12}, \psi_{13})_G = 1$ and so ψ_{12}, ψ_{13} have exactly one constituent in common and it occurs in each with the same multiplicity. Since we can interchange χ_1 and χ_2 if we replace ε by $-\varepsilon$, we can assume without loss that

$$(5.18) \qquad \psi_{13} = \varepsilon(\chi_1 - \chi_3),$$

where χ_3 is an irreducible character of G distinct from χ_1 and χ_2. Since χ_2, χ_3 are distinct, there do not exist expressions of the form (5.17) and (5.18) with $-\varepsilon$ in place of ε, and so ε is uniquely determined.

We argue next that ψ_{1k} has the same form for all k, $2 \leqslant k \leqslant t$, as for $k = 2$ and 3. Indeed, suppose $k > 3$ and assume χ_1 is not a constituent of ψ_{1j}. Since $(\psi_{1j}, \psi_{1k})_G = 1$, $2 \leqslant j \leqslant 3$, by (5.16), it follows therefore from (5.17) and (5.18) that $(-\varepsilon\chi_j, \psi_{1k})_G = 1$, whence $(\chi_j, \psi_{1k})_G = -\varepsilon$, $2 \leqslant j \leqslant 3$. But ψ_{1k} is the sum of two irreducible characters of multiplicities ± 1 and consequently $\psi_{1k} = -\varepsilon(\chi_2 + \chi_3)$ by Theorem 2.4(i). However, this is impossible, as $\deg \psi_{1k} = 0$. Hence χ_1 is a constituent of ψ_{1k}. Since $(\psi_{12}, \psi_{1k})_G = 1$, χ_1 is the only common constituent and it occurs with the same multiplicity in ψ_{12} and ψ_{1k}. We thus have

$$(5.19) \qquad \psi_{1k} = \varepsilon(\chi_1 - \chi_k) \qquad 2 \leqslant k \leqslant t,$$

where the χ_k are suitable irreducible characters of G. Since $(\psi_{1j}, \psi_{1k})_G = 1$ for $j \neq k$, $2 \leqslant j, k \leqslant t$, $\chi_j \neq \chi_k$, for otherwise $(\psi_{1j}, \psi_{1k})_G = 2$ by Theorem 2.4(i). Since $(\psi_{1k}, \psi_{1k})_G = 2$, we conclude similarly that $\chi_k \neq \chi_1$ for $k > 1$.

Finally, we consider ψ_{jk} with $2 \leqslant j, k \leqslant t$ and $j \neq k$. Again by (5.16), we have $(\psi_{jk}, \psi_{1k} - \psi_{1j})_G = 2$. But $\psi_{1k} - \psi_{1j} = \varepsilon(\chi_j - \chi_k)$ and so $(\psi_{jk}, \varepsilon(\chi_i - \chi_j))_G = 2$. By Theorem 2.4(i) and the form of ψ_{jk}, the only possibility is that χ_j, χ_k are constituents of ψ_{jk} of multiplicities ε, $-\varepsilon$, respectively, whence

$$(5.20) \qquad \psi_{jk} = \varepsilon(\chi_j - \chi_k) \qquad 2 \leqslant j, k \leqslant t.$$

But now (5.19) and (5.20) together with $\psi_{jj} = 0$ yield the theorem.

Irreducible characters χ_i of G constructed from the tamely embedded subgroup K of G in the above fashion are called *exceptional* characters of G (for K). As our final result, we derive an elementary property of exceptional characters which we shall need.

Theorem 5.5

If χ is an exceptional character of G for the subgroup K, then $\chi(y)$ is integral for any element y of G not contained in a conjugate of K.

Proof

We preserve the notation preceding Theorem 5.4, so that $t = |C_d|$ and by assumption, $t \geqslant 2$. Moreover, there are t distinct uniquely determined irreducible characters χ_i of G, $1 \leqslant i \leqslant t$, satisfying the conclusion of Theorem 5.4 and $\chi = \chi_i$ for some i. By Theorem 3.6.15, there exists a finite normal extension F_0 of the rationals Q with $F_0 \subseteq F$ such that every irreducible representation of G, K, and $N = N_G(K)$ can be written in F_0. Then $\chi_i(y) \in F_0$ for all i and all y in G. We shall argue that if y is not in a conjugate of K, then $\chi_i^\sigma(y) = \chi_i(y)$ for all σ in the Galois group $G(F_0, Q)$, which will imply that $\chi_i(y) \in Q$. Since $\chi_i(y)$ is an algebraic integer, the theorem will follow.

Setting $\alpha_i = \tilde{\vartheta}_i$, Theorem 5.4 can be written

$$(5.20) \qquad \varepsilon(\chi_j - \chi_i) = \alpha_j^* - \alpha_i^* \qquad 1 \leqslant i, j \leqslant t.$$

Let $\sigma \in G(F_0, Q)$. Then each α_i^σ has the same degree as α_i, does not have K in its kernel, and is 0 whenever α_i is 0. Hence $\alpha_i^\sigma \in I_0(K)$ for all σ and all i. Applying σ to (5.20) yields

$$(5.21) \qquad \varepsilon(\chi_j^\sigma - \chi_i^\sigma) = (\alpha_j^*)^\sigma - (\alpha_i^*)^\sigma = (\alpha_j^\sigma)^* - (\alpha_i^\sigma)^*.$$

If $\alpha_i^\sigma = \alpha_k$ and $\alpha_j^\sigma = \alpha_m$, the uniqueness of the χ_i together with the irreducibility of χ_i^σ, χ_j^σ imply that $\chi_i^\sigma = \chi_k$, $\chi_j^\sigma = \chi_m$. Since m runs from 1 to t as j does, it follows, in particular, that

$$(5.22) \qquad \varepsilon(\chi_i - \chi_i^\sigma) = \alpha_i^* - (\alpha_i^\sigma)^* \qquad 1 \leqslant i \leqslant t.$$

But by Theorem 4.3(ii), both α_i^* and $(\alpha_i^\sigma)^*$ are 0 on y if y is not in a conjugate of K, whence $\chi_i^\sigma(y) = \chi_i(y)$ for all σ in $G(F_0, Q)$, as required.

6. COHERENCE

In this section we shall obtain an important generalization of Theorem 5.4 due to Feit. Once again let K be a subgroup of G disjoint from its conjugates such that $N = N_G(K)$; and, as in (5.14), let $\tilde{\vartheta}_i$, $1 \leqslant i \leqslant t$, be the set of irreducible characters on N induced from the set of all nonprincipal irreducible characters θ_i of a given degree d of K. Put $\eta_i = \tilde{\vartheta}_i$, $1 \leqslant i \leqslant t$, and $n = |N:K|$. In view of Theorem 5.3 and the definition of $I(K)$, as given in the preceding section, the η_i can also be described as the set of all irreducible characters of $I(K)$ of degree dn. They thus form a basis of a submodule of $I(K)$ which we shall denote by $I^d(K)$. We also set $I_0^d(K) = I^d(K) \cap I_0(K)$, so that each $\zeta_{ij} = \eta_i - \eta_j$ is in $I_0^d(K)$ and the generalized characters $\zeta_{1j} = \eta_1 - \eta_j$, $2 \leqslant j \leqslant t$, form a basis of $I_0^d(K)$.

Theorem 4.6 asserts that the induction map * from N to G is an isometry of $I_0(K)$ into $ch_0(G)$ and, in particular, of $I_0^d(K)$ into $ch_0(G)$. Now the conclusion of Theorem 5.4 can be expressed in the following way: When $t \geqslant 2$, the isometry of $I_0^d(K)$ into $ch_0(G)$ can be extended to an isometry τ of $I^d(K)$ into $ch(G)$. Indeed, if ε and χ_i, $1 \leqslant i \leqslant t$, are as in Theorem 5.4, then the mapping

$$(6.1) \qquad\qquad \eta_i^\tau = \varepsilon\chi_i \qquad 1 \leqslant i \leqslant t$$

gives the required isometry. Since the $\varepsilon\chi_i$ are distinct generalized characters of G of norm 1, Theorem 2.4(i) implies that $\sum_{i=1}^{t} a_i\eta_i$ and $\sum_{i=1}^{t} a_i(\varepsilon\chi_i)$ have the same norms for any integers a_i, $1 \leqslant i \leqslant t$. Since the η_i form a basis of $I^d(K)$, τ is thus an isometry of $I^d(K)$ into $ch(G)$. That τ extends the isometry of $I_0^d(K)$ into $ch_0(G)$ is clear since the elements $\eta_1 - \eta_j$ are a basis of $I_0^d(K)$ and

$$(6.2) \qquad (\eta_1 - \eta_j)^\tau = \eta_1^\tau - \eta_j^\tau = \varepsilon\chi_1 - \varepsilon\chi_j = (\eta_1 - \eta_j)^* \qquad 2 \leqslant j \leqslant t.$$

We may now ask the more general question: When can the isometry * from $I_0(K)$ into $ch_0(G)$ be extended to an isometry τ of $I(K)$ into $ch(G)$? Whenever this is true, we shall say that $I(K)$ is *coherent*. More generally if I is a submodule of $I(K)$ we shall call I *coherent* if the isometry of $I \cap I_0(K)$ into $ch_0(G)$ can be extended to one from I into $ch(G)$. This concept of coherence is a very particular case of the general notion of a coherent set of characters defined by Feit and Thompson in their proof of the solvability of groups of odd order.

Using the language of coherence, we have the following corollary of Theorem 5.4:

Theorem 6.1

Let K be an abelian subgroup of G disjoint from its conjugates such that $N = N_G(K)$ is a Frobenius group with kernel K. Then one of the following holds:

(i) *$I(K)$ is coherent.*

(ii) *K is an elementary abelian p-group for some prime p, $|N:K| = |K| - 1$, and $I_0(K) = 0$.*

Proof

Since K is abelian, $C_1(K)$ contains all nonprincipal irreducible characters of K and so $I^1(K) = I(K)$. Hence by the preceding discussion, either $I(K)$ is coherent or $t = 1$, where $t = \dim I(K)$. But by Lemma 5.2 and the proof of Theorem 5.3, $t = (k - 1)/n$, where $k = |K|$ and $n = |N : K|$. Hence $n = k - 1$ when $t = 1$. Let H be a Frobenius complement in N and let x be an element of prime order p in K. Since H induces a regular group of automorphisms of K, the orbit of x under H contains $n = |H|$ distinct elements. But then if $n = k - 1$, we have $n = |K^{\#}|$, in which case the orbit of x contains all elements of $K^{\#}$ and so K is an elementary abelian p-group. Moreover, $I(K)$ is generated by a single irreducible character and so $I_0(K) = 0$.

Feit's results give an extension of Theorem 6.1 to the case that K is nilpotent. [In view of Thompson's theorem, the assumption that $N_G(K)$ is a Frobenius group with kernel K will actually imply the nilpotency of K.] We preserve the notation K, N and n throughout, so that, in particular, every element of $I(K)$ has degree dn for some integer d. The argument is based upon the following crucial theorem, which can be regarded as a generalization of Theorem 5.4.

Theorem 6.2

Suppose I is the direct sum of submodules I_1, I_2, of $I(K)$, where I_1, I_2 are generated by irreducible characters of N, I_1 is coherent, and $I^1(K) \subseteq I_1$. Let ζ_{1j}, $1 \leqslant j \leqslant t_1$, be the distinct irreducible characters of I_1 and assume the following:

    (a) $t_1 \geqslant 2$.

    (b) *If I_2 contains an irreducible character of degree dn, then*

$$\sum_{j=1}^{t_1} \deg (\zeta_{1j})^2 > 2dn^2.$$

Then $I = I_1 \oplus I_2$ is coherent and, except in the case $I = I_1 = I^1(K)$ and $t_1 = 2$, the isometry τ is uniquely determined.

Proof

Since K is nilpotent, $K' \subset K$ and consequently $|C_1(K)| = |K/K'| - 1 > 1$. Hence $I^1(K) \neq 0$. Since $I^1(K) \subseteq I_1$, we can choose the notation so that $\zeta_{11} \in I^1(K)$ in which case $\deg \zeta_{11} = \zeta_{11}(1) = n$. Next let d_i, $2 \leqslant i \leqslant m$, be the set of distinct integers for which I_2 possesses an irreducible character of degree $d_i n$, let ζ_{ij}, $1 \leqslant j \leqslant t_i$, be the irreducible characters of I_2 of degree $d_i n$ and let I^i be the submodule of $I^{d_i}(K)$ generated by ζ_{ij}, $1 \leqslant j \leqslant t_i$. The discussion at the beginning of the section tells us that I^i is coherent whenever $t_i \geqslant 2, 2 \leqslant i \leqslant m$.

Now set $J_r = I_1 \cup I^2 \cdots \cup I^r, 1 \leqslant r \leqslant m$. Suppose we know that J_r is coherent. We shall argue that the isometry τ is uniquely determined on J_r except when $J_r = I^1(K)$ and $t_1 = 2$. Since $J_m = I$, the final statement of the theorem will then follow. If $J_r = I^1(K)$, then the isometry τ of J_r into ch (G) is uniquely determined by Theorem 5.4 if $t_1 \geqslant 3$. Since $t_1 \geqslant 2$ by assumption, either the desired conclusion follows or $I^1(K) \subset J_r$. In the latter case let ζ_{1j}, ζ_{ik} be arbitrary irreducible characters of J_r with deg $\zeta_{1j} = n$ and deg $\zeta_{ik} = d_i n, d_i > 1$. Then $d_i \zeta_{1j} - \zeta_{ik} \in I_0(K)$. Since τ extends *, we have

(6.3)
$$(\zeta_{1j}^{\tau}, (d_i \zeta_{1j} - \zeta_{ik})^*)_G = (\zeta_{1j}, d_i \zeta_{1j} - \zeta_{ik})_N = d_i,$$
$$(\zeta_{ik}^{\tau}, (d_i \zeta_{1j} - \zeta_{ik})^*)_G = (\zeta_{ik}, d_i \zeta_{1j} - \zeta_{ik})_N = -1.$$

Since ζ_{1j}^{τ} has norm 1, the first equation together with Theorem 2.4(i) implies that $d_i \zeta_{1j}^* - \zeta_{ik}^*$ has an irreducible constituent χ_{1j} of multiplicity $\pm d_i$. But by the same theorem,

(6.4)
$$(d_i \zeta_{1j}^* - \zeta_{ik}^*, d_i \zeta_{1j}^* - \zeta_{ik}^*)_G = d_i^2 + 1.$$

Since $d_i \zeta_{1j}^* - \zeta_{ik}^*$ has degree 0, we conclude at once from (6.4) that

(6.5)
$$d_i \zeta_{ij}^* - \zeta_{ik}^* = \varepsilon(d_i \chi_{1j} - \chi_{ik}),$$

for suitable irreducible characters χ_{ik} of G, where $\varepsilon = \pm 1$. Moreover, since χ_{1j}, χ_{ik} occur with distinct multiplicities, each is uniquely determined. But now (6.3) forces $\zeta_{1j}^{\tau} = \varepsilon \chi_{1j}$ and $\zeta_{ik}^{\tau} = \varepsilon \chi_{ik}$. Thus τ is uniquely determined on all irreducible character of J_r and so on J_r.

Hence to prove the theorem, we need only show that each J_r is, in fact, coherent, for then $I = J_m$ will be coherent. We proceed by induction on r. If $r = 1$, then $J_1 = I_1$ is coherent by hypothesis; so we may assume J_{r-1} is coherent for some $r \geqslant 2$ and verify that J_r is coherent. Then by assumption there exist irreducible characters χ_{ij} of G and signs $\varepsilon_{ij} = \pm 1, 1 \leqslant i \leqslant r - 1$, $1 \leqslant j \leqslant t_i$, such that the mapping $\zeta_{ij}^{\tau} = \varepsilon_{ij} \chi_{ij}$ is an isometry of J_{r-1} into ch (G) which extends that of $J_{r-1} \cap I_0(K)$ determined by *. However, since $\zeta_{ij}(1)\zeta_{11} - \zeta_{11}(1)\zeta_{ij}$ has degree 0, we have $0 = \zeta_{ij}(1)\zeta_{11}^{\tau}(1) - \zeta_{11}(1)\zeta_{ij}^{\tau}(1)$ $= \zeta_{ij}(1)\varepsilon_{11} \chi_{11}(1) - \zeta_{11}(1)\varepsilon_{ij} \chi_{ij}(1)$, whence $\varepsilon_{ij} = \varepsilon_{11}$ for all i, j. We put $\varepsilon = \varepsilon_{11}$. We also set $d_{1j} = (1/n) \deg \zeta_{1j}, 1 \leqslant j \leqslant t_1$, so that each d_{1j} is an integer and $d_{11} = 1$.

Now set $\theta_k = (d_r \zeta_{11} - \zeta_{rk})^*, 1 \leqslant k \leqslant t_r$, and note that each θ_k has degree 0. We shall now argue that χ_{11} appears in θ_k with multiplicity εd_r. We set

(6.6)
$$(\chi_{11}, \theta_k)_G = \varepsilon(d_r - a)$$

and proceed to argue that the integer a is 0. Then for $j > 1$, the linearity of the inner product obviously implies

$$(6.7) \qquad (\chi_{1j}, \theta_k)_G = (d_{1j}\chi_{11}, \theta_k)_G - (d_{1j}\chi_{11} - \chi_{1j}, \theta_k)_G.$$

The first term can be computed from (6.6), while the second is equal to $\varepsilon(d_{1j}\zeta_{11} - \zeta_{1j}, d_r\zeta_{11} - \zeta_{rk})_N$ as $d_{1j}\chi_{11} - \chi_{1j}$ has degree 0. Thus

$$(6.8) \qquad (\chi_{1j}, \theta_k)_G = \varepsilon d_{1j}(d_r - a) - \varepsilon d_{1j}d_r = -\varepsilon d_{1j}a \qquad 2 \leqslant j \leqslant t_1.$$

Suppose θ_k has no constituents other than χ_{ij}, $1 \leqslant i \leqslant r - 1$, $1 \leqslant j \leqslant t_i$. Since $\deg \theta_k = 0$ and since τ extends the induction map on J_{r-1}, it follows from this that θ_k is induced from an element α_k of J_{r-1} of degree 0. But then $\beta_k^* = 0$, where $\beta_k = d_r \zeta_{11} - \zeta_{rk} - \alpha_k$ and consequently β_k is orthogonal to every element of J_r by Theorem 4.6, forcing $\beta_k = 0$. But then $\zeta_{rk} \in J_{r-1}$, which is not the case. We conclude that each θ_k possesses an irreducible constituent χ_{rk} with $\chi_{rk} \neq \chi_{ij}$, $1 \leqslant i \leqslant r - 1$, $1 \leqslant j \leqslant t_i$.

On the other hand, as $\deg \theta_k = 0$, Theorem 4.6 also implies that

$$(6.9) \qquad (\theta_k, \theta_k)_G = d_r^2 + 1.$$

But now (6.6), (6.8), and (6.9) together with Theorem 2.4(ii) yield

$$(6.10) \qquad (d_r - a)^2 + \sum_{j=2}^{t_1} d_{1j}^2 a^2 + (\theta_k, \chi_{rk})_G \leqslant d_r^2 + 1.$$

Since $d_{11} = 1$ and $(\theta_k, \chi_{rk})_G \geqslant 1$, this gives

$$(6.11) \qquad -2ad_r + a^2 \sum_{j=1}^{t_1} d_{1j}^2 \leqslant 0.$$

However, since $\deg \zeta_{1j} = d_{1j}n$, condition (b) of the theorem with d_r as d implies that

$$(6.12) \qquad \sum_{j=1}^{t_1} d_{1j}^2 > 2d_r.$$

Since a is an integer, (6.11) and (6.12) together force $a = 0$.

Thus χ_{11} is a constituent of θ_k of multiplicity εd_r. Since $\deg \theta_k = 0$, it follows now from (6.9) that

$$(6.13) \qquad \theta_k = \varepsilon(d_r \chi_{11} - \chi_{rk}) \qquad 1 \leqslant k \leqslant t_r.$$

Moreover, $\theta_k \neq \theta_h$ for $k \neq h$ since $\zeta_{rk} \neq \zeta_{rh}$ and consequently $\chi_{rk} \neq \chi_{rh}$. We now extend the definition of τ to J_r by setting

$$(6.14) \qquad \zeta_{rk}^\tau = \varepsilon \chi_{rk} \qquad 1 \leqslant k \leqslant t_r.$$

Clearly then τ is an isometry of J_r into ch (G). But the θ_k together with $J_{r-1} \cap I_0(K)$ obviously generate $J_r \cap I_0(K)$. Since τ agrees with $*$ on $J_{r-1} \cap I_0(K)$ by induction and on each θ_k by construction, τ is an extension of $*$ on $J_r \cap I_0(K)$, completing the proof of the theorem.

To relate condition (b) to properties of K, we require the following lemma, which is of some independent interest.

Lemma 6.3

If ϕ is an irreducible representation over F of a nilpotent group G, then $(\deg \phi)^2$ divides $|G:Z(G)|$.

Proof

We proceed by induction on $|G|$. We write G as the direct product of its Sylow subgroups P_i, $1 \leqslant i \leqslant m$. By Theorem 3.7.1, ϕ is the tensor product of irreducible representations ϕ_i of P_i. If $m > 1$, then $(\deg \phi_i)^2$ divides $|P_i:Z(P_i)|$ by induction, $1 \leqslant i \leqslant m$. Since $Z(G)$ is the direct product of the $Z(P_i)$ and $\deg \phi$ is the product of the $\deg \phi_i$, the lemma follows. Hence we may assume that $m = 1$, in which case G is a p-group. Next let H be the kernel of ϕ and let $\bar{Z}$ be the image of $Z(G)$ in $\bar{G} = G/H$, so that $\bar{Z} \subseteq Z(\bar{G})$. Now ϕ induces a faithful irreducible representation $\bar{\phi}$ of $\bar{G}$ of the same degree as ϕ. If $H \neq 1$, then $(\deg \bar{\phi})^2$ divides $|\bar{G}:Z(\bar{G})|$ by induction and so divides $|\bar{G}:\bar{Z}|$ as $\bar{Z} \subseteq Z(\bar{G})$. Since $|\bar{G}:\bar{Z}| \leqslant |G:Z(G)|$, the lemma follows. Hence we may also assume that ϕ is faithful. In particular, $Z(G)$ is cyclic by Theorem 3.2.2. Finally, if G is abelian, $\deg \phi = 1$, in which case the lemma is obvious; so we may also assume that G is nonabelian, whence $Z(G) \subset G$.

Since G is a p-group, there exists a normal subgroup L of G with $Z(G) \subset L \subseteq Z_2(G)$ and $|L:Z(G)| = p$. But then $L/Z(G)$ is cyclic and so L is abelian by Lemma 1.3.4. Let V be the representation space of $\bar{\phi}$. We regard V as a faithful G-module and apply Clifford's theorem to the normal subgroup L. Let V_i, $1 \leqslant i \leqslant r$, be the corresponding Wedderburn components. Since F is the complex field and L is abelian, Theorem 3.2.4 implies that V_i is the direct sum of one-dimensional isomorphic L-submodules. Hence L acts on V_i as a group of scalar transformations. But then if $r = 1$, this action must be faithful and so $L \subseteq Z(G)$, which is not the case. Thus $r > 1$.

Now set $C = C_G(L)$. Since $L \subseteq Z_2(G)$, we have for y in $L - Z(G)$ and x in G that $[x, y] \in Z(G)$. Moreover, one verifies directly that the mapping $(x)\alpha = [x, y]$ is a homomorphism of G into $Z(G)$ and, since $y^p \in Z(G)$, that the image of G is $\Omega_1(Z(G))$. But C is the kernel of α and $|\Omega_1(Z(P))| = p$, whence $|G:C| = p$. By Clifford's theorem, C leaves each V_i invariant and G/C induces a transitive permutation group of the V_i. Thus $r = p$. Furthermore, the irreducibility of ϕ on V implies that V_1 is an irreducible C-module.

Finally, if D denotes the kernel of the representation ψ determined by C on V_1, we have $LD/D \subseteq Z(C/D)$, since L induces scalar transformations on V_1. Hence by induction $(\deg \psi)^2$ divides $|C:L|$. But $\deg \phi = p \deg \psi$, while $|G:Z(G)| = p^2 |C:L|$. We conclude that $(\deg \phi)^2$ divides $|G:Z(G)|$, completing the proof.

We shall now derive a consequence of Theorem 6.2. Once this is done, it will be easy to obtain Feit's main result. Here the *square-free part* of a positive integer x denotes, as usual, the smallest integer of the form x/y^2, y an integer.

Theorem 6.4

Let a be the square-free part of $|K:K'|$. If $|K:K'| > [4(n^2 - 1)/a] + 2$, then $I(K)$ is coherent.

Proof

If L is a subgroup of K' normal in N, we denote by $I(L)$ the submodule of $I(K)$ generated by those characters of $I(K)$ whose kernels contain L. Thus $I(1) = I(K)$ and so to prove the theorem we must show that $I(1)$ is coherent. Note that $I(M) \supseteq I(L)$ whenever $M \subseteq L$. Furthermore, if ζ is an irreducible character of N not having K in its kernel, then we know that $\deg \zeta = dn$ and that ζ is induced from an irreducible character ϕ of K of degree d. Moreover, by Theorem 4.3(iii), $\ker \phi \subseteq \ker \zeta$. Hence by Theorem 5.3 the set of irreducible characters of N induced by all nonprincipal irreducible characters of K having L in their kernels is a basis of $I(L)$. In particular, then, $I(K')$ is the subset $I^1(K)$ generated by the irreducible characters of $I(K)$ of degree n. We shall use these facts in the proof.

We claim, first of all, that $I(K')$ is coherent. Since $I(K') = I^1(K)$, this will follow at once from Theorem 4.6 if $\dim I(K') > 1$, so assume that $\dim I(K') = 1$. Then if H is a Frobenius complement in N, the nonidentity elements of K/K' must all lie in a single orbit under the action of H. Thus $|K:K'| = n - 1$ since $n = |H|$. But then certainly $a \leqslant n - 1$, whence

$$(6.15) \qquad \frac{4(n^2 - 1)}{a} + 2 \geqslant 4(n + 1) + 2 > n - 1 = |K:K'|,$$

contrary to assumption.

There thus exists a subgroup L of K' with $L \lhd N$ of least order such that $I(L)$ is coherent. Suppose by way of contradiction that $L \neq 1$. Let M be a maximal subgroup of L such that $M \lhd N$. Then $I(M)$ is not coherent. Set $I_1 = I(L)$ and let I_2 be the submodule of $I(K)$ generated by the irreducible characters of N induced from characters of K having M, but not L, in their kernels. Then $I(M) = I_1 \oplus I_2$. Furthermore, $I^1(K) = I(K') \subseteq I_1 = I(L)$. Hence by the preceding paragraph $t_1 = \dim I_1 \geqslant \dim I^1(K) \geqslant 2$. Since I_1 and I_2 are generated by irreducible characters, we see then that condition (b) of Theorem 6.2 must be violated. Letting ζ_{1j}, $1 \leqslant j \leqslant t_1$, and d_i, $2 \leqslant i \leqslant m$, have the same meaning as in that theorem, we conclude that

$$(6.16) \qquad \sum_{j=1}^{t_1} (\deg \zeta_{1j})^2 \leqslant 2d_i n^2$$

for some i, $2 \leqslant i \leqslant m$. But as $I_1 = I(L)$, the ζ_{1j} include all irreducible characters of N which have L, but not K, in their kernels. It follows at once from this, using Theorem 3.6.14(iv) and (v), that the left side of (6.16) is simply $|N:L| - |N:K|$, whence

$$(6.17) \qquad |N:L| - |N:K| \leqslant 2d_i n^2.$$

We shall next argue that

$$(6.18) \qquad d_i^2 \,|\, |K:L|.$$

By definition, $d_i n$ is the degree of an irreducible character ζ of N having M, but not L, in its kernel and consequently ζ is induced from an irreducible character η of K of degree d_i which has M in its kernel. Since $\bar{K} = K/M$ is nilpotent, it will suffice to show that $\bar{L} = L/M \subseteq Z(\bar{K})$, for then it will follow from the preceding lemma that $d_i^2 \,|\, \bar{K}:\bar{L}|$. Since $|\bar{K}:\bar{L}| = |K:L|$, this will yield (6.18). But by our choice of M, L is clearly a minimal normal subgroup of $\bar{N} = N/M$. However, since K is nilpotent and normal in N, Theorem 2.6.4 implies that $\bar{L} \cap Z(\bar{K})$ is a nontrivial normal subgroup of $\bar{K}$, whence $\bar{L} = \bar{L} \cap Z(\bar{K})$ and $\bar{L} \subseteq Z(\bar{K})$, as required.

Next let b be the square-free part of $|K':L|$ and set $c = (a, b)$. Then it is immediate that the square-free part of $|K:L|$ is $e = ab/c^2$. Hence, by (6.18), $d_i \leqslant \sqrt{(1/e)|K:L|}$. Since $|N:K| = n$, it follows therefore upon dividing (6.18) by n that

$$(6.19) \qquad |K:L| - 1 \leqslant 2n \sqrt{\frac{1}{e}\,|K:L|}.$$

Squaring and dividing by $|K:L|$ yields

(6.20) $$|K:L| - 2 \leqslant \frac{4n^2}{e} - \frac{1}{|K:L|}.$$

However, as e divides $|K:L|$, (6.20) implies the stronger inequality

(6.21) $$|K:L| - 2 \leqslant \frac{4n^2 - 1}{e} = \frac{4n^2c^2 - c^2}{ab}.$$

Finally, since b is the square-free part of $|K':L|$, certainly $|K:K'| b \leqslant |K:L|$. Hence by (6.21) and the fact that $c \leqslant b$, we obtain

(6.22) $$|K:K'| - 2 \leqslant \frac{4n^2c^2 - c^2}{ab^2} \leqslant \frac{4n^2 - 1}{a}.$$

But then $|K:K'| \leqslant (4n^2 - 1/a) + 2$, contrary to hypothesis. Thus $L = 1$ and $I(K)$ is coherent.

We can now readily establish Feit's main result:

Theorem 6.5 (Feit)

Let K be a nilpotent subgroup of G disjoint from its conjugates such that $N = N_G(K)$ is a Frobenius group with kernel K. Then one of the following holds:

(i) $I(K)$ is coherent.
(ii) K is an elementary abelian p-group for some prime p, $|N:K| = |K| - 1$, and $I_0(K) = 0$.
(iii) K is a nonabelian p-group and $|K:K'| \leqslant 4|N:K|^2 + 1$.

Proof

We may assume K is nonabelian, otherwise the theorem follows from Theorem 6.1. As usual, let H be a Frobenius complement in N, so that $n = |H|$. If n were even, then H would contain an element x of order 2 and x would induce by conjugation an automorphism of K of order 2 fixing only the identity. It is an easy argument (which we shall give in Chapter 10) that K must be abelian in this case. Hence n is odd.

Let a be the square-free part of $|K:K'|$. Then we may also assume that

(6.23) $$|K:K'| \leqslant \frac{4(n^2 - 1)}{a} + 2 \leqslant 4n^2 + 1;$$

otherwise $I(K)$ is coherent by Theorem 6.4 and (i) holds. Hence to complete the proof, we need only show that (6.23) forces K to be a p-group, for then (iii) will hold.

Let P_i, $1 \leqslant i \leqslant m$, be the distinct Sylow subgroups of K and assume by way of contradiction that $m > 1$. Since K is nilpotent, we have

(6.24) $$|K:K'| = \prod_{i=1}^{m} |P_i:P_i'|.$$

Now H leaves each P_i invariant as P_i char K and so each $|P_i:P_i'| \equiv 1$ (mod n). Suppose $|P_i|$ is odd. Since n is odd, it follows that, in fact, $|P_i:P_i'| \equiv 1$ (mod $2n$), whence $|P_i:P_i'| \geqslant 2n + 1$. But then if $|P_i|$ were odd for at least two values of i, (6.24) would imply that $|K:K'| \geqslant (2n+1)^2$, contrary to (6.23). Hence we must have $m = 2$ and $|P_i|$ even for $i = 1$ or 2, say $i = 1$.

Thus P_1 is a 2-group and P_2 is a p-group, p odd. Let $|P_1:P_1'| = 2^s$ and $|P_2:P_2'| = p^t$. Then

(6.25) $$2^s = 1 + e_1 n \qquad \text{and} \qquad p^t = 1 + 2e_2 n$$

for suitable integers e_1, e_2. Since $|K:K'| = 2^s p^t = (1 + e_1 n)(1 + 2e_2 n)$, (6.23) forces $e_1 = e_2 = 1$. In particular, $p^t = 2^{s+1} - 1 \equiv -1$ (mod 4), which implies that t is odd. But then p divides a, the square-free part of $|K:K'|$. However, since $n \geqslant 3$, one checks directly that

$$|K:K'| = (n+1)(2n+1) > \frac{4(n^2 - 1)}{p} + 2 \geqslant \frac{4(n^2 - 1)}{a} + 2,$$

contrary to (6.23). This completes the proof.

The significance of the coherence of $I(K)$ rests on the fact that when it holds we can obtain fairly precise information concerning the values of the irreducible characters of G on $K^{\#}$. Indeed, we have

Theorem 6.6

Let K be a nilpotent subgroup of G disjoint from its conjugates such that $N = N_G(K)$ is a Frobenius group with kernel K. Assume that $I(K)$ is coherent and let τ be an isometry of $I(K)$ into ch (G) which extends the induction map of $I_0(K)$ into $\mathrm{ch}_0 (G)$. Then there exists an integer c such that for any irreducible character ζ of $I(K)$ and any element y of $K^{\#}$,

$$\zeta^{\tau}(y) = \zeta(y) + \frac{\deg \zeta}{|N:K|} c.$$

Moreover, if χ is an irreducible character of G not contained in $I(K)^{\tau}$, then χ has a constant integral value on $K^{\#}$.

Proof

Let $\zeta_i, 1 \leqslant i \leqslant t$, be the irreducible characters of $I(K)$ with

$$\deg \zeta_1 = n = |N:K|.$$

We can write

$$(6.26) \qquad \zeta_i^\tau|_N = \sum_{j=1}^{t} a_{ij}\zeta_j + \pi_i \qquad 1 \leqslant i \leqslant t,$$

where the a_{ij} are nonnegative integers and π_i is a character of N having K in its kernel. Using the Frobenius reciprocity theorem and Theorem 2.4(i) together with the coherence of $I(K)$, we have

$$(6.27) \qquad \frac{\deg \zeta_i}{n} a_{i1} - a_{ij} = \left(\zeta_i^\tau|_N, \frac{\deg \zeta_j}{n}\zeta_1 - \zeta_j \right)_N$$

$$= \left(\zeta_i^\tau, \left(\frac{\deg \zeta_j}{n}\zeta_1 - \zeta_j\right)^* \right)_G = \left(\zeta_i^\tau, \frac{\deg \zeta_j}{n}\zeta_1^\tau - \zeta_j^\tau \right)_G$$

$$= \frac{\deg \zeta_j}{n}\delta_{i1} - \delta_{ij},$$

where δ_{ij} has the usual meaning. Solving for a_{ij} and substituting in (6.26), we obtain

$$(6.28) \qquad \zeta_i^\tau|_N = \sum_{j=1}^{t} \delta_{ij}\zeta_j + \frac{a_{i1} - \delta_{i1}}{n} \sum_{j=1}^{t} (\deg \zeta_j)\zeta_j + \pi_i.$$

The first sum reduces to ζ_i. Since the ζ_j are all the irreducible characters of N not having K in their kernel, it follows from Theorem 3.6.14(iv) and (v) that the second sum is simply $\rho_N - \rho_{N/K}$, where ρ_N, $\rho_{N/K}$ denote the characters of the regular representation of N and N/K, respectively. Thus

$$(6.29) \qquad \zeta_i^\tau|_N = \zeta_i + \frac{a_{i1} - \delta_{i1}}{n}(\rho_N - \rho_{N/K}) + \pi_i \qquad 1 \leqslant i \leqslant t.$$

But on $K^\#$, ρ_N, $\rho_{N/K}$, and π_i have the respective values $0, n$, and $\pi_i(1)$. Hence there exists an integer c_i such that

$$(6.30) \qquad \zeta_i^\tau(y) = \zeta_i(y) + c_i \qquad y \in K^\#, 1 \leqslant i \leqslant t.$$

On the other hand, by the coherence of $I(K)$ and Theorem 4.6,

$$(6.31) \qquad \frac{\deg \zeta_i}{n}\zeta_1^\tau(y) - \zeta_i^\tau(y) = \frac{\deg \zeta_i}{n}\zeta_1(y) - \zeta_i(y) \qquad y \in K^\#.$$

Combining (6.30) and (6.31), we conclude at once that

$$(6.32) \qquad c_i = \frac{\deg \zeta_i}{n}c_1 \qquad 1 \leqslant i \leqslant t.$$

Setting $c_1 = c$, the first assertion of the theorem now follows from (6.30) and (6.32).

Suppose that next χ is an irreducible character of G not contained in $I(K)^\tau$. We have

$$(6.33) \qquad \chi|_N = \sum_{j=1}^{t} b_j \zeta_j + \pi,$$

where the b_j are nonnegative integers and π is a character of N with K in its kernel. Proceeding as in (6.27), we obtain

$$(6.34) \qquad \frac{\deg \zeta_j}{n} b_1 - b_i = \left(\chi, \frac{\deg \zeta_j}{n} \zeta_1^\tau - \zeta_j^\tau \right)_G = 0,$$

since $\chi \neq \pm \zeta_k^\tau$ for any k. This yields

$$(6.35) \qquad \chi|_N = \frac{b_1}{n} \sum_{j=1}^{t} (\deg \zeta_j) \zeta_j + \pi = \frac{b_1}{n} (\rho_N - \rho_{N/K}) + \pi.$$

Hence for y in $K^{\#}$, we have $\chi(y) = -b_1 + \pi(1)$, whence χ has constant integral value on $K^{\#}$, thus completing the proof.

To determine the parameter c, and hence the exact values of the exceptional characters on $K^{\#}$, requires additional information. By its definition $I(K)$ is limited to the characters of N with support on K no constituent of which has K in its kernel. There is, however, a character of N with support on K, whose constituents do have K in their kernels: $\tilde{1}_K = \rho_{N/K}$. If we know the decomposition of $1_K^* = \tilde{1}_K^*$, then the exact value of c can be determined as well as the values of the nonexceptional characters on $K^{\#}$.

If we set $I'(K) = \langle I(K), \tilde{1}_K \rangle$ and $I_0'(K) = I'(K) \cap \mathrm{ch}_0(G)$, then $\dim I'(K) = \dim I(K) + 1$ and $\dim I_0'(K) = \dim I_0(K) + 1$. Furthermore, we know that the induction map is actually an isometry of $I_0'(K)$ into $\mathrm{ch}_0(G)$. An important special case of the above considerations occurs when this isometry can be extended to one of $I'(K)$ into $\mathrm{ch}(G)$. This is a stronger requirement than coherence. Examples of these situations will be discussed in detail in Chapters 9 and 13.

In the Frobenius case we have just considered, the module $I(K)$ possessed a basis consisting of irreducible characters. When $N = N_G(K)$ is not a Frobenius group, this need no longer be true. Under these more general circumstances, the conditions required for the coherence of $I(K)$ are considerably more complicated. This problem is studied by Feit and Thompson in Section 10 of the Odd Order paper. In Section 9.4 we shall consider a very particular case of this situation, in which the coherence of $I(K)$ can easily be established.

7. BRAUER'S CHARACTERIZATION OF CHARACTERS

A generalized character χ of G is a complex-valued class function on G. It is natural to ask for criteria which will guarantee that a particular complex-valued class function θ on G is necessarily a generalized character. Since χ is the difference of two characters of G, so also is $\chi|_H$ for any subgroup H of G and hence $\chi|_H$ is a generalized character of H. Clearly then it is necessary that $\chi|_H$ be a generalized character of any subgroup H of G. Brauer's theorem asserts conversely that χ must be a generalized character of G if its restriction to every so-called *elementary* subgroup E of G is a generalized character of E.

A group E is called *elementary* if it is the direct product of a p-group and a cyclic p'-group. Obviously every subgroup of an elementary group is elementary. If we wish to specify the prime p, we shall say that E is *p-elementary*.

Brauer's characterization theorem is a direct consequence of another fundamental result of his which will reveal vividly the importance of elementary subgroups for the study of the characters of G. The proof of this latter theorem which we shall give is the celebrated simplified one due to Brauer and Tate.

Theorem 7.1 (Brauer-Tate)
Every character of G is an integral linear combination of characters of G induced from linear characters of elementary subgroups of G.

We shall first prove the weaker statement that the characters of G are integral linear combinations of characters induced from *arbitrary* irreducible characters of elementary subgroups of G and shall then prove the independent assertion that the set of linear characters of elementary subgroups induces the same module as does the set of all their irrreducible characters.

We break up the proof into a sequence of lemmas, but first we introduce some convenient terminology.

Let $\mathscr{E}$ be the set of all elementary subgroups of G and $\mathscr{E}_p$ the subset of p-elementary subgroups. Define $v(G)$ to be the submodule of ch (G) generated by the set of all characters of G induced from elements of $\mathscr{E}$.

Equivalently we have

(7.1) $$v(G) = \sum_{E \in \mathscr{E}} \text{ch}(E)^*$$

Our aim will be to show that $v(G) = \text{ch}(G)$.

Let Z be the ring of integers, let ω be a primitive complex $|G|$th root of unity, and denote by R the ring $Z[w]$. We know that the irreducible polynomial $f(X)$ for ω over Z is monic. This implies that R has a basis as a Z-module consisting of the elements $1, \omega, \omega^2, \ldots, \omega^{n-1}$, where $n = \deg f(Z)$. We shall need this property of R.

In the proof we shall make use of the extended modules $\text{ch}_R(G)$ and $v_R(G)$ consisting of all linear combinations with coefficients in R of the characters of $\text{ch}(G)$ and $v(G)$, respectively. Clearly

(7.2) $$v(G) \subseteq v_R(G) \qquad \text{and} \qquad \text{ch}(G) \subseteq \text{ch}_R(G).$$

If H is a subgroup of G and $\psi \in \text{ch}_R(H)$, then $\psi = \sum_{i=1}^{t} a_i \psi_i$ for suitable characters ψ_i of H and elements a_i of R, $1 \leqslant i \leqslant t$. We extend the induction map from $\text{ch}(H)$ to $\text{ch}_R(H)$ by setting $\psi^* = \sum_{i=1}^{t} a_i \psi_i^*$. This extended map carries $\text{ch}_R(H)$ into $v_R(G)$. Moreover, $*$ is given in terms of ψ by the usual formula.

Furthermore, if $x \in G$ and p is prime, it follows from Theorem 1.3.1(iii) that x can be written uniquely in the form $x = x_1 x_2$, where x_1 is a p-element, x_2 is a p'-element, and x_1, x_2 commute. We shall call x_1 the p-part of x and x_2 the p'-part of x. In particular, $\langle x_1 \rangle \times \langle x_2 \rangle$ is a p-elementary subgroup and so each element of G lies in an element of $\mathscr{E}_p$ for each prime p.

Finally two elements x, y of G will be said to be p-conjugate if their p'-parts are conjugate in the ordinary sense. Since the p'-part of an element x is a power of x, conjugate elements are also p-conjugate. However, the converse is not necessarily true. Moreover, it is easy to see that the relation of p-conjugacy is an equivalence relation. We can thus speak of the p-classes of G.

We now begin the proof. A key point is the following general property of induced characters.

Lemma 7.2

Let H be a subgroup of G, let $\phi \in \text{ch}(H)$, and let θ be a complex-valued class function of G such that $\theta|_H \in \text{ch}(H)$. Then

$$(\phi(\theta|_H))^* = \phi^* \theta.$$

Proof

Set $\zeta = \phi(\theta|_H)$ and define $\zeta(y) = \phi(y) = 0$ for y in $G - H$. Then for all x in G, we have

(7.3) $\zeta(x) = \phi(x)\theta(x).$

Hence by Theorem 4.3(i), we have for y in G:

(7.4) $\zeta^*(y) = \dfrac{1}{|H|} \sum_{u \in G} \zeta(uyu^{-1}) = \dfrac{1}{|H|} \sum_{u \in G} \phi(uyu^{-1})\theta(uyu^{-1}).$

But $\theta(uyu^{-1}) = \theta(y)$ as θ is a class function on G. Thus (7.4) reduces to

(7.5) $\zeta^*(y) = \theta(y) \dfrac{1}{|H|} \sum_{u \in G} \phi(uyu^{-1}) = \theta(y)\phi^*(y),$

which proves the lemma.

This result enables us to prove:

Lemma 7.3

$v(G)$ *is an ideal of* ch (G).

Proof

Let $\psi \in v(G)$ and $\chi \in$ ch (G). We must show that $\psi\chi \in v(G)$. Now ψ is an integral linear combination of characters ψ_i induced from elementary subgroups of G, $1 \leqslant i \leqslant r$. The desired result will follow from the distributive law if each $\psi_i\chi \in v(G)$. Hence it suffices to treat the case that $\psi = \phi^*$, where ϕ is a character of $E \in \mathscr{E}$. Similarly we may assume that χ is a character of G. But now by Lemma 7.2, we have

$$\psi\chi = \phi^*\chi = (\phi(\chi|_E))^*,$$

which proves the result.

In view of Lemma 7.3, the conclusion $v(G) = $ ch (G) will follow if we can show that $1_G \in v(G)$, for then $v(G)$ will be the unit ideal of ch (G).

The next result reduces our task to showing that $1_G \in v_R(G)$.

Lemma 7.4

If $m1_G \in v_R(G)$, $m \in Z$, *then* $m1_G \in v(G)$. *In particular, if* $1_G \in v_R(G)$, *then* $v(G) = $ ch (G).

Proof

We first argue that $1, \omega, \omega^2, \ldots, \omega^{n-1}$ are linearly independent over ch (G). Indeed let χ_i, $1 \leqslant i \leqslant r$, be the distinct irreducible characters of G

and suppose that for suitable integers c_{ij}, we have

(7.6)
$$\sum_{i=1}^{r} \sum_{j=0}^{n-1} c_{ij} \chi_i \, \omega^j = 0.$$

Setting $d_i = \sum_{j=0}^{n-1} c_{ij} \omega^j$, we have $d_i \in R$ and $\sum_{i=1}^{r} d_i \chi_i = 0$. But the χ_i are linearly independent over F and therefore each $d_i = 0$. Since the ω^j, $0 \leqslant j \leqslant n - 1$, are linearly independent over Z, we conclude that each $c_{ij} = 0$, which proves the assertion.

As an immediate consequence, we obtain that

$$v_R(G) = \sum_{j=0}^{n-1} v(G) \omega^j,$$

where the sum is direct. This in turn implies that

(7.7)
$$\text{ch}\,(G) \cap v_R(G) = v(G).$$

But now if $m1_G \in v_R(G)$, (7.7) implies that $m1_G \in v(G)$. The final assertion now follows from the statement preceding the lemma.

We next prove

Lemma 7.5

If χ is an element of $\text{ch}_R\,(G)$ which takes integral values on G, then the value of $\chi \pmod p$ is constant on each p-class of G.

Proof

If $y \in G$, write $y = uv$, where u is the p'-part and v is the p-part of y. Since χ is constant on each conjugate class of G and since p-conjugate elements have conjugate p'-parts, it will suffice to prove that

(7.8)
$$\chi(y) \equiv \chi(u) \pmod p.$$

If $Y = \langle y \rangle$, we have

(7.9)
$$\chi|_Y = \sum_{i=1}^{t} a_i \psi_i,$$

where the ψ_i are irreducible characters of Y and $a_i \in R$, $1 \leqslant i \leqslant t$. Now as Y is abelian, each ψ_i is a homomorphism of Y into the multiplicative group of complex numbers. Hence if $|v| = p^m$, we have $\psi_i(y)^{p^m} = \psi_i(uv)^{p^m} = \psi_i(u)^{p^m} \psi_i(v)^{p^m} = \psi_i = \psi_i(u)^{p^m}$. But then if we raise (7.9) to the p^mth power and use the binomial theorem we conclude that

(7.10)
$$\chi(y)^{p^m} \equiv \chi(u)^{p^m} \pmod{pR},$$

where pR denotes the principal ideal of R generated by p.

We now make use of the identity

$$Z \cap pR = pZ,$$

which follows at once from the fact that $1, \omega, \ldots, \omega^{n-1}$ is a basis of R over Z. Since $\chi(y)$ and $\chi(u)$ are integers, by hypothesis, the difference of the two sides of (7.10) lies in $Z \cap pR$ and we conclude that

$$(7.11) \qquad\qquad \chi(y)^{p^m} \equiv \chi(u)^{p^m} \,(\mathrm{mod}\ pZ).$$

But $\chi(y)^{p^m} \equiv \chi(y) \,(\mathrm{mod}\ p)$ and $\chi(u)^{p^m} \equiv \chi(u) \,(\mathrm{mod}\ p)$, so (7.8) follows at once from (7.11).

We now bring the elementary subgroups of G explicitly into the argument.

Lemma 7.6

Let $U = \langle u \rangle$, where u is a p'-element and let P be an S_p-subgroup of $C_G(U)$. Then there exists an element ψ in $\mathrm{ch}_R\,(U \times P)$ such that

(i) *$\psi^*(y) \in Z$ for all y in G.*

(ii) *$\psi^*(y) = 0$ if y is not in the p-class of u.*

(iii) *$\psi^*(u) = |C_G(u):P| \not\equiv 0 \,(\mathrm{mod}\ p)$.*

Proof

Since P centralizes U and U is a p'-group, we have, in fact, $UP = U \times P$. Let ψ_i, $1 \leqslant i \leqslant t$, be the irreducible characters of $U \times P$ having P in their kernel, so that each ψ_i is linear. Define

$$(7.12) \qquad\qquad \psi = \sum_{i=1}^{r} \overline{\psi_i(u)}\psi_i.$$

Since ψ_i is constant on the cosets of P, we conclude at once from the orthogonality relations in UP/P that

$$(7.13) \qquad \begin{aligned} \psi(uv) &= \psi(u) = |U| &&\text{for } v \in P, \text{ and} \\ \psi(x) &= 0 &&\text{for } x \in UP - uP. \end{aligned}$$

We shall argue that ψ^* has the required properties. First of all, each $\overline{\psi_i(u)}$ is a $|G|$th root of unity and so is a power of ω. Thus $\psi \in \mathrm{ch}_R\,(UP)$ and so $\psi^* \in v_R(G)$. Moreover, we have for y in G,

$$(7.14) \qquad\qquad \psi^*(y) = \frac{1}{|UP|} \sum_{z \in G} \psi(zyz^{-1}),$$

where $\psi(zyz^{-1}) = 0$ if $zyz^{-1} \notin UP$. Because of (7.13), this reduces to

$$(7.15) \qquad\qquad \psi^*(y) = \frac{1}{|P|} \sigma(y),$$

where $\sigma(y)$ denotes the number of elements z of G such that $zyz^{-1} \in uP$. Now if $zyz^{-1} \in uP$, so does $vzyz^{-1}v^{-1}$ for every v in P. Hence $\sigma(y)$ is divisible by $|P|$ and consequently $\psi^*(y)$ is an integer for all y in G.

Furthermore, it follows from (7.15) that $\psi^*(y) = 0$ unless $zyz^{-1} = uv$ for some v in P. But in the latter case, the p'-part of y is conjugate to u and so y lies in the same p-class as u. Finally if $zuz^{-1} = uv$, $v \in P$, then $v = 1$ since u and uv must have the same orders. Thus $\sigma(u) = |C_G(u)|$ and therefore $\psi^*(u) = |C_G(u) : P|$. Since P is an S_p-subgroup of $C_G(u)$, we conclude that $\psi^*(u)$ is prime to p, completing the proof.

With the aid of Lemma 7.6, we can now prove that certain class functions on G are, in fact, elements of $v_R(G)$.

Lemma 7.7

If θ is an integral-valued class function on G such that $\theta(y)$ is divisible by $|G|$ for all y in G, then $\theta \in v_R(G)$.

Proof

Choose p prime to $|G|$, in which case every element of G is a p'-element and p-conjugacy is the same as conjugacy. Let K_j, $1 \leqslant j \leqslant r$, be the distinct conjugacy classes of G. By the preceding lemma there exists for each j an integral-valued element χ_j of $v_R(G)$ which is 0 on K_i for $i \neq j$ and which has a value m_j dividing $|G|$ on K_j. But then if $\theta(y_j) = d_j|G|$ for y_j in K_j, it follows that

$$(7.16) \qquad \theta(y) = \sum_{j=1}^{r} \frac{d_j |G|}{m_j} \chi_j(y)$$

for all y in G. Since the coefficients are integers, we conclude that $\theta \in v_R(G)$.

Lemma 7.8

For any prime p, there exists an integral-valued element χ of $v_R(G)$ such that $\chi(y) \equiv 1 \pmod{p}$ for all y in G.

Proof

Applying Lemma 7.6 again, we can find for each p-class L_j of G an integral-valued element ζ_j of $v_R(G)$ which is θ on L_i for $i \neq j$ and which has a value prime to p on L_j, $1 \leqslant j \leqslant t$. But then for a suitable integer a_j, we have $a_j \zeta_j(y_j) \equiv 1 \pmod{p}$ for $y_j \in K_j$, $1 \leqslant j \leqslant t$. It follows at once that the function $\chi = \sum_{j=1}^{t} a_j \zeta_j$ is in $v_R(G)$ and has the required property.

Lemma 7.9

Let p be a prime and let $|G| = mp^a$, where $(m, p) = 1$. Then $m 1_G \in v(G)$.

Proof

By Lemma 7.4, it will suffice to prove that $m1_G \in v_R(G)$. Choose χ as in the preceding lemma and set $\zeta = \chi^{p^a}$. Since $v(G)$ is an ideal of ch (G) by Lemma 7.3, so also is $v_R(G)$ an ideal of ch$_R(G)$. Hence $\zeta \in v_R(G)$. Since $\chi(y) \equiv 1 \pmod{p}$, we have $\zeta(y) \equiv 1 \pmod{p^a}$ for all y in G. Now

$$(7.17) \qquad\qquad m1_G = m(1_G - \zeta) + m\zeta.$$

Since $1_G(y) = 1$ for all y in G, it follows that the values of $m(1_G - \zeta)$ are integers divisible by $mp^a = |G|$. But then $m(1_G - \zeta) \in v_R(G)$ by Lemma 7.7 and we conclude from (7.17) that $m1_G \in v_R(G)$.

Finally we obtain our objective:

Lemma 7.10

$v(G) = $ ch (G).

Proof

Write $|G| = p_1^{a_1} p_2^{a_2} \cdots p_k^{a_k}$, where the p_i are distinct primes and set $m_i = |G|/p_i^{a_i}$, $1 \leqslant i \leqslant k$. Then the m_i are relatively prime as a set and so $1 = \sum_{i=1}^{k} c_i m_i$ for suitable integers c_i. But by the preceding lemma $m_i 1_G \in v(G)$ for each i, $1 \leqslant i \leqslant k$. Therefore $1_G = \sum_{i=1}^{k} c_i m_i 1_G \in v(G)$. Since $v(G)$ is an ideal of ch (G), we conclude that $v(G) = $ ch (G).

To complete the proof of the Brauer-Tate theorem, we shall prove

Theorem 7.11 (Brauer)

If E is an elementary group and θ is an irreducible character of E, then θ is induced from a linear character of some subgroup of E.

Let us first prove Theorem 7.1 on the basis of this result. We know that $v(G)$ is spanned by the characters θ^*, where θ ranges over the irreducible characters of E and E ranges over the set $\mathscr{E}$ of elementary subgroups of G. By the theorem, each $\theta = \tilde{\phi}$, where ϕ is a linear character of a subgroup E_1 of E and $\tilde{\phi}$ denotes the character of E induced by ϕ. But then by the transitivity of induction, $\theta^* = \tilde{\phi}^* = \phi^*$. Since $E_1 \in \mathscr{E}$, we see that $v(G)$ is spanned by the set of ϕ^*, where ϕ is a linear character of an elementary subgroup of G, which establishes Theorem 7.1.

We turn now to the proof of Theorem 7.11. We write $E = A \times P$. By Theorems 3.2.4 and 2.11, the irreducible representations of A over F are of degree 1 and those of P are of degree p^i for some i. Moreover, by Theorem 3.7.1 any irreducible representation of E is the tensor product of irreducible representations of A and P, respectively. Hence deg $\theta = p^n$ for some n.

We argue by induction on n. If ϕ is a character of a subgroup H of E, we shall as usual denote by ϕ^* the character induced on E by ϕ. Now if $n = 0$, then ϕ itself is linear and we may take $H = E$ and $\phi = \theta$ to obtain $\theta = \phi^*$. Thus we may assume $n > 0$.

Let λ be a linear character of E. By Theorem 2.6 we have

(7.18) $(\lambda, \theta\bar\theta)_E = (\theta, \lambda\theta)_E$.

But θ is irreducible and $\deg \lambda\theta = (\deg \lambda)(\deg \theta) = \deg \theta$, whence either $\theta = \lambda\theta$ or θ does not appear in $\lambda\theta$. Hence by (7.18), we have that $(\lambda, \theta\bar\theta)_E = 0$ or 1 and it equals 1 if and only if $\theta = \lambda\theta$. Let Λ be the set of all linear characters λ of E such that $\theta = \lambda\theta$. Then our argument shows that

(7.19) $$\theta\bar\theta = \sum_{\lambda \in \Lambda} \lambda + \psi,$$

where ψ is a character of E, all of whose constituents are nonlinear. Hence by the first paragraph of the proof, the degree of each of these constituents is a positive power of p. Thus $\deg \psi$ is divisible by p. Furthermore, $\deg \theta\bar\theta = p^{2n}$ and $n > 0$. We conclude therefore from (7.19) that

(7.20) p divides $|\Lambda|$.

On the other hand, it is immediate from its definition that Λ is a group under multiplication. But now (7.20) and Sylow's theorem imply that Λ contains an element η of order p. Let K be the kernel of η. Now as η is linear, it maps E homomorphically onto the multiplicative group T of the pth roots of unity, which implies that E/K is isomorphic to T. We conclude at once that $|E : K| = p$ and that $A \subseteq K$. Thus $K = A \times Q$, where $Q \subset P$ and $|P : Q| = p$.

Now by its definition, $\eta|_K = 1_K$. Since $1_E \in \Lambda$, it follows from (7.19) that 1_K occurs in $\theta\bar\theta|_K$ with multiplicity at least 2. Since $\theta\bar\theta|_K = (\theta|_K)(\bar\theta|_K)$, Theorem 2.6 now yields that $(\theta|_K, \bar\theta|_K)_K \geq 2$, whence $\theta|_K$ is a reducible character. Hence if ϕ is an irreducible constituent of $\theta|_K$, we conclude that $\deg \phi < \deg \theta$.

On the other hand, the Frobenius reciprocity theorem gives

(7.21) $(\theta|_K, \phi)_K = (\theta, \phi^*)_E$.

Thus θ is a constituent of ϕ^*, and so $\deg \theta \leq \deg \phi^*$. But $\deg \phi^* = |E : K| \deg \phi = p \deg \phi$. Moreover, as $K = A \times Q$ is p-elementary, it follows from the first paragraph of the proof that also $\deg \phi$ is a power of p. The only possibility for our inequalities is that $\deg \phi = p^{n-1}$ and $\deg \phi^* = p^n = \deg \theta$. Since θ is a constituent of ϕ^*, this yields $\theta = \phi^*$.

Finally, by induction there exists a subgroup L of K and a linear character ζ of L such that $\phi = \tilde{\zeta}$, where $\tilde{\zeta}$ is the character of K induced by ζ. But then $\theta = \phi^* = \tilde{\zeta}^* = \zeta^*$ by the transitivity of induction and Theorem 7.11 is proved.

On the basis of Theorem 7.1, we can now easily derive Brauer's characterization of characters. We note that the proof requires only Lemma 7.10, but does not use Theorem 7.11.

Theorem 7.12 (Brauer)

A complex-valued class function θ on G is a generalized character of G if and only if $\theta|_E$ is a generalized character of E for every elementary subgroup E of G.

Proof

Obviously if $\theta \in \mathrm{ch}\,(G)$, then $\theta|_E \in \mathrm{ch}\,(E)$ for all E in $\mathscr{E}$. Conversely, define $u(G)$ to be the set of all class functions θ of G such that $\theta|_E \in \mathrm{ch}\,(E)$ for each E in $\mathscr{E}$. Since each $\mathrm{ch}\,(E)$ is a ring, so also is $u(G)$. To prove the theorem, we must show that $\mathrm{ch}\,(G) = u(G)$. In any case, we have

$$\mathrm{ch}\,(G) \subseteq u(G).$$

Now 1_G is the unit element of $u(G)$. Since $1_G \in v(G) = \mathrm{ch}\,(G)$ by Lemma 7.10, it will suffice to prove that $v(G)$ is an ideal of $u(G)$, for this will imply the desired conclusion $v(G) = \mathrm{ch}\,(G) = u(G)$.

As in the proof of Lemma 7.3, we need only show that $\psi\theta \in v(G)$, where $\psi = \phi^*$, ϕ a character of $E \in \mathscr{E}$, and $\theta \in u(G)$. Since $\theta|_E \in \mathrm{ch}\,(E)$, we have $\psi\theta = (\phi(\theta|_E))^*$ by Lemma 7.2 and the proof is complete.

We conclude this section with an application of Brauer's characterization theorem which we shall need in Chapter 15.

Theorem 7.13 (Brauer)

Let p^n be the highest power of the prime p dividing the order of the group G. If χ is an irreducible character of G whose degree is a multiple of p^n, then

$$\chi(y) = 0$$

for any element y of G whose order is a multiple of p.

Proof

Define the complex-valued class function θ on G by setting

$$(7.22) \qquad \theta(y) = \begin{cases} \chi(y) & \text{if } |y| \text{ is prime to } p \\ 0 & \text{if } y \text{ is divisible by } p. \end{cases}$$

To prove the theorem, we must show that $\theta = \chi$. It will suffice to show that

θ is a generalized character of G. Indeed, assume this to be the case. By (7.22) and the definition of the inner product, we have $(\theta, \theta)_G \leqslant (\chi, \chi)_G$, with equality holding if and only if $\chi = \theta$. But $(\theta, \theta)_G > 0$ as $\theta(1) = \chi(1) \neq 0$, while $(\chi, \chi)_G = 1$ as χ is irreducible. However, $(\theta, \theta)_G$ is an integer since θ is assumed to be a generalized character. Hence $(\theta, \theta)_G = (\chi, \chi)_G$ and $\theta = \chi$. Thus $\chi(y) = \theta(y) = 0$ if y is divisible by p.

By Theorem 7.12 we need only show that $\theta|_E$ is a generalized character of E for every elementary subgroup E of G. If $|E|$ is prime to p, then by (7.22), $\theta|_E = \chi|_E$ and the result is clear. So we may assume $|E|$ is divisible by p. Now $E = A \times B$, where B has prime power order and A is cyclic of order prime to $|B|$. If $|A|$ is divisible by p, we can write $A = P \times A_1$, where P is an S_p-subgroup of A and A_1 is a p'-subgroup of A, by Theorem 1.2.13. Hence $E = P \times Q$, where $Q = A_1 \times B$ is a p'-group. On the other hand, we reach the same conclusion if B is a p-group by setting $P = B$ and $Q = A$.

Now as we have observed in Section 2, a complex-valued class function ϕ on E is a generalized character if and only if $(\phi, \zeta)_E$ is an integer for each irreducible character ζ of E. We proceed to verify this for the function $\phi = \theta|_E$.

By (7.22), $\theta(y) = 0$ for y in $E - Q$ and $\theta(y) = \chi(y)$ for y in Q. Hence

$$(7.23) \quad (\theta|_E, \zeta)_E = \frac{1}{|E|} \sum_{y \in Q} \chi(y)\overline{\zeta(y)} = \frac{|Q|}{|E|} (\chi|_Q, \zeta|_Q)_Q = \frac{1}{|P|} (\chi|_Q, \zeta|_Q)_Q.$$

It will suffice to show that $(1/|P|)\chi(y)$ is an algebraic integer for all y in Q, for then

$$\frac{1}{|P|} (\chi|_Q, \zeta|_Q)_Q = \sum_{y \in Q} \frac{\chi(y)}{|P|} \overline{\zeta(y)}$$

will also be an algebraic integer. But the left side is a rational number, as $\chi|_Q$ and $\zeta|_Q$ are characters of Q. Hence the left side will be a rational integer and (7.23) will give the desired conclusion that $(\theta|_E, \zeta)_E$ is a rational integer.

Finally by Theorem 2.10 we know that

$$\frac{\chi(y) |G : C_G(y)|}{\deg \chi}$$

is an algebraic integer for all y in Q. Since p^n divides $\deg \chi$ by hypothesis, it follows that $(1/p^n)\chi(y) |G : C_G(y)|$ is an algebraic integer. On the other hand, $P \subseteq C_G(y)$ as $y \in Q$, so $|G : C_G(y)|_p \leqslant p^n/|P|$. Since $\chi(y)$ is an algebraic integer, we conclude at once that $(1/|P|)\chi(y)$ is an algebraic integer and the theorem is proved.

EXERCISES

Throughout these exercises F will denote the field of complex numbers.

1. Show that the quaternion group and the dihedral group of order 8 have isomorphic character tables.
2. Determine the character table of A_5.
3. Let $G = G_1 \times G_2$, where G_i has r_i conjugate classes, $1 \leqslant i \leqslant 2$. Prove
    (i) The number of conjugate classes in G is $r_1 r_2$.
    (ii) Let ϕ_i, ψ_i be irreducible representations of G_i with respective characters $\chi_i, \theta_i, 1 \leqslant i \leqslant 2$, and let χ, θ be the characters of the corresponding product representations $\phi_1 \otimes \phi_2$ and $\psi_1 \otimes \psi_2$. Then

    $$(\chi, \theta)_G = (\chi_1, \theta_1)_{G_1}(\chi_2, \theta_2)_{G_2}.$$

    (iii) Use (i) and (ii) to show that every irreducible representation of G over F is equivalent to a product representation.
4. The product of a nonsingular diagonal matrix and a permutation matrix is called a *monomial* matrix. A matrix representation ϕ of G is called *monomial* if $(x)\phi$ is a monomial matrix for all x in G. Prove
    (i) Let ϕ be a monomial representation of G over F. If $(x)\phi = D_x P_x$, where D_x is diagonal and P_x is a permutation matrix, then the mapping $(x)\pi = P_x$ is a permutation representation of G. (One says that ϕ is *transitive* if π is transitive.)
    (ii) Every transitive monomial representation of G over F is equivalent to one induced from a linear representation of some subgroup of G.
5. If G is supersolvable, show that every representation of G over F is monomial.
6. If every representation of G over F is monomial, show that G is solvable.
7. Let $G = SL(2, 3)$. Prove
    (i) G is solvable, but not supersolvable.
    (ii) G possesses a faithful two-dimensional representation over F which is not equivalent to a monomial representation.
8. A group G is *metabelian* if it possesses a normal abelian subgroup K with G/K abelian. Prove that every representation over F of a metabelian group is monomial.
9. Let G be a cyclic group and define the map θ on G by the rule: $\theta(y) = |G|$ if y generates G and $\theta(y) = 0$ if y does not generate G. Show by induction

on $|G|$ that θ is an integral linear combination of characters of permutation representations of G.

10. If G has an irreducible character χ of degree p, p a prime, and G is simple, prove that an S_p-subgroup of G has order p.

11. Let $H \lhd G$ and let χ be an irreducible character of G not having H in its kernel. Prove that $\chi(y) = 0$ for any y in G such that $C_H(y) = 1$.

12. If χ is a nonlinear irreducible character of G, prove that $\chi(y) = 0$ for some y in G.

13. Let χ be a faithful character of G which assumes exactly r distinct values on G. Show that every irreducible character of G occurs as a constituent of one of the characters $1_G = \chi^0, \chi = \chi^1, \chi^2, \ldots, \chi^{r-1}$.

14. Prove that p-conjugacy is an equivalence relation.

15. Let θ be a class function on G. Show that θ is an irreducible character of G if and only if the following three conditions hold:

    (a) $\theta|_E \in \text{ch}(E)$ for every elementary subgroup E of G.
    (b) $(\theta, \theta)_G = 1$.
    (c) $\theta(1) > 0$.

16. Let $A = A(G, F) = F_{n_1} \oplus F_{n_2} \oplus \cdots \oplus F_{n_r}$ be the decomposition of the group algebra A of the group G as the direct sum of simple ideals and let χ_i be the character of the irreducible representation of G determined by a minimal right ideal of F_{n_i}, $1 \leqslant i \leqslant r$. Also let e_i be the primitive idempotent of $Z(A)$ with the property $Ae_i = F_{n_i}$, $1 \leqslant i \leqslant r$ (compare Exercise 3.12). Derive the following expression for e_i:

$$e_i = \frac{\chi_i(1)}{|G|} \sum_{y \in G} \overline{\chi_i(y)} y \qquad 1 \leqslant i \leqslant r.$$

CHAPTER 5

GROUPS OF PRIME POWER ORDER

This chapter treats a variety of topics concerning groups of prime power order, primarily related to their automorphisms and to the structure of certain very special classes of p-groups. We develop the basic properties of the Frattini subgroup, which is of central importance for the study of automorphisms of p-groups and in the final section we introduce the associated Lie ring of a p-group, which is also a useful tool for certain questions concerning automorphisms. In particular, we obtain results about regular groups of automorphisms and also determine conditions under which a nontrivial automorphism of a p-group remains nontrivial when restricted to various characteristic subgroups.

As for the second topic, we determine all p-groups which possess no noncyclic characteristic abelian, normal abelian, or abelian subgroups. In the process of this investigation we give various characterizations of all 2-groups of maximal class. Both topics are closely related to the study of special and extra-special p-groups, and in Section 5 we determine the structure of all extra-special p-groups and, in addition, obtain information about their representations.

1. THE FRATTINI SUBGROUP

Another important characteristic subgroup of a group G is the so-called *Frattini* subgroup, which by definition is the intersection of all the maximal subgroups of G. We denote it by $\Phi(G)$; we also speak of $G/\Phi(G)$ as the *Frattini factor* group of G. We develop some of its properties in the present section.

Theorem 1.1

    (i) $G = \langle x_i \,|\, x_i \in G, \, 1 \leqslant i \leqslant n \rangle$ *if and only if*

$$G = \langle \Phi(G), x_i \,|\, x_i \in G, \, 1 \leqslant i \leqslant n \rangle.$$

    In particular, if $G = \Phi(G) H$ for some subgroup H of G, then $G = H$.

    (ii) *If $H \lhd G$, then H possesses a partial complement in G if and only if $H \not\subseteq \Phi(G)$.*

Proof

Suppose $G = \langle \Phi(G), x_i \,|\, x_i \in G, \, 1 \leqslant i \leqslant n \rangle$, but $G_0 = \langle x_i \,|\, 1 \leqslant i \leqslant n \rangle \subset G$. Then $G_0 \subset M$ for some maximal subgroup M of G. However, $\Phi(G) \subseteq M$ by definition of the Frattini subgroup, so $G = \langle \Phi(G), G_0 \rangle \subseteq M$, a contradiction. Thus $G = G_0$. The converse implication is obvious. As for the final assertion of (i), if $G = \Phi(G) H$, we have $G = \langle \Phi(G), h_i \,|\, 1 \leqslant i \leqslant m \rangle$, where the h_i are the distinct elements of H. But then $G = \langle h_i \,|\, 1 \leqslant i \leqslant m \rangle = H$.

Assume next that $H \lhd G$ with $H \not\subseteq \Phi(G)$. Then there exists a maximal subgroup M of G with $H \not\subseteq M$. But HM is a group as $H \lhd G$ and $HM \supset M$ as $H \not\subseteq M$. Maximality of M forces $G = HM$ and M is a partial complement of H. Conversely suppose $H \subseteq \Phi(G)$ and H has a partial complement K. Then $G = HK \subseteq \Phi(G) K$, whence $G = K$ by (i), contrary to the definition of a partial complement. Thus (ii) also holds.

As a corollary, we have

Corollary 1.2

    If $G/\Phi(G)$ is cyclic, then G is cyclic.

Proof

Choose x in G so that $\Phi(G) x$ generates $G/\Phi(G)$. Then obviously $G = \langle \Phi(G), x \rangle$, so $G = \langle x \rangle$ by the theorem.

In Chapter 6 we shall derive other general properties of the Frattini subgroup, but here we shall limit ourselves to establishing two important properties of it in connection with p-groups.

Theorem 1.3

*The Frattini factor group $P/\Phi(P)$ of a p-group P is elementary abelian.
Furthermore, $\Phi(P) = 1$ if and only if P is elementary abelian.*

Proof

If M is maximal in P, then $M \lhd P$ and $|P : M| = p$. Hence $P' = [P, P] \subseteq M$
as P/M is abelian and $x^p \in M$ for all x in P as $|P/M| = p$. Since these
hold for each maximal subgroup M of P, it follows that $P' \subseteq \Phi(P)$ and
$x^p \in \Phi(P)$ for each x in P. Hence $P/\Phi(P)$ is abelian and the image of each
x in $P - \Phi(P)$ has order p, which implies that P is elementary abelian.

In particular, if $\Phi(P) = 1$, then P is elementary abelian. Conversely, if
P is elementary abelian, then any x_1 in $P^\#$ can be included in a basis
$x_i, 1 \leqslant i \leqslant n$, of P. But then $\langle x_i | 2 \leqslant i \leqslant n \rangle$ is a maximal subgroup of P,
not containing x_1. Since x_1 was arbitrary in $P^\#$, we conclude at once
that $\Phi(P) = 1$.

As with elements of groups, we say that an automorphism ψ of a group
G is a *π-automorphism* if its order is divisible only by primes in the set π
and is a *π'-automorphism* if its order is divisible by no prime in π.

Theorem 1.4 *(Burnside)*

*Let ψ be a p'-automorphism of the p-group P which induces the identity on
$P/\Phi(P)$. Then ψ is the identity automorphism of P.*

Proof

Set $H = \Phi(P)$, $\bar{P} = P/H$, $|\bar{P}| = p^r$, and $|H| = p^m$, so that $|P| = p^{m+r}$.
For any subset $Y = \{y_i | 1 \leqslant i \leqslant n\}$ of P, we know that $P = \langle H, Y \rangle$ if and
only if $P = \langle Y \rangle$. Hence Y generates P if and only if the image of Y in $\bar{P}$
generates $\bar{P}$. But $\bar{P}$, being elementary abelian of order p^r, can be generated
by r, but no fewer than r, elements and we conclude that the same is
true of P.

Let then x_i, $1 \leqslant i \leqslant r$, be a minimal generating system of P. Then for
each h_i in H the elements $x_i' = h_i x_i$, $1 \leqslant i \leqslant r$, also form a minimal generating system of P. Conversely any minimal generating system of P whose
images are the elements $\bar{x}_i$ clearly has this form. Hence there are exactly
p^{mr} minimal generating systems of P whose images in $\bar{P}$ are the ordered set
$\{x_i, 1 \leqslant i \leqslant r\}$. We denote by $\mathcal{M}$ the set of all such minimal generating
systems of P.

Now let ψ be a p'-automorphism of P which induces the identity on $\bar{P}$
and let $\{x_i' | 1 \leqslant i \leqslant r\} \in \mathcal{M}$. Then ψ fixes each coset $Hx_i' = Hx_i$ and con-
sequently $x_i'\psi = h_i' x_i$ for suitable h_i' in H. Thus $\{x_i'\psi | 1 \leqslant i \leqslant r\}$ is also an
element of $\mathcal{M}$. In other words, ψ induces a permutation of the elements of

$\mathcal{M}$. Clearly the number of elements in a cycle of this permutation is a divisor of $t = |\psi|$. Suppose some cycle had degree $s < t$. Then $\psi_1 = \psi^s$ fixes each element of this cycle and so fixes the elements of some minimal generating system $\{x_i' | 1 \leqslant i \leqslant r\}$ of P. But every element of P can be expressed as a product of the x_i' as they generate P. Since ψ_1 is an automorphism of P fixing each x_i', it follows that ψ_1 fixes every element of P, whence $\psi_1 = \psi^s$ is the identity on P, contrary to the fact that $|\psi| = t > s$.

Thus the permutation of $\mathcal{M}$ determined by ψ decomposes as a product of disjoint cycles each of length t. Hence t must divide $|\mathcal{M}| = p^{mr}$. Since $(t, p) = 1$, this forces $t = 1$, whence ψ is the identity on P.

The preceding theorem is one of a great number of results that we shall establish in succeeding sections about p'-automorphisms of p-groups.

2. p'-AUTOMORPHISMS OF ABELIAN p-GROUPS

In Theorem 3.3.2 we have shown that if A is a p'-group of automorphisms of the abelian p-group P and if R is an A-invariant direct factor of P; then $P = R \times S$, where S is also A-invariant. We can repeat this process on R and S if either possesses an A-invariant direct factor. Hence by continuing the process sufficiently, we can express P as

$$P = P_1 \times P_2 \times \cdots \times P_r,$$

where each P_i is A-invariant and no P_i can be decomposed further as the direct product of nontrivial A-invariant subgroups, $1 \leqslant i \leqslant r$. We say that A acts *indecomposably* on P_i or that the A-module P_i is indecomposable. The well-known Krull-Schmidt theorem (which we do not require) asserts the essential uniqueness up to isomorphism of the indecomposable factors of P in any such factorization.

We wish, however, to determine the possible structure of an indecomposable factor. We first prove the following lemma:

Lemma 2.1

Let A be a p'-group of automorphisms of the abelian p-group P and assume that P is not homocyclic. Let P have exponent p^n and set $X = \mho^{n-1}(P)$. Then

(i) P possesses a nontrivial A-invariant subgroup T such that $T \cap X = 1$.
(ii) If T is any A-invariant subgroup of P such that $T \cap X = 1$, then P/T has exponent p^n and $\mho^{n-1}(P/T)$ is the image of X in P/T.

Proof

Let $\{x_i | 1 \leqslant i \leqslant m\}$ be a basis of P with $|x_i| = p^{n_i}$ and $n_i \geqslant n_{i+1}$, $1 \leqslant i \leqslant m$. Then $n_1 = n$ by definition of the exponent and $n_m < n$ as P is not homocyclic. Let r be the largest integer such that $n_r = n$. Also set $y_i = x_i^{p^{n_i-1}}$, $1 \leqslant i \leqslant m$. It is immediate that $\{y_i | 1 \leqslant i \leqslant r\}$ is a basis of $X = \mho^{n-1}(P)$, while $\{y_i | 1 \leqslant i \leqslant m\}$ is a basis of $\Omega_1(P)$. In particular, $X \subset \Omega_1(P)$. Since X and $\Omega_1(P)$ are characteristic in P, they are A-invariant. But X is a direct factor of $\Omega_1(P)$ as $\Omega_1(P)$ is elementary abelian and now Theorem 3.3.2 yields that $\Omega_1(P) = X \times T$, where T is A-invariant. Then $T \neq 1$ and $X \cap T = 1$, proving (i).

Next let T be any A-invariant subgroup of P satisfying (i), set $\bar{P} = P/T$, and let $\bar{X}$, $\bar{x}_i$, $\bar{y}_i$ be the respective images of X, x_i, and y_i in $\bar{P}$. Now the $\bar{x}_i$ generate $\bar{P}$ and, as $|\bar{x}_i| < p^n$ for $i > r$, it follows that $\mho^{n-1}(\bar{P})$ is generated by $\bar{y}_i$, $1 \leqslant i \leqslant r$, whence $\bar{X} = \mho^{n-1}(\bar{P})$. On the other hand, as $X \cap T = 1$, $|\bar{X}| = |X| = p^r$ and so $\{\bar{y}_i | 1 \leqslant i \leqslant r\}$ is, in fact, a basis of $\bar{X}$. In particular, this implies that $|\bar{x}_1| = p^n$ and hence that $\bar{P}$ is of exponent p^n. Thus (ii) also holds.

We can now prove

Theorem 2.2

Let A be a p'-group of automorphisms acting indecomposably on the abelian p-group P. Then P is homocyclic.

Proof

Assume false and let the notation be as in the lemma. Choose T now to be a maximal A-invariant subgroup of P disjoint from X. Then $T \neq 1$ by the lemma. Set $\bar{P} = P/T$ and let $\bar{X}$ be the image of X in $\bar{P}$. Then $\bar{X} = \mho^{n-1}(\bar{P})$ and $\bar{P}$ has exponent p^n. If $\bar{P}$ is not homocyclic, then a further application of the lemma yields that $\bar{P}$ possesses a nontrivial A-invariant subgroup $\bar{T}_1$ with $\bar{X} \cap \bar{T}_1 = \bar{1}$. But then the inverse image T_1 of $\bar{T}_1$ in P is A-invariant, $T \subset T_1$, and $X \cap T_1 \subseteq X \cap T = 1$, contrary to our maximal choice of T. Thus $\bar{P}$ is homocyclic of type $(p^n, p^n, \ldots, p^n)$ and order p^{ns} for some $s \leqslant m$.

Since the elements $\bar{x}_i$, $1 \leqslant i \leqslant m$, generate $\bar{P}$ and $|\bar{x}_i| < p^n$ for $i > r$, we necessarily have $s \leqslant r$. On the other hand, as $|\bar{X}| = |X| = p^r$, the number of basis elements of $\bar{P}$ is at least r. Thus $r = s$.

Now set $Q = \langle x_i | 1 \leqslant i \leqslant r \rangle$, so that $|Q| = p^{rn} = |\bar{P}|$. Hence either Q maps onto $\bar{P}$ or else $Q \cap T \neq 1$. However, $X = \mho^{n-1}(Q)$ and hence the assumption $Q \cap T \neq 1$ would force $X \cap T \neq 1$, which is not the case. Thus Q maps on $\bar{P}$ and $Q \cap T = 1$, which together imply that $P = T \times Q$. But now T is an A-invariant direct factor of P and so $P = T \times R$, where $R \neq 1$ is A-invariant by Theorem 3.3.2, contrary to the fact that A acts indecomposably on P.

We next prove

Theorem 2.3

Let A be a p'-group of automorphisms of the abelian group P. Then we have

$$P = C_P(A) \times [P, A].$$

Proof

If $|A| = n$, we consider the endomorphism $\theta = 1/n \sum_{\phi \in A} \phi$ of P, which we assume to be written additively. Since $\phi\psi$ and $\psi\phi$ run over A as ϕ does, for ψ in A, it follows at once that

(2.1) $$\theta\psi = \psi\theta = \theta$$

for all ψ in A. This in turn yields

(2.2) $$\theta^2 = \theta\left(1/n \sum_{\phi \in A} \phi\right) = 1/n \sum_{\phi \in A} \theta\phi = 1/n(n\theta) = \theta;$$

so also θ is idempotent.

Now set $C = C_P(A)$ and $C_1 = (P)\theta$. If $x \in P$, we have $(x\theta)\phi = x\theta$ for all ϕ in A by (2.1), so $C_1 \subseteq C$. Conversely, if $x \in C$, then

(2.3) $$x\theta = 1/n \sum_{\phi \in A} x\phi = 1/n \sum_{\phi \in A} x = 1/n(nx) = x,$$

so $x \in C_1$. We conclude that $C_1 = C$.

Next set $H = [P, A]$ and $H_1 = \{x - x\theta \mid x \in P\}$. As θ is an endomorphism and P is abelian, H_1 is a subgroup of P. Moreover, $x = x\theta + (x - x\theta)$ for x in P, so $P = C + H_1$. On the other hand, if $x \in C \cap H_1$, we have $x = x\theta$ by the preceding paragraph and $x = y - y\theta$ for some y in P, whence $x = x\theta = (y - y\theta)\theta = 0$, as θ is idempotent. It follows that $P = C \oplus H_1$. In addition, our calculation shows that H_1 is the kernel of θ.

Finally, by definition, H is generated by the elements $-x + x\phi$, $x \in P$, $\phi \in A$ [$x^{-1}(x\phi)$ in multiplicative notation]. But $(-x + x\phi)\theta = -x\theta + x\phi\theta = -x\theta + x\theta = 0$, which implies that $H \subseteq H_1$. Conversely, for x in P, we have $x - x\theta = 1/n \ [\sum_{\phi \in A} (x - x\phi)] \in H$ as each $x - x\phi \in H$. Thus $H_1 \subseteq H$, whence $H_1 = H$ and the desired conclusion $P = C \oplus H$ is established.

Theorem 2.4

If A is a p'-group of automorphisms of the abelian p-group P which acts trivially on $\Omega_1(P)$, then $A = 1$.

Proof

By the preceding theorem, $P = C \times H$, where $C = C_P(A)$ and $H = [P, A]$. By hypothesis $\Omega_1(P) \subseteq C_P(A) = C$, so $\Omega_1(P) \subseteq \Omega_1(C)$. On the other hand, obviously $\Omega_1(P) = \Omega_1(C) \times \Omega_1(H)$, whence $\Omega_1(H) = 1$. We conclude that $H = 1$ and $P = C$. Thus A acts trivially on P and, as A is a group of automorphisms of P, we have $A = 1$, as asserted.

3. p'-AUTOMORPHISMS OF p-GROUPS

We shall be primarily interested in relating the actions of p'-automorphisms of a p-group P to their induced actions on certain subgroups and factor groups of P. In particular, we shall determine conditions under which these induced automorphisms remain nontrivial.

We begin with a definition which generalizes the situation considered in Theorem 3.3.4. Let A be a subgroup of Aut G and let

$$G = G_0 \supseteq G_1 \supseteq \cdots \supseteq G_n = 1$$

be a normal series of G. We say that A *stabilizes* the given series if each G_i is A-invariant and A acts trivially on each factor G_{i-1}/G_i, $1 \leqslant i \leqslant n$.

As an almost immediate consequence of the definition, we have

Lemma 3.1

A subgroup A of Aut G stabilizes the normal series

$$G = G_0 \subseteq G_1 \subseteq \cdots \subseteq G_n = 1$$

of G if and only if A normalizes each G_i and $[G_i, A] \subseteq G_{i+1}$, $0 \leqslant i \leqslant n - 1$.

Proof

Set $\bar{G}_i = G_i/G_{i+1}$ and let $\bar{x}$ be the image in $\bar{G}_i$ of the element x of G_i. Then A stabilizes the given series if A normalizes each G_i and $\bar{x}\phi = \bar{x}$ for all $\bar{x}$ in $\bar{G}_i$, ϕ in A, $0 \leqslant i \leqslant n - 1$. This last equality is equivalent to the assertion $\bar{x}^{-1}(\bar{x}\phi) = \bar{1}$ or $[x, \phi] \in G_{i+1}$, from which the lemma follows at once.

We now prove

Theorem 3.2

Let A be a p'-group of automorphisms of the p-group P which stabilizes some normal series of P. Then $A = 1$.

Proof

Let $P = P_0 \supseteq P_1 \supseteq \cdots \supseteq P_n = 1$ be a normal series of P stabilized by A. We argue by induction on n. Now A induces a group of automorphisms of P_1 and stabilizes the normal series P_i, $1 \leqslant i \leqslant n$, of P_1, and so A acts trivially on P_1 by induction. Furthermore, A acts trivially on P/P_1 by assumption. Hence $[x, \phi] \in P_1$ for x in P, ϕ in A, by the lemma, whence $x\phi = xz$, $z \in P_1$. Since ϕ acts trivially on P_1, this yields $x\phi^2 = (xz)\phi = (x\phi)(z\phi) = (xz)z = xz^2$, and we conclude readily by induction that $x\phi^i = xz^i$ for all i. In particular, this holds for $i = m$, where $m = |\phi|$, and yields $x = x\phi^m = xz^m$, whence $z^m = 1$. But $(m, p) = 1$, as A is a p'-group. Since z is a p-element, it follows that $z = 1$. Thus $x\phi = x$ for all x in P and all ϕ in A, giving the desired conclusion $A = 1$.

This last result is often phrased in the following form, which we state as a corollary:

Corollary 3.3

If a subgroup A of Aut P, P a p-group, stabilizes a normal series of P, then A is a p-group.

Proof

By the theorem, A possesses no nontrivial p'-automorphisms and so is a p-group.

With the aid of the preceding theorem and with our first application of the three-subgroup lemma, we now prove the following result of Thompson:

Theorem 3.4

Let $A \times B$ be a group of automorphisms of the p-group P with A a p'-group and B a p-group. If A acts trivially on $C_P(B)$, then $A = 1$.

Proof

Now $C_P(B)$ is invariant under A as well as B, since A centralizes B. Assume A acts trivially on $C_P(B)$ and let Q be an $(A \times B)$-invariant subgroup of P containing $C_P(B)$ of maximal order such that A acts trivially on Q. If $Q = P$, then $A = 1$; so we may assume that $Q \subset P$. Then $R = N_P(Q) \supset Q$ by Theorem 1.2.11(ii), and R is $(A \times B)$-invariant by Theorem 2.1.1(i).

Let S be a minimal $(A \times B)$-invariant subgroup of R which contains Q properly and set $\bar{S} = S/Q$. Since $\Phi(\bar{S})$ char $\bar{S}$, our minimal choice of S implies that $\Phi(\bar{S}) = \bar{1}$ and so $\bar{S}$ is elementary abelian. It follows therefore from Lemma 2.6.3 that $C_{\bar{S}}(B) \neq \bar{1}$. But $C_{\bar{S}}(B)$ is $(A \times B)$-invariant and consequently $\bar{S} = C_{\bar{S}}(B)$, again by our minimal choice of S. Thus $[S, B] \subseteq Q$.

But $[Q, A] = 1$, as A acts trivially on Q, and hence

$$[S, B, A] = 1.$$

On the other hand, $[B, A] = 1$ as B centralizes A, and so

$$[B, A, S] = 1.$$

But now the three-subgroup lemma yields

$$[A, S, B] = 1.$$

Thus $[A, S] \subseteq C_S(B) \subseteq C_P(B) \subseteq Q$. But now Lemma 3.1 implies that A stabilizes the normal series $S \supset Q \geq 1$ of S. Since A is a p'-group, it follows therefore from Theorem 3.2 that A acts trivially on S, contrary to our maximal choice of Q.

We shall next extend some of the results of the preceding section to arbitrary p-groups.

Theorem 3.5

If A is a p'-group of automorphisms of the p-group P, then $P = CH$, where $C = C_P(A)$ and $H = [P, A]$. In particular, if $H \subseteq \Phi(P)$, then $A = 1$.

Proof

Consider first the case $H \subseteq Z(P)$; and for ϕ in A, define the mapping α_ϕ of P into P by setting $x\alpha_\phi = x^{-1}(x\phi)$ for x in P. For x, y in P, we have $(xy)\alpha_\phi = (xy)^{-1}(xy)\phi = y^{-1}x^{-1}(x\phi)y\phi = x^{-1}(x\phi)y^{-1}(y\phi)$, as $x^{-1}(x\phi) \in H$ $\subseteq Z(P)$. Thus $(xy)\alpha_\phi = (x\alpha_\phi)(y\alpha_\phi)$ and so α_ϕ is an endomorphism of P for each ϕ in A. Clearly the kernel of α_ϕ is precisely $C_P(\phi)$, while its image is contained in H. Since $H \subseteq Z(P)$, α_ϕ thus maps P into an abelian group and so $P' = [P, P]$ is contained in the kernel of α_ϕ. Hence $P' \subseteq C_P(\phi)$ for all ϕ in A and we conclude that $P' \subseteq C$.

Now set $\bar{P} = P/P'$, $\bar{C} = C_P(A)$, and $\bar{H} = [\bar{P}, A]$. Since $\bar{P}$ is abelian, $\bar{P} = \bar{C} \times \bar{H}$ by Theorem 2.3. It is also clear that $\bar{H}$ is the image of H in $\bar{P}$. Hence $P = C_1 H$, where C_1 denotes the inverse image of $\bar{C}$ in P. But A acts trivially on both P' and $\bar{C}$, whence A stabilizes the normal series $C_1 \supseteq P' \supseteq 1$ and now Theorem 3.2 yields that A acts trivially on C_1. Thus $C_1 \subseteq C$ and $P = CH$.

Assume next that $H \nsubseteq Z(P)$, whence certainly $H \neq 1$. Now $H \triangleleft P$ by Theorem 2.2.1(iii) and the discussion of Chapter 2, Section 6, and consequently $K = H \cap Z(P) \neq 1$ by Theorem 2.6.4. In addition, K is A-invariant. We now define $D = \langle x \in P | [x, A] \subseteq K \rangle$. Clearly $C \subseteq D$. Set $\bar{P} = P/K$ and again put $\bar{C} = C_P(A)$, $\bar{H} = [\bar{P}, A]$. If $x \in P$ and $[x, A] \subseteq K$, then

A centralizes the image of x in $\bar{P}$. It follows therefore from the definition of D that D maps into $\bar{C}$. Conversely, if $\bar{x} \in \bar{C}$, $[\bar{x}, A] = \bar{1}$ and $[x, A] \subseteq K$ for any representative x of $\bar{x}$ in P. Thus $x \in D$ and we conclude that $\bar{C}$ is the image of D in $\bar{P}$. Furthermore, we also have that $\bar{H}$ is the image of H in $\bar{P}$.

Since $K \neq 1$, $|\bar{P}| < |P|$ and hence by induction on $|P|$ we have $\bar{P} = \bar{C}\bar{H}$. But then $P = DH$ by the preceding paragraph. If $[x, A] \subseteq K$ for all x in P, then $H \subseteq K \subseteq Z(P)$, contrary to assumption; so $D \subset P$. Now D is A-invariant, as both K and $\bar{C}$ are. Hence by induction and the fact that $C \subseteq D$, we obtain $D = C[D, A]$. Since $[D, A] \subseteq H$ and $P = DH$, the desired conclusion $P = CH$ follows in this case as well.

Finally if $H \subseteq \Phi(P)$, we have $P = C\Phi(P)$, whence $P = C$ by Theorem 1.1, which implies that $A = 1$.

This last result has the following important consequence:

Theorem 3.6

If A is a p'-group of automorphisms of the p-group P, then

$$[P, A, A] = [P, A].$$

In particular, if $[P, A, A] = 1$, then $A = 1$.

Proof

Set $H = [P, A]$, $H_1 = [H, A] = [P, A, A]$, and $C = C_P(A)$. Then H, H_1, and C are each A-invariant. We apply the preceding theorem to both P and H to obtain $P = CH$ and $H = (H \cap C)H_1$, whence $P = CH_1$. Hence for x in P, we can write $x = yz$, where $y \in C$ and $z \in H_1$, so that $x^{-1}(x\phi) = z^{-1}y^{-1}(y\phi)(z\phi) = z^{-1}(z\phi)$ for any ϕ in A. But $z^{-1}(z\phi) \in H_1$ as $z \in H_1$ and H_1 is A-invariant. We conclude that $H_1 \supseteq H$. On the other hand, clearly $H_1 = [H, A] \subseteq [P, A] = H$, whence $H_1 = H$.

Finally, if $H_1 = 1$, then $H = 1$ and A acts trivially on P, forcing $A = 1$.

Several reduction-type arguments that we shall later encounter lead to a p-group P and a p'-automorphism ϕ of P with the property that ϕ acts trivially on *every* proper ϕ-invariant subgroup of P. Our next result, which covers a slight generalization of this situation, shows that the existence of such a p'-automorphism imposes a considerable restriction on P.

Theorem 3.7

Let A be a p'-group of automorphisms of the p-group P and assume that for some nonidentity element ψ of A, ψ acts trivially on every proper A-invariant normal subgroup of P. Then the following conditions hold:

(i) $P' = [P, P] \subseteq Z(P)$.

    (ii) *P/P' is elementary abelian, A acts irreducibly on P/P', and ψ acts nontrivially on P/P'.*

    (iii) *Either P is elementary abelian or P has class 2, $P' = Z(P) = \Phi(P)$ is elementary abelian, and ψ acts trivially on P'.*

Proof

First, ψ acts trivially on P' as P' is a proper A-invariant normal subgroup of P. Hence ψ does not act trivially on $\bar{P} = P/P'$; otherwise ψ would stabilize the normal series $P \supset P' \supseteq 1$ of P and it would follow that $\psi = 1$, which is not the case. Suppose we can write $\bar{P} = \bar{P}_1 \times \bar{P}_2$, where $\bar{P}_i \neq 1$ and $\bar{P}_i$ is A-invariant. Then $P = P_1 P_2$ and P_i is a proper A-invariant normal subgroup of P, where P_i is the inverse image of $\bar{P}_i$ in P, $1 \leqslant i \leqslant 2$. But then ψ is the identity on each P_i and so also on P, a contradiction. Thus A acts indecomposably on $\bar{P}$ (which is therefore homocyclic by Theorem 2.2). If $\Omega_1(\bar{P}) \subset \bar{P}$, then ψ acts trivially on the inverse image of $\Omega_1(\bar{P})$ in P, which is then a proper A-invariant normal subgroup of P, and so ψ acts trivially on $\Omega_1(\bar{P})$. But then ψ acts trivially on $\bar{P}$ by Theorem 2.4, a contradiction. Thus $\bar{P} = \Omega_1(\bar{P})$ is elementary abelian. Since A acts indecomposably on $\bar{P}$, we conclude now from Maschke's theorem that A acts irreducibly on $\bar{P}$. Thus (ii) holds.

Now let $B = \langle \psi^A \rangle$ be the normal closure of ψ in A. Since ψ acts trivially on P' and P' is A-invariant, it follows that B acts trivially on P'. Set $H = [P, B]$. If $H \subseteq P'$, we have $1 = [H, B] = [P, B, B]$, whence $B = 1$ by Theorem 3.6, a contradiction. Thus $H \nsubseteq P'$. Moreover, since B and P are each A-invariant, Theorem 2.2.1(iii) and (ix) implies that $H \lhd P$ and that H is A-invariant. If $H \subset P$, then ψ acts trivially on H and so also on the image $\bar{H}$ of H in $\bar{P}$. But $\bar{H}$ is a nontrivial A-invariant subgroup of $\bar{P}$, whence $\bar{H} = \bar{P}$ by the irreducible action of A on $\bar{P}$. This contradicts the fact that ψ acts nontrivially on $\bar{P}$. Hence we must have $H = P$.

Since B centralizes P' and $P' \lhd P$, we have $[P', P, B] = 1$ and $[B, P', P] = 1$, whence $[P, B, P'] = 1$ by the three-subgroup lemma. Since $[P, B] = P$, it follows that P' centralizes P and hence that $P' \subseteq Z(P)$, proving (i).

Assume finally that P is not elementary abelian. Since $\bar{P} = P/P'$ is elementary abelian, we have $P' \neq 1$ and consequently $P' \subseteq Z(P) \subset P$. But then the image $\bar{Z}$ of $Z(P)$ in $\bar{P}$ is a proper A-invariant subgroup of $\bar{P}$, whence $\bar{Z} = \bar{1}$ by the irreducibility of A on $\bar{P}$. Hence $Z(P) = P'$ and P is of class 2. Since $P' \subseteq \Phi(P)$, it follows similarly that $P' = \Phi(P)$. Furthermore, if $x, y \in P$, then $[x, y] = z \in P' = Z(P)$ and so $[x, y^p] = z^p$ by Lemma 2.2.2(i). But $y^p \in Z(P)$ as $\bar{P}$ is elementary, which implies that $z^p = 1$. Thus $[x, y]^p = 1$ for all x, y in P. Since P' is abelian and is generated by the set of all such $[x, y]$, it follows that P' is elementary abelian. Thus (iii) also holds and the proof is complete.

The preceding theorem suggests the introduction of the following term: A *p*-group P is called *special* if either P is elementary abelian or P is of class 2 and $P' = Z(P) = \Phi(P)$ is elementary abelian. Note that as $P' = \Phi(P)$ in either case, our conditions imply that P/P' is elementary abelian. As we shall see, the particular case that P has class 2 and $|P'| = p$ is of great importance. Such a *p*-group is said to be *extra-special*.

As a corollary of the theorem, we have

Theorem 3.8

Let A be a p'-group of automorphisms of the p-group P and let ψ be an element of $A^{\#}$. Then P possesses an A-invariant special subgroup Q such that A acts irreducibly on $Q/\Phi(Q)$, ψ acts nontrivially on $Q/\Phi(Q)$, and ψ acts trivially on $\Phi(Q)$.

Proof

Choose Q to be a minimal A-invariant subgroup of P on which ψ acts nontrivially. Then certainly ψ acts trivially on every proper A-invariant normal subgroup of Q and so Q has the required properties by Theorem 3.7 and the definition of a special *p*-group.

As an application of Theorem 3.7 we shall next derive an extension of Theorem 2.4 to nonabelian *p*-groups. However, the following example shows that the desired generalization is not universally valid. If $P = \langle x, y \mid x^4 = y^4 = 1 \text{ and } y^{-1}xy = x^{-1} \rangle$ is a quaternion group, the mapping ϕ of P into P defined by $(x^i y^j)\phi = y^i(xy)^j$, $1 \leqslant i, j \leqslant 4$, is easily checked to be an automorphism of P of order 3 fixing the element $x^2 = y^2$. But x^2 is the unique element of order 2 in P and so $\Omega_1(P) = \langle x^2 \rangle$. Thus ϕ is a nontrivial $2'$-automorphism of P which acts trivially on $\Omega_1(P)$.

However, no such counterexample exists when p is odd. Furthermore, in Section 6, using different methods, we shall show that the desired generalization holds for $p = 2$ for certain special values of the order of the p'-automorphisms involved.

Our results for odd p depend on the following general lemma on *p*-groups of class at most 2 (both parts of which are false for the quaternion group).

Lemma 3.9

Let P be a p-group of class at most 2 with p odd. Then
  (i) $\Omega_1(P)$ is of exponent p.
  (ii) If $P/Z(P)$ is elementary abelian, then $(xy)^p = x^p y^p$ for all x, y in P.

Proof

Let $x, y \in P$ and set $z = [x, y]$. Since $\text{cl}(P) \leqslant 2, z \in Z(P)$ and so z commutes with both x and y. But then by Lemma 2.2.2, we have

$$(3.1) \qquad (xy)^i = z^{1/2 \, i(i-1)} x^i y^i \qquad \text{and} \qquad [y^i, x] = z^i$$

for all i.

If x and y have order p, then by (3.1) we have $1 = [1, x] = [y^p, x] = z^p$ and $(xy)^p = z^{1/2 \, p(p-1)} x^p y^p = z^{1/2 \, p(p-1)}$. Since p is odd and $z^p = 1$, it follows that $(xy)^p = 1$. Thus the product of two elements of P of order p has order 1 or p, which implies that $\Omega_1(P)$ is of exponent p.

Now assume that $P/Z(P)$ is elementary abelian, in which case

$$1 = [y^p, x] = z^p.$$

But now (3.1) yields $(xy)^p = x^p y^p$.

Theorem 3.10

If A is a p'-group group of automorphisms of the p-group P with p odd which acts trivially on $\Omega_1(P)$, then $A = 1$.

Proof

We proceed by induction on $|P|$. Certainly $\Omega_1(Q) \subseteq \Omega_1(P)$ for any subgroup Q of P. Hence if Q is any proper A-invariant subgroup of P, A acts trivially on $\Omega_1(Q)$ and so acts trivially on Q by induction. But now it follows from Theorem 3.7 (with ψ any element of $A^\#$) that P is a special p-group, that A acts trivially on P', and irreducibly on P/P'. In particular, $\text{cl}(P) \leqslant 2$.

Hence if $x \in P$ and $\phi \in A$, Lemma 3.9 implies that $(x^{-1}(x\phi))^p = (x^{-1})^p (x\phi)^p = (x^p)^{-1}(x^p\phi)$. But $x^p \in P'$, as P/P' is elementary abelian, and so ϕ fixes x^p. It follows therefore that $(x^{-1}(x\phi))^p = 1$. Since $[P, A]$ is generated by the set of all such elements $x^{-1}(x\phi)$, we conclude that $[P, A] \subseteq \Omega_1(P)$. Since A acts trivially on $\Omega_1(P)$ by assumption, we see that A stabilizes the normal series $P \supseteq \Omega_1(P) \supseteq 1$ of P, whence $A = 1$ by Theorem 3.2.

If Q is the special A-invariant subgroup of P of Theorem 3.8, it may very well happen that some element of $A^\#$ acts trivially on Q. It is therefore natural to ask whether there exists an A-invariant subgroup of P class at most 2 on which no element of $A^\#$ acts trivially. The following theorem, which answers the question affirmatively, is due to Thompson and appears in the Odd-Order paper.

Theorem 3.11 (Thompson)

A p-group P possesses a characteristic subgroup C with the following properties:

(i) $\operatorname{cl}(C) \leqslant 2$ *and* $C/Z(C)$ *is elementary abelian.*

(ii) $[P, C] \subseteq Z(C)$.

(iii) $C_P(C) = Z(C)$,

(iv) *Every nontrivial $p′$-automorphism of P induces a nontrivial automorphism of C.*

Remark   We note that C need not be special; in particular, $Z(C)$ need not be elementary abelian.

Proof

Suppose first that a characteristic subgroup C of P exists satisfying condition (iii). Let ψ be a $p′$-automorphism of P which acts trivially on C and set $A = \langle \psi \rangle$. Then $[C, A] = 1$, so $[C, A, P] = 1$. Since $[P, C] \subseteq C$ as C char P, we also have $[P, C, A] = 1$, whence $[A, P, C] = 1$ by the three-subgroup lemma. Thus $[A, P] \subseteq C_P(C)$ and so $[A, P] \subseteq C$ by (iii). But then A stabilizes the normal series $P \supseteq C \supseteq 1$ of P and so $A = 1$. Thus $\psi = 1$ and it follows that (iii) implies (iv). Hence it will suffice to prove that C exists satisfying (i), (ii), and (iii).

We separate the next point of the proof as an independent lemma:

Lemma 3.12

If M is a normal subgroup of the p-group P maximal subject to being abelian, then $C_P(M) = M$.

Proof

We have $M \subseteq H = C_P(M)$ as M is abelian. Suppose $H \supset M$. Set $\bar{P} = P/M$ and let $\bar{H}$ be the image of H in $\bar{P}$. We have $H \lhd P$, whence $\bar{H} \subset \bar{P}$ and $\bar{H} \neq \bar{1}$, so $\bar{H} \cap Z(\bar{P}) \neq \bar{1}$. If $\bar{X}$ is a subgroup of $\bar{H} \cap Z(\bar{P})$ of order p, then $\bar{X} \lhd \bar{P}$, the inverse image X of $\bar{X}$ in P is normal in P, and $X \subseteq H$. Since H centralizes M, we have $M \subseteq Z(X)$. But X/M, being of order p, is cyclic and consequently X is abelian by Lemma 1.3.4. Since $X \lhd P$, our maximal choice of M is contradicted.

We return now to the proof of Theorem 3.11 and let M be a normal subgroup of P maximal subject to being abelian, so that $C_P(M) = M$ by the preceding lemma. Consider the case M char P. We shall argue that $C = M$ satisfies the required conditions. We have $C_P(C) = C$, so (iii) holds. Also $C = Z(C)$ is of class 1, $C/Z(C)$ is trivial, and $[P, C] \subseteq C = Z(C)$, whence also (i) and (ii) hold. Hence it remains to treat the case that no characteristic abelian subgroup of P is a maximal abelian normal subgroup of P.

Let D be a maximal characteristic abelian subgroup of P and let M be a maximal abelian normal subgroup of P containing D, so that $D \subset M$. Since M is abelian, we have $M \subseteq H = C_P(D)$, whence $D \subset H$. Furthermore, H char P. Set $\bar{P} = P/D$ and let $\bar{H}$ be the image of H in $\bar{P}$. Then $\bar{H} \neq 1$ and so $\bar{C} = \bar{H} \cap \Omega_1(Z(\bar{P})) \neq \bar{1}$. If C denotes the inverse image of $\bar{C}$ in P, we argue now that C has the required properties.

First of all, the inverse image K of $\Omega_1(Z(\bar{P}))$ is characteristic in P by Theorem 2.2.1(iv) and consequently $C = H \cap K$ char P. Since $C \subseteq H = C_P(D)$, we have $D \subseteq Z(C)$. But $Z(C)$ is a characteristic abelian subgroup of P as C char P. Hence $Z(C) = D$ by our maximal choice of D. But then $C/Z(C) = \bar{C}$ is elementary abelian and $\mathrm{cl}\,(C) = 2$. Furthermore, since $\bar{C} \subseteq Z(\bar{P}), [\bar{P}, \bar{C}] = \bar{1}$, whence $[P, C] \subseteq D = Z(C)$. Thus C satisfies conditions (i) and (ii).

Finally, set $Q = C_P(C)$ and suppose $Q \nsubseteq C$. Since $Z(C) = D = C_C(C)$, we have $Q \cap C = D$. Also $Q \subseteq H$ as Q centralizes D. Hence if $\bar{Q}$ denotes the image of Q in $\bar{P}$, we have $\bar{Q} \subseteq \bar{H}, \bar{Q} \cap \bar{C} = \bar{1}, \bar{Q} \lhd \bar{P}$, and $\bar{Q} \neq \bar{1}$. But then by Theorem 2.6.4, we have $\bar{1} \neq \bar{Q} \cap \Omega_1(Z(\bar{P})) \subseteq \bar{H} \cap \Omega_1(Z(\bar{P})) = \bar{C}$, which implies that $\bar{Q} \cap \bar{C} \neq \bar{1}$, a contradiction. We conclude that $Q \subseteq C$ and hence that $Q = Z(C)$. Thus (iii) also holds and the theorem is proved.

A characteristic subgroup C of a p-group P which satisfies the conditions of Theorem 3.11 will be called a *critical* subgroup of P.

When p is odd, we have the following corollary:

Theorem 3.13

For odd p, a p-group P possesses a characteristic subgroup D of class at most 2 and of exponent p such that every nontrivial p'-automorphism of P induces a nontrivial automorphism of D.

Proof

Let C be a critical subgroup of P and set $D = \Omega_1(C)$. Then D is of exponent p by Lemma 3.9(i). Clearly also $\mathrm{cl}\,(D) \leqslant 2$. Since D char C char P, we have D char P. Furthermore, since p is odd, a nontrivial p'-automorphism of C induces a nontrivial automorphism of D by Theorem 3.10 and now the theorem follows from Theorem 3.11(iv).

We remark that our conditions imply that $Z(D)$ and $D/Z(D)$ are each elementary abelian. However, D need not be special since we may very well have $D' \subset Z(D)$.

Our last sequence of theorems shows that for many questions a study of p'-automorphisms of p-groups can be reduced to the study of p'-automorphisms of p-groups having class at most 2.

We conclude this section with some properties of a regular group of automorphisms (compare Section 2.7) of a p-group and with a generalization of Theorem 3.3.3 to arbitrary p-groups.

Theorem 3.14

Let A be a regular group of automorphisms of a p-group P. Then we have
   (i) A is a p'-group.
   (ii) A possesses no noncyclic abelian subgroups.
   (iii) A subgroup of A of order qr, q and r primes, is cyclic.

Proof

Let B be an S_p-subgroup of A. Then B acts on $V = \Omega_1(Z(P))$, which is elementary abelian and so $C_V(B) \neq 1$ by Lemma 2.6.3. Since the elements of $A^{\#}$ fix only the element 1 of G and since B fixes the elements of $C_V(B)$, this forces $B = 1$. Thus A is a p'-group.

Suppose next that C is a noncyclic abelian subgroup of A. Then some S_q-subgroup Q of C is noncyclic by Theorem 1.3.1(ii). But then $V = \langle C_V(\phi) | \phi \in Q^{\#} \rangle$ by Theorem 3.3.3. Since $V = \Omega_1(Z(P)) \neq 1$, this forces $C_V(\phi) \neq 1$ for some ϕ in $Q^{\#}$, again contradicting the regularity of A.

Finally, let D be a subgroup of A of order qr, q and r primes. If $q = r$, then $|D| = q^2$, so D is an abelian q-group, whence D is cyclic by the preceding paragraph. Thus we may assume that $q > r$. If Q, R denote S_q- and S_p-subgroups of D, then $D = QR$ and, by Theorem 1.3.8, we have $Q \triangleleft D$. If $C_D(Q) \supset Q$, then $C_D(Q) = D$ and D is abelian, whence cyclic. Hence we may also assume $C_D(Q) = Q$. But now Theorem 3.4.3 is applicable to the action of D on V and yields that $C_V(R) \neq 1$, giving the same contradiction as above. All parts of the theorem are proved.

Theorem 3.15

Let A be a p'-group of automorphisms of a p-group P and let H be an A-invariant normal subgroup of P. Then $C_{P/H}(A)$ is the image of $C_P(A)$ in P/H. In particular, if A is a regular group of automorphisms of P or if $C_P(A) = 1$, then A is a regular group of automorphisms of P/H or $C_{P/H}(A) = 1$, respectively.

Proof

Set $\bar{P} = P/H$, let $\bar{K} = C_{\bar{P}}(A)$, and let K be the inverse image of $\bar{K}$ in P. Clearly $C_P(A)$ maps into $\bar{K}$ and so $C_P(A) \subseteq K$. Hence to prove the first assertion, it will suffice to show that $K = HC_K(A)$. But since A centralizes $\bar{K}$, it follows that K is A-invariant and $[K, A] \subseteq H$. However, $K = [K, A]C_K(A)$ by Theorem 3.5, whence $K = HC_K(A)$, as required.

In particular, if $C_P(A) = 1$, our argument shows that $C_{\bar{P}}(A) = \bar{1}$. Finally, if A is a regular group of automorphisms of P, then $C_P(B) = 1$ for any nontrivial subgroup B of A, whence $C_{\bar{P}}(B) = \bar{1}$ and consequently A is a regular group of automorphisms of $\bar{P}$.

Theorem 3.16

Let P be a p-group and let Q be a noncyclic abelian q-group of automorphisms of P, q a prime distinct from p. Then

$$P = \prod_{x \in Q^\#} C_P(x).$$

In particular, P is generated by its subgroups $C_P(x)$ for x in $Q^\#$.

Proof

It is understood, of course, that the above product is to be taken for some fixed ordering x_i, $1 \leqslant i \leqslant n$, of the elements of $Q^\#$. We proceed by induction on $|P|$. Setting $Z = \Omega_1(Z(P))$, it follows from Theorem 3.3.3 that $Z_j = C_Z(x_j) \neq 1$ for some j. But then the theorem holds in $\bar{P} = P/Z_j$ by induction. Since $C_P(x_i)$ maps onto $C_{\bar{P}}(x_i)$ for each i, $1 \leqslant i \leqslant n$, by the preceding theorem, we conclude at once that $P = Z_j \prod_{i=1}^{n} C_P(x_i)$. But Z_j is contained in $C_P(x_j)$ and lies in the center of P, whence $P = \prod_{i=1}^{n} C_P(x_i)$, as asserted.

4. p-GROUPS OF SMALL DEPTH

As we have just seen, a p-group P which is itself a regular group of automorphisms of a group of prime power order possesses no noncyclic abelian subgroups. Clearly then it is of interest to determine the structure of all p-groups with this property. We shall carry this out in the present section and at the same time shall determine all p-groups which have respectively no noncyclic normal or noncyclic characteristic subgroups. It turns out that the structure of this last class of groups is intimately connected with that of extra-special groups, which were defined in the preceding section.

It will be convenient to introduce the terms *depth*, *normal depth*, and *characteristic depth* of a p-group P to denote the maximum of $m(A)$, where A ranges respectively over all abelian, all normal abelian, and all characteristic abelian subgroups of P. We write $d(P), d_n(P), d_c(P)$ for the depth, normal depth, and characteristic depth of P, respectively. (We have used "depth" rather than the more customary term "rank" because the latter term will be needed for our later discussion of simple groups.)

We are thus interested in determining all p-groups in which $d(P) = 1$, $d_n(P) = 1$, or $d_c(P) = 1$. We shall also study the case $d(P) = 2$ and $d_n(P) = 2$ when p is odd.

We begin with the following result:

Lemma 4.1

Let $P = \langle x \rangle$ be a cyclic p-group of order p^n, $n \geq 2$, and set $A = \text{Aut } P$. Then we have

  (i) If $p = 2$ and $n = 2$, then $A = \langle \alpha \rangle$, where $x\alpha = x^{-1}$ and $|A| = 2$.
  (ii) If $p = 2$ and $n > 2$, then A is an abelian 2-group of type $(2^{n-2}, 2)$ and order 2^{n-1} with basis α, β, where $x\alpha = x^5$ and $x^\beta = x^{-1}$.
  (iii) If p is odd, A is abelian of order $p^{n-1}(p - 1)$ and an S_p-subgroup of A is cyclic with generator α, where $x\alpha = x^{1+p}$.

Proof

By Theorem 1.3.10(i), A is abelian in all cases. Furthermore, any element α of A is determined by its effect on x; also $x\alpha = x^i$, where $(p^n, i) = 1$. Conversely for each such i there is an element of A taking x into x^i. Thus $|A| = |\phi(p^n)|$, where ϕ is Euler's ϕ-function, and consequently $|A| = p^{n-1}(p - 1)$.

Suppose $p = 2$, in which case $|A| = 2^{n-1}$. If $n = 2$, $|A| = 2$ and the only nontrivial automorphism of P is given by $x\alpha = x^3 = x^{-1}$, so (i) holds. To prove (ii), observe that

$$(4.1) \qquad 5^{2^{n-2}} = (1 + 2^2)^{2^{n-2}} \equiv 1 \ (\text{mod } 2^n)$$

and

$$(4.2) \qquad 5^{2^j} \not\equiv 1 \ (\text{mod } 2^n) \qquad \text{if } j < n - 2.$$

Let α be the automorphism of P determined by $x\alpha = x^5$. Then inductively we obtain $x\alpha^i = x^{5^i}$. Since $|x| = 2^n$, (4.1) and (4.2) together imply that $x\alpha^{2^j} \neq x$ if $1 \leq j < n - 2$ and that $x\alpha^{2^{n-2}} = x$. Thus $|\alpha| = 2^{n-2}$. On the other hand, we also have

$$(4.3) \qquad 5^j \not\equiv -1 \ (\text{mod } 2^n) \qquad \text{for all } j,$$

whence $\alpha^j \neq \beta$ for any j, where $\beta \in A$ and $x\beta = x^{-1}$. Since $|A| = 2^{n-1}$, it follows that α, β is a basis of A, so (ii) holds.

Suppose finally that p is odd. Then the order of an S_p-subgroup A_p of A is p^{n-1}. Observe now that

$$(4.4) \qquad\qquad (1 + p)^{p^j} \equiv 1 \;(\mathrm{mod}\; p^{j+1})$$

and

$$(4.5) \qquad\qquad (1 + p)^{p^j} \not\equiv 1 \;(\mathrm{mod}\; p^{j+2}),$$

as p is odd. But then, as in the preceding paragraph, the element $\alpha \in A$ given by $x\alpha = x^{1+p}$ is of order p^{n-1}. Hence $A_p = \langle \alpha \rangle$ is cyclic and (iii) also holds.

Corollary 4.2

   The following conditions hold:
   (i) *If $p = 2$ and $n > 2$, set $\gamma = \alpha^{2^{n-3}}$. Then $\Omega_1(A)$ is abelian of type $(2, 2)$ with basis γ, β and*

$$x\beta = x^{-1} \qquad x\gamma = x^{5^{2^{n-3}}} = x^{1+2^{n-1}} \qquad x(\gamma\beta) = x^{-1-2^{n-1}} = x^{-1+2^{n-1}}.$$

   Furthermore, γ is the only element of $A^{\#}$ which acts trivially on $\mho^1(P) = \langle x^2 \rangle$.
   (ii) *If p is odd, set $\gamma = \alpha^{p^{n-2}}$. Then $\Omega_1(A_p) = \langle \gamma \rangle$, where A_p is the S_p-subgroup of A and*

$$x\gamma = x^{1+p^{n-1}}.$$

   Furthermore, $\langle \gamma \rangle$ is the only nonidentity subgroup of A_p which acts trivially on $\mho^1(P) = \langle x^p \rangle$.

The various statements of the corollary follow at once from the description of A given the lemma.

With the aid of the corollary, using the methods of semidirect products as described in Section 2.5, we now construct a number of particular p-groups. If $p = 2$, assume below that $m > 3$, while if p is odd, assume $m > 2$. We define

$$M_m(p) = \langle x, y \mid x^{p^{m-1}} = y^p = 1, x^y = x^{1+p^{m-2}} \rangle.$$

The existence of such a group $M_m(p)$ of order p^m follows from our general construction procedure provided we set $m = n + 1$ in the preceding corollary and use the automorphism γ to determine the action of y on $\langle x \rangle$.

Similarly, using $\gamma\beta$ when $p = 2$, there exists a group S_m for $m > 3$ defined by

$$S_m = \langle x, y \,|\, x^{2^{m-1}} = y^2 = 1, \ x^y = x^{-1+2^{m-2}} \rangle.$$

The group S_m of order 2^m is called a *semidihedral* group. We also introduce the notation D_m, Q_m for the dihedral and generalized quaternion groups of order 2^m (defined in Section 2.5). Here $m \geq 2$ for D_m and $m \geq 3$ for Q_m. For brevity, we also set $D = D_3$ and $Q = Q_3$.

Finally, in each case (including D_m and Q_m), we set $H = \langle x \rangle$ and refer to H as a *maximal cyclic generator* of the given group.

The following omnibus theorem gives a large number of properties of these various groups:

Theorem 4.3

The following holds:
   (i) *Set $P = M_m(p)$. Then*
       (a) cl $(P) = 2$ *and* $|P'| = p$.
       (b) $\Phi(P) = Z(P)$ *is cyclic of order p^{m-2}.*
       (c) $\Omega_i(P)$ *is abelian of type (p^i, p), $1 \leq i \leq m - 2$.*
   (ii) *Set $P = D_m$, $m \geq 3$, Q_m, or S_m. Then*
       (a) cl $(P) = m - 1$.
       (b) $\Phi(P) = P'$ *is cyclic of order 2^{m-2}.*
       (c) $|Z(P)| = 2$ *and $P/Z(P)$ is isomorphic to D_{m-1}.*
       (d) *P possesses no noncyclic abelian subgroups of order 8.*
       (e) *If $P = D_m$, then $\Omega_1(P) = P$, $d(P) = 2$, $d_c(P) = 1$, and $d_n(P) = 2$ or 1 according as $m = 3$ or $m > 3$. Furthermore, the maximal subgroups of P are cyclic or dihedral.*
       (f) *If $P = Q_m$, then $\Omega_1(P) = Z(P)$ and $d(P) = 1$. Furthermore, the maximal subgroups of P are cyclic or generalized quaternion.*
       (g) *If $P = S_m$, then $\Omega_1(P)$ is isomorphic to D_{m-1}, $d(P) = 2$, and $d_c(P) = 1$. Furthermore, the maximal subgroups of P are cyclic, generalized quaternion, or dihedral.*
   (iii) *No two of the groups $M_m(p)$, D_m, Q_m, or S_m are isomorphic.*

Proof

Set $P = M_m(p)$, D_m, Q_m, or S_m as the case may be and let $P = \langle x, y \rangle$ with x, y satisfying the appropriate relations. In the first case,

$$(x^p)^y = (x^y)^p = (x^{1+p^{m-2}})^p = x^p,$$

so x^p commutes with y as well as x and hence $x^p \in Z(P)$. On the other hand, it is immediate that neither x nor $x^i y$ is in $Z(P)$. Thus $Z(P) = \langle x^p \rangle$ is cyclic of order p^{m-2}. Since $P/\Phi(P)$ is elementary abelian, $x^p \in \Phi(P)$, whence

$Z(P) \subseteq \Phi(P)$. If $\Phi(P) \supset Z(P)$, then $|P/\Phi(P)| = p$ and P would be cyclic by Corollary 1.2. Thus $Z(P) = \Phi(P)$ and cl $(P) = 2$.

Furthermore, $[x, y] = x^{p^{m-2}} = z$, so that z is of order p. But then

$$(4.6) \qquad [x^i, y] = z^i \qquad \text{and} \qquad (yx^j)^p = z^{jp(p-1)/2} x^{jp}$$

by Lemma 2.2.2. If p is odd, it follows that $(yx^j)^p = x^{jp}$, whence yx^j has order dividing p^i if and only if $p^{m-i-1} | j$. We conclude from this that $\Omega_i(P) = \langle x^{p^{m-i-1}}, y \rangle$ is elementary abelian of type (p^i, p), $1 \leqslant i \leqslant m - 2$. On the other hand, if $p = 2$, (4.6) gives

$$(4.7) \qquad (yx^j)^2 = z^j x^{2j} = x^{2j + 2^{m-2}j}.$$

Since $m > 3$ in the definition of $M_m(2)$, it again follows that yx^j has order dividing p^i if and only if $p^{m-i-1} | j$, and we reach the same conclusion as when p is odd. Thus all parts of (i) hold.

Now consider (ii), in which case $p = 2$ and either $x^y = x^{-1}$ or $x^y = x^{-1+2^{m-2}}$ and $m > 3$. But then correspondingly $[x, y] = x^{-2}$ or $x^{-2+2^{m-2}}$ and we conclude in either case that $x^2 \in P'$, whence $|P/P'| \leqslant 4$. Since $P' \subseteq \Phi(P)$, it follows as in the proof of (i) that $|P/\Phi(P)| = 4$ and hence that $P' = \Phi(P)$. Furthermore, $[x^i, y] = x^{-2i}$ or $x^{(-2+2^{m-2})i}$ and so y commutes with x^i if and only if $i | 2^{m-2}$. Since yx^j does not centralize x for any j, we conclude that $\langle x^{2^{m-2}} \rangle = Z(P)$, whence $|Z(P)| = 2$.

Set $\bar{P} = P/Z(P) = \langle \bar{x}, \bar{y} \rangle$. Then $|\bar{x}| = 2^{m-2}$ and so $\bar{x}^{\bar{y}} = \bar{x}^{-1}$ in all cases. Since either $y^2 = 1$ or $y^2 = x^{2^{m-2}}$, we also have $\bar{y}^2 = 1$. Thus $\bar{P}$ is isomorphic to D_{m-1}. If $m - 1 \geqslant 3$, then cl $(\bar{P}) = m - 2$ by induction, while if $m - 1 = 2$, cl $(\bar{P}) = 1 = m - 2$, as then $\bar{P}$ is abelian. We conclude in either case that cl $(P) = m - 1$.

Observe next that in D_m, $(xy)^2 = x(yxy) = xx^{-1} = 1$, so that both xy and y have order 2. But then $\Omega_1(D_m) \supseteq \langle xy, y \rangle = \langle x, y \rangle = D_m$. In Q_m we have similarly $(x^iy)^2 = x^{2^{m-2}}$ for all i, so x^iy is never of order 2. Hence $\Omega_1(Q_m) = \langle x^{2^{m-2}} \rangle = Z(Q_m)$. Finally, in S_m we have $(x^iy)^2 = x^{i2^{m-2}}$, so that x^iy is of order 2 if and only if i is even. But then $\Omega_1(S_m) = \langle x^2y, y \rangle = \langle x^2, y \rangle$. Setting $x_1 = x^2$, we obtain $|x_1| = 2^{m-1}$ and

$$x_1^y = (x^2)^y = (x^2)^{-1+2^{m-2}} = x^{-2} = x_1^{-1},$$

and we see that $\Omega_1(S_m)$ is isomorphic to D_{m-1}.

The remaining parts of (ii) are proved by similar calculations which we omit.

Finally $\Omega_1(D_m)$, $\Omega_1(Q_m)$, and $\Omega_1(S_m)$ have distinct orders, so none of the groups D_m, Q_m, or S_m are isomorphic. Since $\Omega_1(M_m(2))$ is abelian of type $(2, 2)$, it follows likewise that $M_m(2)$ is isomorphic to none of the other three groups of order 2^m, and so (iii) also holds.

Each of the groups $M_m(p)$, D_m, $m \geqslant 3$, Q_m, and S_m possesses a maximal cyclic subgroup of order p^{m-1}. The next theorem shows that these groups are characterized among all nonabelian p-groups by this property.

Theorem 4.4

Let P be a nonabelian p-group of order p^m which contains a cyclic subgroup H of order p^{m-1}. Then
(i) If p is odd, P is isomorphic to $M_m(p)$.
(ii) If $p = 2$ and $m = 3$, then P is isomorphic to D or Q.
(iii) If $p = 2$ and $m > 3$, then P is isomorphic to $M_m(2)$, D_m, Q_m, or S_m.
Furthermore, in each case H is a maximal cyclic generator of P.

Proof

Since P is nonabelian, we have $m \geqslant 3$. We also have $H \lhd P$ and P/H is cyclic order p. Furthermore, $H \not\leqslant Z(P)$; otherwise P would be abelian by Lemma 1.3.4. Hence $H = C_P(H)$. Thus P/H is isomorphic to a subgroup of Aut H of order p. We set $H = \langle x \rangle$, so that $|x| = p^n$ with $n = m - 1 \geqslant 2$.

Consider first the case p odd. Then by Corollary 4.2, there must exist an element u in $P - H$ such that $x^u = x^{1+p^{m-2}}$. Then $P = \langle x, u \rangle$ and $(x^p)^u = (x^u)^p = x^p$, whence x^p centralizes both x and u and so lies in $Z(P)$. Since $|P:\langle x^p \rangle| = p^2$, Lemma 1.3.4 implies that $\langle x^p \rangle = Z(P)$ and that $Z(P) = \Phi(P)$. In particular, cl $(P) = 2$. Now $u^p \in H$, but u^p does not generate H, since otherwise P would be cyclic. It follows that $u^p = x^{ap}$ for some a. Set $y = ux^{-a}$. Since p is odd and $P/Z(P)$ is elementary abelian, we have $y^p = (ux^{-a})^p = u^p x^{-ap} = 1$ by Lemma 3.9(ii). But $x^y = x^u = x^{1+p^{m-2}}$ and $P = \langle x, y \rangle$, which proves that P is isomorphic to $M_m(p)$. Thus (i) holds.

Next assume $p = 2$ and $m = 3$, so that $|x| = 4$. Then H possesses a unique nontrivial automorphism and so for any y in $P - H$ we have $P = \langle x, y \rangle$ and $x^y = x^{-1}$. Since P is nonabelian, we again have $y^2 = x^{2a}$ for some a. If a is even, $y^2 = 1$ and P is isomorphic to D; while if a is odd, $y^2 = x^2$ and P is isomorphic to Q.

Suppose finally that $p = 2$ and $m > 3$. In this case if $u \in P - H$, there are three possibilities for the action of y on x:

$$(4.8) \qquad x^u = x^{1+2^{m-2}} \qquad x^u = x^{-1} \qquad x^u = x^{-1+2^{m-2}}.$$

Moreover, in each case, we again have $u^2 = x^{2a}$. If the first possibility holds, we choose c to satisfy the congruence

(4.9) $a + c(1 + 2^{m-3}) \equiv 0 \pmod{2^{m-2}}$,

which we can do, as $m > 3$. But then if we set $y = ux^c$ we obtain

(4.10) $y^2 = (ux^c)^2 = u^2(x^c)^u x^c = x^{2a} x^{c(1+2^{m-2})} x^c = x^{2a + 2c(1+2^{m-3})}$.

Now (4.9) and (4.10) give $y^2 = 1$ as $|x| = 2^{m-1}$. Since $x^y = x^u$, we conclude that P is isomorphic to $M_m(2)$.

In the remaining two cases of (4.8), we compute easily that $Z(P) = \langle x^{2^{m-2}} \rangle$ is of order 2. On the other hand, $u^2 \in H$, so u^2 centralizes x as well as u. Thus $u^2 \in Z(P)$ and so $u^2 = x^{a 2^{m-2}}$ for some a. If a is even, then $u^2 = 1$ and it follows that P is isomorphic to D_m or S_m according as the second or third case of (4.8) holds. On the other hand, if a is odd, we have $u^2 = x^{2^{m-2}}$, so that P is isomorphic to Q_m if $x^u = x^{-1}$.

There remains the case $u^2 = x^{2^{m-2}}$ and $x^u = x^{-1+2^{m-2}}$. We set $y = ux$ so that

$$y^2 = (ux)^2 = u^2 x^u x = x^{2^{m-2}} x^{-1+2^{m-2}} x = 1,$$

and we conclude at once that P is isomorphic to S_m, which establishes (iii).

Furthermore, the proof of the theorem shows that H can be taken as a maximal cyclic generator of P in each case.

The groups D_m, Q_m, and S_m each have class $m - 1$ and have commutator factor groups of order 4. Our next result shows that they are characterized among all 2-groups by either of these properties.

Theorem 4.5

Let P be a nonabelian 2-group of order 2^m in which either $\mathrm{cl}(P) = m - 1$ or $|P/P'| = 4$, $m > 1$. Then P is isomorphic to D_m, Q_m, or S_m.

Proof

Suppose $\mathrm{cl}(P) = m - 1$. Once again Lemma 1.3.4 implies that $|P/\Phi(P)| \geqslant 4$, whence also $|P/P'| \geqslant 4$. If the equality were strict, the lower central series of P would necessarily terminate in less than $m - 1$ steps, whence $\mathrm{cl}(P) < m - 1$. Thus $|P/P'| = 4$; and so it will suffice to show that this last condition implies that P has the required structure.

Suppose $m = 3$. Since P is nonabelian, P is not of exponent 2 by Lemma 1.3.5 and so contains a cyclic subgroup of order 4. But then P is isomorphic to D or Q by the preceding theorem. Hence we may also assume $m > 3$.

Since $P' \lhd P$ and $P' \neq 1$, we can choose Z of order 2 in $P' \cap Z(P)$. Setting $\bar{P} = P/Z$, it follows that $\bar{P}'$ is the image of P', whence also $|\bar{P}/\bar{P}'| = 4$. Since $m > 3$, $\bar{P}$ is nonabelian and consequently by induction $\bar{P}$ is isomorphic to D_{m-1}, Q_{m-1}, or S_{m-1}. Let $\bar{H}$ be a maximal cyclic generator of $\bar{P}$ and let H be its inverse image in P. If H is cyclic, then P is isomorphic to $M_m(2)$, D_m, Q_m, or S_m by the preceding theorem. However, the case $M_m(2)$ cannot arise, for then by Theorem 3.4(i), $|P/P'| = 2^{m-1} > 4$. Thus the theorem holds in this case.

Consider the case that H is noncyclic. Since $Z \subseteq Z(H)$ and H/Z is cyclic, H is abelian by Lemma 1.3.4. Since $|Z| = 2$ and $|H| = 2^{m-1}$, the only possibility is that $H = \langle x, z \rangle$ with $|x| = 2^{m-2}$, $|z| = 2$, and $\langle z \rangle = Z$. Since $m > 3$, $\mho^1(H) = \langle x^2 \rangle$ and $X = \mho^1(H) \cap \Omega_1(H) = \langle x^{2^{m-3}} \rangle$ is of order 2 and X char $H \triangleleft P$. Hence $X \subseteq Z(P)$ and so $\bar{X} \subseteq Z(\bar{P})$, where $\bar{X}$ is the image of X in $\bar{P}$. Since $\bar{X} \neq 1$, it follows from Theorem 4.3(ii) that $\bar{X} = Z(\bar{P}) \subseteq \bar{P}'$ whence $X \subseteq P'$. But then we can apply induction to $\tilde{P} = P/X$ as we did to P/Z to obtain that $\tilde{P}$ is isomorphic to D_{m-1}, Q_{m-1}, or S_{m-1}. On the other hand, as x, z is a basis of H, the image $\tilde{H}$ of H in $\tilde{P}$ is abelian of type $(2^{m-3}, 2)$. Since $\tilde{P}$ contains no noncyclic abelian subgroups of order 8, by Theorem 4.3(ii) the only possibility is $m = 4$.

But in this case we have $|P/XZ| = 4$ and $XZ \subseteq P' \cap Z(P)$. Since P is nonabelian, this forces $XZ = Z(P)$ and $P/Z(P)$ elementary, whence $P = \langle Z(P), y_1, y_2 \rangle$ for suitable elements y_1, y_2. It follows at once from this that $[y_1, y_2]$ generates P', which is therefore cyclic, contrary to the fact that $XZ \subseteq P'$ and XZ is elementary abelian of type $(2, 2)$. This completes the proof.

Since $|P/P'| \geqslant p^2$ in any nonabelian p-group, consideration of the lower central series of P shows that $\mathrm{cl}\,(P) \leqslant m - 1$ if $|P| = p^m$. For this reason a p-group of class exactly $m - 1$ is said to be of *maximal class*. The preceding theorem is therefore a classification of all 2-groups of maximal class. Blackburn has studied p-groups of maximal class in great detail and, in particular, has classified them in the case $p = 3$.

With these specialized results at our disposal we turn now to an analysis of p-groups P in which $d_c(P) = 1$. We require the following three lemmas:

Lemma 4.6

Let C be an extra-special subgroup of the p-group P such that $[P, C] \subseteq Z(C)$. Then $P = CC_P(C)$.

Proof

Given x in P, it will suffice to show that there exists y in C such that xy^{-1} centralizes C, for then $x = yu$, $u \in C_P(C)$ and the desired conclusion follows. If ϕ_x, ϕ_y denote the automorphisms induced by conjugation by x, y, respectively, we must thus produce y in C such that $\phi_x = \phi_y$ on C.

But ϕ_x acts trivially on $C/Z(C)$ in as much as $[P, C] \subseteq Z(C)$. Hence we are reduced to establishing the following result: If ψ is an automorphism of C which acts trivially on $C/Z(C)$, then ψ is an inner automorphism of C.

Let $x_i, 1 \leqslant i \leqslant n$, be elements of C whose images in $C/Z(C)$ form a basis for $C/Z(C)$ and let $Z(C) = \langle z \rangle$, so that $|z| = p$ and $|C| = p^{n+1}$. We have $x_i\psi = x_i z^{a_i}$ for suitable a_i, $0 \leqslant a_i < p$, $1 \leqslant i \leqslant n$. Thus there are at most p^n distinct automorphisms of C which act trivially on $C/Z(C)$.

On the other hand, if $u_j, 1 \leqslant j \leqslant p^n$, are a set of coset representatives of $Z(C)$ in C, then for each j the corresponding inner automorphism ϕ_{u_j} of C leaves each coset of $Z(C)$ invariant as $\mathrm{cl}\,(C) = 2$, and hence acts trivially on $C/Z(C)$. Moreover, $\phi_{u_j} \neq \phi_{u_k}$ if $j \neq k$, otherwise $u_j u_k^{-1}$ acts trivially on C, whence $u_j u_k^{-1} \in Z(C)$ and u_j, u_k determine the same coset of $Z(C)$, a contradiction. Thus the inner automorphisms of C give p^n distinct automorphisms of C which act trivially on $C/Z(C)$. Hence by the preceding paragraph every automorphism with this property is inner, as required.

Lemma 4.7

Let P be a p-group in which $d_c(P) = 1$ and let C be a critical subgroup of P. Then
  (i) $Z(C)$ is cyclic and C is the central product of $Z(C)$ and a subgroup E, where either E is extra-special or $E = 1$.
  (ii) If $R = C_P(E)$, then $P = ER$ and $C_R(Z(C)) = Z(C)$. In particular, P is the central product of E and R.

Proof

Since C char P, we must have $d_c(C) = 1$, so that, in particular, $Z = Z(C)$ is cyclic. We have $C_P(C) = Z$, as C is a critical subgroup of P (compare Theorem 3.11). Hence if $Z = C$, the lemma follows with $R = P$ and $E = 1$. Thus we may assume $C \supset Z$, in which case C is nonabelian. Furthermore, if C is extra-special, then $P = CC_P(C) = C$ by the preceding lemma since a critical subgroup C satisfies the condition $[P, C] \subseteq Z$. In this case the lemma follows with $E = P$ and $R = Z$. Thus we may also assume that C is not extra-special. Since C/Z is elementary abelian and C is nonabelian, this forces $|Z| > p$.

If $x, y \in C$, then $x^p \in Z$ and consequently $[x, y]^p = [x^p, y] = 1$ by Lemma 2.2.2. Since $C' \subseteq Z$ and C' is generated by all such $[x, y]$, it follows that $C' = \Omega_1(Z)$ is of order p. Set $\bar{C} = C/C'$, let $\bar{Z}$ be the image of Z in $\bar{C}$, and let $\bar{A}$ be a maximal cyclic subgroup of $\bar{C}$ containing $\bar{Z}$. Since C/Z is elementary abelian, $\bar{A}$ is clearly a cyclic subgroup of maximal order in $\bar{C}$ and consequently $\bar{C} = \bar{A} \times \bar{E}$ by Lemma 1.3.3. Our conditions imply that

$\bar{E}$ is elementary abelian and $|\bar{A}:\bar{Z}| = p$ or 1. In the first case, $\bar{Z}\bar{E} = \mho^1(\bar{C})\Omega_1(\bar{C})$ char $\bar{C}$ and, in the second case, obviously $\bar{Z}\bar{E}$ char $\bar{C}$. Hence if E denotes the inverse image of $\bar{E}$ in C and if we set $D = EZ$; then D char C, whence D char P. But then also $d_c(D) = 1$, so that $Z(D)$ is also cyclic. But clearly $Z \subseteq Z(D)$, while $\bar{Z}$ is a maximal cyclic subgroup of the image $\bar{Z}\bar{E}$ of D in $\bar{C}$, and so we must have $Z = Z(D)$. On the other hand, as $D = EZ$, we have $Z(E) \subseteq Z(D) = Z$. Since $E \cap Z = C'$, this implies that $Z(E) = C'$. Moreover, $E \supset Z(E)$, as otherwise C would be cyclic. Hence $E' \neq 1$, forcing $E' = C'$ and also $E/E' = E/C' = \bar{E}$ to be elementary abelian. Thus $\Phi(E) = E' = Z(E)$ and we conclude that E is extra-special.

Since $[P, C] \subseteq Z$, certainly $[P, E] \subseteq Z$. But $\mho^1(E) \subseteq Z(E) = \Omega_1(Z)$ and it follows easily that, in fact, $[P, E] \subseteq \Omega_1(Z) = Z(E)$. Hence by the preceding lemma, $P = ER$, where $R = C_P(E)$.

In particular, as $E \subseteq C$, we have $C = E(C \cap R)$, $Z \subseteq R$, and $R \cap E = \Omega_1(Z)$. This implies that $C/C' = \bar{C} = \bar{B} \times \bar{E}$, where $\bar{B}$ is the image of $C \cap R$ in $\bar{C}$. But $\bar{C} = \bar{A} \times \bar{E}$ with $\bar{A}$ cyclic and hence $\bar{B}$ is cyclic. Furthermore, $\bar{B} \supseteq \bar{Z}$ and $\bar{Z} \neq 1$ as $|Z| > p$. Since $C' = \Omega_1(Z)$, it follows therefore that $C \cap R$ is cyclic. Since $C \cap R$ centralizes E, this yields $C \cap R \subseteq Z(C)$, whence $C \cap R = Z$. We conclude that $C = D = EZ$ is the central product of the extra-special group E and the cyclic group Z.

Finally, $C_R(Z)$ centralizes both E and Z and consequently $C_R(Z) \subseteq C_P(C) = Z$ and all parts of the lemma are proved.

The effect of the preceding lemma is to reduce the classification of p-groups P with $d_c(P) = 1$ to the study of extra-special p-groups and of p-groups which contain a self-centralizing cyclic normal subgroup H. In Theorem 4.4 we have already considered the particular case that H is a maximal subgroup. For the general case we do not need a complete analysis, but simply the following lemma:

Lemma 4.8

Let P be a nonabelian p-group which contains a cyclic subgroup H of order p^n such that $C_P(H) = H$. Then

(i) $n \geqslant 2$ and if $n = 2$, then P is isomorphic to $M_3(p)$, p odd, D, or Q.

(ii) If $n > 2$, one of the following two statements holds:

(a) P is isomorphic to D_{n+1}, Q_{n+1}, or S_{n+1}, or

(b) $M = C_P(\mho^1(H))$ is isomorphic to $M_{n+1}(p)$ and $\Omega_1(M)$ char P.

Proof

If $|P:H| = p$, then H is maximal in P and the lemma follows from Theorem 4.4. Hence we may assume $|P:H| > p$. Since $C_P(H) = H$,

$\bar{P} = P/H$ is isomorphic to a subgroup of Aut H. Since $|\bar{P}| > p$, Lemma 4.1 implies that $n > 2$. Let $\bar{M}$ be the subgroup of $\bar{P}$ whose elements induce the trivial automorphism on $\mho^1(H)$ and let M be its inverse image in P, so that $M = C_P(\mho^1(H))$. By Corollary 4.2, $|\bar{M}| = p$ and if $H = \langle x \rangle$, then we can choose y in $M - H$ so that $x^y = x^{1+p^{n-1}}$. Since H is a maximal subgroup of M, Theorem 4.4 now yields that M is isomorphic to $M_{n+1}(p)$. Thus to complete the proof, we need only show that $\Omega_1(M)$ char P.

If $\bar{P}$ is cyclic, then $\bar{M} = \Omega_1(\bar{P})$. Since $\Omega_1(P)$ maps into $\Omega_1(\bar{P})$, it follows that $\Omega_1(P) \subseteq \Omega_1(M)$, whence $\Omega_1(M) = \Omega_1(P)$ char P. On the other hand, if $\bar{P}$ is noncyclic, Lemma 4.1 forces $p = 2$ and P must contain an element u such that $x^u = x^{-1}$. But then $\mho^1(H) = \langle x^2 \rangle \subseteq P'$. But $P' \subseteq H$ as $\bar{P}$ is abelian by Lemma 4.1, whence P' is cyclic. Hence $\mho^1(H)$ char P' char P and consequently also $M = C_P(\mho^1(H))$ char P. But then $\Omega_1(M)$ char P in this case as well.

We can now easily establish the following result of Philip Hall:

Theorem 4.9 (P. Hall)

Let P be a p-group which contains no noncyclic characteristic abelian subgroups. Then P is the central product of subgroups E and R, where either $E = 1$ or E is extra-special and either R is cyclic or $p = 2$ and R is isomorphic to D_m, Q_m, or S_m, $m \geqslant 4$.

Proof

Let C be a critical subgroup of P and set $Z = Z(C)$. By Lemma 4.7, Z is cyclic and P is the central product of two subgroups E and R, where either $E = 1$ or E is extra-special, $Z \vartriangleleft R$ and $C_R(Z) = Z$. If R is cyclic or is isomorphic to D_m, Q_m, or S_m, $m \geqslant 4$, the theorem follows; so we may assume that R is of none of these forms. Furthermore, if R is isomorphic to $M_3(p)$, D, or Q, then $R/\Omega_1(Z)$ is elementary abelian and consequently $P/\Omega_1(Z) = ER/\Omega_1(Z)$ is also elementary abelian. Thus $\Omega_1(Z) = P' = \Phi(P)$ and P is extra-special. Again the theorem follows. So we may also assume that R is not of one of these forms.

But now Lemma 4.8 implies that $|Z| = p^n$, $n > 2$, that $M = C_R(\mho^1(Z))$ is isomorphic to $M_{n+1}(p)$, and that $\Omega_1(M)$ char R. Since $P = ER$, it follows that $C_P(\mho^1(Z)) = EM$. But $\mho^1(Z)$ char Z char C char P, whence EM char P. Since any characteristic subgroup of EM is thus characteristic in P, it will suffice to show that $d_c(EM) > 1$, for then $d_c(P) > 1$, contrary to hypothesis.

Set $F = \Omega_1(EM)$. We shall argue that $Z(F)$ is noncyclic, which will prove that $d_c(EM) > 1$. Since M centralizes E and $E \cap M = E'$ is of order 1 or p, an element of F of order p is the product of elements of E and M, each of order at most p^2. This implies that $F \subseteq E\Omega_2(M)$. But $\Omega_2(M)$ is abelian of type (p^2, p) by Theorem 4.3(i) as $|M| = p^{n+1} \geqslant p^4$. Hence $F \cap M \subseteq Z(F)$. But $\Omega_1(M) \subseteq F \cap M$ and $\Omega_1(M)$ is abelian of type (p, p), giving the desired conclusion $Z(F)$ noncyclic.

As a corollary of the theorem, we have

Theorem 4.10

    (i) *If P is a p-group with no noncyclic abelian normal subgroups, then either P is cyclic or $p = 2$ and P is isomorphic to D_m, $m \geqslant 4$, Q_m, or S_m.*

    (ii) *If P is a p-group with no noncyclic abelian subgroups, then either P is cyclic or $p = 2$ and P is isomorphic to Q_m.*

Proof

Suppose $d_n(P) = 1$. Then certainly $d_c(P) = 1$; so by the preceding theorem, $P = ER$, where E, R satisfy the conditions of the theorem. In particular, (i) follows if $E = 1$; so we may assume $E \neq 1$.

Now any abelian subgroup of E of type (p, p) containing E' is normal in E and hence is normal in P. Since $d_n(P) = 1$, $E' = Z(E)$ is forced to be the unique subgroup of order p in E, whence $d(E) = 1$. Now let $x \in E - E'$ and set $H = \langle x \rangle$, $K = C_E(H)$. Since $x^p \in E'$ and $|x| > p$, we must have $\langle x^p \rangle = E'$ and $|x| = p^2$. We claim $K = H$. If not, then we can choose y in $K - H$, so certainly $y \in E - E'$. But then also $\langle y^p \rangle = E'$ and $|y| = p^2$. Replacing y by an appropriate power, we can assume without loss that $y^p = x^p$. Since y and x commute and $y \notin H$, it follows that $u = yx^{-1}$ is of order p and $u \notin E'$, a contradiction. Thus $H = K = C_E(H)$ and now Theorem 4.4 yields that E is isomorphic to $M_3(p)$, D, or Q. But $M_3(p)$ and D each contain noncyclic abelian subgroups by Theorem 4.3, so E must be isomorphic to Q. In particular, $p = 2$.

If $|R| \leqslant 2$, then $R \subseteq E$ and $P = E$ is quaternion. Hence we may assume $|R| > 2$, in which case R contains a cyclic normal subgroup L of order 4 by the structure of R. But then $L \lhd P$. If H is any subgroup of order 4 of E, H is also cyclic and $H \lhd P$. Since E and R commute elementwise, HL is thus an abelian normal subgroup of P of exponent 4. Since $|E \cap R| = 2$, $|HL| = 8$ and consequently HL is noncyclic, contrary to $d_n(P) = 1$. Thus (i) holds.

Finally, Theorem 4.3 shows that among the groups satisfying (i), only the cyclic groups and Q_m possess no noncyclic abelian subgroups; so (ii) follows at once from (i).

Theorem 4.10 in turn has the following important consequence:

Theorem 4.11

Let A be a regular group of automorphisms of a p-group P. Then the S_q-subgroups of A are cyclic for odd q and are cyclic or generalized quaternion for $q = 2$.

Proof

This follows at once from Theorem 4.10(ii) together with Theorem 3.14(ii).

To complete the classification of p-groups P for which $d_c(P) = 1$, it still remains to determine the structure of all extra-special p-groups. We prefer to carry this out in the next section along with the determination of other properties of extra-special groups.

We shall instead conclude the present section with a discussion of p-groups P in which $d_n(P) \leqslant 2$, p odd. Our principal result will be that in such a group, necessarily also $d(P) \leqslant 2$. Using this fact, Blackburn has completely classified all such groups (for $p = 2$, the classification is still open), but we shall not present his full results here. However, with the aid of the above property, we shall also derive a result on the automorphisms of such groups which we shall later need.

Our results depend upon a preliminary lemma, but first we establish two elementary facts.

Lemma 4.12

If x, y are elements of a p-group with $\langle x, y \rangle$ noncyclic, then $\langle y, y^x \rangle \subset \langle x, y \rangle$.

Proof

Set $Q = \langle y, y^x \rangle$ and $P = \langle x, y \rangle$. Clearly $Q \subseteq P$. Suppose $Q = P$. Since $[y, x] \in P'$, we have $[y, x] \in Q'$. But $[y, x] = y^{-1}y^x$ and consequently the coset $Q'y$ generates Q/Q'. Hence $Q/\Phi(Q)$ is cyclic and therefore $Q = P$ is cyclic by Corollary 1.2, contrary to hypothesis. Thus $Q \subset P$, as asserted.

Lemma 4.13

Let G be an arbitrary group and let A be a subgroup of Aut G which stabilizes a normal series of G of the form $G \supseteq H \supseteq 1$ with H abelian. Then A is abelian.

Proof

Let $\phi, \psi \in A$ and let $x \in G$. Then $x\phi = yx$ and $x\psi = zx$ with y, z in H. Furthermore, ϕ and ψ act trivially on H. But then a direct calculation gives

$$(4.11) \qquad (x)[\phi, \psi] = (x)\phi^{-1}\psi^{-1}\phi\psi = y^{-1}z^{-1}yzx = [y, z]x.$$

Since H is abelian, it follows that $(x)[\phi, \psi] = x$ and, as x is arbitrary, we conclude that $[\phi, \psi]$ acts trivially on G. Thus $[\phi, \psi] = 1$ for all ϕ, ψ in A and so A is abelian.

Lemma 4.14

Let P be a p-group, p odd, and let A be a maximal abelian normal subgroup of P with $m(A) = d_n(P)$. Then $\Omega_1(C_P(\Omega_1(A))) = \Omega_1(A)$.

Proof

By definition of $d_n(P)$, there exists a normal abelian subgroup A of P with $m(A) = d_n(P)$ and so we can always choose A to satisfy the conditions of the lemma. We must show that whenever an element x of P of order p centralizes $\Omega_1(A)$, then $x \in \Omega_1(A)$.

Let $x \in C_P(\Omega_1(A))$ with $x^p = 1$ and set $B_1 = \langle \Omega_1(A), x \rangle$. Let $B_1 \subset B_2 \subset \cdots \subset B_n = \langle A, x \rangle$ be an ascending chain of subgroups, each of index p in its successor, so that $B_i \lhd B_{i+1}$, $1 \leqslant i \leqslant n - 1$. We shall argue that $B_1 \lhd B_n = \langle A, x \rangle$. Indeed, suppose $B_1 \lhd B_m$ for some $m \leqslant n - 1$. Clearly $B_m = B_1(A \cap B_m)$. Since $A \lhd P$, $A \cap B_m \lhd B_m$ and consequently $[B_1, A \cap B_m] \subseteq B_1 \cap (A \cap B_m)$. Since B_1 and $A \cap B_m$ are each abelian, $[B_1, A \cap B_m]$ thus centralizes each of them and so lies in $Z(B_m)$. But also $B_1(A \cap B_m)/[B_1, A \cap B_m]$ is abelian and therefore B_m has class at most 2. Now let z be an element of order p in B_m. Since $B_m = (A \cap B_m)\langle x \rangle$, we have $z = yx^k$ for some integer k and some y in A. Since z and x^k have order 1 or p, it follows from Lemma 3.9(i) that $y = zx^{-k}$ has order 1 or p inasmuch as cl$(B_m) \leqslant 2$. Thus $y \in \Omega_1(A)$ and so $z \in B_i$. We conclude therefore that $B_1 = \Omega_1(B_m)$. But then B_1 char $B_m \lhd B_{m+1}$ and so $B_1 \lhd B_{m+1}$. Thus $B_1 \lhd B_n = \langle A, x \rangle$, as asserted.

Since $\Omega_1(A)$ and $B_1 = \langle \Omega_1(A), x \rangle$ are each normal in $\langle A, x \rangle$ and x is of order p, it follows that $B_1/\Omega_1(A) \subseteq Z(B_n/\Omega_1(A))$. Thus x centralizes $A/\Omega_1(A)$ as well as $\Omega_1(A)$ and so stabilizes the normal series $A \supseteq \Omega_1(A) \supset 1$ of A. This assertion holds for every x of order p which centralizes $\Omega_1(A)$.

We use this result to show that $D = \Omega_1(C_P(\Omega_1(A)))$ has exponent p; equivalently, that the set of elements of order 1 or p in D form a subgroup. If false, then there must exist x, y of order p in D such that $(xy)^p \neq 1$. Among all such choices of x, y, choose x, y so that $\langle x, y \rangle$ has minimal order. Lemma 3.9(i) implies that $\langle x, y \rangle$ has class at least 3. Hence by Lemma 4.12, $\langle y, y^x \rangle \subset \langle x, y \rangle$. Since y and y^x are each of order p, it follows therefore from our minimal choice of $\langle x, y \rangle$ that $y^{-1}y^x = [y, x]$ has order 1 or p. On the other hand, y and x each stabilize the normal series $A \supseteq \Omega_1(A) \supset 1$ of A and so $[y, x]$ centralizes A by Lemma 4.13. However,

$C_P(A) = A$ by Lemma 3.12 as A is a maximal abelian normal subgroup of P. Since $[y, x]^p = 1$, we conclude that $[y, x] \in \Omega_1(A)$. But then $[y, x]$ centralizes x and y which lie in the centralizer of $\Omega_1(A)$. This implies that $[y, x]$ is in the center of $\langle x, y \rangle$ and hence that $\langle x, y \rangle$ has class at most 2, which is not the case. This contradiction shows that D has exponent p, as asserted.

Finally, $\Omega_1(A) \subseteq D$ as A is abelian. If $\Omega_1(A) \subset D$, choose $E \lhd P$ with $\Omega_1(A) \subset E \subseteq D$ and $|E : \Omega_1(A)| = p$. By Lemma 1.3.4, E is abelian. Since D is of exponent p, E must be elementary abelian and consequently $m(E) = m(A) + 1 > d_n(P)$. Since $E \lhd P$, this is impossible and so $\Omega_1(A) = D$, completing the proof.

We remark that Lemma 4.14 is false in general for $p = 2$, the dihedral group of order 16 being a counterexample.

We can now prove

Theorem 4.15

Let P be a p-group in which $d_n(P) \leqslant 2$, p odd. Then the following conditions hold:

(i) $d(P) \leqslant 2$.
(ii) If ψ is an automorphism of P of prime order $q \neq p$, then q divides $p^2 - 1$. In particular, $q < p$.

Proof

Choose A in accordance with the preceding lemma, so that $m(A) \leqslant 2$, whence $\Omega_1(A)$ is elementary abelian of order p or p^2. Suppose that P contains an elementary abelian subgroup E of type (p, p, p) and set $E_1 = C_E(\Omega_1(A))$. Then $E_1 \subseteq \Omega_1(A)$ by the preceding lemma. On the other hand, as E/E_1 induces a group of linear transformations of $\Omega_1(A)$ as a vector space over Z_p, $|E/E_1| \leqslant p$ by Theorem 2.8.1 and consequently $m(E_1) \geqslant 2$. Since $m(\Omega_1(A)) \leqslant 2$, it follows that $E_1 = \Omega_1(A)$ and that $m(E_1) = 2$. But E centralizes $E_1 = \Omega_1(A)$, whence $E = E_1$. However, this is impossible since $m(E) = 3$. Thus (i) holds.

To prove (ii), let D be a ψ-invariant subgroup of P of minimal order on which ψ acts nontrivially. Then D is a special p-group of exponent p by Theorems 3.7 and 3.10. Furthermore, $d(D) \leqslant 2$ by (i). If D is abelian, then ψ induces a linear transformation of D as a vector space over Z_p of order q and Theorem 2.8.1 implies that q divides $p^2 - 1 = (p - 1)(p + 1)$. Since p is odd, certainly $q < p$.

If D is nonabelian, then $m(Z(D)) = 1$ since otherwise $m(Z(D)) = 2$ and any subgroup N of D of order p^3 containing $Z(D)$ would be elementary abelian by Lemma 1.3.4 and the fact that D is of exponent p. Thus D is extra-special. Let E be a normal subgroup of D of order p^2 and set $C = C_D(E)$. Since $E \subseteq Z(C)$, we reach the same contradiction if $C \supset E$. Hence $C = E$ and now Theorem 2.8.1 yields that $|D/E| = p$. Thus $|D| = p^3$ and so $\bar{D} = D/\Phi(D)$ is elementary abelian of order p^2. But ψ induces an automorphism of $\bar{D}$ of order q by Theorem 1.4 and the desired conclusions follow as in the preceding paragraph. Thus (ii) also holds.

5. EXTRA-SPECIAL p-GROUPS

We shall now analyze the structure of extra-special p-groups and shall also derive some properties of their representations.

We begin with the definition of an additional group of order p^3 in the case that p is odd. We set

$$M(p) = \langle x, y, z \mid x^p = y^p = z^p = 1, [x, z] = [y, z] = 1, \text{ and } [x, y] = z \rangle.$$

Then $M(p)$ is the semidirect product of the elementary abelian group $H = \langle x, z \rangle$ of type (p, p) by the group $\langle y \rangle$ of order p, where y is determined by the automorphism ϕ of H of order p given by $x\phi = xz$ and $z\phi = z$. Thus $M(p)$ has order p^3 and class 2. Moreover, by definition, $\Omega_1(M(p)) = M(p)$ and, as p is odd, it follows also that $M(p)$ is of exponent p. In particular, $M(p)$ is not isomorphic to $M_3(p)$, which is also of order p^3.

We first prove

Theorem 5.1

A nonabelian p-group P of order p^3 is extra-special and is isomorphic to one of the groups $M_3(p)$, $M(p)$, D, or Q.

Proof

If P contains a cyclic subgroup of order p^2, then P is isomorphic to $M_3(p)$, D, or Q by the results of the preceding section, so we may assume P possesses no such subgroup. But then P must be of exponent p. Since P is nonabelian, this forces p to be odd. Let H be a maximal subgroup of P, so that $|H| = p^2$ and hence H is elementary abelian of type (p, p). We have $|Z(P)| = p$, since otherwise P would be abelian by Lemma 1.3.4. Since $H \triangleleft P$, $H \cap Z(P) \neq 1$ and hence $Z(P) \subset H$. By the same lemma, $P/Z(P)$ is elementary abelian of order p^2. In particular, this implies that $Z(P) = P' = \Phi(P)$ and P is extra-special. Moreover, if we choose y in $P - H$ and x in $H - Z(P)$, it follows that $[x, y] = z \in Z(P)$. Since $P = \langle Z(P), x, y \rangle$ and P is nonabelian, $z \neq 1$, whence $P = \langle x, y, z \rangle$ is isomorphic to (Mp).

For simplicity of notation, we set $M = M(p)$ and $N = M_3(p)$. Furthermore, for any extra-special p-group E, we shall denote by E^k the central product of k copies of E. Then $Z(E) = Z(E^k)$ and $E^k/Z(E)$ is elementary abelian, so that E^k is also an extra-special group. For completeness, set $E^0 = 1$. Finally if E and F are extra-special groups, it will be understood in the balance of the section that EF is to denote their central product.

With these conventions, we can now establish our main result:

Theorem 5.2

An extra-special p-group P is the central product of $r \geqslant 1$ nonabelian subgroups of order p^3. Moreover, we have

(i) *If p is odd, P is isomorphic to $N^k M^{r-k}$, while if $p = 2$, P is isomorphic to $D^k Q^{r-k}$ for some k. In either case, $|P| = p^{2r+1}$.*

(ii) *If p is odd and $k \geqslant 1$, $N^k M^{r-k}$ is isomorphic to NM^{r-1}, the groups M^r and NM^{r-1} are not isomorphic, M^r is of exponent p, and $d_c(NM^{r-1}) > 1$.*

(iii) *If $p = 2$, then $D^k Q^{r-k}$ is isomorphic to DQ^{r-1} if k is odd and to Q^r if k is even, and the groups Q^r and DQ^{r-1} are not isomorphic.*

Proof

For x in $P - Z(P)$, there exists y in P such that $[x, y] = z \neq 1$. Then $\langle z \rangle = Z(P)$ as $P' = Z(P)$ is of order p. Furthermore, x^p and y^p lie in $Z(P)$ as $P/Z(P)$ is elementary abelian, and so $P_1 = \langle x, y, z \rangle$ is a nonabelian group of order p^3. By Theorem 5.1 P_1 is extra-special. Since $[P, P] \subseteq Z(P) = Z(P_1)$, certainly $[P, P_1] \subseteq Z(P_1)$. But now Lemma 4.6 implies that $P = P_1 R$, where $R = C_P(P_1)$. Since R centralizes P_1, $Z(R) \subseteq Z(P)$ and so $Z(R) = Z(P)$. Hence either $R = Z(R) \subseteq P_1$, in which case $P = P_1$, or else R is nonabelian. In the latter case $R' = P' = Z(P)$ and $R/Z(P) \subseteq P/Z(P)$ is elementary abelian, so that R is extra-special. But now it follows by induction that R is the central product of nonabelian subgroups P_i, $2 \leqslant i \leqslant r$, of order p^3 and that $|R| = p^{2r-1}$. Thus P is the central product of P_i, $1 \leqslant i \leqslant r$, and as $P_1 \cap R = Z(R)$, $|P| = p^{2r+1}$. Furthermore, Theorem 5.1 yields that P_i is isomorphic to M or N if p is odd and to D or Q if $p = 2$. Since the factors P_i commute elementwise, they can be written in any order and we conclude that all parts of (i) hold.

Assume now that p is odd. Since M has exponent p and since the distinct components of M^r commute elementwise, it follows that M^r is of exponent p. For the same reason $\Omega_1(NM^{r-1}) = \Omega_1(N)M^{r-1}$. But $\Omega_1(N)$ is abelian of type (p, p) and so $\Omega_1(N)$ char $\Omega_1(NM^{r-1})$ char NM^{r-1}. Thus $d_c(NM^{r-1}) \geqslant 2$. Since NM^{r-1} has exponent p^2, it is not isomorphic to M^r. Thus to complete the proof of (ii), we need only show that $N^k M^{r-k}$ and NM^{r-1}

are isomorphic for all $k \geqslant 1$. This will follow immediately if we prove that N^2 and NM are isomorphic.

Now $P = N^2$ has generators $\langle x_1, y_1, x_2, y_2 \rangle$ with $\langle x_1, y_1 \rangle$ centralizing $\langle x_2, y_2 \rangle$ and $|x_i| = p^2$, $|y_i| = p$, $x_i^{y_i} = x_i^{1+p}$, $1 \leqslant i \leqslant 2$. Furthermore, $\langle x_1^p \rangle = \langle x_2^p \rangle = Z(P)$. Replacing x_2 by an appropriate power, we can suppose that $x_1^p = x_2^p$. Setting $u_2 = x_2 x_1^{-1}$, we then have $u_2^p = (x_2 x_1^{-1})^p = x_2^p (x_1^p)^{-1} = 1$. Furthermore, y_2 does not centralize u_2 and consequently $\langle y_2, u_2 \rangle = P_1$ must be isomorphic to M. But now as in the proof of (i), we have $P = P_1 P_2$, where P_2 is also extra-special of order p^3. If P_2 were isomorphic to M, then P would be isomorphic to M^2 and so would be of exponent p, which is not the case. Thus P_2 is isomorphic to N and $P = N^2$ is isomorphic to MN, completing the proof of (ii).

Finally, assume that $p = 2$. We first argue that D^2 and Q^2 are isomorphic. If $P = Q^2$, then $P = \langle x_1, y_1, x_2, y_2 \rangle$ with $\langle x_1, y_1 \rangle$ centralizing $\langle x_2, y_2 \rangle$, $x_i^{y_i} = x_i^{-1}$, $x_i^2 = y_i^2 = z$, and $z^2 = 1$, $1 \leqslant i \leqslant 2$. Set $P_1 = \langle x_1, y_1 x_2 \rangle$ and $P_2 = \langle x_2, y_2 x_1 \rangle$. Then $y_1 x_2$ and $y_2 x_1$ are each of order 2 and conjugate x_1, x_2, respectively, into their inverses. Thus P_1, P_2 are both isomorphic to D. But x_1 centralizes x_2, y_2, and x_1 and so centralizes P_2. Similarly, $y_1 x_2$ centralizes x_2. Finally,

$$(y_2 x_1)^{y_1 x_2} = y_2^{y_1 x_2} x_1^{y_1 x_2} = y_2^{x_2} x_1^{y_1} = y_2^{-1} x_1^{-1} = (z y_2)(z x_1) = y_2 x_1.$$

Thus $y_2 x_1$ and $y_1 x_2$ also commute, whence P_1 centralizes P_2. We conclude that Q^2 and D^2 are isomorphic. This in turn implies that $D^k Q^{r-k}$ is ismorphic to $D Q^{r-1}$ or Q^r according as k is odd or even.

To complete the proof of (iii), it remains to show that $D Q^{r-1}$ and Q^r are not isomorphic, which we shall accomplish by proving that they have distinct numbers of cyclic subgroups of order 4. Consider Q^r, which we write as $Q = Q_1 Q_2 \cdots Q_r$. Set $\langle z \rangle = Z(Q^r)$. Let $\langle x \rangle$ be a cyclic subgroup of order 4 and write $x = x_1 x_2 \cdots x_r$ with $x_i \in Q_i$, $1 \leqslant i \leqslant r$. Then we have

$$(5.1) \qquad x = z^a x_{i_1} x_{i_2} \cdots x_{i_h} \qquad x_{i_j} \in Q_j - \langle z \rangle, \ 1 \leqslant j \leqslant k,$$

and $a = 0$ or 1. If $a = 1$, then $z x_{i_1} = x_{i_1}^{-1}$ and $x_{i_1}^{-1} \in Q_{i_1} - \langle z \rangle$. Conversely if $x_{i_j} \in Q_{i_j} - \langle z \rangle$, $1 \leqslant j \leqslant h$, with $i_j \neq i_k$ if $j \neq k$, then x_{i_j} and x_{i_k} commute for all j, k. Hence if we set $x = x_{i_1} x_{i_2} \cdots x_{i_k}$, we obtain $x^2 = z^h$ and consequently x has order 4 if and only if h is odd. Furthermore, if h is odd, $x^{-1} = x_{i_1}^{-1} x_{i_2}^{-1} \cdots x_{i_h}^{-1} = x_{i_1}^{-1} x_{i_2} \cdots x_{i_h}$. Similarly, if x_{i_k} is replaced by $x_{i_k}^{-1}$, then x is replaced by x^{-1}, $1 \leqslant k \leqslant h$. Finally we note that x and x^{-1} generate the same cyclic subgroup of order 4.

Since there are exactly six elements in $Q_i - \langle z \rangle$, the preceding analysis shows that for a given choice of the indices $i_1, i_2, \ldots, i_h$, h odd, the number of distinct cyclic subgroups of order 4 obtained is precisely 3^h. But clearly distinct sets of indices determine disjoint sets of cyclic subgroups of order 4. We conclude that the total number m of cyclic subgroups of order 4 in Q^r is given by

$$(5.2) \qquad\qquad m = \sum_h 3^h \binom{r}{h},$$

where h runs over all odd integers from 1 to r. But now using the binomial formula, we can rewrite (5.2) as

$$(5.3) \qquad m = 1/2\{(1 + 3)^r - (1 - 3)^r\} = 1/2\{2^{2r} - (-2)^r\}.$$

An entirely similar calculation, which we leave as an exercise, yields that the number n of cyclic subgroups of order 4 in DQ^{r-1} is given by

$$(5.4) \qquad\qquad n = 1/2\{2^{2r} + (-2)^r\}.$$

Together (5.3) and (5.4) yield the desired conclusion $m \neq n$, completing the proof of the theorem.

As a corollary we have the following sharpening of Philip Hall's theorem for odd p:

Theorem 5.3

For odd p, a p-group P in which $d_c(P) = 1$ is isomorphic to the central product of a cyclic group and M^r for some r.

We shall next analyze the representations of extra-special p-groups. For a group of order p^3, we have

Theorem 5.4

Let P be an extra-special p-group of order p^3 and let F be a field of characteristic 0 or prime to p, which contains a primitive p^2-root of unity. Then

    (i) *F is splitting field of P.*

    (ii) *P has exactly $p^2 + p - 1$ inequivalent irreducible representations over F, p^2 of degree 1 and $p - 1$ of degree p. Those of degree p are faithful and represent a generator of $Z(P)$ by distinct scalar matrices.*

Proof

If $x \in P - Z(P)$, then $|C_P(x)| = p^2$, so x has exactly p conjugates. Thus $P - Z(P)$ consists of $(p^3 - p)/p = p^2 - 1$ conjugate classes. Since each element of $Z(P)$ is conjugate only to itself, there are precisely $p^2 + p - 1$

conjugate classes in G. Hence by Theorem 3.6.14 this is the number of irreducible representations of G over an algebraic closure L of F. Since $|P/Z(P)| = p^2$, p^2 of these are of degree 1 by Theorem 3.2.4, and so there are $p - 1$ nonlinear representations. Since P/N is abelian for any nontrivial normal subgroup of P, the nonlinear representations must all be faithful.

Suppose $p = 2$, in which case P is isomorphic to D or Q by Theorem 5.1. But if i is a primitive fourth root of unity in F, the matrices $\begin{pmatrix} i & 0 \\ 0 & -i \end{pmatrix}$ and $\begin{pmatrix} 0 & 1 \\ \varepsilon & 0 \end{pmatrix}$ generate a group isomorphic to D if $\varepsilon = 1$ and to Q if $\varepsilon = -1$, which is clearly irreducible. Thus the one nonlinear irreducible representation of P can be written in F. Since clearly the linear representations of P can also be written in F, F is a splitting field of P by Theorem 3.5.9.

Suppose then that p is odd, in which case P is isomorphic to $M_3(p)$ or $M(p)$ by Theorem 5.1. In the first case, let $P = \langle x, y \mid x^{p^2} = y^p = 1$ and $x^y = x^{1+p} \rangle$. Let ω be a primitive p^2-root of unity in F, and consider the mappings ϕ_i, $1 \le i \le p - 1$, of P into $GL(p, F)$ determined by

$$(5.5) \qquad x\phi_i = \operatorname{diag}\left(\omega^{i(1+(p-1)p)}, \ldots, \omega^{i(1+p)}, \omega^i\right)$$

$$y\phi_i = \begin{pmatrix} 0 & 1 & 0 & \cdots & 0 \\ 0 & 0 & 1 & \cdots & 0 \\ & & & \vdots & \\ 1 & 0 & 0 & \cdots & 0 \end{pmatrix}.$$

One verifies easily that each ϕ_i is an isomorphism of P onto an irreducible group of matrices, so that each ϕ_i is an irreducible matrix representation of P over L. Since $(x^p)\phi_i$ is the scalar matrix $\omega^{ip}I$ and since $\langle x^p \rangle = Z(P)$, ϕ_i and ϕ_j are inequivalent for $i \ne j$. Thus the $p - 1$ nonlinear irreducible representations of P are all of degree p and can be written in F. Since the linear representations of P can also be written in F, F is again a splitting field of P.

If $P = \langle x, y, z \mid x^p = y^p = z^p = 1, [x, z] = [y, z] = 1, [x, y] = z \rangle$ is isomorphic to $M(p)$ and if $\eta = \omega^p$, the same argument applies provided we define ϕ_i, $1 \le i \le p - 1$, on the generators x, y of P by

$$(5.6) \qquad x\phi_i = \operatorname{diag}\left(\eta^{i(p-1)}, \ldots, \eta^i, 1\right) \qquad y\phi_i = \begin{pmatrix} 0 & 1 & 0 & \cdots & 0 \\ 0 & 0 & 1 & \cdots & 0 \\ & & & \vdots & \\ 1 & 0 & 0 & \cdots & 0 \end{pmatrix}.$$

By Theorem 5.2, every extra-special p-group P is the central product of extra-special groups of order p^3. Hence by Theorems 2.7.1 and 2.7.2 the irreducible representations of P are all obtained as tensor products of irreducible representations of the individual factors of P and so can be determined from the preceding theorem. We shall not attempt to give a complete statement, but shall content ourselves with the following result, which we shall need later.

Theorem 5.5

Let P be an extra-special p-group of order p^{2r+1} and let F be a field of characteristic 0 or prime to p which contains a primitive p^2-root of unity. Then the faithful irreducible representations of P over F are all of degree p^r.

Proof

Since the dimension over F of the tensor product of vector spaces is the product of their individual dimensions, the conclusion follows at once from the preceding theorem together with the fact that P, being of order p^{2r+1}, is the central product of r extra-special groups of order p^3.

6. THE ASSOCIATED LIE RING

Many problems concerning p-groups, particularly questions about their automorphisms, can be transformed into questions concerning the corresponding associated Lie ring that are often easier to treat. We shall now describe this ring and shall then give a few applications of the technique.

First of all, a *Lie ring* is a set R together with two binary operations, addition and Lie multiplication, denoted, respectively, by $x + y$ and $[x, y]$ for x, y in R which satisfy the following conditions:

(6.1) R is an abelian group under addition,

(6.2) $[x + y, z] = [x, z] + [y, z]$ and $[x, y + z] = [x, y] + [x, z]$,

(6.3) $[x, x] = 0$,

(6.4) $[[x, y], z] + [[y, z], x] + [[z, x], y] = 0$,

for all x, y, z in R. Here 0 is the identity for addition and, as usual, $-x$ will denote the additive inverse of x. Formula (6.4) is known as the *Jacobi* identity.

Any associative ring R can be made into a Lie ring by defining the Lie multiplication by the rule

$$[x, y] = xy - yx,$$

as is easily verified.

A Lie ring R is called a *Lie algebra* over a field F if F operates on R in such a way that R is a vector space over F with respect to addition and

(6.5) $a[x, y] = [ax, y] = [x, ay]$

for all x, y in R and a in F.

Given any group, there is a natural way of associating a Lie ring with it, which is primarily of value for the study of p-groups (and nilpotent groups). For this reason we shall define it only in the case of a p-group P. Let $P = P_1 \supset P_2 \supset \cdots \supset P_{n+1} = 1$ be the lower central series of P, so that $P_i = L_i(P) = [P_{i-1}, P] = [P, P, \ldots, P]$ (i factors). The construction depends upon the following lemma, where we are using the notation $x \equiv y \pmod{H}$ for $xy^{-1} \in H$:

Lemma 6.1

Let $x, x' \in P_i$, $y, y' \in P_j$, and $z \in P_k$. Then we have
  (i) $[x, y] \in P_{i+j}$.
  (ii) If $x \equiv x' \pmod{P_{i+1}}$ and $y \equiv y' \pmod{P_{j+1}}$, then
      $[x, y] \equiv [x', y'] \pmod{P_{i+j+1}}$.
  (iii) $[xx', y] \equiv [x, y][x', y] \pmod{P_{i+j+1}}$ and
      $[x, yy'] \equiv [x, y][x, y'] \pmod{P_{i+j+1}}$.
  (iv) $[x, y, z][y, z, x][z, x, y] \equiv 0 \pmod{P_{i+j+k+1}}$.
  (v) For any nonnegative integer a,
      $[x, y]^a \equiv [x^a, y] \equiv [x, y^a] \pmod{P_{i+j+1}}$.

Proof

We shall prove by induction on j that $[P_i, P_j] \subseteq P_{i+j}$, and this will establish (i). For $j = 1$, this is immediate from the definition, so assume $j > 1$. Set $H = [P_1, P_i, P_{j-1}][P_i, P_{j-1}, P_1]$. It follows directly from our induction assumption that $H \subseteq P_{i+j}$, so we need only show that $[P_i, P_j] \subseteq H$. But $H \triangleleft P$ by Theorem 2.2.1(ix) and so we can apply the three-subgroup lemma in P/H to conclude that $[P_{j-1}, P_1, P_i] \subseteq H$. However, $[P_{j-1}, P_1, P_i] = [[P_{j-1}, P_1], P_i] = [P_j, P_i] = [P_i, P_j]$, giving the desired conclusion $[P_i, P_j] \subseteq H$.

Now we prove (ii). Let $x' = xu$, $u \in P_{i+1}$. Then $[x', y] = [xu, y] =$

$[x, y][x, y, u][u, y]$ by Lemma 2.2.4(i). But by (i), both $[x, y, u]$ and $[u, y]$ lie in P_{i+j+1}, so $[x', y] \equiv [x, y] \pmod{P_{i+j+1}}$. Similarly, $[x', y'] \equiv [x', y]$ $\pmod{P_{i+j+1}}$ and (ii) follows.

Again by Lemma 2.2.4(i) and (i), we have $[xx', y] = [x, y][x, y, x']$ $[x', y] \equiv [x, y][x', y] \pmod{P_{i+j+1}}$. The second relation of (iii) follows similarly. Furthermore, (v) follows at once from (iii) by induction on a.

To prove (iv), we use the identity

(6.6) $[x, y^{-1}, z]^y[y, z^{-1}, x]^z[z, x^{-1}, y]^x = 1.$

Set $w = [x, y^{-1}, z]$. Then $w \in P_{i+j+k}$ by (i). Since $w^y = w[w, y]$, another application of (i) yields that $w^y \equiv w \pmod{P_{i+j+k+1}}$. Furthermore, since P_{i+j}/P_{i+j+1} is abelian, the elements $[x, y]^{-1}$ and $[x, y^{-1}]$ have the same images in this factor group, so $w^y \equiv [[x, y]^{-1}, z] \pmod{P_{i+j+k+1}}$. Repeating this argument, we conclude finally that $w^y \equiv [x, y, z]^{-1} \pmod{P_{i+j+k+1}}$. By symmetry, the corresponding result holds for the other two terms of (6.6) and consequently

(6.7) $[x, y, z]^{-1}[y, z, x]^{-1}[z, x, y]^{-1} \equiv 1 \pmod{P_{i+j+k+1}}.$

Finally, taking inverses in (6.7), we obtain (iv).

Now set $L_i = P_i/P_{i+1}$, $1 \leqslant i \leqslant n$. Then each L_i is an abelian group which we consider to be written additively. We let L be the direct sum of the groups $L_i, 1 \leqslant i \leqslant n$, so that L is an abelian group. We make L into a Lie ring by introducing a Lie product on L. We first define $[\bar{x}, \bar{y}]$ for $\bar{x}$ in L_i and $\bar{y}$ in L_j as the image of $[x, y]$ in L_{i+j}, where x, y are representatives of $\bar{x}, \bar{y}$ in P_i, P_j, respectively. By parts (i) and (ii) of the lemma, $[\bar{x}, \bar{y}]$ is, in fact, a well-defined element of L_{i+j}, determined independently of the choice of the coset representatives x, y. (It is, of course, to be understood that $L_k = 0$ if $k > n$.) For $\bar{x}$ in L_i, $\bar{y}$ in L_j, and $\bar{z}$ in L_k, the linearity conditions (6.2) follow from part (iii) and the Jacobi identity (6.4) from part (iv) of the lemma. Since $[x, x] = 1$, we also have $[\bar{x}, \bar{x}] = 1$ for any $\bar{x}$ in L_i. We now extend the definition of the Lie product to all of L by means of linearity. When we do this, conditions (6.2), (6.3), and (6.4) are seen to hold when $\bar{x}, \bar{y}, \bar{z}$ are arbitrary elements of L. Thus L is a Lie ring.

L is called the *associated Lie ring* of P. We denote it by $L(P)$. If each L_i is of exponent p, then $L(P)$ will actually be a Lie algebra over Z_p. Indeed, in this case L is a vector space over Z_p. Furthermore, condition (6.5) follows from part (v) of the lemma.

A Lie ring L of the form $L = L_1 \oplus L_2 \oplus \cdots \oplus L_n$ with $[L_i, L_j] \subseteq L_{i+j}$ and each L_i a p-group is called a *homogeneous* Lie ring of characteristic p. It is not difficult to show that there exist such Lie rings which are not of the form $L(P)$ for some p-group P. This is due to the fact the power structure in a p-group imposes, in general, some limitations on the possible homogeneous Lie rings of characteristic p that can arise as associated Lie rings.

Now let ϕ be an automorphism of P. Since each P_i char P, ϕ induces an automorphism of each L_i and hence of $L(P)$ as an abelian group (which we denote by the same letter). If $L(P)$ is a Lie algebra over Z_p, this induced automorphism will also be a linear transformation of $L(P)$ as a vector space over Z_p. Since $[x, y]\phi = [x\phi, y\phi]$ for all x, y in P, it follows at once from the definition of $L(P)$ that

$$[\bar{x}, \bar{y}]\phi = [\bar{x}\phi, \bar{y}\phi].$$

Thus ϕ also preserves the Lie multiplication of $L(P)$ and so by definition, ϕ is an automorphism of $L(P)$ as a Lie ring or Lie algebra over Z_p. Furthermore, if ϕ is a p'-automorphism of P and if ϕ^h induces the identity automorphism of $L(P)$, then ϕ^h acts trivially on each $L_i = P_i/P_{i+1}$ and so ϕ^h stabilizes the lower central series of P. But then ϕ^h is the identity on P by Theorem 3.2. Thus ϕ has the same order on $L(P)$ as it has on P. We have thus proved:

Theorem 6.2

Let ϕ be an automorphism of the p-group P. Then ϕ induces an automorphism of the associated Lie ring or Lie algebra $L(P)$ of P. If $m = |\phi|$ is prime to p, the induced automorphism of $L(P)$ is also of order m.

It is because of Theorem 6.2 that we are able to translate questions about automorphisms of P into those of automorphisms of $L(P)$. The advantage of working in $L = L(P)$, particularly when L is a Lie algebra over Z_p, is that we can pass to the extended Lie algebra $L_F = L \otimes_{Z_p} F$ for any extension field F of Z_p. Thus if ϕ has order m, we can take F to be $Z_p(\omega)$, where ω is a primitive mth root of unity, in which case the characteristic roots of ϕ as a linear transformation of L_F lie in F.

That L_F is, in fact, a Lie algebra is clear, for if v_i, $1 \leqslant i \leqslant t$, is a basis of L over Z_p, the products $[v_i, v_j]$ are well-defined elements of L and hence also of L_F. Since the v_i are also a basis of L_F over F, we can extend the Lie product to all of L_F by linearity. When we do this, L_F becomes a Lie algebra over F. Furthermore, an automorphism ϕ of L induces in a natural way an automorphism of L_F.

To exploit this situation, we need the following general lemma:

Lemma 6.3

Let T be an irreducible linear transformation of V/Z_p and let $m = |T|$, $n = \dim_{Z_p} V$. Then

   (i) $m \mid (p^n - 1)$.
   (ii) For some primitive mth root of unity over Z_p, the characteristic roots of T on V are ω^{p^i}, $0 \leqslant i \leqslant n - 1$, and they are all distinct.

Proof

Since T acts irreducibly on V/Z_p, the characteristic polynomial $f(X)$ of T is irreducible over Z_p. Adjoin a root ω of $f(X)$ to Z_p and set $F = Z_p(\omega)$. Then $[F:Z_p] = n$ as $f(X)$ is of degree $n = \dim_{Z_p} V$. Thus $F = GF(p^n)$. Furthermore, we know that the Galois group of F over Z_p is cyclic of order n and is generated by an automorphism σ taking a into a^p for all a in F. Since ω is a root of $f(X)$ over Z_p, so also are $\omega^{\sigma^i} = \omega^{p^i}$, $0 \leqslant i \leqslant n - 1$. If $0 \leqslant i, j \leqslant n - 1$ and $i \neq j$, then $\omega^{\sigma^i} \neq \omega^{\sigma^j}$, since otherwise σ^i and σ^j would determine the same automorphism of F. Thus ω^{p^i}, $0 \leqslant i \leqslant n - 1$, are the characteristic roots of T and they are all distinct.

Finally since $f(X) \mid (X^m - 1)$, we have $\omega^m = 1$. On the other hand, since the characteristic roots of T^j are the jth power of those of T and as $|T| = m$, it follows that $\omega^j \neq 1$ for $1 \leqslant j < m$. Thus ω is a primitive mth root of unity. Since the multiplicative group of $GF(p^n)$ is cyclic of order $p^n - 1$, m must divide $p^n - 1$ and the lemma is proved.

The lemma shows that $p^n - 1$ is an upper bound for the order of T. That this upper bound can actually be achieved can be seen by identifying V with the additive group of $GF(p^n)$ and defining T by the rule $vT = v\zeta$ for all v in $V = GF(p^n)$, where ζ is a generator of the multiplicative group of $GF(p^n)$. Then it is immediate that T is an irreducible linear transformation of V of order $p^n - 1$. Thus as an elementary consequence of the lemma, we have

Corollary 6.4

Let P be an elementary abelian p-group of order p^n. Any automorphism of P which acts irreducibly on P has order dividing $p^n - 1$ and P possesses such an automorphism of order $p^n - 1$.

We shall now use the associated Lie ring to determine an upper bound for the order of a p'-automorphism of an extra-special p-group P which acts trivially on P' and irreducibly on $\bar{P} = P/P'$. Although $\bar{P}$ admits an irreducible automorphism of order $|\bar{P}| - 1$ by the preceding corollary, we shall see that a bound for ϕ is considerably smaller. Our argument applies equally well for any nonabelian special p-group, so we consider this more general case.

Theorem 6.5

Let ϕ be a p'-automorphism of the nonabelian special p-group P and assume that ϕ acts trivially on P' and irreducibly on P/P'. If $|\phi| = m$ and $|P/P'| = p^n$, then m divides $p^r + 1$ for some integer $r \leqslant n/2$.

Proof

Consider $L = L(P)$. In this case $L = L_1 \oplus L_2$, L_1 is elementary abelian, L_2 is elementary abelian, L is a Lie algebra over Z_p, and ϕ determines an automorphism (also denoted by ϕ) of L of order m which acts trivially on L_2 and irreducibly on L_1. By Lemma 6.3, m divides $p^n - 1$ and the characteristic roots of ϕ on L_1 are $\omega^{p^i}, 0 \leqslant i \leqslant n - 1$, for some primitive mth root of unity over Z_p and they are distinct. We set $F = Z_p(\omega)$ and $M_i = L_i \otimes_{Z_p} F, 1 \leqslant i \leqslant 2$, so that $L_F = M_1 \oplus M_2$. Then ϕ can be considered as an automorphism of L_F leaving the subspaces M_i invariant. Moreover, M_1 possesses a basis $v_i, 0 \leqslant i \leqslant n - 1$, consisting of characteristic vectors of ϕ:

$$(6.8) \qquad\qquad v_i \phi = \omega^{p^i} v_i.$$

In addition, ϕ acts trivially on M_2.

We claim $[v_i, v_j] \neq 0$ for some i, j. If not, then $[M_1, M_1] = 0$. But then $[M_1, M_2] = [M_2, M_1] = [M_2, M_2] = 0$ by definition of L and L_F, whence $[L_F, L_F] = 0$. But L is a subset of L_F and the Lie product in L_F agrees with that of L on L, so $[L, L] = 0$, which is not the case.

Choose $i, j, 0 \leqslant i, j \leqslant n - 1$ so that $[v_i, v_j] = v \neq 0$. Then certainly $i \neq j$; so we may assume $i < j$. Since $v \in M_2$ and ϕ preserves the Lie product, we obtain, using (6.8),

$$v = v\phi = [v_i, v_j]\phi = [v_i \phi, v_j \phi] = [\omega^{p^i} v_i, \omega^{p^j} v_j] = \omega^{p^i + p^j} v.$$

Since $v \neq 0$, this yields

$$(6.9) \qquad \omega^{p^i + p^j} = 1 \qquad \text{for some } i, j, 0 \leqslant i < j \leqslant n - 1.$$

But as ω is a primitive mth root of unity and $(m, p) = 1$, it follows from (6.9) that

$$m \,|\, (p^t + 1) \qquad \text{where } t = j - i.$$

Since m also divides $p^n - 1$, it thus divides $(p^t + 1) + (p^n - 1) = p^n + p^t = p^t(p^{n-t} + 1)$, whence also

$$m \,|\, (p^{n-t} + 1).$$

Since $r = \min (t, n - t) \leqslant n/2$, the theorem follows.

In the case that P is extra-special and p is odd, it can be shown that the bound $p^{n/2} + 1$ can always be achieved.

As a corollary of the theorem we obtain the following extension of Theorem 3.10:

Theorem 6.6

Let ϕ be an automorphism of the 2-group P and assume $|\phi|$ is a Mersenne prime greater than 3. Then ϕ acts nontrivially on $\Omega_1(P)$.

Proof

If the theorem is false, we reduce by induction as in the proof of Theorem 3.10 to the case that P is a nonabelian special 2-group and that ϕ acts trivially on P' and irreducibly on $\bar{P} = P/P'$. Set $|\bar{P}| = 2^n$. By assumption $|\phi| = 2^m - 1$ for some $m > 2$. But now $2^m - 1$ divides $2^r + 1$ for suitable $r \leqslant n/2$ by Theorem 6.5. Writing $r = am + b$ with $0 \leqslant b < m$, we obtain by successive division by $2^m - 1$ that $2^m - 1$ must divide $2^b + 1$. But $2^b + 1 < 2^m - 1$ since $m \geqslant 3$ and $0 \leqslant b < m$, and we reach a contradiction.

A variety of results of this general nature can be derived by these techniques; we shall list some as exercises. For example, using the associated Lie ring G. Higman has studied regular automorphisms of prime order q of p-groups P and has shown that the class of P is bounded by a suitable function of q, independent of p.

EXERCISES

1. Let A be a subgroup of Aut G which stabilizes the normal series $G = G_0 \supseteq G_1 \supseteq \cdots \supseteq G_n = 1$. Prove
   (i) $\pi(A) \subseteq \pi(G)$.
   (ii) If G is nilpotent, then A is nilpotent.
   (iii) If each $G_i \lhd G$, then A is nilpotent.
2. Let P be a 2-group of order 64 in which $Z(P) = P'$ and $Z(P)$ is elementary abelian of order 4. If P possesses an automorphism of order 5, show that P is special and is uniquely determined up to isomorphism.
3. If P is a p-group of class at least $m \geqslant 3$, show that $L_{m-1}(P)$ is abelian and hence show that P possesses a characteristic abelian subgroup which is not contained in $Z(P)$.
4. Let P be a 2-group and let A be a subgroup of Aut P of odd order. Assume that A acts trivially on every characteristic abelian subgroup of P and that $[P, A] = P$. Prove that P is a nonabelian special group. (Use Exercise 3.)

5. Let P be a 2-group of class 2 in which P' is elementary abelian. Prove
   (i) $\Omega_2(P)$ has exponent 4.
   (ii) If α is an automorphism of P of odd order which acts trivially on $\Omega_2(P)$, then $\alpha = 1$.

6. Complete the proof of all parts of Theorem 4.3.

7. (i) If G is dihedral of order 8, prove that Aut G is isomorphic to G.
   (ii) If G is a quaternion group, prove that Aut G is isomorphic to the symmetric group S_4.

8. Give a direct proof of Theorem 4.10(i) utilizing Theorem 4.4.

9. Let P be a p-group and let Q be a normal subgroup of P which contains no normal elementary abelian subgroup of P of order p^2. Show that either Q is cyclic of $p = 2$ and Q is dihedral, semi-dihedral, or generalized quaternion.

10. Let P be a 2-group in which $Z(P)$ is cyclic and let Q be an elementary abelian subgroup of P of order 4 such that $|P : C_P(Q)| \leqslant 2$. Prove that $Q \lhd P$.

11. Let P be a 2-group of class 2 such that $Z(P)$ is cyclic and $P/Z(P)$ is elementary abelian. If A is a subgroup of Aut P of odd order, show that $[P, A]$ is extra-special.

12. Let P be an extra-special p-group and let F be a field of characteristic not p which contains a p^2-root of unity. Show that P has exactly $p - 1$ inequivalent nonlinear irreducible representations over F.

13. Let P be a p-group and let A be an elementary abelian subgroup of Aut P of order q^2, q a prime, $q \neq p$. Assume that A possesses exactly two distinct subgroups A_i of order q such that $C_P(A_i) \neq 1$, $1 \leqslant i \leqslant 2$. Prove that

$$P = C_P(A_1) \times C_P(A_2).$$

14. Construct a 3-group of maximal class of order 3^5.

15. Prove that there are precisely $\frac{1}{2}[2^{2r} + (-2)^r]$ distinct cyclic subgroups of order 4 in DQ^{r-1}.

16. Let R be an associative ring and define a new product by the rule $[x, y] = xy - yx$ for x, y in R. Show that with respect to this operation of multiplication and the original operation of addition R is a Lie ring.

17. If P is a p-group such that P/P' is elementary abelian, show that the associated Lie ring of P is a Lie algebra over Z_p.

18. Let P be an extra-special p-group of order p^{2r+1} and exponent p, p odd. Construct an automorphism of P of order $p^r + 1$ which acts irreducibly on P/P' and trivially on P'.

19. Let P be a special p-group in which $|P'| = |P/P'| = p^n$ and assume that P possesses an automorphism α which acts irreducibly on both P/P' and P' and has the same characteristic polynomial on each of them regarded as vector spaces over Z_p. Prove that $|\alpha| \leqslant p^{n-1} - 1$.

20. Let P be a p-group of class at most $p + 1$ such that P/P' is elementary abelian of order p^n and assume P admits an automorphism α of order $p^n - 1$ such that $C_P(\alpha) \neq 1$. Prove that $p^n = 2, 4, 8,$ or 9.

21. Using the associated Lie ring, show that a p-group which admits an automorphism of order 3 fixing only the identity element has class at most 2.

22. Let P be the semidirect product of an elementary abelian p-group A of order p^{p^n} and a cyclic group $B = \langle y \rangle$ of order p^n, where y cyclically permutes the elements of a basis of A. Assume $p \equiv 1 \pmod 4$. Prove

(i) P has class p^n.

(ii) P possesses an automorphism α of order 4 which fixes only the identity element of P with $y^\alpha = y^{-1}$.

CHAPTER 6

SOLVABLE AND π-SOLVABLE GROUPS

We develop here certain basic properties of solvable groups as particular cases of theorems on the wider classes of π-separable and π-solvable groups. Primarily we are concerned with the existence of so-called *Hall* subgroups in solvable groups and in conditions for *p*-stability. Our results on Hall subgroups are derived from the Schur-Zassenhaus theorem, which provides a general result in this direction. Underlying all our arguments are certain general properties of the Fitting and Frattini subgroups of a group which we establish in Section 1. In Section 4 we also derive Philip Hall's basic criterion for a group to be solvable. In the final section we discuss *p*-stability in *p*-solvable groups.

1. THE FITTING AND FRATTINI SUBGROUPS

In this section we shall derive some further properties of the Frattini subgroup of a group G which are related to another important characteristic subgroup of G, the *Fitting* subgroup of G. To define it, we need the following preliminary result:

Lemma 1.1

   If H and K are normal nilpotent subgroups of G, then so is HK.

Proof

We know that $HK \lhd G$ and we proceed by induction on $|G|$ to show that it is nilpotent. If $HK \subset G$, the assertion follows by induction, so we may assume $G = HK$. Now $Z(K) \neq 1$ by Corollary 2.6.5 and $Z(K) \lhd G$. Then $N = [H, Z(K)] \lhd G$. If $N = 1$, then $Z(K)$ centralizes H and so $Z(K) \subseteq Z(HK) = Z(G)$. Thus $Z(G) \neq 1$ in this case. We argue to the same conclusion if $N \neq 1$. Now $N \subseteq H$ as $H \lhd G$ and so $L = N \cap Z(H) \neq 1$ by another application of Corollary 2.6.5. But $L \subseteq N \subseteq Z(K)$, so $L \subseteq Z(G)$. Thus $Z(G) \neq 1$ in this case as well. But then $G/Z(G)$ is nilpotent by induction and we conclude at once that G is nilpotent.

As an immediate corollary we have

Theorem 1.2

The subgroup of G generated by all its nilpotent normal subgroups is a nilpotent normal subgroup of G.

This subgroup is thus the unique maximal nilpotent normal subgroup of G. It is called the *Fitting* subgroup of G and will be denoted by $F(G)$.

For a given group $G, F(G)$ may, of course, be trivial. However, this is never the case in a solvable group, for a minimal normal subgroup of such a group is always abelian and so is nilpotent. In fact, in a solvable group, we can assert even more:

Theorem 1.3

If G is solvable, then $C_G(F(G)) \subseteq F(G)$.

Proof

Set $F = F(G)$ and $C = C_G(F)$ and assume by way of contradiction that $C \not\subseteq F$, so that $C \supset C \cap F$. Since C and $C \cap F$ are each normal in G, we can refine the series $G \supseteq C \supset C \cap F \supseteq 1$ to a chief series $G = G_1 \supset G_2 \supset \cdots \supset G_n = 1$. If $C = G_{s+1}$ and $C \cap F = G_{r+1}$, then $s < r$. Thus $G_r \subseteq C$. Since $F \neq 1$, and F is nilpotent, we also have $C \cap F \neq 1$, whence $G_r \supset G_{r+1}$. Furthermore, G_r/G_{r+1} is abelian by Theorem 2.4.2, whence $[G_r, G_r] \subseteq G_{r+1} = C \cap F$. Since $G_r \subseteq C$ and C centralizes F, it follows that $L_3(G_r) = [G_r, G_r, G_r] = 1$. But then G_r is nilpotent and so $G_r \subseteq F$, by definition of F, as $G_r \lhd G$. Thus $G_r \subseteq C \cap F = G_{r+1}$, contrary to $G_r \supset G_{r+1}$.

We shall also need the following general property of $F(G)$:

Theorem 1.4

Let M be a maximal subgroup of G and set $L = \bigcap_{x \in G} M^x$, so that $L \lhd G$. Set $\bar{G} = G/L$, $\bar{F} = F(\bar{G})$, and let $\bar{M}$ be the image of M in $\bar{G}$. Then either

$\bar{F} = \bar{1}$ or *the following conditions hold:*
  (i) *$\bar{F}$ is a minimal normal subgroup of $\bar{G}$.*
  (ii) *$\bar{F}$ is an elementary abelian p-group for some prime p.*
  (iii) *$C_{\bar{G}}(\bar{F}) = \bar{F}$.*
  (iv) *$\bar{F} \cap \bar{M} = \bar{1}$.*
  (v) *$|G : M| = p^n$ for some n.*

Proof

Assume $\bar{F} \neq \bar{1}$, whence $Z(\bar{F}) \neq \bar{1}$. Let $\bar{P} \neq \bar{1}$ be an S_p-subgroup of $\Omega_1(Z(\bar{F}))$ for some prime p. Then $\bar{P} \lhd \bar{G}$ and $\bar{P}$ is elementary abelian. We argue that $\bar{G} = \bar{P}\bar{M}$. Since $\bar{M}$ is maximal in $\bar{G}$ and since $\bar{P}\bar{M}$ is a group, the desired assertion will follow if we show that $\bar{P} \nsubseteq \bar{M}$. In fact, we shall prove that $\bar{M}$ possesses no nontrivial normal subgroups of $\bar{G}$. Indeed, if $\bar{N}$ were such a subgroup, then $\bar{N} \subseteq \bar{M}^{\bar{x}}$ for all $\bar{x}$ in $\bar{G}$, whence $N \subseteq \bigcap_{x \in G} M^x = L$, where N is the inverse image of $\bar{N}$ in G. Since $\bar{G} = G/L$, this gives $\bar{N} = \bar{1}$, a contradiction. In particular, $\bar{G} = \bar{P}\bar{M}$ and so (v) holds.

Now set $\bar{C} = C_{\bar{G}}(\bar{P})$ and note that $\bar{F} \subseteq \bar{C}$ as $\bar{P} \subseteq Z(\bar{F})$. Moreover, $\bar{C} \lhd \bar{G}$ and so $\bar{C} \cap \bar{M} \lhd \bar{M}$. But as $\bar{G} = \bar{P}\bar{M}$ and $\bar{P}$ centralizes $\bar{C} \cap \bar{M}$, it follows that $\bar{C} \cap \bar{M} \lhd \bar{G}$, whence $\bar{C} \cap \bar{M} = 1$ by the preceding paragraph. Since $\bar{P} \subseteq \bar{F} \subseteq \bar{C}$, we have $\bar{G} = \bar{C}\bar{M}$ with $\bar{C} \cap \bar{M} = \bar{P} \cap \bar{M} = \bar{1}$. But then $|\bar{G}| = |\bar{C}||\bar{M}| = |\bar{P}||\bar{M}|$ and we conclude that $\bar{P} = \bar{F} = \bar{C}$. This gives (i) to (iv) at once, and the theorem is proved.

We remark that this last result can easily be translated into a general property of primitive permutation groups.

As a corollary we have

Theorem 1.5

If M is a maximal subgroup of a solvable group G, then $|G : M| = p^n$ for some prime p.

Proof

Preserving the above notation, $\bar{G}$ is solvable and $\bar{G} \neq \bar{1}$, so $\bar{F} \neq \bar{1}$ and the conclusion follows from part (v) of the theorem.

Our next result gives some important relations between Fitting and Frattini subgroups.

Theorem 1.6

Set $F = F(G)$ and $\Phi = \Phi(G)$. Then we have
  (i) *$[F, F] \subseteq \Phi \subseteq F$.*
  (ii) *$F/\Phi = F(G/\Phi)$.*

Proof

Set $\bar{G} = G/\Phi$, $\bar{F} = F(\bar{G})$, and let K be the inverse image of $\bar{F}$ in G. If P is an S_p-subgroup of K, its image is an S_p-subgroup of the nilpotent group $\bar{F}$ and so is normal in $\bar{G}$. Hence $\Phi P \lhd G$ and consequently $G = \Phi N_G(P)$ by Theorem 1.3.7. But then $G = N_G(P)$ by Theorem 5.1.1(i) and so $P \lhd G$. Since this is true for each S_p-subgroup of K, K is nilpotent by Theorem 2.3.5. Thus $K \subseteq F$. On the other hand, the image of F in $\bar{G}$ is certainly a nilpotent normal subgroup of $\bar{G}$ and so lies in $\bar{F}$. Hence $F \subseteq K$ and we conclude that $K = F$, that $\Phi \subseteq F$, and that $F/\Phi = \bar{F}$.

It thus remains to prove that $[F, F] \subseteq \Phi$. We apply Theorem 1.4 with M and L as in that theorem. Set $\tilde{G} = G/L$ and let $\tilde{F}$ be the image of F in $\tilde{G}$, so that $\tilde{F} \subseteq F(\tilde{G})$. By the theorem $F(\tilde{G})$ is abelian and hence so is $\tilde{F}$. But then $[F, F] \subseteq L \subseteq M$. Since this holds for each maximal subgroup M of G, we conclude that $[F, F] \subseteq \Phi$, as Φ is by definition the intersection of all maximal subgroups of G.

2. THE SCHUR-ZASSENHAUS THEOREM

If π is a set of primes, a subgroup H of G will be called an S_π-*subgroup* of G provided H is a π-group and $|G:H|$ is divisible by no primes in π. Such a subgroup is also called a *Hall* subgroup of G. When $\pi = \{p\}$, H is simply a Sylow p-subgroup of G, which we continue to designate as an S_p-subgroup.

By Sylow's theorem G possesses an S_p-subgroup and any two S_p-subgroups are conjugate in G. For an arbitrary set of primes π a group G may or may not possess an S_π-subgroup and, if it does, it may or may not be true that any two of them are conjugate in G. The Schur-Zassenhaus theorem gives an important sufficient condition for the existence and conjugacy of S_π-subgroups in G (actually $S_{\pi'}$-subgroups in the notation of the theorem).

If H is an S_π-subgroup of G and H possesses a complement K in G, then $|K| = |G:H|$ and $|G:K| = |H|$, which together imply that K is an $S_{\pi'}$-subgroup of G. Conversely if G possesses an S_π-subgroup H and an $S_{\pi'}$-subgroup K, then clearly $G = HK$ with $H \cap K = 1$, so each is a complement of the other.

With these preliminary remarks, we now prove

Theorem 2.1 (Schur-Zassenhaus)

Let H be a normal S_π-subgroup of G. Then we have
 (i) G possesses an $S_{\pi'}$-subgroup K which is a complement to H in G.
 (ii) If either H or G/H is solvable, then any two S_π-subgroups of G
     are conjugate in G.

Proof

If $H = 1$, then G itself is an $S_{\pi'}$-subgroup and the theorem is obvious, so we may assume throughout that $H \neq 1$. Suppose (i) is false and among all pairs G, H violating the desired conclusion, choose G of least order. Let P be a nontrivial S_p-subgroup of H. Since $H \lhd G$, Theorem 1.3.7 implies that $G = HN$, where $N = N_G(P)$. Consider first the case $N \subset G$. We have $H \cap N \lhd N$ and $G/H = HN/H$ isomorphic to $N/H \cap N$. Since $|G:H|$ is prime to $|H|$, it follows that $|N:H \cap N|$ is prime to $|H \cap N|$. Hence $H \cap N$ is a normal S_π-subgroup of N. By induction N possesses an $S_{\pi'}$-subgroup K. But then $|K| = |N:H \cap N| = |G:H|$ and so K is an $S_{\pi'}$-subgroup of G, contrary to our choice of G.

Hence $N = G$ and so $P \lhd G$. This argument applies to each Sylow subgroup of H and consequently H must be nilpotent. Set $\bar{G} = G/Z(H)$ and let $\bar{H}$ be the image of H in $\bar{G}$. Then $\bar{H}$ is an S_π-subgroup of $\bar{G}$ and so by induction $\bar{G}$ possesses an $S_{\pi'}$-subgroup $\bar{K}$. Let L be the inverse image of $\bar{K}$ in G, so that $|L:Z(H)| = |\bar{K}| = |\bar{G}:\bar{H}| = |G:H|$. If $L \subset G$, we again apply induction to obtain that L possesses an $S_{\pi'}$-subgroup K. Then $|K| = |G:H|$ and so K is an $S_{\pi'}$-subgroup of G, contrary to our choice of G. Thus $G = L$, whence $H = Z(H)$ and so H is abelian.

In this case we use an averaging argument to construct an $S_{\pi'}$-subgroup. Let x_i, $1 \leqslant i \leqslant m$, be a set of left coset representatives of H in G. If $\bar{G} = G/H$, the images $\bar{x}_i$ of x_i in $\bar{G}$ are distinct and include all the elements of $\bar{G}$, so $|\bar{G}| = m$. It will be convenient to use letters α, β, γ for the elements of $\bar{G}$ and to write x_α for the element x_i with the property $\bar{x}_i = \alpha$. In this notation $x_\alpha x_\beta$ and $x_{\alpha\beta}$ determine the same coset of H in G and so we have

$$(2.1) \qquad\qquad x_\alpha x_\beta = x_{\alpha\beta} f(\alpha, \beta),$$

where $f(\alpha, \beta) \in H$. This holds for each α, β in $\bar{G}$ and so f is a function from $\bar{G} \times \bar{G}$ to H. We apply the associative law:

$$(2.2) \quad (x_\alpha x_\beta)x_\gamma = x_{\alpha\beta} f(\alpha, \beta)x_\gamma = x_{\alpha\beta} x_\gamma f(\alpha, \beta)^{x_\gamma} = x_{(\alpha\beta)\gamma} f(\alpha\beta, \gamma) f(\alpha, \beta)^{x_\gamma}$$

$$(2.3) \quad x_\alpha(x_\beta x_\gamma) = x_\alpha x_{\beta\gamma} f(\beta, \gamma) = x_{\alpha(\beta\gamma)} f(\alpha, \beta\gamma) f(\beta, \gamma).$$

Since $(x_\alpha x_\beta)x_\gamma = x_\alpha(x_\beta x_\gamma)$ and $(\alpha\beta)\gamma = \alpha(\beta\gamma)$, (2.2) and (2.3) yield

(2.4) $f(\alpha\beta, \gamma)f(\alpha, \beta)^{x_\gamma} = f(\alpha, \beta\gamma)f(\beta, \gamma)$

for all α, β, $\gamma \in \bar{G}$. The function f will thus be recognized as a 2-cocycle from G to the abelian group H.

Our aim will be to replace each x_α by another coset representative y_α so that the y_α form a group. The argument will depend on (2.4) together with the fact that $n = |H|$ and m are relatively prime.

For each δ in $\bar{G}$, we set

(2.5) $$g(\delta) = \prod_{\alpha \in \bar{G}} f(\alpha, \delta).$$

Keep β, γ fixed in (2.4) and let α run through $\bar{G}$. We multiply the resulting equations, rearranging terms in the product as H is abelian, to obtain

(2.6) $$\prod_{\alpha \in \bar{G}} f(\alpha\beta, \gamma) \prod_{\alpha \in \bar{G}} f(\alpha, \beta)^{x_\gamma} = \prod_{\alpha \in \bar{G}} f(\alpha, \beta\gamma) \prod_{\alpha \in \bar{G}} f(\beta, \gamma).$$

Since $\alpha\beta$ ranges over G as α does, (2.5) and (2.6) together give

(2.7) $g(\gamma)g(\beta)^{x_\gamma} = g(\beta\gamma)[f(\beta, \gamma)]^m.$

Since $(n, m) = 1$, there exists an integer r such that $rm \equiv 1 \pmod{n}$. Put $h(\delta) = g(\delta)^{-r}$ for each δ in G and take as new coset representatives of H in G the elements $y_\alpha = x_\alpha h(\alpha)$.

We claim that the set $K = \{y_\alpha | \alpha \in \bar{G}\}$ is a subgroup of G, which will follow if we prove the $y_\beta y_\gamma = y_{\beta\gamma}$ for all β, γ in $\bar{G}$. Indeed, we have

(2.8) $y_\beta y_\gamma = x_\beta h(\beta)x_\gamma h(\gamma) = x_\beta x_\gamma h(\beta)^{x_\gamma}h(\gamma) = x_{\beta\gamma}f(\beta, \gamma)h(\beta)^{x_\gamma}h(\gamma).$

Since $y_{\beta\gamma} = x_{\beta\gamma}h(\beta\gamma)$, the desired conclusion will follow from (2.8) provided we show that

(2.9) $h(\gamma)h(\beta)^{x_\gamma} = h(\beta\gamma)f(\beta, \gamma)^{-1}.$

But (2.9) follows at once by raising (2.7) to the $-m$ power and using both the definition of h and the fact that $f(\beta, \gamma)^{-rm} = f(\beta, \gamma)^{-1}$ by our choice of r.

Thus K is a subgroup of G of order $m = |G/H|$ and so K is an $S_{\pi'}$-subgroup of G. This completes the proof of (i).

We prove (ii) by induction on $|G|$. Let K, K_1 be two S_π-subgroups of G and hence two complements of H in G. Suppose H contains a nontrivial proper subgroup N with $N \triangleleft G$. Then KN/N and K_1N/N are S_π-subgroups of G/N and so are conjugate in G/N. Hence a conjugate of K_1 in G lies in KN and we need only show that this conjugate is itself conjugate to K. Thus without loss we may assume that $K_1 \subseteq KN = G_1$. Since $N \subset H$,

$G_1 \subset G$ and hence K_1 is conjugate to K by induction. Thus we may suppose that H is itself a minimal normal subgroup of G.

Let M be a maximal normal π'-subgroup of G. Then $|KM|$ divides $|K||M|$ and so KM is a π'-subgroup of G, whence $|KM| = |K|$ as K is an $S_{\pi'}$-subgroup of G. Thus $K = KM$ and so $M \subseteq K$. Similarly $M \subseteq K_1$. If $M \neq 1$, then K/M and K_1/M are conjugate in G/M, whence K and K_1 are conjugate in G. So we may also assume that G has no nontrivial normal π'-subgroups.

Suppose next that $\bar{G} = G/H$ is solvable. Let $\bar{R}$ be a minimal normal subgroup of $\bar{G}$, so that $\bar{R}$ is an elementary abelian p-group for some prime p in π'. If R denotes its inverse image in G, we have $|R| = |H||\bar{R}|$. Since $G = HK = RK$, it follows that $|R \cap K| = |\bar{R}|$. But $|\bar{R}|$ is the order of an S_p-subgroup of R as $p \in \pi'$. Hence $P = R \cap K$ is an S_p-subgroup of R. Likewise $P_1 = R \cap K_1$ is an S_p-subgroup of R. Now P and P_1 are conjugate in R by Sylow's theorem. Hence replacing K_1 by suitable conjugate, we can assume without loss that $P_1 = P$. Thus P is normal in both K and K_1 as $R \lhd G$. Since P is a π'-group, P is not normal in G by the preceding paragraph, whence by induction K and K_1 are conjugate in $N_G(P)$. Thus we may also assume that G/H is not solvable.

By the hypothesis of (ii), H must therefore be solvable. But then $H' = [H, H] \subset H$. Since $H' \lhd G$ and H is a minimal normal subgroup of G, $H' = 1$ and H is abelian. In this minimal case, we again use an averaging argument. Since $G = HK$ and since K, K_1 are each isomorphic to G/H, we have for any x_1 in K_1 that $x_1 = xf(x)$, where $x \in K$ and $f(x)$ is a suitable element of H and where x ranges over K as x_1 ranges over K_1. Furthermore, if $y_1 \in K_1$ and $y_1 = yf(y)$, $y \in K$, $f(y) \in H$, then $x_1 y_1$ and xy lie in the same coset of H in G. Since $x_1 y_1 \in K_1$ and $xy \in K$, we thus have $x_1 y_1 = xyf(xy)$. Hence

$$(2.10) \qquad xyf(xy) = xf(x)yf(y) = xyf(x)^y f(y),$$

which implies that for all x, y in K,

$$(2.11) \qquad f(xy) = f(x)^y f(y).$$

Thus f is a 1-cocycle from K to H.

Now set $z = \prod_{x \in K} f(x)$. Then for a fixed y, if we multiply (2.11) over all x in K and rearrange terms, we obtain

$$(2.12) \qquad z = z^y f(y)^m,$$

where $m = |K|$. If again r is determined by $rm \equiv 1 \pmod{n}$, where $n = |H|$, it follows from (2.12) that

(2.13) $$z^r = (z^y)^r f(y)^{rm} = (z^r)^y f(y).$$

Finally setting $u = z^r$, (2.13) gives $u = u^y f(y)$, whence

(2.14) $$u^{-1} yu = yf(y)$$

for all y in K. But $yf(y) \in K_1$ and so (2.14) shows that $u^{-1} Ku = K_1$. Thus K and K_1 are conjugate and the theorem is proved.

Remark   Under the hypothesis of the theorem, either H or G/H has odd order, so that by the Feit-Thompson theorem H or G/H must, in fact, be solvable. Thus once it is established that all groups of odd order are solvable, the hypothesis on solvability in part (ii) of the Schur-Zassenhaus theorem can be dropped. The same remark will apply to a few other results below.

The theorem has the following important consequence:

Theorem 2.2
Let A be a π'-group of automorphisms of the π-group G, and suppose G or A is solvable. Then for each prime p in π, we have
   (i) A leaves invariant some S_p-subgroup of G.
   (ii) Any two A-invariant S_p-subgroups of G are conjugate by an element of $C_G(A)$.
   (iii) Any A-invariant p-subgroup of G is contained in an A-invariant S_p-subgroup of G.
   (iv) If H is any A-invariant normal subgroup of G, then $C_{G/H}(A)$ is the image of $C_G(A)$ in G/H.

Proof
Let G^* be the semidirect product of G by A, so that G is a normal S_π-subgroup of G^*, A is an S_π-subgroup of G^*, and, as A is isomorphic to G^*/G, either G or G^*/G is solvable. Hence by part (ii) of the Schur-Zassenhaus theorem, any other $S_{\pi'}$-subgroup of G^* is conjugate to A. Since $G^* = GA$, this conjugating element can clearly be assumed to lie in G.

Now let P be an S_p-subgroup of G and set $N = N_{G^*}(P)$, so that $G^* = GN$ by Theorem 1.3.7. Thus $N/G \cap N$ is isomorphic to G^*/G and hence to A. Since $G \cap N$ is a normal S_π-subgroup of N, part (i) of the Schur-Zassenhaus theorem implies that N possesses an $S_{\pi'}$-subgroup B. But then B is an $S_{\pi'}$-subgroup of G^* and so $B^x = A$ for some x in G. However, B leaves P invariant as $B \subseteq N = N_G(P)$, and consequently A leaves the S_p-subgroup P^x of G invariant, proving (i).

Suppose next that A leaves two S_p-subgroups P and Q of G-invariant. Then $P = Q^x$ for some x in G and consequently A^x leaves $Q^x = P$ invariant. Since A also leaves P invariant, A and A^x therefore both lie in $N = N_{G^*}(P)$ and so each is an $S_{\pi'}$-subgroup of N. Since either $G \cap N$ or $N/G \cap N$ is solvable, it follows that $(A^x)^y = A$ for some element y in $G \cap N$ by another application of the Schur-Zassenhaus theorem. Set $z = xy$, so that $z \in G$. Now y normalizes P and consequently $Q^z = Q^{xy} = P^y = P$. Thus P and Q are conjugate by z. On the other hand, $[A, z] \subseteq A$, as $z = xy$ normalizes A. But $[A, z] \subseteq G$, as $G \triangleleft G^*$. Thus $[A, z] \subseteq A \cap G = 1$. We conclude that $z \in C_G(A)$, proving (ii).

Next let Q be an A-invariant p-subgroup of G and let P be a maximal A-invariant p-subgroup of G containing Q. Then $N = N_G(P)$ is A-invariant by Theorem 2.1.1(i), so by (i) there exists an A-invariant S_p-subgroup R of N. But $P \subseteq R$, whence $R = P$ by our maximal choice of P. Theorem 1.2.11(ii) implies now that P is an S_p-subgroup of G. Thus (iii) also holds.

Finally, set $\bar{G} = G/H$, let $\bar{C} = C_{\bar{G}}(A)$, and let $C = C_G(A)$. Clearly $\bar{C}$ contains the image of C in $\bar{G}$. Hence it will suffice to show that for each prime p in $\pi(\bar{C})$, an S_p-subgroup of C maps onto an S_p-subgroup of $\bar{C}$. Let $\bar{P}$ be an S_p-subgroup of $\bar{C}$, let K be the inverse image of $\bar{P}$ in G, and let P be an A-invariant S_p-subgroup of K. Then A centralizes $PH/H = \bar{P}$. Since PH/H is isomorphic to $P/P \cap H$, it follows at once from Theorem 5.3.15 that $C_P(A)$ maps onto $\bar{P}$, as required.

A more elementary result of the same type is the following:

Theorem 2.3

If A is a p-group of automorphisms of G with the property $C_G(A) = 1$, then G is a p'-group.

Proof

Again we consider the semidirect product G^* of G by A and let P^* be an S_p-subgroup of G^* containing A. Then $P = P^* \cap G$ is an S_p-subgroup of G by Theorem 1.3.8. Assume $P \neq 1$. Since $P \triangleleft P^*$, $P \cap Z(P^*) \neq 1$ by Theorem 2.6.4. But A centralizes $P \cap Z(P^*)$, contrary to our hypothesis $C_G(A) = 1$. Thus $P = 1$ and G is a p'-group.

Finally we prove

Theorem 2.4

If A is a noncyclic abelian π'-group of automorphisms of the π-group G, then

$$G = \langle C_G(\alpha) \mid \alpha \in A^{\#} \rangle.$$

Proof

By Theorem 1.3.1, some S_q-subgroup Q of A is noncyclic. Now Q leaves invariant an S_p-subgroup P of G for each p in $\pi(G)$. Moreover, $P = \langle C_P(\alpha) \,|\, \alpha \in Q^* \rangle$ by Theorem 5.3.16. Since G is generated by a set of S_p-subgroups as p ranges over $\pi(G)$, the theorem follows.

3. π-SEPARABLE AND π-SOLVABLE GROUPS

We shall now study a basic class of groups which generalizes that of solvable groups. In the next section we shall apply the results we obtain to the study of solvable groups.

If π is a set of primes, we shall say that G is π-*separable* if every composition factor of G is either a π'-group or a π-group; and we shall say that G is π-*solvable* if every composition factor of G is either a π'-group or a p-group for some prime p in π.

Clearly π-separability and π'-separability are equivalent. Furthermore, π-solvability implies π-separability. For a single prime p, the notions of p-separable and p-solvable are obviously equivalent, but in general a π-separable group need not be π-solvable. There are many ways of describing a solvable group in this terminology. For example, G is solvable if and only if it is p-solvable for every prime p in $\pi(G)$. Note also that every composition factor of a π-solvable π-group must be a p-group for some prime p in π and so such a group is solvable. Finally if G is solvable, it is certainly π-solvable for every set of primes π.

If H and K are normal π-subgroups of an arbitrary group G, then so also is HK as $|HK|$ divides $|H|\,|K|$. Hence G possesses a unique maximal normal π-subgroup, which we denote by $O_\pi(G)$. Clearly $O_\pi(G)$ char G. Furthermore, by definition of $O_\pi(G)$, we have $O_\pi(\bar{G}) = \bar{1}$, where $\bar{G} = G/O_\pi(G)$. In $\bar{G}$, we consider the unique maximal normal π'-subgroup $O_{\pi'}(\bar{G})$ and denote its inverse image in G by $O_{\pi,\pi'}(G)$. Similarly, we define $O_{\pi,\pi',\pi}(G)$ to be the inverse image in G of $O_\pi(G/O_{\pi,\pi'}(G))$. Continuing the definition in the obvious way, we thus obtain a sequence of characteristic subgroups of G:

$$(3.1) \qquad 1 \subseteq O_\pi(G) \subseteq O_{\pi,\pi'}(G) \subseteq O_{\pi,\pi'\pi}(G) \subseteq \cdots .$$

This sequence is called the *upper* π-series of G. Similarly, we define the *lower* π-series of G to be

$$(3.2) \qquad 1 \subseteq O_{\pi'}(G) \subseteq O_{\pi',\pi}(G) \subseteq O_{\pi',\pi,\pi''}(G) \subseteq \cdots .$$

The π-*length* of a π-separable group G is by definition the number of factors of the *lower* π-series of G that are π-groups. (This may not be the same as the number of such factors of the upper π-series of G.)

Obviously the upper (lower) π-series of G is the same as the lower (upper) π'-series of G.

Our first result is an easy consequence of the definitions:

Theorem 3.1

(i) *If G is π-separable, the upper and lower π-series of G terminate in G. Conversely if the upper or lower π-series terminates in G, then G is π-separable.*

(ii) *Subgroups and homomorphic images of π-separable (π-solvable) groups are π-separable (π-solvable).*

(iii) *A minimal normal subgroup of a π-separable group is either a π-group or a π'-group.*

(iv) *In any group G, $O_\pi(G/O_\pi(G)) = 1$.*

Proof

First of all, (iv) has been observed above. We next prove (iii); so let K be a minimal normal subgroup of the π-separable group G. Then K is characteristically simple, whence K is the direct product of isomorphic simple groups K_i, $1 \leqslant i \leqslant n$, by Theorem 2.1.4. Since $K \lhd G$, there exists a composition series of G in which K_1 is the last nontrivial term, whence K_1 is a composition factor of G. Since G is π-separable, K_1, and hence each K_i, is thus either a π- or a π'-group, proving (iii).

Next observe that as an immediate consequence of the definitions, homomorphic images and normal subgroups of a π-separable (π-solvable) group G have the same property. Now let H be any subgroup of G, let K be a minimal normal subgroup of G, and set $\bar{G} = G/K$. Then by induction the image $\bar{H}$ of H in $\bar{G}$ is π-separable (π-solvable). Hence to complete the proof of (ii), we need only show that $H \cap K$ is π-separable (π-solvable). Since K is a π-group or π'-group by (iii), $H \cap K$ is certainly π-separable. If G is π-solvable, so is K as $K \lhd G$, so K is either a π'-group or a solvable π-group. In either case, it is clear that $H \cap K$ is π-solvable, and (ii) is proved.

If the upper or lower π-series of G terminates in G, it can be refined to a composition series, each of whose factors will then be either a π- or a π'-group, so G is π-separable. Conversely suppose G is π-separable and assume, say, that the upper π-series of G terminates in a proper subgroup H of G. Setting $\bar{G} = G/H$, we then must have $O_\pi(\bar{G}) = O_{\pi'}(\bar{G}) = \bar{1}$. But $\bar{G}$ is

π-separable by (ii) and so a minimal normal subgroup $\bar{K}$ of $\bar{G}$ (possibly $\bar{G}$ itself) is either a π- or a π'-group by (iii). Correspondingly $\bar{K} \subseteq O_\pi(\bar{G})$ or $\bar{K} \subseteq O_{\pi'}(\bar{G})$; in either case, we have a contradiction. Thus (i) also holds and the theorem is proved.

The following property of π-separable groups is fundamental.

Theorem 3.2

If G is π-separable and $\bar{G} = G/O_{\pi'}(G)$, then

$$C_{\bar{G}}(O_\pi(\bar{G})) \subseteq O_\pi(\bar{G}).$$

In particular, if $O_{\pi'}(G) = 1$, then $C_G(O_\pi(G)) \subseteq O_\pi(G)$.

Proof

$\bar{G}$ is π-separable and $O_{\pi'}(\bar{G}) = \bar{1}$ by Theorem 3.1. Hence it will suffice to treat the special case $O_{\pi'}(G) = 1$.

Set $H = O_\pi(G)$ and $C = C_G(H)$. Then $C \cap H = Z(H)$ and so we must prove that $C = Z(H)$. We have $O_\pi(C)$ char $C \lhd G$, so $O_\pi(C)$ is a normal π-subgroup of G and hence $O_\pi(C) \subseteq H$. Thus $O_\pi(C) \subseteq C \cap H = Z(H)$. On the other hand, $Z(H) \lhd G$ and $Z(H) \subseteq C$, so that $Z(H) \subseteq O_\pi(C)$. We conclude that $O_\pi(C) = Z(H)$.

Assume now by way of contradiction that $C \supset Z(H)$. Then $C \supset O_\pi(C)$ by the preceding paragraph. Now C is π-separable by Theorem 3.1, so $L = O_{\pi,\pi'}(C) \supset O_\pi(C)$. Since $L/O_\pi(C)$ is a π'-group, $Z(H) = O_\pi(C)$ is thus a normal S_π-subgroup of L and hence by the Schur-Zassenhaus theorem $Z(H)$ possesses a complement $K \neq 1$ in L which is an $S_{\pi'}$-subgroup of L. But $K \subseteq C$ and C centralizes $Z(H)$, whence $L = Z(H) \times K$ and, as K is a π'-group, we have K char L char $C \lhd G$. Thus $K \lhd G$ and consequently $K \subseteq O_{\pi'}(G) = 1$, a contradiction.

As an immediate corollary we have

Theorem 3.3

If P is an S_p-subgroup of the p-solvable group G, then

$$C_G(P \cap O_{p',p}(G)) \subseteq O_{p',p}(G).$$

In particular, $Z(P) \subseteq O_{p',p}(G)$.

Proof

Set $Q = P \cap O_{p',p}(G)$, so that Q is an S_p-subgroup of $O_{p',p}(G)$. Hence Q maps onto $O_p(\bar{G})$, where $\bar{G} = G/O_{p'}(G)$. But then $C_G(Q)$ maps into $C_{\bar{G}}(O_p(\bar{G}))$ and consequently $C_G(Q) \subseteq O_{p',p}(G)$ by Theorem 3.2. Since $Z(P)$ centralizes Q, it follows, in particular, that $Z(P) \subseteq O_{p',p}(G)$.

It is Theorem 3.2 that enables us to reformulate effectively many problems about p-solvable groups in terms of groups of linear transformations over Z_p. Indeed, as a second corollary, we have

Theorem 3.4

Let G be a p-solvable group in which $O_{p'}(G) = 1$ and set $H = O_p(G)$. Then G/H is faithfully represented on $H/\Phi(H)$ regarded as a vector space over Z_p.

Proof

We have $\Phi(H)$ char $H \lhd G$, so $\Phi(H) \lhd G$. Set $\bar{G} = G/\Phi(H)$ and let $\bar{H}$ be the image of H in $\bar{G}$, so that $\bar{H} = H/\Phi(H)$ is an elementary abelian normal p-subgroup of $\bar{G}$. If $\bar{C} = C_{\bar{G}}(\bar{H})$, we know that $\bar{G}/\bar{C}$ is thus represented as a group of linear transformations of $\bar{H}$ as a vector space over Z_p. On the other hand, $\bar{G}/\bar{H}$ is isomorphic to G/H by the second isomorphism theorem. Hence to complete the proof, it will suffice to show that $\bar{H} = \bar{C}$.

First of all, let $\bar{x}$ be a p'-element of $\bar{C}$ and let x be a representative of $\bar{x}$ in G, which we can assume is also a p'-element. Then x induces by conjugation a p'-automorphism of H which acts trivially on $\bar{H} = H/\Phi(H)$. By Theorem 5.1.4, this implies that x acts trivially on H; that is, $x \in C_G(H)$. But $C_G(H) \subseteq H$ by Theorem 3.2. Thus $x \in H$ and so $\bar{x} = \bar{1}$. We conclude that $\bar{C}$ is a p-group. But $\bar{C} \lhd \bar{G}$ and so the inverse image C of $\bar{C}$ is normal in G and is a p-group. Hence $C = H$ and $\bar{C} = \bar{H}$, as required.

Using the Schur-Zassenhaus theorem we can also establish the existence of S_σ-subgroups in π-separable groups for suitable sets of primes σ, a result which will be basic for the study of solvable groups.

Theorem 3.5

If G is π-separable and p, q are primes in π, π', respectively, then G possesses an S_σ-subgroup for $\sigma = \pi$, $\sigma = \{\pi, q\}$, and $\sigma = \{p, q\}$.

Proof

We argue by induction on $|G|$. Let M be a minimal normal subgroup of G and set $\bar{G} = G/M$, so that $\bar{G}$ is π-separable. By induction $\bar{G}$ possesses an S_σ-subgroup $\bar{H}$ for each choice of σ. Let H be the inverse image of $\bar{H}$ in G. Then H is π-separable and so if $H \subset G$, H possesses an S_σ-subgroup by induction which is clearly an S_σ-subgroup of G.

Hence we may assume $H = G$, whence $\bar{G} = \bar{H}$ is a π-separable σ-group. Consider next the case that M is a π-group. If $\sigma = \pi$ or $\sigma = \{\pi, q\}$, then G itself is a σ-group and the theorem holds trivially. Hence we can assume $\sigma = \{p, q\}$. If P is an S_p-subgroup of M, we have as usual that $G = MN$, where $N = N_G(P)$. If $N \subset G$, then by induction N possesses an S_σ-subgroup K. But N contains an S_p-subgroup of M and hence one of G as well. Furthermore, N maps on $\bar{G}$, M is a π-group, and $q \in \pi'$, which together imply that N contains an S_q-subgroup of G. Thus K is, in fact, an S_σ-subgroup of G. On the other hand, if $N = G$, then $P \lhd G$ and so if $P \neq 1$, then $P = M$, as M is a minimal normal subgroup of G. In this case, G itself is a σ-group and again the theorem holds trivially. Finally if $P = 1$, then M is a p'-group as well as a q'-group and so is a σ'-group. But then G possesses an S_σ-subgroup by the Schur-Zassenhaus theorem.

Hence by Theorem 3.1(iii) it remains to consider the case that M is a π'-group. If $\sigma = \pi$, then M is a normal $S_{\pi'}$-subgroup of G and the theorem follows again by the Schur-Zassenhaus theorem. On the other hand, if $\sigma = \{\pi, q\}$ or $\{p, q\}$, we let Q be an S_q-subgroup of M and now set $N = N_G(Q)$. Then $G = MN$ and the theorem follows by the same argument as in the preceding paragraph.

If we assume G is π-solvable or π'-solvable (or invoke the solvability of groups of odd order), we can use part (ii) of Theorem 2.1 to obtain results on the conjugacy of S_π-subgroups of G.

Theorem 3.6

Assume G is π-solvable or π'-solvable and let K be an S_π-subgroup of G. If L is any π-subgroup of G, then $L^x \subseteq K$ for some x in G. In particular, L is contained in an S_π-subgroup of G and any two S_π-subgroups of G are conjugate.

Proof

Our hypothesis implies that G is π-separable, so K exists by the preceding theorem. We prove the first statement by induction on $|G|$. Let M be a minimal normal subgroup of G, so that $\bar{K} = KM/M$ is an S_π-subgroup of $\bar{G} = G/M$. Since $\bar{G}$ is either π-solvable or π'-solvable, we have $\bar{L}^{\bar{x}} \subseteq \bar{K}$ for some $\bar{x}$ in $\bar{G}$, where $\bar{L}$ is the image of L in $\bar{G}$. But then $L^x \subseteq KM$ for some x in G. If M is a π-group, so is MK, whence $M \subseteq K$ as K is an S_π-subgroup of G. In this case we have $L^x \subseteq K$, as desired.

We can therefore assume that M is a π'-group. By Theorem 3.1(ii), K or M must be solvable according as G is π- or π'-solvable. Correspondingly, KM is π- or π'-solvable. Hence if $KM \subset G$ we can apply induction to conclude that $(L^x)^y \subseteq K$ for some y in KM, whence $L^z \subseteq K$ with $z = xy$.

Suppose finally that $G = KM$. Set $G_1 = LM$. If G is π-solvable, then L is solvable. Thus either L or M is solvable. Now clearly L is an S_π-subgroup of G_1. Furthermore, $G = G_1 K$ and $|G| = |M||K|$, whence $|G_1 \cap K| = |L|$.

Hence also $G_1 \cap K$ is an S_π-subgroup of G. But then by Theorem 2.1(ii), $L^x = G_1 \cap K \subseteq K$ for some x in G and the first assertion of the theorem is proved.

Finally, if $L^x \subseteq K$, then $L \subseteq K^{x^{-1}} = K_1$ and K_1 is an S_π-subgroup of G. Moreover, if L is itself an S_π-subgroup of G, then $|L| = |K|$ and so $L^x = K$. Thus the final statement also holds.

4. SOLVABLE GROUPS

Since a solvable group is π-solvable for every set of primes π, Theorems 3.5 and 3.6 yield as a corollary the following basic properties of solvable groups:

Theorem 4.1 (P. Hall)
If G is solvable, then
   (i) *G possesses an S_π-subgroup for any set of primes π.*
   (ii) *Any two S_π-subgroups of G are conjugate.*
   (iii) *Any π-subgroup of G is contained in an S_π-subgroup.*

This result, because of its obvious relation with Sylow's theorem, is often called the *extended* Sylow theorem for solvable groups. We wish to derive a slight refinement of this result which depends upon the following lemma:

Lemma 4.2
If H and K are subgroups of G such that $|G : H|$ and $|G : K|$ are relatively prime, then
   (i) *$|G : H \cap K| = |G : H||G : K|$.*
   (ii) *$G = HK$.*

Proof
Set $g = |G|$, $m = |G : H|$, $n = |G : K|$, and $a = |H \cap K|$. Then $|H| = ah$ and $|K| = ak$ for suitable integers h, k. Hence $g = ahm = akn$, which implies that $hm = kn$. Since $(m, n) = 1$ by hypothesis, this gives $h = nr$ and $k = mr$ for some integer r. But then also

(4.1)
$$g = amnr.$$

On the other hand,

(4.2) $g = |G| \geqslant |HK| = |H||K|/|H \cap K| = (ah)(ak)/a = amnr^2.$

Now (4.1) and (4.2) force $r = 1$. Hence $|HK| = amn = g$ and so $HK = G$.

Furthermore, $|G : H \cap K| = amn/a = mn = |G : H||G : K|$, and the lemma is proved.

We now prove

Theorem 4.3 (P. Hall)

Let G be a solvable group and let $\pi(G) = \{p_i \mid 1 \leqslant i \leqslant n\}$. Then there exist S_{p_i}-subgroups P_i of $G, 1 \leqslant i \leqslant n$, such that $P_i P_j = P_j P_i$ is a group for all i, j.

Proof

Let $g = |G| = p_1^{e_1} p_2^{e_2} \cdots p_n^{e_n}$. First of all, by Theorem 4.1(i) with $\pi = p_i'$, G possesses an $S_{p_i'}$-subgroup H_i, $1 \leqslant i \leqslant n$. Then $|G : H_i| = p_i^{e_i}$ and hence $|G : H_i|$ and $|G : H_j|$ are relatively prime. But then $|G : H_i \cap H_j| = p_i^{e_i} p_j^{e_j}$ by Lemma 4.2 and consequently $H_i \cap H_j$ is an S_π-subgroup of G with $\pi = \pi(G) - \{p_i, p_j\}$. Since $|H_i : H_i \cap H_j| = p_j^{e_j}$, it follows now by another application of Lemma 4.2 that for $i \neq j \neq k \neq i$, we have $|H_i : H_i \cap H_j \cap H_k| = p_j^{e_j} p_k^{e_k}$, whence $H_i \cap H_j \cap H_k$ is an S_π-subgroup of G with $\pi = \pi(G) - \{p_i, p_j, p_k\}$. Repeated application of this argument yields that the 2^n intersections of the H_i, including the empty intersection G, are S_π-subgroups of G for appropriate sets of primes π.

In particular, $P_i = \bigcap_{j \neq i} H_j$ is an S_{p_i}-subgroup of G and $\bigcap_{k \neq i, j} H_k = Q_{ij}$ is an $S_{\{p_i, p_j\}}$-subgroup of G. But $P_i P_j \subseteq Q_{ij}$ and $|P_i P_j| = |Q_{ij}|$, which together imply that $P_i P_j = P_j P_i = Q_{ij}$ is a group. Since this holds for all i, j, the theorem is proved.

The proof of the theorem implies, in fact, that $P_{i1} P_{i2} \cdots P_{ik}$ is a group for any subset, $\{i_i, i_2, \ldots, i_k\}$.

A set of Sylow subgroups which satisfy the conditions of the theorem is called a *Sylow system* of G.

Philip Hall's renowned characterization of solvable groups asserts that the existence of $S_{p'}$-subgroups in a group G for all p implies that G is solvable. We turn now to the proof of this beautiful result.

We first prove

Theorem 4.4

If a group G possesses three solvable subgroups whose indices are pairwise relatively prime, then G is solvable.

Proof

Let H_i, $1 \leqslant i \leqslant 3$, be the three given subgroups of G. If $H_1 = 1$, then $|G : H_1| = |G|$. Then $|G : H_2|$ must be relatively prime to $|G|$, which is possible only if $H_2 = G$, whence G is solvable in this case. Hence we may assume $H_i \neq 1$, $1 \leqslant i \leqslant 3$. Let M be a minimal normal subgroup of H_1. Since H_1 is solvable, M is an elementary abelian p-group for some prime p. Since H_2 and H_3 have coprime indices, we can assume that p does not divide, say, $|G : H_2|$, in which case H_2 contains an S_p-subgroup of G. Hence if P_1 denotes an S_p-subgroup of H_1, we have $P_1 \subseteq P^x$ for some x in G. Since H_2^x has the same properties as H_2, we can replace H_2 by H_2^x and so can assume without loss that H_2 contains P_1. But M, being normal in H_1, is contained in every S_p-subgroup of H_1. Hence $M \subseteq H_1 \cap H_2$.

Now by Lemma 4.2, we have $G = H_1 H_2$. Hence if $y \in G$, $y = y_1 y_2$ with $y_i \in H_i$, $1 \leqslant i \leqslant 2$, and consequently $M^y = M^{y_1 y_2} = M^{y_2} \subseteq H_2$. But then the normal closure $K = M^G = \langle M^y \mid y \in G \rangle \subseteq H_2$. Since H_2 is solvable, so is K. Furthermore, it is immediate that the subgroups KH_i/K of G/K satisfy the conditions of the theorem. Hence by induction G/K is solvable. We conclude that G is solvable.

We now prove

Theorem 4.5 (P. Hall)
G is solvable if and only if G possesses an $S_{p'}$-subgroup for every prime p.

Proof
Obviously we can restrict ourselves to p in $\pi(G)$. If G is solvable, the conclusion follows from Theorem 4.1(i). Conversely let $|G| = p_1^{e_1} p_2^{e_2} \cdots p_n^{e_n}$ with $p_1, p_2, \cdots p_n$ distinct primes. If $n = 1$, G is a p_1-group and so is solvable. If $n = 2$, then G is solvable by Burnside's theorem. Hence we may assume $n > 2$. Let H_i be an $S_{p_i'}$-subgroup of G, $1 \leqslant i \leqslant n$, which exists by hypothesis.

We argue by induction on $|G|$ that each H_i is solvable. Since $|G : H_i| = p_i^{e_i}$, H_1, H_2, and H_3 have pairwise relatively prime indices and so the solvability of G will then follow from the preceding theorem. Now by Lemma 4.2, $H_1 \cap H_j$ is an S_π-subgroup of G with $\pi = \pi(G) - \{p_1, p_j\}$ and consequently $H_1 \cap H_j$ is an $S_{p_i'}$-subgroup of H_1, $2 \leqslant j \leqslant n$. Hence by induction, H_1 is solvable. Similarly, H_2, H_3 are solvable and the theorem is proved.

The study of solvable groups and, in particular, supersolvable groups is a very rich portion of finite group theory. The theory of system normalizers, Carter subgroups, and formations has been investigated in great detail and contains many important and interesting results. However, as these results do not appear to have direct applicability to the various problems we shall discuss, we conclude the general development of solvable groups at this point.

5. p-STABILITY IN p-SOLVABLE GROUPS

Our results on p-stability (Chapter 3, Section 8) together with the general properties of p-solvable groups established above lead at once to the following theorem:

Theorem 5.1
Let G be a p-solvable group in which $O_p(G) = 1$ and assume that either $p \geqslant 5$ or $p = 3$ and $SL(2, 3)$ is not involved in G. Then G is p-stable.

Proof
Suppose G possesses a faithful representation on V over $GF(p^n)$ in which some p-element x of G has a quadratic minimal polynomial. Set $P = \langle x \rangle$ and $H = O_{p'}(G)$. Since $O_p(G) = 1$, Theorem 3.2 implies that $C_G(H) \subseteq H$ and hence that $C_P(H) = 1$. On the other hand, P induces by conjugation a group of automorphisms of H of order prime to $|H|$ and so P leaves an S_q-subgroup Q of H invariant for each q in $\pi(H)$ by Theorem 2.2. Since $\Omega_1(P)$ does not centralize H, it does not centralize some Q. For such a choice of Q, we have $C_P(Q) = 1$. Set $K = PQ$. Then $O_p(K) \subseteq P$ and $[O_p(K), Q] \subseteq P \cap Q = 1$. Thus $O_p(K) \subseteq C_P(Q) = 1$. We conclude that K is a solvable group containing x and having no nontrivial normal p-subgroups. Furthermore, $SL(2, 3)$ is not involved in K if $p = 3$. Hence K is p-stable by Theorem 3.8.4(e). Since K is faithfully represented on V, x does not have a quadratic minimal polynomial on V, a contradiction.

In view of the conclusion of the theorem, it will be convenient to call a p-solvable group G strongly p-solvable if either $p \geqslant 5$ or $p = 3$ and $SL(2, 3)$ is not involved in G.

We have seen in Theorem 3.3 that in a p-solvable group G we have $Z(P) \subseteq O_{p',p}(G)$ for any S_p-subgroup P of G. The importance of the preceding theorem lies in the fact that if G is strongly p-solvable, not only is $Z(P) \subseteq O_{p',p}(G)$, but also so is every normal abelian subgroup of P. Indeed we have:

Theorem 5.2
If P is an S_p-subgroup of the strongly p-solvable group G, then every normal abelian subgroup of P is contained in $O_{p',p}(G)$.

Proof
It clearly suffices to prove the theorem for $G/O_{p'}(G)$, which is also strongly p-solvable. Hence without loss we can assume that $O_{p'}(G) = 1$. Set

$R = O_p(G)$, $V = R/\Phi(R)$, and $\bar{G} = G/R$. Then by Theorem 3.4, $\bar{G}$ is faithfully represented on V as a vector space over Z_p. But $\bar{G}$ is also strongly p-solvable and $O_p(\bar{G}) = \bar{1}$. Hence by Theorem 5.1, the representation of $\bar{G}$ on V is p-stable.

Now let A be an abelian normal subgroup of P and let $\bar{A}$ be its image in $\bar{G}$. Since $A \lhd P$, $[P, A] \subseteq A$ and since A is abelian, this gives $[P, A, A] = 1$. But then $[R, A, A] = 1$ and consequently

$$[R/\Phi(R), A\Phi(R)/\Phi(R), A\Phi(R)/\Phi(R)] = 1 \qquad \text{that is, } [V, \bar{A}, \bar{A}] = 1.$$

But now Theorem 2.6.6 implies that each $\bar{x}$ in $\bar{A}$ induces a linear transformation of V which satisfies the polynomial $(X - 1)^2$. Since the representation is p-stable, this is possible only if each $\bar{x}$, in fact, satisfies the polynomial $X - 1$. Thus $\bar{A}$ acts trivially on V and, as the representation of $\bar{G}$ on V is faithful, this yields $\bar{A} = \bar{1}$, whence $A \subseteq R = O_p(G)$.

The following slight extension of this result will be very important for us (see Section 8.1).

Theorem 5.3

Let G be a strongly p-solvable group, K a normal subgroup of G, and P a p-subgroup of K such that $G = KN_G(P)$. Then if A is a p-subgroup of $N_G(P)$ with the property $[P, A, A] = 1$, we have

$$AC_G(P)/C_G(P) \subseteq O_p(N_G(P)/C_G(P)).$$

Remark   Taking $K = O_{p',p}(G)$ and letting P be an S_p-subgroup of K, we have $G = KN_G(P)$ by Theorem 1.3.7. If Q is an S_p-subgroup of G containing P and A is an abelian normal subgroup of Q, then certainly $[P, A, A] = 1$. By the preceding theorem, $A \subseteq P$ and so certainly $AC_G(P/C_G(P) \subseteq O_p(N_G(P)/C_G(P))$. Thus Theorem 5.2 is, in fact, a special case of Theorem 5.3.

Proof

Set $N = N_G(P)$ and let $P = P_1 \supset P_2 \supset \cdots \supset P_{n+1} = 1$ be an N-invariant normal series of P such that each $\bar{P}_i = P_i/P_{i+1}$, $1 \leqslant i \leqslant n$, is elementary abelian and such that N acts irreducibly on $\bar{P}_i$. Let H_i be the kernel of the representation of N on $\bar{P}_i$. Since $\bar{N}_i = N/H_i$ acts faithfully and irreducibly on $\bar{P}_i$ as a vector space over Z_p, we have $O_p(\bar{N}_i) = \bar{1}$ by Theorem 3.1.3.

On the other hand, as $[P, A, A] = 1$, certainly $[\bar{P}_i, \bar{A}_i, \bar{A}_i] = 1$, where $\bar{A}_i$ denotes the image of A in $\bar{N}_i$. But now it follows from Theorem 2.6.6, exactly as in the proof of the preceding theorem, that $\bar{A}_i = \bar{1}$, whence $A \subseteq H_i$ for all

i, $1 \leqslant i \leqslant n$. We conclude that $A \subseteq H = \bigcap_{i=1}^{n} H_i$. But H stabilizes the normal series P_i, $1 \leqslant i \leqslant n+1$, of P. Since H/C is a subgroup of Aut P, where $C = C_G(P)$, Corollary 5.3.3 now yields that H/C is a p-group. But $H/C \lhd N/C$, so $H/C \subseteq O_p(N/C)$. Thus $AC/C \subseteq O_p(N/C)$ and the theorem is proved.

We note that the argument shows that Theorem 5.3 is, in fact, valid for any group which involves only p-stable subgroups.

EXERCISES

1. Let G be a solvable group in which $F(G)$ is a p-group. Prove that $O_{p'}(G) = 1$ and that $F(G) = O_p(G)$.
2. Let H, K be S_π-subgroups of G and assume H and K are nilpotent. Prove that H and K are conjugate in G.
3. Let A be a π'-group of automorphisms of the π-group G. Prove that $[G, A, A] = [G, A]$.
4. If G is a solvable group with abelian Sylow subgroups, show that $Z(G) \cap G' = 1$.
5. Let H and K be $S_{\{p,q\}}$-subgroups of the solvable group G. If X is a subgroup of G with $X \subseteq O_p(H) \cap K$, show that $X \subseteq O_p(K)$.
6. Let G be a p-solvable group and let Q be a p'-subgroup of G such that $|N_G(Q)/C_G(Q)|$ is divisible by p. Prove that Q does not normalize an S_p-subgroup of G.
7. Let G be p-solvable, let P be a fixed S_p-subgroup of G, and denote by $\mathcal{H}(P)$ the set of subgroups H of G such that (a) H has p-length at most 2, (b) $P \subseteq H$, and (c) $\pi(H)$ consists of at most two primes. Prove
    (i) $G = \langle H \mid H \in \mathcal{H}(P) \rangle$.
    (ii) If M and N are subgroups of G containing P such that $H = (H \cap M)(H \cap N)$ for all H in $\mathcal{H}(P)$, then $G = MN$.
8. Let G be p-solvable with $O_{p'}(G) = 1$. Let Q be a p'-subgroup of G and A a p-subgroup of $N_G(Q)$ such that $[A, Q] = Q$. Prove that $[O_p(G), A, Q] = 1$.
9. Show that any two Sylow systems of a solvable group G are conjugate in G.
10. Let P_i, $1 \leqslant i \leqslant n$, be a Sylow system of the solvable group G. Prove
    (i) For each subset π of $\pi(G)$, there exists an S_π-subgroup G_π of G such that $P_i \cap G_\pi$ is a Sylow subgroup of G_π.
    (ii) If $C = \bigcap_{\pi \subseteq \pi(G)} N_G(G_\pi)$, then C is nilpotent.
11. Let p be a prime in $\pi(G)$, set

$$\mathcal{B} = \{B \mid B \lhd G, \ B \text{ is a } p\text{-group, and } O_p(G/C_G(B)) = 1\},$$

and let $R = \langle B \mid B \in \mathscr{B} \rangle$. Prove

    (i) $R \in \mathscr{B}$.

    (ii) R is abelian.

12. Let G be p-solvable with $O_{p'}(G) = 1$. Let P be an S_p-subgroup of G and let $B = Z(P)^G$ be the normal closure of $Z(P)$ in G. Prove

    (i) B is an abelian p-group.

    (ii) $O_p(G/C_G(B)) = 1$ (hence $B \in \mathscr{B}$ in the notation of Exercise 11).

    (iii) $C_G(B)$ is the largest normal subgroup of G which centralizes $Z(P)$.

13. Show that either of the following conditions imply that G has p-length 1.

    (a) G is p-solvable and an S_p-subgroup of G is abelian.

    (b) G is strongly p-solvable and an S_p-subgroup of G has class 2.

14. Let G be p-solvable with $O_{p'}(G) = 1$ and let P be an S_p-subgroup of G, p odd. Prove that every *cyclic* normal subgroup of P lies in $O_p(G)$.

CHAPTER 7

FUSION, TRANSFER, AND
p-FACTOR GROUPS

We begin with Alperin's fundamental theorem which describes the conjugacy of p-elements of a group G. This theorem asserts that such conjugacy, which can be regarded as a "global" property of G is, in fact, completely determined by "local" properties—specifically, by the structure of the normalizers of the nonidentity p-subgroups of G. On the basis of this result, we are able to give a concise treatment of all the standard applications of the transfer homomorphism, including the theorems of Burnside, Frobenius, and Grün on the existence of nontrivial p-factor groups. In Section 5 we introduce the general notion of weak closure and study its relation to the particular concept of p-normality. Then in the final two sections we study groups with very restricted classes of Sylow p-subgroups, which provides an opportunity to apply a number of our general theorems to obtain information about the fusion of p-elements in such groups.

1. LOCAL FUSION

If x and y are conjugate elements in G, then obviously $|x| = |y|$. Hence if $\pi(\langle x \rangle) = \{p_i | 1 \leqslant i \leqslant r\}$, Theorem 1.3.1 implies that $x = x_1 x_2 \cdots x_r$ and

$y = y_1 y_2 \cdots y_r$ with x_i, y_i uniquely determined p_i-elements of $\langle x \rangle, \langle y \rangle$, respectively. Raising x and y to the appropriate powers, the conjugacy of x and y implies the conjugacy of x_i and $y_i, 1 \le i \le r$. Because of this, many questions of conjugacy in general can be reduced to problems about conjugacy of elements of prime power order. Furthermore, because of Sylow's theorem, conjugacy of such elements can in turn be reduced to the study of conjugacy of elements of a fixed Sylow subgroup of G.

If P is a fixed S_p-subgroup of the group G, then obviously two elements of P that are conjugate in P are conjugate in G. Determination of the conjugacy classes of a given p-group may not be easy to accomplish. However, this question is not the one which will primarily concern us; rather we shall be interested in the converse problem: when are distinct conjugate classes of P part of the same conjugate class of G?

Thus we say that two elements x, y of P are *fused* in G if x and y are conjugate in G, but not in P. In this case the distinct conjugate classes of P in which x and y lie are part of a single conjugate class in G. More generally two subsets X, Y of P are said to be *fused* in G if they are conjugate in G, but not in P.

If x, y lie in a subgroup P_1 of P, it may happen that x and y are conjugate in $N_G(P_1)$. (If x, y are conjugate in P, this is indeed the case with $P_1 = P$.) However, x and y may very well be conjugate in G without the conjugation taking place in the normalizer of some subgroup of P containing them. A slightly more general situation is the following: There exist subgroups P_1 and P_2 of P with $x \in P_1, y \in P_2$, such that x is conjugate in $N_G(P_1)$ to an element z which lies in P_2 and z in turn is conjugate to y in $N_G(P_2)$. We shall give an exercise to illustrate that x and y may be conjugate in this latter fashion without being conjugate in the normalizer of any subgroup of P. Clearly we can generalize this procedure to any finite number of subgroups of P. Thus by considering the normalizers of all nonidentity p-subgroups of P, we can study the fusion that takes place in these normalizers by the process just described. Conjugacy of this type we can regard as "local conjugacy" or "local fusion," in the sense that it is determined in the "neighborhood" of the S_p-subgroup P of G.

We formalize this in the following definition: Two subsets X, Y of P are said to be *locally conjugate* or *locally fused* in G provided there exists a sequence of subgroups P_i of $P, 1 \le i \le n + 1$, and elements x_i of $N_G(P_i), 1 \le i \le n$, such that

$$(1.1) \qquad X^{x_1 x_2 \cdots x_i} \subseteq P_{i+1} \quad \text{and} \quad X^{x_1 x_2 \cdots x_n} = Y.$$

On its face, it would appear that the elements x and y of P could be fused in G without being locally fused. However, this is, in fact, not possible as Alperin's remarkable theorem will demonstrate. Some work of Burnside and Wielandt perhaps foreshadowed this striking result; and we conclude this introductory section with Burnside's classical theorem:

Theorem 1.1 (Burnside)
If P is an S_p-subgroup of G, then two normal subsets of P are conjugate in G if and only if they are conjugate in $N_G(P)$. In particular, two elements of $Z(P)$ are conjugate in G if and only if they are conjugate in $N_G(P)$.

Proof
Obviously any element of $Z(P)$ is itself a normal subset of P and also two subsets of P conjugate in $N_G(P)$ are conjugate in G. Hence we need only prove that if X, Y are normal subsets of P with $Y = X^u$, $u \in G$, then $Y = X^z$ with $z \in N_G(P)$. Set $N = N_G(Y)$, so that $P \subseteq N$, as Y is a normal subset of P. But Y is also a normal subset of P^u, as $Y = X^u$ and X is a normal subset of P. Hence also $P^u \subseteq N$. Then P and P^u are S_p-subgroups of N and consequently $P^{uv} = P$ for some v in N. Setting $z = uv$, we then have $z \in N_G(P)$ and $X^z = X^{uv} = Y^v = Y$, as required.

2. ALPERIN'S THEOREM

Alperin's results will show not only that all fusion is local, but that considerable restriction can be placed upon the subgroups P_i of P and the elements x_i of $N_G(P_i)$ which effect the local conjugation. For the subsequent applications it will be necessary to establish his results in a very precise form. We therefore begin with some definitions involving Sylow groups and their intersections.

If P and Q are S_p-subgroups of G, we shall say that the intersection $P \cap Q$ is *tame* provided $N_P(P \cap Q)$ and $N_Q(P \cap Q)$ are each S_p-subgroups of $N_G(P \cap Q)$.

In general, $N_P(P \cap Q)$ and $N_Q(P \cap Q)$ are p-subgroups of $N_G(P \cap Q)$, but one or both may fail to be an S_p-subgroup of $N_G(P \cap Q)$. If $P \cap Q = 1$, then $N_P(P \cap Q) = P$ and $N_Q(P \cap Q) = Q$, so in this case $P \cap Q$ is always a tame intersection. Likewise, if $P = Q$, then $P \cap Q = P$ and in this case also $P \cap Q$ is a tame intersection.

Now let P be a fixed S_p-subgroup of G. Then if Q, R are two S_p-subgroups of G we shall say that R is *related to Q with respect to P* provided there exist S_p-subgroups Q_i, $1 \leqslant i \leqslant n$, such that

(a) $P \cap Q_i$ is a tame intersection, $1 \leqslant i \leqslant n$.

(b) There exist p-elements x_i of $N_G(P \cap Q_i)$, $1 \leqslant i \leqslant n$, such that $R^x = Q$, where $x = x_1 x_2 \cdots x_n$.

(c) $P \cap R \subseteq P \cap Q_1$ and $(P \cap R)^{x_1 x_2 \cdots x_i} \subseteq P \cap Q_{i+1}$, $1 \leqslant i \leqslant n - 1$.

Whenever this is the case we shall write $R \sim_P Q$, and if there is no danger of confusion we shall simply write $R \sim Q$. If we wish to refer to the conjugating element x, we shall write $R \sim Q$ via x.

Condition (c) amounts to the fact that as we conjugate from R to Q, we are "keeping track" of what is happening to $P \cap R$. Although the definition does not specify the final intersection when we apply x_n, this intersection is, in fact, determined. Indeed,

$$(P \cap R)^x = ((P \cap R)^{x_1 x_2 \cdots x_{n-1}})^{x_n} \subseteq (P \cap Q_n)^{x_n} \subseteq P \cap Q_n,$$

as $x_n \in N_G(P \cap Q_n)$.

Since this last inclusion may be proper, we cannot necessarily reverse our steps, and so the relation $R \sim_P Q$ is not necessarily symmetric. On the other hand, if $P \cap Q$ is a tame intersection, then obviously $Q \sim_P Q$ with $n = 1$, $x_1 = 1$, and $Q_1 = Q$; so our relation is reflexive.

Alperin's principal result, from which the conclusions on fusion follow directly, is the following: If Q is any S_p-subgroup of G, then the relation $Q \sim_P P$ necessarily holds. We carry this out in a sequence of lemmas, the first of which shows that the given relation is transitive. We emphasize that throughout P is a fixed S_p-subgroup of G and we drop the subscript P.

Lemma 2.1

If Q, R, S are S_p-subgroups of G such that $S \sim R$ and $R \sim Q$, then $S \sim Q$.

Proof

Suppose $y_i, T_i, 1 \leqslant i \leqslant m$, and $z_i, U_i, 1 \leqslant i \leqslant r$, are elements and S_p-subgroups of G which realize the relations $S \sim R$ and $R \sim Q$ with respect to P, respectively. Set $n = m + r$ and define

$$(2.1) \qquad x_i = \begin{cases} y_i \\ z_{i-m} \end{cases} \quad \text{and} \quad Q_i = \begin{cases} T_i & 1 \leqslant i \leqslant m \\ U_{i-m} & m + 1 \leqslant i \leqslant n. \end{cases}$$

We claim that the elements x_i and the S_p-subgroups Q_i, $1 \leqslant i \leqslant n$, effect the desired conclusion $S \sim Q$.

Indeed, $P \cap Q_i$ is a tame intersection and x_i is a p-element of $N_G(P \cap Q_i)$ for all i inasmuch as corresponding statements hold for $P \cap T_i$, $P \cap U_i$, y_i, and z_i. Furthermore, if $y = y_1 y_2 \cdots y_m$ and $z = z_1 z_2 \cdots z_r$, then

$x = yz = x_1 x_2 \cdots x_n$. Since $S^y = R$ and $R^z = Q$, we have $S^x = Q$. Thus conditions (a) and (b) of the definition of $S \sim Q$ hold.

Now $P \cap S \subseteq P \cap T_1 = P \cap Q_1$, while if $1 \leqslant i \leqslant m - 1$, then

$$(2.2) \qquad (P \cap S)^{x_1 x_2 \cdots x_i} = (P \cap S)^{y_1 y_2 \cdots y_i} \subseteq P \cap T_{i+1} = P \cap Q_{i+1}.$$

Furthermore,

$$(P \cap S)^{x_1 x_2 \cdots x_m} = (P \cap S)^y \subseteq P \cap R,$$

as we have observed above. But then

$$(2.3) \qquad (P \cap S)^{x_1 x_2 \cdots x_m} \subseteq P \cap U_1 = P \cap Q_{m+1},$$

as $P \cap R \subseteq P \cap U_1$.

Finally, for $m + 1 \leqslant i \leqslant n - 1$, we have

$$(2.4) \qquad (P \cap S)^{x_1 x_2 \cdots x_i} = ((P \cap S)^y)^{x_{m+1} \cdots x_i} \subseteq (P \cap R)^{z_1 z_2 \cdots z_{m-i}}$$

$$\subseteq P \cap U_{i-m+1} = P \cap Q_{i+1}.$$

But now (2.2), (2.3), and (2.4) together show that also condition (c) holds. Thus $S \sim Q$, as asserted.

Lemma 2.2

Let Q, R be S_p-subgroups of G such that $P \cap R \supseteq P \cap Q$, $R \sim P$ via x, and $Q^x \sim P$. Then $Q \sim P$.

Proof

By the preceding lemma, it will be enough to show that $Q \sim Q^x$. Let $x = x_1 x_2 \cdots x_n$ and Q_i, $1 \leqslant i \leqslant n$, be given in accordance with the definition $R \sim P$ via x. We claim that $Q \sim Q^x$ is given by the same elements x_i and S_p-subgroups Q_i. Indeed, conditions (a) and (b) clearly hold as Q is conjugated into Q^x by the element x. As for (c), $P \cap Q \subseteq P \cap R$ by hypothesis and so $P \cap Q \subseteq P \cap Q_1$. But then

$$(P \cap Q)^{x_1 x_2 \cdots x_i} \subseteq (P \cap R)^{x_1 x_2 \cdots x_i} \subseteq P \cap Q_{i+1} \qquad 1 \leqslant i \leqslant n - 1,$$

as required.

Lemma 2.3

Let Q, R be S_p-subgroups of G such that $R \cap Q \supset P \cap Q$ and $R \sim P$. Suppose $S \sim P$ for all S_p-subgroups S of G with the property $|S \cap P| > |Q \cap P|$. Then $Q \sim P$.

Proof

Let $R \sim P$ via x, so that $R^x = P$. Then $P \cap Q^x = R^x \cap Q^x = (R \cap Q)^x$. But by hypothesis, $|R \cap Q| > |P \cap Q|$, whence $|P \cap Q^x| > |P \cap Q|$. Hence

$Q^x \sim P$ by our second assumption. Since $R \sim P$, the desired conclusion $Q \sim P$ will follow from the preceding lemma provided we show that $P \cap R \supseteq P \cap Q$. But $P \cap R \supseteq P \cap (R \cap Q) \supseteq P \cap (P \cap Q) = P \cap Q$, as required.

Lemma 2.4

Let Q be an S_p-subgroup of G such that $P \cap Q$ is a tame intersection. If $S \sim P$ for all S_p-subgroups S of G with the property $|S \cap P| > |Q \cap P|$, then $Q \sim P$.

Proof

If $Q = P$, then we know that $Q \cap P$ is a tame intersection and that $Q \sim P$; hence we may assume $Q \neq P$, in which case $P \cap Q \subset P$. Set $P_0 = N_P(P \cap Q)$ and $Q_0 = N_Q(P \cap Q)$, so that P_0, Q_0 are each S_p-subgroups of $N = N_G(P \cap Q)$ since $P \cap Q$ is a tame intersection. Let K be the subgroup of N generated by all its p-elements. Then clearly Q_0 and P_0 are S_p-subgroups of K, whence $Q_0^y = P_0$ for some y in K. But then we can write $x = x_1 x_2 \cdots x_n$, where each x_i is a p-element of K. Take $Q_i = Q$ for $1 \leqslant i \leqslant n$. Then certainly $P \cap Q_i$ is a tame intersection for all i and it follows immediately from the definition that $Q \sim Q^x$.

On the other hand, $P \cap Q^x \supseteq P \cap Q_0^x = P \cap P_0 = P_0$. But $P_0 \supset P \cap Q$ by Theorem 1.2.11(ii), since $P \supset P \cap Q$. Hence $|P \cap Q^x| > |P \cap Q|$ and consequently $Q^x \sim P$ by hypothesis. Thus we have both $Q \sim Q^x$ and $Q^x \sim P$, whence $Q \sim P$ by Lemma 2.1.

With the aid of these lemmas, we can now prove

Theorem 2.5

For any S_p-subgroups P and Q of G, we have $Q \sim_p P$.

Proof

We argue by induction on $|P : P \cap Q|$. If $|P : P \cap Q| = 1$, then $P = Q$ and the theorem holds; so we may suppose that $P \cap Q \subset P$. Let D be an S_p-subgroup of $N_G(P \cap Q)$ which contains $N_P(P \cap Q)$ and let S be an S_p-subgroup of G containing D. Then $P \cap S \supseteq P \cap D = N_P(P \cap D) \supset P \cap Q$, so $P \cap S \supset P \cap Q$. Hence by induction $S \sim P$. Suppose $S \sim P$ via the element x. It will suffice to show that $Q^x \sim P$, for then Lemma 2.2 with S in place of R will give the desired conclusion $Q \sim P$.

Now $P \cap Q^x \supseteq P \cap (P \cap Q)^x$, while $(P \cap Q)^x \subseteq S^x = P$, whence $P \cap (P \cap Q)^x = (P \cap Q)^x$, and consequently

$$(2.5) \qquad\qquad P \cap Q^x \supseteq (P \cap Q)^x.$$

If $P \cap Q^x \supset (P \cap Q)^x$, then $|P:P \cap Q^x| < |P:P \cap Q|$, as $(P \cap Q)^x$ and $P \cap Q$ have the same order. But then $Q^x \sim P$ by induction. Hence we may assume that (2.5) is an equality.

Since D is an S_p-subgroup of $N_G(P \cap Q)$, it follows therefore that D^x is an S_p-subgroup of $N_G((P \cap Q)^x) = N_G(P \cap Q^x)$. Now let E be an S_p-subgroup of $N_G(P \cap Q^x)$ containing $N_{Q^x}(P \cap Q^x)$ and let T be an S_p-subgroup of G containing E. Then $T \cap Q^x \supseteq E \supseteq N_{Q^x}(P \cap Q^x) \supset P \cap Q^x$. If $T \sim P$, then the first condition of Lemma 2.3 is satisfied with T, Q^x in the roles of R, Q, respectively. Since the second condition of the lemma holds by our induction assumption, it follows that $Q^x \sim P$, as required. Hence it will suffice to prove that, in fact, $T \sim P$. But $P \cap T \supseteq P \cap Q^x$, so if $P \cap T \supset P \cap Q^x$, this assertion will follow from our induction assumption. Hence we may also assume that $P \cap T = P \cap Q^x$.

We argue under these conditions that $P \cap T$ is a tame intersection, in which case the conclusion $T \sim P$ will follow from Lemma 2.4 in view of our induction assumption. First of all, we have that $D^x \subseteq P$ and that D^x is an S_p-subgroup of $N_G(P \cap Q^x) = N_G(P \cap T)$. Furthermore, since $E \subseteq T$ and E is an S_p-subgroup of $N_G(P \cap Q^x)$, we also have that $N_T(P \cap T)$ is an S_p-subgroup of $N_G(P \cap T)$. Thus $P \cap T$ is a tame intersection and the theorem is proved.

Theorem 2.5 leads at once to Alperin's main result on fusion:

Theorem 2.6 (Alperin)

Let A and B be two subsets of an S_p-subgroup P of G and suppose that $A^x = B$. Then there exist elements x_i and S_p-subgroups Q_i of $G, 1 \leqslant i \leqslant n$, and an element y of $N_G(P)$ which satisfy the following conditions:

     (i) $x = x_1 x_2 \cdots x_n y$.
     (ii) $P \cap Q_i$ is a tame intersection, $1 \leqslant i \leqslant n$.
     (iii) x_i is a p-element of $N_G(P \cap Q_i), 1 \leqslant i \leqslant n$.
     (iv) $A \subseteq P \cap Q_1$, while $A^{x_1 x_2 \cdots x_i} \subseteq P \cap Q_{i+1}, 1 \leqslant i \leqslant n$.

Proof

By Theorem 2.5, $P^{x^{-1}} \sim P$ via some element u. Let Q_i and x_i, $1 \leqslant i \leqslant n$, be S_p-subgroups and elements of G which give rise to this relation, so that, in particular, $u = x_1 x_2 \cdots x_n$ and $(P^{x^{-1}})^u = P$. Setting $y = u^{-1}x$, it follows that $y \in N_G(P)$ and $x = uy$. Since $B = A^x \subseteq P$, we have $A \subseteq P \cap P^{x^{-1}}$. Hence $A^{x_1 x_2 \cdots x_i} \subseteq (P \cap P^{x^{-1}})^{x_1 \cdots x_i} \subseteq P \cap Q_{i+1}, 1 \leqslant i \leqslant n-1$, by definition of $P^{x^{-1}} \sim P$ via u and by our choice of Q_i and x_i. For the same reason $P \cap Q_i$ is a tame intersection and $x_i \in N_G(P \cap Q_i), 1 \leqslant i \leqslant n$, and the theorem is proved.

The theorem applies, in particular, of course, to elements of P. We note also that the element y need not be a p-element.

There is another form of Alperin's theorem that is more convenient for some applications. Observe, first of all, that if we put $Q_{n+1} = P$, we have that $P \cap Q_{n+1}$ is a tame intersection. Furthermore, as we have seen above $A^u \subseteq P$, so $A^u = A^{x_1 x_2 \cdots x_n} \subseteq Q_{n+1}$. In addition, if we set $y = x_{n+1}$, then $x_{n+1} \in N_G(P \cap Q_{n+1})$. Now put $A = A_0$ and set $A = A_0^{x_1 x_2 \cdots x_i}, 1 \leqslant i \leqslant n + 1$, so that $A_{n+1} = B$. Our conditions imply that A_{i-1} and A_i both lie in $P \cap Q_{i+1}$ and are conjugate by the element x_i. Thus we have (replacing $n + 1$ by m):

Theorem 2.7 (Alperin)

If A and B are subsets of the S_p-subgroup P of G that are conjugate in G, then there exist S_p-subgroups Q_i of G with $P \cap Q_i$ a tame intersection, $1 \leqslant i \leqslant m$, and subsets $A = A_0, A_1, A_2, \ldots, A_m = B$ such that
  (i) *$A_{i-1} \subseteq P \cap Q_i, A_i \subseteq P \cap Q_i$.*
  (ii) *$A_i = A_{i-1}^{y_i}$ for some y_i in $N_G(P \cap Q_i), 1 \leqslant i \leqslant m$.*

Theorem 2.6 simply asserts, in addition, that for $1 \leqslant i \leqslant m - 1$ the element y_i can be taken as a p-element, while y_m can be taken in $N_G(P)$ and Q_m can be taken as P.

3. TRANSFER AND THE FOCAL SUBGROUP

The study of fusion of p-elements is very closely related to the question of whether a given group G possesses a nontrivial p-*factor* group—that is, a proper normal subgroup of index a power of the prime p. The well-known theorems of Burnside, Frobenius, and Grün give conditions for the existence of nontrivial p-factor groups. Strikingly simple proofs of all these theorems can be obtained from Alperin's theorem. To carry this out, however, we need a property of the so-called *focal* subgroup of an S_p-subgroup P of G, which in turn depends upon the *transfer* homomorphism of G into P/P'. We shall derive these results in the present section.

If G possesses a proper normal subgroup K such that $\bar{G} = G/K$ is a p-group, then $\bar{G}' \subset \bar{G}$ and if L is the inverse image of $\bar{G}'$ in G, then L is a proper normal subgroup of G and G/L is an *abelian p-group*. Thus G has a nontrivial p-factor group if and only if it has a nontrivial abelian p-factor group. A very simple description can be given of the maximal abelian p-factor group. Indeed, we have

Theorem 3.1

   Let P be an S_p-subgroup of G. Then
   (i) There exists a normal subgroup K of G such that G/K is isomorphic
       to $P/P \cap G'$.
   (ii) If K is a normal subgroup of G such that G/K is an abelian p-group,
        then $P \cap G' \subseteq K$ and G/K is isomorphic to a homomorphic image
        of $P/P \cap G'$.

Proof

   Assume $K \lhd G$ and G/K is an abelian p-group. Then $G' \subseteq K$ as G/K is
abelian and $G = KP$ as G/K is a p-group. In particular, $P \cap G' \subseteq K$ and
by the third isomorphism theorem G/K is isomorphic to $P/P \cap K$, which
together imply that $P/P \cap K$ is a homomorphic image of $P/P \cap G'$. Thus
(ii) holds.

   Now $P \cap G'$ is an S_p-subgroup of G', as $G' \lhd G$, and $\bar{G} = G/G'$ is
abelian. Hence if K denotes the inverse image of $O_{p'}(\bar{G})$ in G, we see that
$P \cap G' = P \cap K$, $K \lhd G$, and G/K is an abelian p-group isomorphic to
$P/P \cap G'$; and so (i) also holds.

   Theorem 3.1 shows the significance of the subgroup $P \cap G'$ and tells us
that G possesses a unique maximal abelian p-factor group, isomorphic to
$P/P \cap G'$. We call $P \cap G'$ the *focal* subgroup of P in G.

   We shall need a description of $P \cap G'$ in terms of fused elements of P.
To obtain this result requires some information about the transfer homomorphism, which we proceed to develop. Although we shall be primarily
interested in the transfer of G into P/P', it is more convenient in the
beginning to consider an arbitrary abelian group A. The existence of this
homomorphism depends upon the following theorem:

Theorem 3.2

   Let G be a group, H a subgroup of G, and ϕ a homomorphism of H into an
abelian group A. Let y_i, $1 \le i \le n$, be a complete set of right coset representatives of H in G. For x in G, if $y_i x \in H y_{i'(x)}$ write

$$y_i x = h_i(x) y_{i'(x)}$$

or the appropriate element $h_i(x)$ of H. Then we have
   (i) The mapping $x\tau = \prod_{i=1}^{n} h_i(x)\phi$ is a homomorphism of G into A.
   (ii) τ is determined independently of the choice of the coset representa-
        tives y_i, $1 \le i \le n$, of H in G.

Proof

Because ϕ is a homomorphism, we can rewrite $x\tau$ as

$$(3.1) \qquad\qquad x\tau = \left(\prod_{i=1}^{n} h_i(x) \right)\phi.$$

Hence for x_1, x_2 in G we have

$$(3.2) \quad (x_1\tau)(x_2\tau) = \left(\prod_{i=1}^{n} h_i(x_1) \right)\phi\left(\prod_{i=1}^{n} h_i(x_2) \right)\phi = \left(\prod_{i=1}^{n} h_i(x_1) \prod_{i=1}^{n} h_i(x_2) \right)\phi.$$

On the other hand,

$$(3.3) \qquad\qquad (x_1 x_2)\tau = \left(\prod_{i=1}^{n} h_i(x_1 x_2) \right)\phi.$$

If u, v denote the terms in the parentheses of the right side of (3.2) and (3.3), respectively, τ will be a homomorphism provided we prove that $u\phi = v\phi$, or equivalently that $u = kv$ for some element k of the kernel K of ϕ. Since A is abelian, $H' \subseteq K$. Consequently it will suffice to prove that $v \equiv u \pmod{H'}$. Suppose we can show that v is equal to the product of the $2n$ elements $h_i(x_1)$, $h_i(x_2)$, $1 \leqslant i \leqslant n$, in *some* order. Since any rearrangement of these terms does not affect the coset of H' in which the product lies, the desired conclusion $v \equiv u \pmod{H'}$ will then follow, since by (3.2) u is by definition a product of these $2n$ elements.

To prove the required assertion, note, first of all, that by definition of $h_i(x_1 x_2)$, we have

$$(3.4) \qquad\qquad y_i(x_1 x_2) = h_i(x_1 x_2)y_{i'(x_1 x_2)}.$$

On the other hand,

$$(3.5) \qquad y_i(x_1 x_2) = (y_i x_1)x_2 = h_i(x_1)y_{i'(x_1)}x_2 = h_i(x_1)(y_j x_2),$$

where we have set $j = i'(x_1)$. Thus

$$(3.6) \qquad\qquad y_i(x_1 x_2) = h_i(x_1)h_j(x_2)y_{j'(x_2)},$$

which together with (3.4) yields

$$(3.7) \qquad\qquad h_i(x_1 x_2) = h_i(x_1)h_j(x_2) \qquad 1 \leqslant i \leqslant n.$$

Since $v = \prod_{i=1}^{n} h_i(x_1 x_2)$, the desired conclusion will follow from (3.7) provided we show that j runs over the set $S = \{1, 2, \ldots, n\}$ (in some order) as i does. But the mapping π_{x_1} from S to S defined by the rule

$$(3.8) \qquad\qquad (i)\pi_{x_1} = i'(x_1)$$

is clearly a permutation of S. Since $i'(x_1) = j$ by definition, j runs over S and we conclude that τ is a homomorphism.

Suppose now that $\bar{y}_i$, $1 \leqslant i \leqslant n$, is another set of coset representatives of H in G and let $\bar{\tau}$ be the corresponding homomorphism of G into A, defined by the corresponding elements $\bar{h}_i(x)$ for x in G, $1 \leqslant i \leqslant n$. We must prove that $\bar{\tau} = \tau$. Setting

$$(3.9) \qquad u = \prod_{i=1}^{n} h_i(x) \qquad \text{and} \qquad \bar{u} = \prod_{i=1}^{n} \bar{h}_i(x)$$

and, arguing as in the proof of (i), it will suffice to show that $u \equiv \bar{u} \pmod{H'}$. If the $\bar{y}_i$ are a permutation of the y_i, then the $\bar{h}_i(x)$ are a permutation of the $h_i(x)$ and the desired conclusion follows at once in this case. Hence replacing the $\bar{y}_i$ by a suitable permutation of them, we may assume without loss that y_i and $\bar{y}_i$ lie in the same coset of H, $1 \leqslant i \leqslant n$.

Thus $\bar{y}_i = z_i y_i$, $z_i \in H$, $1 \leqslant i \leqslant n$, whence

$$(3.10)$$

$$\bar{y}_i x = z_i y_i x = z_i h_i(x) y_{i'(x)} = z_i h_i(x) z_{i'(x)}^{-1} z_{i'(x)} y_{i'(x)} = z_i h_i(x) z_{i'(x)}^{-1} \bar{y}_{i'(x)}.$$

It follows from (3.10) and the definition of $\bar{h}_i(x)$ that

$$(3.11) \qquad \bar{h}_i(x) = z_i h_i(x) z_{i'(x)}^{-1} \qquad 1 \leqslant i \leqslant n.$$

But now (3.9) and (3.11) yield

$$(3.12) \qquad \bar{u} \equiv u \left(\prod_{i=1}^{n} z_i \prod_{i=1}^{n} z_{i'(x)}^{-1} \right) \pmod{H'}.$$

However, the mapping $(x)\pi_x = i'(x)$ is a permutation of $S = \{1, 2, \ldots, n\}$ and consequently the second product is simply the inverse of the first. Thus $\bar{u} \equiv u \pmod{H'}$ and the theorem is proved.

The homomorphism τ is called the *transfer* or *transfer homomorphism* of G into A (relative to H and ϕ). For most applications, one is interested in the case that $H = P$ is an S_p-subgroup of G, $A = P/P^*$, where P^* is a subgroup of P containing P', and ϕ is the natural homomorphism of P on P/P^*.

By the theorem, $x\tau$ is determined independently of the choice of the coset representatives of H in G. We shall now choose these coset representatives in a very particular way, which will itself be a function of the element x, and on the basis of this choice will establish the following result:

Theorem 3.3

Let τ be the transfer of G into an abelian group A relative to the subgroup H of G and the homomorphism ϕ of H into A. Then for any element x of G, there exists a set of t elements x_i of G, $1 \leqslant i \leqslant t$, with t and x_i depending upon x, with the following properties:

   (i) $x_i x^{r_i} x_i^{-1} \in H$ *for suitable positive integers* r_i, $1 \leqslant i \leqslant t$.

   (ii) $\displaystyle\sum_{i=1}^{t} r_i = n = |G : H|.$

   (iii) $x\tau = \left(\displaystyle\prod_{i=1}^{t} x_i x^{r_i} x_i^{-1} \right)\phi.$

Proof

With the notation as in Theorem 3.2 and with the coset representatives y_i of H in G, $1 \leqslant i \leqslant n$, we consider the permutation π_x of $S = \{1, 2, \ldots, n\}$ given in (3.8). We decompose π_x as a product of disjoint cycles and renumber the y_i in such a way that the decomposition of π_x assumes the form

$$(3.13) \quad (12 \cdots r_1)(r_1 + 1 \cdots r_1 + r_2)(r_1 + r_2 + 1 \cdots r_1 + r_2 + r_3) \cdots .$$

Let t be the number of cycles of π_x. Then their respective lengths are r_i and $\displaystyle\sum_{i=1}^{t} r_i = n = |G : H|.$ Thus (ii) holds for these integers r_i.

Now let $x_1, x_2, \ldots, x_t$ be the coset representatives of the cosets labeled $1, r_1 + 1, \ldots, r_1 + r_2 + \cdots + r_{t-1} + 1$, respectively. Then by definition of π_x we have that $x_i x^j$ is a coset representative of H in G corresponding to the $(j + 1)$st coset of the ith cycle of π_x and so the elements

$$(3.14) \qquad\qquad \{x_i x^j | 1 \leqslant i \leqslant t, 0 \leqslant j \leqslant r_i - 1\}$$

form a complete set of coset representatives of H in G. Furthermore, $x_i x^{r_i} \in H x_i$ by definition of r_i, whence $x_i x^{r_i} x_i^{-1} \in H$ and so condition (i) holds with this choice of the elements x_i, $1 \leqslant i \leqslant t$.

We now compute $x\tau$, using the coset representatives (3.14). Set $y_k = x_i x^j$ (k a function of i and j) and consider $y_k x = h_k(x)y_{k'(x)}$. If $j < r_i - 1$, then $y_k x = x_i x^{j+1} = y_{k'(x)}$ is one of the coset representatives (3.14). But this implies that $h_k(x) = 1$ whenever $j < r_i - 1$. Hence $x\tau$ is the product of those $(h_k(x))\phi$ which correspond to the elements $y_k = x_i x^{r_i - 1}$. For such y_k, we have $y_k x = x_i x^{r_i} \in H x_i$, whence $y_k x = (x_i x^{r_i} x_i^{-1})x_i$ with $x_i x^{r_i} x_i^{-1} \in H$ and $x_i = y_{k'(x)}$. It follows that $h_k(x) = x_i x^{r_i} x_i^{-1}$ for each of these y_k and we conclude that

$$(3.15) \qquad x\tau = \prod_{i=1}^{t} (x_i x^{r_i} x_i^{-1})\phi.$$

Since ϕ is a homomorphism, (iii) follows at once from (3.15) and the theorem is proved.

Theorem 3.3 enables us to give the following description of the focal subgroup.

Theorem 3.4

If P is an S_p-subgroup of G, then the focal subgroup $P \cap G'$ is generated by the set of all elements $x^{-1}y$ with $x, y \in P$ and x conjugate to y in G.

Proof

Set $P^* = \langle x^{-1}x^u \mid x \in P, \; u \in G, \; \text{and} \; x^u \in P \rangle$. We must show that $P^* = P \cap G'$. Since $x^{-1}x^u = x^{-1}u^{-1}xu = [x, u]$, we clearly have $P' \subseteq P^* \subseteq P \cap G'$. In particular, P/P^* is abelian.

Now let ϕ be the natural homomorphism of P on P/P^* and let τ be the transfer of G into P/P^* relative to P and ϕ. If K denotes the kernel of τ, it will suffice to prove that G/K is isomorphic to P/P^*. Indeed, if this is the case, then P/P^* will be a homomorphic image of $P/P \cap G'$ by Theorem 3.1, which will imply that $|P/P \cap G'| \geqslant |P/P^*|$. But since $P^* \subseteq P \cap G'$, the reverse inequality also holds, giving the desired conclusion $P^* = P \cap G'$.

Now let $x \in P$ and choose the elements x_i of G and the integers r_i, $1 \leqslant i \leqslant t$, to satisfy the conditions of Theorem 3.3. Then with $n = |G:P|$, we have

$$(3.16) \qquad x_i x^{r_i} x_i^{-1} \in P, \; 1 \leqslant i \leqslant t,$$

and

$$(3.17) \qquad x\tau \equiv \prod_{i=1}^{t} x_i x^{r_i} x_i^{-1} \pmod{P^*}.$$

Since P/P^* is abelian, we can rewrite (3.17) as

$$(3.18) \quad x\tau = \prod_{i=1}^{t} x^{r_i} x^{-r_i} x_i x^{r_i} x_i^{-1} \equiv \left(\prod_{i=1}^{t} x^{r_i}\right)\left(\prod_{i=1}^{t} x^{-r_i} x_i x^{r_i} x_i^{-1}\right) \pmod{P^*}.$$

But $x^{-r_i} x_i x^{r_i} x_i^{-1} = (x^{r_i})^{-1} x_i x^{r_i} x_i^{-1} \in P^*$ since x^{r_i} and $x_i x^{r_i} x_i^{-1}$ lie in P and are conjugate in G. Thus (3.18) reduces to

$$(3.19) \qquad x\tau \equiv \prod_{i=1}^{t} x^{r_i} = x^{\Sigma_{i=1}^{t} r_i} = x^n \pmod{P^*}.$$

On the other hand, $(n, p) = 1$, as $|G : P| = n$ is relatively prime to p. Hence if $x \notin P^*$, it follows from (3.19) that $x\tau \notin P^*$. In other words, τ maps representatives of the distinct cosets of P^* in P onto distinct cosets of P^* in P and consequently τ maps P onto P/P^*. Clearly then $(G)\tau = P/P^*$, whence G/K is isomorphic to P/P^*, as required.

As an immediate corollary we have

Theorem 3.5

If P is an S_p-subgroup of G, then the transfer of G into $P/P \cap G'$ relative to P is an epimorphism.

4. THEOREMS OF BURNSIDE, FROBENIUS, AND GRÜN

The assertion that G has a nontrivial p-factor group or equivalently a description of the focal subgroup of G is a "global" property of G. The classical results that utilize transfer derive such global information from purely "local" assumptions. We shall now establish these results together with some new ones on the basis of Alperin's theorem and the focal subgroup theorem of the previous section. We begin with the following result:

Theorem 4.1

If P is an S_p-subgroup of G, then $P \cap G'$ is generated by the subgroups $[H, N_G(H)]$, where H ranges over the set of all nonidentity tame intersections $H = P \cap Q$, Q an S_p-subgroup of G.

Proof

Denote by P^* the subgroup of G generated by all such subgroups $[H, N_G(H)]$. Since $H \lhd N_G(H)$, $[H, N_G(H)] \subseteq H \subseteq P$, so P^* is contained in P as well as in G'. Thus $P^* \subseteq P \cap G'$. On the other hand, by Theorem 3.4,

$$P \cap G' = \langle x^{-1}y \,|\, x, y \in P, x \text{ and } y \text{ conjugate in } G \rangle.$$

Hence it will suffice to show that $x^{-1}y \in P^*$ for all such x, y in P.

By Theorem 2.7 there exist elements $x = x_0, x_1, \ldots, x_m = y$ and S_p-subgroups Q_i of G with $H_i = P \cap Q_i$ a tame intersection such that x_{i-1} and x_i lie in H_i and $x_i = x_{i-1}^{y_i}, y_i \in N_G(H_i), 1 \leqslant i \leqslant m$. But then $x_{i-1}^{-1}x_i = x_{i-1}^{-1}y_i^{-1}x_{i-1}y_i = [x_{i-1}, y_i] \in [H_i, N_G(H_i)] \subseteq P^*$ for each i. Since

$$x^{-1}y = x_0^{-1}x_m = (x_0^{-1}x_1)(x_1^{-1}x_2) \cdots (x_{m-1}^{-1}x_m),$$

it follows that $x^{-1}y \in P^*$, and the theorem is proved.

We next establish Grün's first theorem, which gives another description of the focal subgroup.

Theorem 4.2 (Grün)

If P is an S_p-subgroup of G, then
$P \cap G' = \langle P \cap N_G(P'), \; P \cap Q' \mid Q \text{ ranging over all } S_p\text{-subgroups of } G \rangle.$

Proof

Let P^* denote the right side of the above statement. Then clearly $P^* \subseteq P \cap G'$ and, as in the preceding theorem, we need only show that $x^{-1}y \in P^*$ for x, y in P and x conjugate to y in G. Let $Q_i, H_i, y_i, 1 \leqslant i \leqslant m$, be as in the preceding theorem. Again we need only show that $x_{i-1}^{-1}x_i = [x_{i-1}, y_i] \in P^*$ for each i. Now x_{i-1} and x_i are in $H_i = P \cap Q_i$ and $y_i \in N_G(H_i)$. Furthermore, by Theorems 2.6 and 2.7, we can choose y_i to be a p-element for $i < m$ and can choose y_m to be in $N_G(P)$. Hence for $i < m$, x_{i-1} and y_i lie in an S_p-subgroup R_i of G, whence $[x_{i-1}, y_i] \in R_i'$ and so $x_{i-1}^{-1}x_i \in P \cap R_i' \subseteq P^*$ in this case. On the other hand, $x_{m-1}^{-1}x_m = [x_{m-1}, y_m] \in P \cap N_G(P)' \subseteq P^*$, as $x_{m-1} \in P$ and $y_m \in N_G(P)$. This completes the proof.

Let P be an S_p-subgroup of G. If $G = PO_{p'}(G)$, we say that G has a *normal p-complement* [inasmuch as $O_{p'}(G) \lhd G$ and $P \cap O_{p'}(G) = 1$].

As a corollary to Grün's theorem, we have Burnside's well-known sufficient condition for a group to have a normal p-complement.

Theorem 4.3 (Burnside)

If an S_p-subgroup of G lies in the center of its normalizer in G, then G has a normal p-complement.

Proof

Let P be an S_p-subgroup of G and set $N = N_G(P)$. By assumption, $P \subseteq Z(N)$. Since $P \subseteq N$, it follows, in particular, that P is abelian. Hence $Q' = 1$ for any S_p-subgroup of G and so $P \cap Q' = 1$. Furthermore, P is a normal Hall subgroup of N and so has a complement H in N by the Schur-Zassenhaus theorem. Thus $N = PH$ with $P \cap H = 1$. But $P \subseteq Z(N)$, whence P centralizes H and consequently $N = P \times H$. It follows that $N' = (P \times H)' = H'$ and hence that $P \cap N' = P \cap H' = 1$. We conclude therefore from Grün's theorem that $P \cap G' = 1$.

But now Theorem 3.1(i) yields that G possesses a normal subgroup K such that G/K is isomorphic to $P/P \cap G' = P$. Since $|G|/|K| = |G/K| = |P|$, it follows at once that K is a p'-group, whence $K = O_{p'}(G)$. Thus G has a normal p-complement.

The proof of Burnside's theorem yields the following sharper result:

Theorem 4.4

If an S_p-subgroup P of G is abelian and $N = N_G(P)$, then
(i) $P \cap G' = P \cap N'$ and $P = (P \cap N') \times (P \cap Z(N))$.
(ii) *The maximal p-factor group of G is isomorphic to $P \cap Z(N)$.*

Proof

The first part of the preceding proof, together with Grün's theorem, implies that $P \cap G' = P \cap N'$. Furthermore, if H is a complement of P in N, then H is a p'-group and, as P is abelian, Theorem 5.2.3 yields that $P = P_1 \times P_2$, where $P_1 = C_P(H)$ and $P_2 = [P, H]$. But clearly $P_1 = P \cap Z(PH) = P \cap Z(N)$ and $P_2 = P \cap N'$, proving (i). Now (ii) follows from Theorem 3.1.

Our next result, due to Frobenius, gives a necessary and sufficient condition for a group to have a normal p-complement.

Theorem 4.5 (Frobenius)

G possesses a normal p-complement if and only if one of the following conditions holds:
(a) $N_G(H)/C_G(H)$ *is a p-group for every nonidentity p-subgroup of G.*
(b) $N_G(H)$ *has a normal p-complement for every nonidentity p-subgroup of G.*

Proof

Suppose first that G has a normal p-complement K. Let H be a nonidentity p-subgroup of G and set $N = N_G(H)$. Since $N/N \cap K$ and NK/K are isomorphic, we have that $N/N \cap K$ is a p-group. But $N \cap K$ is a p'-group and therefore $N \cap K$ is a normal p-complement in N. Furthermore, $[H, N \cap K] \subseteq H \cap K = 1$ as $H \lhd N$ and $N \cap K \lhd N$. Thus $N \cap K \subseteq C = C_G(H)$. Hence N/C is a homomorphic image of the p-group $N/N \cap K$ and so is itself a p-group. We conclude that conditions (a) and (b) both hold.

Conversely suppose (a) or (b) holds. If (b) holds, then $N = N_G(H)$ has a normal p-complement for any p-subgroup $H \neq 1$ of G. But then by the argument of the preceding paragraph, N/C is a p-group, where $C = C_G(H)$. Hence (b) implies (a) and consequently we need only show that G has a normal p-complement under assumption (a).

We argue by induction on G and suppose first that G has a proper normal subgroup G_1 such that G/G_1 is a p-group. Let H be a nontrivial p-subgroup of G_1 and set $N = N_G(H)$ and $C = C_G(H)$, so that by assumption N/C is a p-group. But $N \cap G_1 = N_{G_1}(H)$ and $C \cap G_1 = C_{G_1}(H)$. Since

N/C is a p-group, so also is $N \cap G_1/C \cap G_1 = N_{G_1}(H)/C_{G_1}(H)$. Thus G_1 satisfies condition (a) and so by induction G_1 possesses a normal p-complement K_1. Since K_1 char $G_1 \lhd G$, $K_1 \lhd G$. But G/G_1 and G_1/K_1 are each p-groups and hence so is G/K_1. We conclude at once that K_1 is a normal p-complement in G.

Thus to complete the proof of the theorem, it will suffice to show that G has a nontrivial p-factor group under assumption (a). This is equivalent, we know, to proving that $P \cap G' \subset P$, where P is an S_p-subgroup of G. We shall show, in fact, that $P \cap G' = P'$. This will follow at once from Theorem 4.1 provided we prove that $[H, N] \subseteq P'$ for every nontrivial tame intersection $H = P \cap Q$, where Q is an S_p-subgroup of G and $N = N_G(H)$. By assumption N/C is a p-group, where $C = C_G(H)$. On the other hand, as H is a tame intersection, $P \cap N$ is an S_p-subgroup of N, whence $N = (P \cap N)C$. But then $[H, N] = [H, (P \cap N)C] = [H, P \cap N]$ as C centralizes H. Since H and $P \cap N$ lie in P, we conclude that $[H, N] \subseteq P'$, as required.

In Chapter 8, using other methods, we shall show that for odd p there exists a *single* nontrivial p-subgroup H of G such that the existence of a normal p-complement in $N_G(H)$ suffices to imply the existence of one in G.

We conclude with two other results of some interest.

Theorem 4.6

If the S_p-subgroup P of G has trivial intersection with its distinct conjugates, then any two elements of P that are conjugate in G are conjugate in $N_G(P)$.

Proof

Let $x, y \in P$ with x conjugate to y in G and let $x = x_0, x_1, x_2, \ldots, x_m = y$, $H_i = P \cap Q_i$, and y_i be as in the proof of Theorem 4.1. Since x_{i-1} and x_i are in H_i, $P \cap Q_i \neq 1$ and consequently $P = Q_i$, $1 \leqslant i \leqslant m$. Thus $H_i = P$ and $y_i \in N_G(P)$ for all i, whence $u = y_1 y_2 \cdots y_m \in N_G(P)$. Since $x^u = y$, the theorem follows.

Theorem 4.7

Let $P \cap Q$ be an intersection of maximal order of two distinct S_p-subgroups of G. Then the only conjugates of $P \cap Q$ in G contained in P are conjugates of $P \cap Q$ in $N_G(P)$.

Proof

Set $A = P \cap Q$ and suppose $B = A^x \subseteq P$. Then by Theorem 2.7, we have $A = A_0, A_1, A_2 \ldots, A_m = B$, $H_i = P \cap Q_i, \langle A_{i-1}, A_i \rangle \subseteq H_i$, and $A_i = A_{i-1}^{y_i}$

for suitable y_i in $N_G(H_i)$, where each H_i is a tame intersection. Now if $Q_i \neq P$, then $H_i = P \cap Q_i = A_{i-1} = A_i$, since otherwise $|P \cap Q_i| > |A_i| = |A| = |P \cap Q|$, contrary to the fact that $P \cap Q$ is an intersection of S_p-subgroups of maximal order. Thus $A_{i-1} = A_i$ whenever $P \neq Q_i$ and consequently $B = A^y$, where $y = y_{i_1} y_{i_2} \cdots y_{i_r}$ with i_j running over those indices for which $Q_{i_j} = P$, proving the theorem.

5. WEAK CLOSURE AND p-NORMALITY

In this section we derive some additional consequences of Alperin's theorem which relate to the basic concept of weak closure. If H and K are subgroups of G, the *weak closure* of K in H *with respect to* G is by definition the subgroup of H generated by all conjugates of K in G which lie in H and is denoted by

$$V(\mathrm{ccl}_G(K); H).$$

(Here " ccl " is an abbreviation of " conjugate class ").

Thus, for example, in this terminology a corollary of Theorem 4.7 is the assertion

$$V(\mathrm{ccl}_G(P \cap Q); P) = V(\mathrm{ccl}_N(P \cap Q); P),$$

where P, Q are as in the theorem and $N = N_G(P)$.

If $K = V(\mathrm{ccl}_G(K); H)$, we say that K is *weakly closed* in H (with respect to G). Clearly in this case K must be a subgroup of H, for if $K^x \subseteq H$, then $K^x \subseteq K$ as K is weakly closed in H. But then $K = K^x \subseteq H$ as $|K^x| = |K|$. Obviously H is weakly closed in itself.

We shall be concerned here with some results in the case that $H = P$ is an S_p-subgroup of G and K is a characteristic subgroup of P. We first prove

Theorem 5.1
Let K be a characteristic subgroup of the S_p-subgroup P of G. Then K is weakly closed in P if and only if K is normal in every S_p-subgroup of G in which it lies.

Proof
Suppose $K \subseteq Q = P^x$, equivalently $K^{x^{-1}} \subseteq P$, $x \in G$. Then by definition K is weakly closed in P if and only if $K^{x^{-1}} \subseteq K$ and hence if and only if $K^{x^{-1}} = K$ for any such x.

But then if K is weakly closed in P, $K^x = K$ and so $K = K^x \operatorname{char} P^x = Q$. Conversely, suppose $K \lhd Q$. Since $K \operatorname{char} P$, $K^x \operatorname{char} P^x = Q$ and so K, K^x

are two normal subgroups of Q that are conjugate in G. But then by Burnside's theorem (Theorem 1.1), $K^{xy} = K$ for some y in $N_G(Q)$. On the other hand, $K^{xy} = K^x$ as K^x char Q. Thus $K^x = K$, whence K is weakly closed in P.

We remark that the proof shows that K need not be characteristic, but need only satisfy the weaker condition $K \lhd N_G(P)$.

Of particular interest is the case $K = Z(P)$. If $Z(P)$ is weakly closed in P, we say that G is p-*normal*. (Clearly this concept depends only upon the prime p and not upon the particular S_p-subgroup P of G.)

If P is abelian, then $P = Z(P)$ and certainly G is p-normal. Grün's second theorem, which we now prove, extends Theorem 4.4 on groups with abelian S_p-subgroups to arbitrary p-normal groups.

Theorem 5.2 (Grün)

If P is an S_p-subgroup of the p-normal group G and if $N = N_G(Z(P))$, then

$$P \cap G' = P \cap N'.$$

Proof

Set $H = N_G(P)$. Since $Z(P)$ char P, H normalizes $Z(P)$ and so $H \subseteq N$, whence $P \cap H' \subseteq P \cap N'$. Furthermore, by Grün's first theorem,

$$P \cap G' = \langle P \cap H', P \cap Q' \mid Q \text{ ranging over all } S_p\text{-subgroups of } G \rangle.$$

Hence to prove that $P \cap G' \subseteq P \cap N'$, it will suffice to show that $P \cap Q' \subseteq P \cap N'$, for all S_p-subgroups Q of G. Since obviously

$$P \cap N' \subseteq P \cap G',$$

this will be enough to establish the theorem.

Set $D = P \cap Q'$ with $Q = P^x$, $x \in G$, and let $M = N_G(D)$. Since $D \subseteq P$, we have $Z(P) \subseteq M$, and since $D \subseteq Q' \subseteq Q$, we also have $Z(P)^x \subseteq M$. Let R, S be S_p-subgroups of M containing $Z(P)$ and $Z(P)^x$, respectively. If $S^u = R$, $u \in M$, we have $Z(P)^{xu} \subseteq R$. Hence if T is an S_p-subgroup of G containing R, we see that both $Z(P)$ and $Z(P)^{xu}$ lie in T. But G is p-normal and consequently $Z(T)$ is weakly closed in T. Since $Z(P)$ and $Z(P)^{xu}$ are conjugates of $Z(T)$ contained in T, it follows that $Z(P) = Z(P)^{xu} = Z(T)$. We conclude therefore that $y = xu \in N = N_G(Z(P))$.

Now $u \in M = N_G(G)$ and consequently

$$D = D^u = (P \cap Q')^u = (P \cap (P')^x)^u = P^u \cap (P')^y.$$

Thus $D \subseteq (P')^y \subseteq N'$ since both P and y lie in N. Since also $D \subseteq P$, it follows that $D = P \cap Q' \subseteq P \cap N'$ and the theorem is proved.

There exist other deeper results, notably the Hall-Wielandt theorem, which give conditions on weakly closed subgroups W of P other than $Z(P)$ for $P \cap G'$ to equal $P \cap N'$ with $N = N_G(W)$. (See M. Hall [1], pp. 206–212.) This theorem does not seem to be a direct consequence of Alperin's theorem; and, as we do not require it, we shall not prove it here.

We conclude with a well-known result of Burnside related to nonweakly closed subgroups of P.

Theorem 5.3 (Burnside)

Let K be a normal subgroup of the S_p-subgroup P of G and assume K is contained as a nonnormal subgroup of some S_p-subgroup of G. Then there is a p-subgroup H of P containing K such that if r is the number of distinct conjugates of K contained in $N_G(H)$, then $(r, p) = 1$ and $r > 1$.

Proof

We have $K \subseteq P^x$ and $K \ntriangleleft P^x$ for some x in G. Thus $K^{x^{-1}} \subseteq P$ and $K^{x^{-1}} \ntriangleleft P$. We know from Alperin's theorem that we can conjugate $K^{x^{-1}}$ into K in a finite number of steps $K^{x^{-1}} = K_0, K_1, K_2, \ldots, K_m = K$ involving only tame intersections. Hence at some stage we must have $K_{i-1} \ntriangleleft P$ and $K_i \triangleleft P$. Set $L_0 = K_{i-1}$ and $L_1 = K_i$. Then our results imply that $\langle L_0, L_1 \rangle \subseteq P \cap Q$, where Q is an S_p-subgroup of G with $P \cap Q$ a tame intersection, that L_0, L_1 are conjugate in $N = N_G(P \cap Q)$, and that there exists an element y in G such that $L_1^y = K$ and $(P \cap Q)^y \subseteq P$.

Since $P \cap Q$ is a tame intersection, $R = N_P(P \cap Q)$ is an S_p-subgroup of N. Now $L_1 \triangleleft R$ as $L_1 \triangleleft P$ and $R \subseteq P$. On the other hand, $L_1 \ntriangleleft N$, for otherwise $L_0 = L_1$ and $L_0 \triangleleft P$, which is not the case. But then $r = |N : N_N(L_1)| > 1$ and is prime to p. Now r is the number of conjugates of L_1 in N; and, furthermore, as $L_1 \subseteq P \cap Q$ and $P \cap Q \triangleleft N$, these conjugates all lie in $P \cap Q$. Finally if we set $H = (P \cap Q)^y$, we see that $L_1^y = K \subseteq H \subseteq P$ and that r is the number of conjugates of K in $N_G(H)$. Since $(r, p) = 1$ and $r > 1$, the theorem is proved.

6. ELEMENTARY APPLICATIONS

We shall apply some of the preceding results to establish a number of important specialized theorems:

Theorem 6.1

Let P be an S_p-subgroup of G, where p is the smallest prime in $\pi(G)$. If $p > 2$, assume $d_n(P) \leqslant 2$, while if $p = 2$, assume P is cyclic. Then G has a normal p-complement.

Proof

Suppose first that p is odd. If H is a nontrivial subgroup of G, $H \subseteq Q$ for some S_p-subgroup Q of G. Since $d_n(Q) = d_n(P) \leqslant 2$, Theorem 5.4.15(i) implies that $d(H) \leqslant 2$, whence certainly $d_n(H) \leqslant 2$. Set $N = N_G(H)$ and $C = C_G(H)$, so that $\bar{N} = N/C$ is isomorphic to a subgroup of Aut H. We argue that $\bar{N}$ is a p-group. Indeed if not, then $\bar{N}$ would contain an element y of prime order $q \neq p$ which determines an automorphism of H of order q. But since $d_n(H) \leqslant 2$, Theorem 5.4.15(ii) implies that $q < p$. However, $q \in \pi(G)$ under these conditions, contrary to the fact that p is the smallest prime in $\pi(G)$. Thus $\bar{N}$ is a p-group for any p-subgroup $H \neq 1$ of G and now Theorem 4.5 yields that G possesses a normal p-complement.

Suppose now that $p = 2$, in which case P is cyclic. Setting $N = N_G(P)$ and $C = C_G(P)$, we have that N/C is a $2'$-group of automorphisms of P. But Aut P is a 2-group by Lemma 5.4.1 and consequently $N = C$. Thus $P \subseteq Z(N)$ and the desired conclusion follows in this case from Burnside's normal p-complement theorem.

In view of Theorem 5.4.11 concerning regular groups of automorphisms, it is of interest to know the structure of groups whose Sylow subgroups are all cyclic. This we can derive as a consequence of Theorem 6.1.

Theorem 6.2

If the Sylow subgroups of G are all cyclic, then G is metacyclic. In particular, G is solvable.

Proof

By induction on $|G|$, we first prove that G is solvable. Let P be an S_p-subgroup of G, where p is the smallest prime in $\pi(G)$. Since P is cyclic, certainly $d_n(P) \leqslant 2$. Hence G possesses a normal p-complement K by Theorem 6.1. Since the Sylow subgroups of K are also all cyclic, K is solvable by induction. Since $G = PK$ with $K \triangleleft G$, we conclude that G is solvable.

Now set $F = F(G)$. The Sylow subgroups of F, being subgroups of those of G, are cyclic. Since F is nilpotent, it follows that F is abelian, and hence, by Theorem 1.3.1(ii), that F is cyclic. But $C_G(F) \subseteq F$ by Theorem 6.1.3 and consequently G/F is isomorphic to a subgroup of Aut F. But Aut F is abelian as F is cyclic. Since the Sylow subgroups of G/F are also all cyclic, another application of Theorem 1.3.1(ii) yields that G/F is cyclic. Thus G is metacyclic, as asserted.

A group G is said to possess a *Sylow tower* if there exists a normal series $G = G_0 \supset G_1 \supset \cdots \supset G_n = 1$ in G such that each G_i/G_{i+1}, $0 \leqslant i \leqslant n - 1$, is isomorphic to a Sylow subgroup of G. Clearly such a group G is necessarily solvable. As a second consequence of Theorem 6.2, we have

Theorem 6.3

Let G be a group of odd order such that for every prime p in $\pi(G)$, we have $d_n(P) \leqslant 2$, where P is an S_p-group of G. Then G possesses a Sylow tower.

Proof

If p is the smallest prime in $\pi(G)$, we can apply Theorem 6.1, since p is odd, to conclude that G has a normal p-complement G_1. Then G_1 satisfies the same conditions as G; so by induction G_1 possesses a normal series with the required properties. Since G/G_1 is an S_p-subgroup of G, it follows at once that G has a Sylow tower.

A further consequence of the same type is the following:

Theorem 6.4

A simple nonabelian group has order divisible either by the cube of its smallest prime or by 12.

Proof

Let P be an S_p-subgroup of G, where p is the smallest prime and suppose $|P| \leqslant p^2$. Then P is either cyclic or abelian of type (p, p). In either case $d_n(P) \leqslant 2$. Hence if $p > 2$ or $p = 2$ and P is cyclic, G has a normal p-complement and so is not simple.

Consider the remaining case that $p = 2$ and P is of type $(2, 2)$ and set $N = N_G(P)$, $C = C_G(P)$. If $N = C$, then Burnside's theorem applies to yield that G has a normal 2-complement; and again G is not simple. On the other hand, if $N \supset C$, then N/C, being of odd order, must contain an element of order 3 which cyclically permutes the three elements of $P^{\#}$. In this case, 12 divides $|G|$ and the theorem is proved.

In view of the solvability of groups of odd order, a simple group, in fact, has order divisible by 8 or 12. Thompson's work on minimal simple groups shows that actually the order of a simple group is divisible by either $2^6 \cdot 5$ or 12.

The preceding results deal with groups whose Sylow subgroups are of very restricted types. We conclude with a general consequence of Burnside's transfer theorem:

Theorem 6.5

If P is an S_p-subgroup of G and A is a maximal abelian normal subgroup of P, then

$$C_G(A) = A \times D,$$

where D is a p'-group.

Proof

Set $C = C_G(A)$. Since $A \lhd P$, P normalizes C and consequently $P \cap C$ is an S_p-subgroup of C by Theorem 1.3.8. But $P \cap C = C_P(A) = A$ by Lemma 5.3.12. Thus A is an S_p-subgroup of C. Since $A \subseteq Z(C)$, Burnside's theorem applies to yield that C possesses a normal p-complement D. Hence $C = AD$, where D is a p'-group. Since D centralizes A, we have, in fact, $C = A \times D$ and the theorem is proved.

7. GROUPS WITH DIHEDRAL SYLOW 2-SUBGROUPS

As an application of Grün's first theorem we shall analyze the fusion of 2-elements in groups with dihedral Sylow 2-subgroups. Of particular importance is the fusion of elements of order 2. In any group G, an element of order 2 is customarily called an *involution* and we shall use this term for such an element. It will also be convenient to call an abelian group of type (2, 2) a *four-group*. Thus a four-group is another name for a dihedral group of order 4. We first treat the case of dihedral groups of order 4, which is considerably easier.

Theorem 7.1

Let G be a group in which an S_2-subgroup is a four-group. Then one of the following holds:
   (i) $N_G(S) \supset C_G(S)$, G has no normal subgroups of index 2, and G has one conjugate class of involutions.
  (ii) $N_G(S) = C_G(S)$, G has a normal 2-complement, and G has three conjugate classes of involutions.
In particular, $C_G(x)$ has a normal 2-complement for any involution x of G.

Proof

Set $N = N_G(S)$ and $C = C_G(S)$. If $N = C$, Burnside's transfer theorem implies that G has a normal 2-complement K. Since G/K is isomorphic to S and S has three classes of involutions, it follows that the involutions of S lie in distinct conjugate classes in G. Since every involution of G is conjugate to one in S by Sylow's theorem, G has three classes of involutions, proving (ii).

Suppose, on the other hand, that $N \supset C$, in which case N/C must contain an element of order 3 which cyclically permutes the three involutions of S. But then $S \cap Z(N) = 1$, whence G has no normal subgroups of index 2 by Theorem 4.4. Furthermore, since the involutions of S are conjugate to each other in N, G has only one class of involutions. Thus (i) also holds.

Finally, let x be an involution of G and set $G_1 = C_G(x)$. Then x, being in the center of G_1, is conjugate only to itself in G_1. On the other hand, G_1 contains a conjugate of S and so G_1 has more than one class of involutions. But then G_1 has a normal 2-complement by (ii).

Theorem 7.1 tells us that either G has a normal 2-complement or else the three conjugate classes of involutions of S are fused to a single class in G.

We turn now to the case of dihedral groups of order at least 8 and first prove the following preliminary result which augments the conclusions obtained in Theorem 5.4.3.

Lemma 7.2

Let $S = \langle x, y \mid y^2 = x^{2^n} = 1, x^y = x^{-1}, n \geqslant 2 \rangle$ be a dihedral group of order at least 8. Set $z = x^{2^{n-1}}$, $H = \langle x \rangle$, $T_0 = \langle y, z \rangle$, and $T_1 = \langle xy, z \rangle$. Then we have

(i) $\langle z \rangle = Z(S)$, $\langle x^2 \rangle = S' = \Phi(S)$, and $\Omega_1(S') = Z(S)$.

(ii) $\langle z \rangle = \Omega_1(H)$ and H contains every cyclic subgroup of S of order at least 4.

(iii) T_0 and T_1 are four-groups and are not conjugate in S. Furthermore, any four-subgroup of S is conjugate to T_0 or T_1.

(iv) $|N_S(T_i) : C_S(T_i)| = 2$ and $C_S(T_i) = T_i$, $0 \leqslant i \leqslant 1$.

(v) S has three conjugate classes of involutions, represented by the elements z, y, and xy, respectively.

(vi) Aut S is a 2-group.

Proof

First of all, (i) has been proved in Theorem 5.4.3. For the same reason we know that the elements of $S - H$ are all involution, which implies (ii) as well as the fact that T_0, T_1 are four-groups.

Let $u \in S$ and set $y^u = v$. Since $u = yx^j$ or x^j for some j, we have $y^u = y^{x^j} = x^{-j}yx^j = yx^{2j}$ in either case. Thus $v = yx^{2j}$ and, for each choice of j, v is conjugate to y. Similarly, yx is conjugate to yx^{2j+1} for all j. Furthermore, z is conjugate only to itself in S. Since the elements yx^i and z include all the involutions of S, we conclude that S has three classes of involutions, proving (v). Moreover, T_0 and T_1 cannot be conjugate in S, for otherwise $y \in T_0$ would be conjugate to one of the involutions z, yx, and $yxz = yx^{1+2^{n-1}}$ of T_1, which is not the case.

Next let T be an arbitrary four-subgroup of S. Since $|S/H| = 2$, $T \cap H \neq 1$, whence $z \in T$. Hence $T = \langle z, yx^i \rangle$ for some i. By the preceding paragraph there exists u in S such that $(yx^i)^u = y$ or yx according as i is even or odd. Since u centralizes z, we conclude correspondingly that $T^u = T_0$ or T_1. Thus (iii) holds.

The preceding analysis shows that for u in S, $y^u = y$ only if $u = y, z$, or yz, while $(xy)^u = yx$ only if $u = yx, z$, or yzx, so $C_S(y) = T_0$ and $C_S(yx) = T_1$. It follows at once that $C_S(T_i) = T_i$, $0 \leqslant i \leqslant 1$. On the other hand, $N_i = N_S(T_i) \supset T_i$ by Theorem 1.2.11(ii) since $S \supset T_i$, $0 \leqslant i \leqslant 1$. Since N_i/T_i acts as a group of linear transformations of T_i as a vector space over Z_2, Theorem 2.8.1 implies that $|N_i/T_i| = 2$, $0 \leqslant i \leqslant 1$, and so (iv) also holds.

Finally, H is the unique cyclic subgroup of S of order more than 2, whence H char S. But then if ϕ is a $2'$-automorphism of S, ϕ acts trivially on both H and S/H by Lemma 5.4.1 and consequently ϕ stabilizes the normal series $S \supset H \supset 1$ of S. But then $\phi = 1$ by Theorem 5.3.2. Thus Aut S is a 2-group, which establishes (vi) and completes the proof.

We now prove

Theorem 7.3

Let G be a group with a dihedral S_2-subgroup S of order at least 8 and let T_0, T_1 be representatives of the two conjugate classes of four-groups in S. Then one of the following holds:

(i) *G has no normal subgroups of index 2, G has one conjugate class of involutions, and $|N_G(T_i) : C_G(T_i)| = 6$ for both $i = 0$ and 1.*

(ii) *G has a normal subgroup of index 2, but no normal subgroup of index 4, G has two conjugate classes of involutions, and $|N_G(T_i) : C_G(T_i)|$ is 6 for one value of i and 2 for the other value of i, $0 \leqslant i \leqslant 1$.*

(iii) *G has a normal 2-complement, G has three conjugate classes of involutions, and $|N_G(T_i) : C_G(T_i)| = 2$ for both $i = 0$ and 1.*

In particular, if z is the involution of $Z(S)$, then $C_G(z)$ has a normal 2-complement.

Proof

We shall determine $S \cap G'$ by means of Grün's theorem. First of all, if $N = C_G(S)$ and $C = C_G(S)$, then N/C is a 2-group by part (vi) of the preceding lemma. Since S is an S_2-subgroup of N, we thus have $N = SC$. Since $C \lhd N$, $S \cap C = Z(S)$ is an S_2-subgroup of C. But $Z(S)$, being of order 2, is cyclic and so C possesses a normal 2-complement K by Theorem 6.1. Since $K \subset C$ centralizes S, it follows that $N = S \times K$, whence $S \cap N' = S'$. We conclude therefore from Grün's first theorem that

$$(7.1) \qquad S \cap G' = \langle S \cap Q' \mid Q \text{ ranging over all } S_2\text{-subgroups of } G \rangle.$$

Let the notation for the elements and subgroups of S be as in the preceding lemma. Hence if $Q = S^u$, $u \in G$, we have $Q' = \langle x^2 \rangle^u$, so $S \cap Q'$ is cyclic of order at most 2^{n-1}. Thus for any single S_2-subgroup Q of G, we never have $H = S \cap Q'$. Furthermore, if $|S \cap Q'| > 2$, then $S \cap Q' \subset H$ by Lemma 7.2(ii). Finally, if $|S \cap Q'| = 2$, then either $S \cap Q' = \langle z \rangle \subset H$ or $S \cap Q' = yx^i$ for some i. We conclude that either $S \cap G' = \langle x^2 \rangle = S'$ or that

$$(7.2) \qquad S \cap G' = \langle x^2, yx^{i_1}, yx^{i_2}, \ldots, yx^{i_r} \rangle$$

for suitable integers i_j and S_2-subgroups Q_j of G such that $S \cap Q'_j = \langle yx^{i_j} \rangle$, $1 \leqslant j \leqslant r$. Moreover, if (7.2) holds, $S \cap G' = \langle x^2, y \rangle$ if all i_j are even, $S \cap G' = \langle x^2, yx \rangle$ if all i_j are odd, and $S \cap G' = \langle x^2, y, yx \rangle = S$ in the remaining case.

Consider first the case $S \cap G' = S$. Then (7.2) holds and i_j is even, i_k is odd for suitable j, k, say, $j = 1$ and $k = 2$. Then yx^{i_1}, yx^{i_2} are conjugate in S to y and yx. Hence replacing Q_1, Q_2 by appropriate conjugates, we can assume without loss that

$$(7.3) \qquad S \cap Q'_1 = \langle y \rangle \qquad \text{and} \qquad S \cap Q'_2 = \langle yx \rangle.$$

Thus $\langle y \rangle = \Omega_1(Q'_1) = Z(Q_1)$ and $\langle yx \rangle = \Omega_1(Q'_2) = Z(Q_2)$. Since $Z(S)$ is conjugate to $Z(Q_i)$ for each i, it follows that both y and yx are conjugate to z in G. In particular, G has only one class of involutions.

Furthermore, by the preceding lemma, $|N_S(T_0) : C_S(T_0)| = 2$, so there exists an element u in $N_S(T_0)$ such that

$$(7.4) \qquad z^u = z \qquad y^u = yz \qquad (yz)^u = y.$$

On the other hand, $\langle y \rangle = Z(Q_1)$, so $C_1 = C_G(y)$ contains both Q_1 and T_0. Hence if S_1 is an S_2-subgroup of C_1 containing T_0, then S_1 is an S_2-subgroup of G and $\langle y \rangle = Z(S_1)$. But then, as with S, we have $|N_{S_1}(T_0) : C_{S_1}(T_0)| = 2$, so there must exist an element v in $N_{S_1}(T_0)$ such that

$$(7.5) \qquad y^v = y \qquad z^v = yz \qquad (yz)^v = z.$$

Setting $w = uv$, it follows at once from (7.4) and (7.5) that

$$(7.6) \qquad z^w = yz \qquad (yz)^w = y \qquad y^w = z.$$

Thus $w \in N_G(T_0)$ and w cyclically permutes the three involutions of T_0, whence w^3 is the least power of w contained in $C_G(T_0)$. We conclude at once that $|N_G(T_0) : C_G(T_0)| = 6$.

A similar calculation with yx and T_1 in place of y and T_0 yields also $|N_G(T_1) : C_G(T_1)| = 6$. Thus all parts of (i) hold when $S \cap G' = S$.

Suppose next that $|S : S \cap G'| = 2$. Then G possesses a normal subgroup K of index 2, but no normal subgroup of index 4 (inasmuch as the factor group by such a normal subgroup would necessarily be abelian). In this case $S \cap G' = \langle x^2, xy^i \rangle$ with $i = 0$ or 1. For definiteness, assume $i = 0$. Then the preceding argument shows that y is conjugate to z in G and that $|N_G(T_0) : C_G(T_0)| = 6$. Furthermore, yx is not conjugate to z in this case, for if $yx = z^u$ with u in G, then $yx \in S \cap Q'$, where $Q = S^u$, whence $S \cap G' = S$, contrary to our present assumption. Thus G has two classes of involutions in this case. In addition, we must also have $|N_G(T_1) : C_G(T_1)| = 2$, otherwise this index would be 6 and $N_G(T_1)$ would contain an element which cyclically permutes the involutions of T_1. But then yx and z would be conjugate in G, which we have just shown is not the case. Thus (ii) holds when $|S : S \cap G'| = 2$.

Finally assume that $|S : S \cap G'| \geqslant 4$, whence $S' = S \cap G'$. By Theorem 3.1 there exists a normal subgroup K of G such that $S' = S \cap G' = S \cap K$ and G/K is isomorphic to $S/S \cap G'$. But then S' is an S_2-subgroup of K and, being cyclic, K possesses a normal 2-complement L by Theorem 6.1. Since L char $K \lhd G$, $L \lhd G$ and G/L is a 2-group. Since $|L|$ is odd, we conclude that L is a normal 2-complement in G. The remaining parts of (iii) follow at once from this.

Finally, if $G_1 = C_G(z)$, then $S \subseteq G_1$ and z is conjugate only to itself in G_1. But now the preceding proof shows that condition (iii) must hold in G_1, since otherwise z would be conjugate to y or yx in G_1. Hence G_1 has a normal 2-complement by (iii) and the theorem is proved.

EXERCISES

1. Let $G = SL(3, p)$, p odd, set $P = \left\{ \begin{pmatrix} 1 & 0 & 0 \\ a & 1 & 0 \\ b & c & 1 \end{pmatrix} \middle| a, b, c \in Z_p \right\}$, $x_1 = \begin{pmatrix} 1 & 0 & 0 \\ 1 & 1 & 0 \\ 0 & 0 & 1 \end{pmatrix}$,

$x_2 = \begin{pmatrix} 1 & 0 & 0 \\ 0 & 1 & 0 \\ 0 & 1 & 1 \end{pmatrix}$, $z = \begin{pmatrix} 1 & 0 & 0 \\ 0 & 1 & 0 \\ 1 & 0 & 1 \end{pmatrix}$, and $P_i = \langle x, z \rangle$, $1 \leqslant i \leqslant 2$. Prove

   (i) P is an S_p-subgroup of G and is extra-special of order p^3 with center $\langle z \rangle$.
   (ii) P_i is a tame intersection, $1 \leqslant i \leqslant 2$.
   (iii) x_i and z are conjugate in $N_G(P_i)$, $1 \leqslant i \leqslant 2$, and hence x_1 and x_2 are conjugate in G.
   (iv) x_1 and x_2 are not conjugate in the normalizer of any subgroup of P containing them.

2. Let G be a group with cyclic Sylow subgroups. Prove that $G = \langle x, y \rangle$ with $x^m = y^n = 1$, $x^y = x^r$, $r^n \equiv 1 \pmod{m}$, $|G| = mn$, and $(n(r - 1), m) = 1$.

3. Let G be a group with no normal subgroup of index 2 and let P be an S_2-subgroup of G. Prove
   (i) If Q is a maximal subgroup of P, then Q contains a representative of every conjugate class of involutions of G. (Consider the transfer of G into P/Q.)
   (ii) If A is an elementary abelian normal subgroup of P of order 4 and x is an involution of G, then $C_G(A)$ contains a conjugate of x.
4. Let G be a group with a generalized quaternion S_2-subgroup. Prove that either G has a normal 2-complement or else $SL(2, 3)$ is involved in G.
5. Let H_1, H_2 be subgroups of G with $H_2 \subseteq H_1$ and let τ_i, τ denote, respectively, the transfer of G into H_i/H_i' and of H_1 into H_2/H_2' with respect to the natural maps of H_i on H_i/H_i'. Prove that

$$(G)\tau_1\tau = (G)\tau_2.$$

By analogy with Lemma 7.2 and Theorem 7.3, the next two exercises describe the possible fusion in a group with semi-dihedral S_2-subgroups.

6. Let $P = \langle x, y \mid y^2 = x^{2^n} = 1, \ y^{-1}xy = x^{-1+2^{n-1}} \rangle$ be semi-dihedral of order 2^{n+1}, $n \geqslant 3$. Prove
   (i) The elements of order 2 in P are $z = x^{2^{n-1}}$ and yx^j, j even. The elements of order 4 in P are $x^{2^{n-2}}$ and yx^j, j odd.
   (ii) $\Phi(P) = P'$ and $Z(P) = \langle z \rangle$.
   (iii) If $A = \langle x \rangle$, then $\langle z \rangle = \Omega_1(A)$ and any cyclic subgroup of P order at least 4 intersects A nontrivially.
   (iv) P has two conjugate classes of involutions represented by y and z.
   (v) Every four subgroup of P is conjugate to $T_0 = \langle y, z \rangle$. Moreover, $T_1 = \langle yx, z \rangle$ and $T_2 = \langle x^{2^{n-2}} \rangle$ are nonconjugate cyclic subgroups of P of order 4.
   (vi) Aut P is a 2-group.
   (vii) $|N_P(T_i) : C_P(T_i)| = 2$, $0 \leqslant i \leqslant 1$.
7. Let G be a group with semi-dihedral S_2-subgroups P and let T be a representative of the conjugate class of four groups in P. Show that exactly one of the following statements holds:
   (i) G has no normal subgroups of index 2, G has one conjugate class of involutions and of elements of order 4 and $|N_G(T) : C_G(T)| = 6$.
   (ii) G has a normal subgroup of index 2, but no normal subgroup of index 4, and either
      (a) G has one conjugate class of involutions and two of elements or order 4 and $|N_G(T) : C_G(T)| = 6$, or
      (b) G has two conjugate classes of involutions and one of elements of order 4 and $|N_G(T) : C_G(T)| = 2$.
   (iii) G has a normal 2-complement, G has two conjugate classes of involutions and two of elements of order 4 and $|N_G(T) : C_G(T)| = 2$.

8. Let G be a group with S_2-subgroup $\langle P = x_1, x_2, y \mid x_1^4 = x_2^4 = y^2 = 1,$ $x_2 x_1 = x_1 x_2$, $x_1^y = x_2$, and $x_2^y = x_1 \rangle$. Discuss the possible fusion of 2-elements in G.

9. Let K be a pronormal subgroup of G with $K \subseteq P$, P an S_p-subgroup of G. Prove that K is weakly closed in P with respect to G. (Compare Exercise 1.4.)

10. Let H be a strongly p-solvable subgroup of G with $O_{p'}(H) = 1$, let P be an S_p-subgroup of H and B be a noncyclic elementary abelian normal subgroup of P, and let L be the largest normal subgroup of H which centralizes B. Assume that for every x in $B^{\#}$, $[C_G(x), B, B] = 1$. Prove
    (i) $V = V(\mathrm{ccl}_G(B); P) \subseteq P \cap L$.
    (ii) $H = L N_G(V)$.

11. Let G be a group in which the normalizer of every nonidentity p-subgroup is p-solvable for some prime p and let P be an S_p-subgroup of G. Assume that $Z(P)$ is noncyclic and that P normalizes no nontrivial p'-subgroups of G. Prove that $Z(P)$ centralizes every p'-subgroup of G that it normalizes.

12. If the S_p-subgroups of G are nonabelian and metacyclic, p odd, show that G has a normal subgroup of index p.

13. Let H be an abelian Hall subgroup of G with $H \subseteq Z(N_G(H))$. Prove that G possesses a normal H-complement.

p-CONSTRAINED AND
p-STABLE GROUPS

In this chapter we shall discuss a number of closely related topics which embody the central ideas of Chapter IV of the Odd Order paper and which have far-reaching applications in classification problems. In Chapter 15 we shall give one such application to the study of groups with a self-centralizing Sylow 2-subgroup of order 4. Some recent work of Glauberman on one of these topics enables us to give a uniform, general treatment of the entire material so that the results hold for any group G such that the normalizer of every nonidentity p-subgroup of G, p odd, is both *p-constrained* and *p-stable*.

The general concepts of p-constraint and p-stability arose out of the attempt to carry over the ideas of the Odd Order paper to the analysis of groups with dihedral Sylow 2-subgroups, but it appears now that they will be useful in the study of simple groups in general. Basic definitions and properties are discussed in Section 1.

In Section 2 we prove Glauberman's theorem, which gives a universal property of p-constrained and p-stable groups which sharpens some earlier results of Thompson. This result is then applied to obtain a condition for a group to have a normal p-complement, for odd p, which considerably strengthens Frobenius' criterion. In Section 4 we generalize Alperin's theorem in order to study the conjugacy of p-elements in groups in which the normalizer of every nonidentity p-subgroup is both p-constrained and p-stable, or, more generally, is what we call of *Glauberman type*. This is followed by a fundamental result of Thompson, the so-called *transitivity theorem*, which deals with the set of all q-subgroups of a given group G which are normalized by a fixed p-subgroup A of G having certain specified properties, p, q being distinct primes.

The chapter culminates in the so-called *Maximal Subgroup theorem*, which considers the set $N(P)$ of all normalizers of nonidentity subgroups of a fixed Sylow p-subgroup P of the group G and provides a sufficient condition for $N(P)$ [more precisely for a certain well-defined subset $N^*(P)$ of $N(P)$] to possess *a unique* maximal element.

1. p-CONSTRAINT AND p-STABILITY

Theorems 6.3.3 and 6.5.3 show that a strongly p-solvable group G has the following two properties:

(A) If P is an S_p-subgroup of $O_{p',p}(G)$, then

$$C_G(P) \subseteq O_{p',p}(G).$$

(B) Let K be a normal subgroup of G and let P be a p-subgroup of K such that $G = KN_G(P)$. Then if A is a p-subgroup of $N_G(P)$ with the property $[P, A, A] = 1$, we have

$$AC_G(P)/C_G(P) \subseteq O_p(N_G(P)/C_G(P)).$$

In the study of groups of odd order and groups with dihedral S_2-subgroups, one is dealing with a situation in which, for suitable primes p, the normalizers of every nonidentity p-subgroup satisfy both conditions (A) and (B). In the case of groups of odd order, this will be a consequence of the fact that these normalizers are strongly p-solvable. However, for groups with dihedral S_2-subgroups, these normalizers need not even be p-solvable. What is remarkable is that many of the arguments that one must carry out depend solely upon the fact that these normalizers satisfy conditions (A) and (B). It is therefore natural to introduce terms for groups which satisfy one or the other of these conditions.

A group G which satisfies condition (A) will be called *p-constrained*.

As noted at the end of the proof of Theorem 6.5.3, condition (B) holds for any group G which involves no non-p-stable groups. Now, the notion of p-stability has thus far been defined only for groups with no nontrivial normal p-subgroups. Hence no confusion will arise if we take condition (B) itself as the definition of p-stability for groups which do have a nontrivial normal p-subgroup. Since we want this concept primarily for the normalizers of nonidentity p-subgroups of a given group, it will be entirely sufficient for our purposes to limit the definition to such groups. Hence we define:

A group G in which $O_p(G) \neq 1$ which satisfies condition (B), where p is an odd prime, will be called *p-stable*.

Throughout the balance of the chapter, p-stability will be used only in the above sense. In the present section we shall derive some elementary properties of p-constrained and p-stable groups.

Theorem 1.1

Let G be a p-constrained group. Then we have
  (i) If $G \supset O_{p'}(G)$, then $O_{p',p}(G) \supset O_{p'}(G)$. In particular, G is not simple.
  (ii) If $\bar{G} = G/O_{p'}(G)$, then $C_{\bar{G}}(O_p(\bar{G})) \subseteq O_p(\bar{G})$.
  (iii) If P is an S_p-subgroup of $O_{p',p}(G)$, then every P-invariant p'-subgroup of G is contained in $O_{p'}(G)$.

Proof

First of all, (i) is an immediate consequence of the definition of p-constraint. Next let P be an S_p-subgroup of $O_{p',p}(G)$ and set $N = N_G(P)$. Then $G = O_{p'}(G)N$ by Theorem 1.3.7 and consequently N maps onto $\bar{G}$. This implies that there exists a subgroup C of N whose image is $C_{\bar{G}}(O_p(\bar{G}))$. Since P maps onto $O_p(\bar{G})$ and $P \lhd N$, it follows that $[C, P] \subseteq O_{p'}(G) \cap P = 1$. Thus $C \subseteq C_G(P) \subseteq O_{p',p}(G)$ as G is p-constrained, whence $C_{\bar{G}}(O_p(\bar{G})) \subseteq O_p(\bar{G})$, proving (ii).

Finally, let K be a P-invariant p'-subgroup of G and let $\bar{K}, \bar{P}$ be the images of K, P in $\bar{G}$. Then $\bar{P} = O_p(\bar{G})$, so $[\bar{K}, \bar{P}]$ is both a p-group and a p'-group. Hence $\bar{K}$ centralizes $\bar{P}$. Since $C_{\bar{G}}(\bar{P})$ is a p-group by (ii), it follows that $\bar{K} = \bar{1}$, whence $K \subseteq O_{p'}(G)$.

In view of Theorem 3.8.4 and the remark following Theorem 6.5.3 we have the following result:

Theorem 1.2

Assume that G does not involve $SL(2, p)$, p odd, and, in particular, is either strongly p-solvable or has dihedral S_2-subgroups. Then G is p-stable.

Finally we have the following extension of Theorem 6.5.2:

Theorem 1.3

Let G be a group in which $O_p(G) \neq 1$ which is both p-constrained and p-stable. If P is an S_p-subgroup of G and A is an abelian normal subgroup of P, then $A \subseteq O_{p',p}(G)$.

Proof

Set $Q = P \cap O_{p',p}(G)$, so that $G = O_p(G)N_G(Q)$ by Theorem 1.3.7. Our conditions on A imply that $A \subseteq N_G(Q)$ and that $[Q, A, A] = 1$. Since G is p-stable, $A \subseteq C_G(Q)$. But $C_G(Q) \subseteq O_{p',p}(G)$, as G is also p-constrained. We conclude that $A \subseteq Q$, proving the theorem.

Theorem 1.3 is usually applied in the following slightly more general form:

Corollary 1.4

Let G be a group, P an S_p-subgroup of G, and Q a nontrivial p-subgroup of P, p odd. Assume that $H = N_G(Q)$ is p-constrained and p-stable and also that Q is an S_p-subgroup of $O_{p',p}(H)$. Then Q contains every abelian normal subgroup of P.

Proof

Let A be an abelian normal subgroup of P. Then $A \cap H \lhd P \cap H$ and so $[Q, A \cap H, A \cap H] = 1$. The argument of the preceding theorem shows that the conclusion $A \cap H \subseteq O_{p',p}(H)$ follows (under the assumption of constraint and stability) from the above commutator condition together with the fact that Q is an S_p-subgroup of $O_{p',p}(H)$, but does not require that $P \cap H$ be an S_p-subgroup of H. Hence $A \cap H = A \cap Q = N_A(Q)$. On the other hand, $AQ = R$ is a p-group; so if $Q \subset R$, then $N_R(Q) = A_0 Q \supset Q$ by Theorem 1.2.11(ii), where $A_0 \subseteq A$. But then $A_0 = N_A(Q) \nsubseteq Q$. Thus in the present case we must have $AQ = Q$, whence $A \subseteq Q$.

2. GLAUBERMAN'S THEOREM

We have seen in Theorem 1.3 that in a p-constrained and p-stable group G, $O_{p',p}(G)$ contains every normal abelian subgroup A of an S_p-subgroup P of G. One may ask whether, among all such normal abelian subgroups of P, there exists a characteristic one, X, such that $G = O_p(G)N_G(X)$; and, in particular, if $O_p(G) = 1$, if there exists one which is normal in G. The remarkable fact is that such a characteristic subgroup X of P always exists and, moreover, can be constructed from P alone, independently of the p-constrained, p-stable group G of which P is an S_p-subgroup. We shall establish this difficult theorem in the present section. Its proof is due to Glauberman and depends, in part, upon some results and concepts of Thompson. As we shall see in succeeding sections and chapters, this result is of great importance in the study of simple groups.

To define this subgroup X requires two definitions. For any p-group P, we first let $A(P)$ be the set of abelian subgroups of P of *maximal* order.

The elements of $A(P)$ have the following basic property, analogous to Lemma 5.3.12.

Lemma 2.1

If $A \in A(P)$, then $A = C_P(A)$; in particular, $Z(P) \subseteq A$.

Proof

Indeed, as A is abelian, so is $\langle A, x \rangle$ for any x in $C_P(A)$ by Lemma 1.3.4. The maximality of A forces $x \in A$ and the lemma follows.

We now define

$$J(P) = \langle A \mid A \in A(P) \rangle.$$

$J(P)$ is called the *Thompson* subgroup of P.

It is the subgroup $Z(J(P))$ which turns out to be our desired subgroup X.

Since any automorphism of P clearly permutes the elements of $A(P)$ among themselves, it leaves $J(P)$ invariant and so $J(P)$ is a characteristic subgroup of P. Hence also $Z(J(P))$ char P. $J(P)$ has a number of interesting properties which we shall need:

Lemma 2.2

Let P be an S_p-subgroup of G. Then we have
    (i) If R is a subgroup of P which contains an element of $A(P)$, then $A(R) \subseteq A(P)$ and $J(R) \subseteq J(P)$.
   (ii) If Q is an S_p-subgroup of G containing $J(P)$, then $J(Q) = J(P)$.
  (iii) If $Q = P^x$, $x \in G$, then $J(Q) = J(P)^x$.
  (iv) $J(P)$ is characteristic in any p-subgroup of G in which it lies.

Proof

If $A \subseteq R \subseteq P$ with $A \in A(P)$, then obviously $A \in A(R)$. Thus the elements of $A(R)$ are of the same order as those of $A(P)$ and so $A(R) \subseteq A(P)$, whence $J(R) \subseteq J(P)$. In particular, $J(P) = J(R)$, if $J(P) \subseteq R$.

If $Q = P^x$, $x \in G$, then clearly $A(Q) = \{A^x \mid A \in A(P)\}$, so $J(Q) = J(P)^x$. If $J(P) \subseteq Q$, then certainly $A \subseteq Q$ for A in $A(P)$, whence $A(P) \subseteq A(Q)$. Thus $J(P) \subseteq J(Q)$. But as $J(P)$ and $J(Q)$ have the same orders, this yields $J(P) = J(Q)$.

Finally, if $J(P) \subseteq S$, S a p-subgroup of G, and if Q is an S_p-subgroup of G containing S, then $J(P) = J(Q)$ by the preceding paragraph. But then $J(Q) = J(S)$ by the first paragraph, whence $J(P) = J(S)$. Since $J(S)$ char S, all parts of the lemma hold.

In the literature another slightly different definition of $J(P)$ also appears, in which $A(P)$ consists of the abelian subgroups A of P for which $m(A)$ rather than $|A|$ is maximal and $J(P)$ is generated by the elements of the corresponding set $A(P)$. This alternative Thompson subgroup has the same properties listed in Lemma 2.2.

Glauberman's theorem depends upon some nontrivial properties of the set $A(P)$, which we proceed now to establish. We first prove a simple lemma:

Lemma 2.3

Let $A \in A(P)$ and let B be a subgroup of P. Then B normalizes A if and only if

$$[B, A, A] = 1.$$

Proof

If B normalizes A, then $[B, A] \subseteq A$, so $[B, A, A] = 1$ as A is abelian. Conversely, if $[B, A, A] = 1$, then $[B, A]$ centralizes A, whence $[B, A] \subseteq A$ by Lemma 2.1. This implies that B normalizes A.

Theorem 2.4 (Thompson)

Let $A \in A(P)$ and suppose that $M = [x, A]$ is abelian for the element x of P. Then $MC_A(M) \in A(P)$.

Proof

Set $C = C_A(M)$. Since M is abelian, clearly MC is an abelian group. Hence we need only show that $|MC| \geq |A|$, for then $MC \in A(P)$ by definition of $A(P)$. Since $C_P(A) = A$ and M is abelian, we have $C \cap M \supseteq A \cap M = C_M(A)$. Hence

(2.1) $\qquad |MC| = |M||C|/|C \cap M| \geq |M||C_A(M)|/|C_M(A)|.$

Hence the desired conclusion $|MC| \geq |A|$ will follow from (2.1) provided we can prove that

(2.2) $\qquad\qquad\qquad |M/C_M(A)| \geq |A/C_A(M)|.$

To establish (2.2), it will clearly suffice to show that whenever u, v are elements of A lying in distinct cosets of $C_A(M)$, then the elements $[x, u]$

and $[x, v]$ of M lie in distinct cosets of $C_M(A)$. Suppose then that

(2.3) $$[x, u] \equiv [x, v] \,(\text{mod } C_M(A)).$$

Then $y = [x, u]^{-1}[x, v] \in C_M(A)$. But

(2.4) $$y = (x^{-1}x^u)^{-1}(x^{-1}x^v) = (x^u)^{-1}x^v$$

and y centralizes A, so that

(2.5) $$y = y^{u^{-1}} = ((x^u)^{-1}x^v)^{u^{-1}} = x^{-1}x^{vu^{-1}} = [x, vu^{-1}].$$

Since y centralizes A, it follows that $[x, vu^{-1}, a] = 1$ for every a in A. But then $[x, a, vu^{-1}] = 1$ by Lemma 2.2.5(i) as A and $[x, A]$ are abelian. Thus vu^{-1} centralizes $[x, a]$ for all a in A and we conclude that $vu^{-1} \in C_A(M)$, contrary to the fact that u and v lie in distinct cosets of $C_A(M)$ in A.

We remark that in the applications A will normalize M and M will normalize A. In this case, $A/C_A(M)$ is isomorphic to a subgroup of Aut M, while $M/C_M(A)$ is isomorphic to a subgroup of Aut A. Thus the theorem asserts in this case a property of the corresponding subgroups of Aut M and Aut A.

Theorem 2.5 (Thompson Replacement Theorem)

Let $A \in A(P)$ and let B be an abelian subgroup of P. Assume A normalizes B, but B does not normalize A. Then there exists an element A^* in $A(P)$ with the following properties:

(i) $A \cap B \subset A^* \cap B.$
(ii) A^* *normalizes* $A.$

Proof

Now AB is a group in which B is a normal subgroup. Since B is abelian, $N = N_B(A)$ normalizes B as well as A, so also $N \lhd AB$. Furthermore, since B does not normalize A by hypothesis, $N \subset B$. Since $B/N \lhd AB/N$, $B/N \cap Z(AB/N) \neq 1$ by Theorem 2.6.4 and so we can choose x in $B - N$ so that its image lies in $Z(AB/N)$. Then $[x, A] \subseteq N$. Setting $M = [x, A]$, we have that M is abelian as $N \subseteq B$ is abelian by assumption. Therefore $A^* = MC_A(M) \in A(P)$, by the preceding theorem. We show that A^* has the required properties.

First of all, M normalizes A as $M \subseteq N = N_B(A)$. Since $C_A(M) \subseteq A$, it follows that A^* normalizes A. Furthermore, $A \cap B$ centralizes both x and A, so $A \cap B \subseteq A^*$. On the other hand, $M = [x, A] \not\subseteq A$ as $x \notin N$, so

$M(A \cap B) \supset A \cap B$. But $M \subseteq N \subseteq B$ and also $M \subseteq A^*$. Thus

$$A^* \cap B \supseteq M(A \cap B) \supset A \cap B,$$

completing the proof.

As a corollary, we have

Theorem 2.6

Let B be an abelian normal subgroup of P. Then there exists an element A in $A(P)$ such that B normalizes A.

Proof

In this case every element of $A(P)$ normalizes B. But then if we choose A in $A(P)$ so that $A \cap B$ is maximal, Thompson's replacement theorem implies that B must normalize A.

The proof of Glauberman's theorem requires an extension of Thompson's results to the case that B is a normal subgroup of P of class at most 2 such that $B = [B, B] \subseteq Z(J(P))$.

Theorem 2.7 (Glauberman Replacement Theorem)

Let P be a p-group, p odd, and let B be a normal subgroup of P of class at most 2 such that $B' \subseteq Z(J(P))$. If A is an element of $A(P)$ which is not normalized by B, then there exists an element A^* of $A(P)$ with the following properties:

(i) $A \cap B \subset A^* \cap B$.
(ii) A^* normalizes A.

Proof

Set $Q = AB$. Since $A \subseteq Q$, $A(Q) \subseteq A(P)$ and $J(Q) \subseteq J(P)$ by Lemma 2.2(i). Furthermore, $Z(J(P))$ centralizes $A \subseteq J(P)$, so $Z(J(P)) \subseteq A$ by Lemma 2.1. Since $A \subseteq J(Q)$, it follows that $Z(J(P)) \subseteq Z(J(Q))$. Hence $B' \subseteq Z(J(Q))$. Thus the hypothesis of the theorem holds also for Q. Since $A(Q) \subseteq A(P)$, it will suffice to show that there exists an element A^* in $A(Q)$ with the required properties. Hence without loss we can assume that $P = AB$.

Since B is of class at most 2, $B' \subseteq Z(B)$. But $B' \subseteq Z(J(P)) \subseteq A$ and consequently $B' \subseteq Z(P)$ in this case.

For the sake of clarity, we incorporate a portion of the proof into an independent lemma. It will be convenient to introduce the symbol $[B, A; i]$ which we define inductively as follows:

$$[B, A; i = [[B, A; i - 1], A]$$

for $i > 0$ with $[B, A; 0] = B$.

Lemma 2.8

Let P be a p-group of the form $P = BA$ with $B \lhd P$, $B' \subseteq Z(P)$, and A abelian; and let n be the least positive integer such that $[B, A; n]$ is abelian. Then the following conditions hold:

    (i) $L_i(P) \equiv [B, A; i - 1] \pmod{B'}$ for all $i \geqslant 2$.

    (ii) $[B, A; i + 1)] \subseteq [B, A; i]$ for all $i \geqslant 0$.

    (iii) If $[B, A; n + 1] = 1$, then $n \leqslant 2$ and cl $(P) \leqslant 4$.

Proof

Note, first of all, that $[B, A; k] = 1$ for k sufficiently large as P is nilpotent; so that the integer n is well defined.

Since (i) is a property of P/B' and since B/B' is abelian, we need clearly prove (i) only in the case that B is abelian. Now $L_i(P) \subseteq B$ for all $i \geqslant 2$, as P/B is abelian. Since B is abelian, it follows that for any x in $L_i(P)$, b in B, and a in A, we have $[ba, x] = a^{-1}b^{-1}x^{-1}bax = a^{-1}x^{-1}ax = [a, x]$. This implies that

$$(2.6) \qquad L_{i+1}(P) = [P, L_i(P)] = [BA, L_i(P)] = [A, L_i(P)] = [L_i(P), A]$$

for all $i \geqslant 2$. We see then that (i) will follow at once from (2.6) by induction once we prove that $P' = L_2(P) = [B, A]$.

By Theorem 2.2.1(i), we have for a in A, b in B, and x in P,

$$(2.7) \qquad\qquad\qquad [ab, x] = [a, x]^b[b, x].$$

But $[a, x] \in B$ and B is abelian, whence (2.7) reduces to

$$(2.8) \qquad\qquad\qquad [ab, x] = [a, x][b, x],$$

which implies that $P' \subseteq [A, P][B, P]$. However, $[B, P] = [B, A]$ by the argument of the preceding paragraph; and a similar argument shows that $[A, P] = [A, B] = [B, A]$. Thus $P' = [B, A]$ and (i) holds.

As for (ii), it follows immediately from Theorem 2.2.1(iii) by induction on i that A normalizes each $[B, A; i]$. This in turn implies that $[B, A; i] \subseteq [B, A; i + 1]$.

Assume now that $[B, A; n + 1] = 1$. Then by (i), $L_{n+2}(P) \subseteq B'$. But $B' \subseteq Z(P)$ and consequently $L_{n+3}(P) = 1$.

Let m be the greatest integer not exceeding $\frac{1}{2}(n + 4)$. Since $n \geqslant 1$, we have $m \geqslant 2$. Furthermore, by its definition $2m \geqslant n + 3$. Now by Lemma 5.6.1(i),

$$(2.9) \qquad\qquad [L_m(P), L_m(P)] \subseteq L_{2m}(P) \subseteq L_{n+3}(P) = 1,$$

whence $L_m(P)$ is abelian. But then $[B, A; m - 1]$ must be abelian by (i).

Since $m - 1$ is positive, it follows therefore from our definition of n that $m - 1 \geqslant n$. Thus

$$n \leqslant m - 1 \leqslant \frac{1}{2}(n + 4) - 1 = \frac{n}{2} + 1,$$

so $n \leqslant 2$. Since $L_{n+3}(P) = 1$, this yields $L_5(P) = 1$ and consequently $\mathrm{cl}(P) \leqslant 4$, proving (iii).

With the aid of Lemma 2.8, we now prove Theorem 2.7. We again let n be the least positive integer such that $[B, A; n]$ is abelian. We distinguish two cases:

Case 1 $[B, A; n + 1] \neq 1$. Let r be the least positive integer such that $[B, A; r] = 1$. Then $r \geqslant n + 2 \geqslant 3$ as $n \geqslant 1$. Hence $[B, A; r - 3]$ is well defined. Furthermore, $[B, A; r - 2]$ does not centralize A, since otherwise $[B, A; r - 1] = 1$, which is not the case. Hence we can choose x in $[B, A; r - 3]$ such that A does not centralize $[x, A]$. Let $M = [x, A]$. Since $r \geqslant n + 2$, we have

(2.10) $M \subseteq [B, A; r - 2] \subseteq [B, A; n]$

by Lemma 2.8(ii) and therefore M is abelian by our choice of n. Hence $A^* = MC_A(M) \in A(P)$ by Thompson's theorem, 2.4.

Now $[B, A \cap B, A] \subseteq [B, B, A] \subseteq [Z(P), A] = 1$ and $[A \cap B, A, B] \subseteq [A, A, B] = 1$, so $[A, B, A \cap B] = 1$ by the three-subgroup lemma. Hence $A \cap B$ centralizes $[B, A]$ and so $A \cap B$ centralizes $[B, A; i]$ for all i by Lemma 2.8(ii). In particular, $A \cap B$ centralizes M and hence A^* by (2.10). On the other hand, $M \nsubseteq A$, since A does not centralize M. But $M \subseteq B$. Thus $A^* \cap B \supseteq M(A \cap B) \supset A \cap B$.

Furthermore, since $C_A(M)$ centralizes A, we have $[A^*, A, A] = [MC_A(M), A, A] = [M, A, A] \subseteq [B, A; r] = 1$, so A^* normalizes A by Lemma 2.3. Therefore A^* has the required properties.

Case 2 $[B, A; n + 1] = 1$. Then $n \leqslant 2$ by Lemma 2.8(iii). But $[B, A; 2] \neq 1$, as B does not normalize A, so $n = 2$. We shall prove that $[x, A]$ is abelian for any x in B. Let $u, v \in A$ and apply Theorem 2.2.3(i) with x, u^{-1}, and $w = [x, v]$ in the roles of x, y, and z, respectively, to obtain

(2.11) $[x, u, w]^{u^{-1}}[u^{-1}, w^{-1}, x]^w[w, x^{-1}, u^{-1}]^x = 1.$

Since $B' \subseteq Z(P)$, each of these three commutators can be seen to lie in $Z(P)$, while the third is, in fact, 1. Hence (2.11) reduces to

(2.12) $[x, u, w][u^{-1}, w^{-1}, x] = 1.$

Furthermore, since $[u^{-1}, w^{-1}]$ and x are in B and $B' \subseteq Z(P)$, it follows from Lemmas 2.2.4(iii) and 2.2.5(ii) that

(2.13)

$$[u^{-1}, w^{-1}, x]^{-1} = [[u^{-1}, w^{-1}], x]^{-1} = [[u^{-1}, w^{-1}]^{-1}, x] = [[w^{-1}, u^{-1}], x].$$

Now (2.12) and (2.13) together with $w = [x, v]$ give

(2.14) $$[[x, u], [x, v]] = [[[x, v]^{-1}, u^{-1}], x].$$

We shall simplify the term $[[x, v]^{-1}, u^{-1}]$. Set $\bar{P} = P/B'$, $\bar{A} = AB'/B'$, and $\bar{B} = B/B'$. Since $[B, A; 3] = 1$, $[\bar{B}, \bar{A}, \bar{A}]$ commutes with $\bar{A}$. But it also commutes with $\bar{B}$, as $\bar{B}$ is abelian. Hence $[\bar{B}, \bar{A}, \bar{A}] \subseteq Z(\bar{P})$. We can therefore apply Lemma 2.2.5(ii) twice to the group $[\bar{B}, \bar{A}]\bar{A}$ to obtain that

(2.15) $$[[x, v]^{-1}, u^{-1}] \equiv [[x, v], u^{-1}]^{-1} \equiv [x, v, u] \pmod{B'}.$$

Since v and u commute and $[x, A]B'/B' \subseteq B/B'$ is abelian, Lemma 2.2.5(i) also yields that

(2.16) $$[x, v, u] \equiv [x, u, v] \pmod{B'}.$$

Since $B' \subseteq Z(P)$, it follows finally from (2.14), (2.15), and (2.16) that

(2.17) $$[[x, u], [x, v]] = [[x, v, u], x] = [[x, u, v], x].$$

By symmetry, we also have

(2.18) $$[[x, v], [x, u]] = [[x, v, u], x] = [[x, u, v], x].$$

Since $[[x, v], [x, u]] = [[x, u], [x, v]]^{-1}$ by Lemma 2.4(iii), we conclude that

(2.19) $$[[x, u], [x, v]]^2 = 1;$$

and, as p is odd, this yields $[[x, u], [x, v]] = 1$. Since u and v are arbitrary elements of A, we have thus proved that $[x, A]$ is abelian for any x in B.

Since B does not normalize A, $[B, A]$ does not centralize A and so we can choose x in B so that $[x, A]$ does not centralize A. We set $M = [x, A]$ and apply Theorem 2.4 to obtain that $A^* = MC_A(M) \in A(P)$. As in case 1, $A \cap B$ centralizes $[B, A]$ and so $A \cap B \subseteq C_A(M)$ as $M \subseteq [B, A]$. Since $[x, A]$ does not centralize A and $M \subseteq B$, we again have $A^* \supseteq M(A \cap B) \supset A \cap B$. Since $[B, A; 3] = 1$, we also have $[A^*, A, A] = [MC_A(M), A, A] = 1$; again A^* has the required properties.

We remark that the oddness of p was used only in case 2, where we had $[B, A; 3] = 1$. Hence Theorem 2.7 is valid for $p = 2$ under the stronger assumption $[B, A; 3] \neq 1$.

As in the case of Theorem 2.6, we also have the following corollary:

Theorem 2.9

Under the assumptions of Theorem 2.7, there exists an element A of A(P) such that B normalizes A.

Our main objective will be obtained as a corollary of the following theorem, which is a consequence of Glauberman's replacement theorem.

Theorem 2.10 (Glauberman)

Let B be a nontrivial normal p-subgroup of the p-stable group G, p odd. If P is an S_p-subgroup of G, then $B \cap Z(J(P))$ is a normal subgroup of G.

Proof

Assume the theorem is false for G and suppose B is a normal p-subgroup of G of least order for which the theorem is false. Set $Z = Z(J(P))$ and let B_1 be the normal closure of $Z \cap B$ in G. Since $B \lhd G$, we have $B_1 \subseteq B$ and, as $Z \cap B \subseteq B_1$, we also have $Z \cap B_1 = Z \cap B$. Hence by our minimal choice of B, we must have $B = B_1$.

Now $B' = [B, B] \subset B$, so $Z \cap B'$ is a normal subgroup of G. Since $Z \lhd P$, we have that $[Z \cap B, B] \subseteq Z \cap B'$. But then for any x in G we have

(2.20) $[(Z \cap B)^x, B] = [Z \cap B, B]^x \subseteq (Z \cap B')^x = Z \cap B',$

as B and $Z \cap B'$ are each normal in G. Since B is generated by all such $(Z \cap B)^x$, it follows that $B' = [B, B] \subseteq Z \cap B'$. Thus $B' \subseteq Z$ and, in particular, $B \cap Z$ centralizes B'. Since B' char B, $B' \lhd G$ and so every conjugate of $Z \cap B$ in G also centralizes B'. But then we see that B itself centralizes B', whence $B' \subseteq Z(B)$. We conclude therefore that $\mathrm{cl}\,(B) \leqslant 2$ and that $B' \subseteq Z(J(P))$. Thus B has the structure required for application of Glauberman's replacement theorem and its corollary.

Let L be the largest normal subgroup of G which normalizes $Z \cap B$. Then $P \cap L$ is an S_p-subgroup of L by Theorem 1.3.8. Since $J(P \cap L)$ char $P \cap L$, it follows therefore from Theorem 1.3.7 that $G = LN$, where $N = N_G(J(P \cap L))$. If $J(P) \subseteq P \cap L$, then $J(P) = J(P \cap L)$ by Lemma 2.2(ii). In this case N normalizes $Z = Z(J(P))$ and so normalizes $Z \cap B$. But then $G = LN$ normalizes $Z \cap B$ and $Z \cap B \lhd G$. Thus we may assume that $J(P) \nsubseteq L \cap P$.

By Theorem 2.9 and Lemma 2.3, there exists an element A in $A(P)$ such that $[B, A, A] = 1$. Since $B \subseteq L$ and G is p-stable, it follows from the definition that $AC/C \subseteq O_p(G/C)$, where $C = C_G(B)$. But also C centralizes $Z \cap B$. Hence LC is a normal subgroup of G which normalizes $Z \cap B$. Our maximal choice of L forces $C \subseteq L$. Hence certainly $AL/L \subseteq O_p(G/L)$. However, we claim that $O_p(G/L) = 1$. Indeed, let K be the inverse image of

$O_p(G/L)$ in G. Then $P \cap K$ is an S_p-subgroup of K and so maps onto $O_p(G/L)$. Hence $K = L(P \cap K)$. But $P \cap K$ normalizes both Z and B and so normalizes $Z \cap B$. Thus $P \cap K \subseteq L$, whence $K = L$ and the desired conclusion $O_p(G/L) = 1$ follows. Since A maps into $O_p(G/L)$, we conclude that $A \subseteq L$.

It follows now from Lemma 2.2(i) that $J(P \cap L) \subseteq J(P)$. Since $Z \subseteq A \subseteq J(P \cap L)$, this implies that $Z \cap B \subseteq Z(J(P \cap L))$. Setting $X = Z(J(P \cap L))$ and applying Theorem 1.3.7, we obtain that $G = LN_G(X)$. Since L normalizes $Z \cap B$, it follows that the normal closure B of $Z \cap B$ in G lies in X. In particular, B is abelian.

Since $J(P) \nsubseteq L \cap P$, there exists an element A_1 in $A(P)$ such that $A_1 \nsubseteq L$. We claim that $[B, A_1, A_1] \neq 1$. Indeed, if $[B, A_1, A_1] = 1$, then the argument carried out above on A can now be repeated for A_1 to yield that $A_1 \subseteq L$, contrary to our choice of A_1.

Finally, among all such choices of A_1, choose A_1 so that $|A_1 \cap B|$ is maximal. By Lemma 2.3, B does not normalize A_1 and so Thompson's replacement theorem can be applied to yield that there exists an element A^* in $A(P)$ such that $A_1 \cap B \subset A^* \cap B$ and A^* normalizes A_1. Because of our maximal choice of A_1, it follows that $A^* \subseteq P \cap L$. Hence $X = Z(J(P \cap L)) \subseteq A_1$. But $B \subseteq X$. Therefore,

$$[B, A_1, A_1] \subseteq [X, A_1, A_1] \subseteq [A^*, A_1, A_1] = 1,$$

as A^* normalizes A_1, contrary to the fact that $[B, A_1, A_1] \neq 1$. The proof is complete.

We now obtain at once

Theorem 2.11 (Glauberman)

Let G be a group with $O_p(G) \neq 1$ which is p-constrained and p-stable, p odd. If P is an S_p-subgroup of G, then

$$G = O_{p'}(G)N_G(Z(J(P))).$$

In particular, if $O_{p'}(G) = 1$, then $Z(J(P)) \lhd G$.

Proof

By Theorems 1.1(ii) and 1.3.7, it will suffice to prove the corresponding assertion in $G/O_{p'}(G)$. Hence without loss we may assume to begin with that $O_{p'}(G) = 1$ and argue that $Z(J(P)) \lhd G$. Then by Theorem 1.3 $Z(J(P)) \subseteq O_p(G)$, inasmuch as $Z(J(P))$ is a normal abelian subgroup of P. Taking $O_p(G)$ as B in Theorem 2.10, it follows that $Z(J(P)) = Z(J(P)) \cap B \lhd G$, as required.

3. THE GLAUBERMAN-THOMPSON NORMAL p-COMPLEMENT THEOREM

For odd p, or if $|G|$ is prime to 3, Thompson has shown that there exist two characteristic subgroups of an S_p-subgroup P of G such that the existence of normal p-complements in both their normalizers implies that G itself has a normal p-complement. Glauberman's theorem gives a refinement of this result for odd p and, in fact, implies that the existence of a normal p-complement in $N_G(Z(J(P)))$ is enough to guarantee one in G.

Theorem 3.1 (Glauberman-Thompson)

If P is an S_p-subgroup of G, p odd, and if $N_G(Z(J(P))$ has a normal p-complement, then so also does G.

Proof

We proceed by induction on $|G|$, so that, in particular, any proper subgroup of G containing P possesses a normal p-complement. Suppose the theorem false. Then by Frobenius' theorem, there exists a nontrivial p-subgroup H of G such that $N_G(H)$ does not have a normal p-complement. Among all such subgroups, choose H so that an S_p-subgroup of $N = N_G(H)$ has maximal order. Without loss we can clearly assume that $P \cap N$ is an S_p-subgroup of N.

We argue that $P \subseteq N$. If not, set $R = P \cap N$, $L = N_N(Z(J(R)))$, and $M = N_G(Z(J(R)))$, so that $L \subseteq M$ and $R \subset P$. But then $R \subset N_P(R)$. Since $Z(J(R))$ char $J(R)$ char R, we have $N_P(R) \subseteq M$ and consequently $P \cap M \supset R$. Thus an S_p-subgroup of M has order greater than that of N and so M has a normal p-complement by our maximal choice of H. Since $L \subseteq M$, it follows at once that L has a normal p-complement. On the other hand, $N \subset G$ as $P \nsubseteq N$ and we conclude from our induction assumption that N possesses a normal p-complement, contrary to our choice of H. Thus $P \subseteq N$, as asserted. This forces $N = G$, since otherwise N would again have a normal p-complement by induction.

Clearly our hypothesis carries over to $G/O_{p'}(G)$. Hence if $O_{p'}(G) \neq 1$, $G/O_{p'}(G)$ would have a normal p-complement by induction and so G would have one as well. Thus $O_{p'}(G) = 1$. Since $G = N_G(O_p(G))$, we can assume $H = O_p(G)$ without loss. If $H = P$, then $Z(J(P))$ char $P \triangleleft G$, so $G = N_G(Z(J(P)))$ has a normal p-complement by our hypothesis. Hence also $H \subset P$.

Now set $\bar{G} = G/H$ and let $\bar{P}$ be the image of P in $\bar{G}$, so that $\bar{P} \neq 1$. Set

$\bar{N}_1 = N_{\bar{G}}(Z(J(\bar{P})))$ and let N_1, H_1 be the inverse images of N_1 and $Z(J(\bar{P}))$, respectively, in G. Then $N_1 = N_G(H_1)$ and $H \subset H_1$. Also $P \subset N_1$, as $\bar{P} \subseteq \bar{N}_1$. Since $H = O_p(G)$ and $H \subset H_1$, we have $N_1 \subset G$. Since N_1 contains P, N_1 thus has a normal p-complement by induction and consequently so also does $\bar{N}_1$. But now applying induction to $\bar{G}$, we conclude that $\bar{G}$ possesses a normal p-complement.

Thus $\bar{G} = O_{p',p}(\bar{G})$ and so $G = O_{p,p',p}(G)$. In particular, G is p-solvable. If G is strongly p-solvable, then G is p-constrained and p-stable, so Glauberman's theorem applies. Since $O_{p'}(G) = 1$, we conclude that $Z(J(P)) \lhd G$. But then G has a normal p-complement by hypothesis. On the other hand, it follows at once from the definition that G is strongly p-solvable if $p \geqslant 5$ or if $p = 3$ and the S_2-subgroups of G are abelian. Hence to complete the proof, we need only show that the S_2-subgroups of G are, in fact, abelian when $p = 3$.

By Theorem 6.2.2, $\bar{P}$ normalizes an S_q-subgroup $\bar{Q}$ of $O_{p'}(\bar{G})$ for each prime q and so normalizes $Z(\bar{Q})$. Let G_1 be the inverse image of $\bar{P}Z(\bar{Q})$ in G, so that $G_1 = PQ_1$, where Q_1 is an abelian q-group isomorphic to $Z(\bar{Q})$. If $G_1 \subset G$, then by induction G_1 has a normal p-complement, which in this case must be Q_1 itself. But then $[H, Q_1] \subseteq H \cap Q_1 = 1$ and so Q_1 centralizes H. However, $C_G(H) \subseteq H$ as $H = O_p(G)$ and $O_{p'}(G) = 1$, by Theorem 6.3.2. This contradiction shows that $G = G_1 = PQ_1$. Thus S_2-subgroups of G are indeed abelian and so G is strongly p-solvable when $p = 3$. The theorem is proved.

4. GROUPS WITH SUBGROUPS OF GLAUBERMAN TYPE

In this section we shall establish a fundamental conjugation property for the p-elements of a group G, p odd, in which the normalizer of every non-identity p-subgroup is both p-constrained and p-stable. This result is based upon a generalization of Alperin's theorem. However, it turns out that the proof does not require the full force of these assumptions but only the consequence of them, which is given by Glauberman's theorem.

For this reason we shall say that a group G is of *Glauberman type* (with respect to the prime p) provided

$$(4.1) \qquad\qquad G = O_{p'}(G)N_G(Z(J(P))),$$

where P is an S_p-subgroup of G. We note that we do not require p to be odd.

To motivate our conjugation theorem, we first prove:

Theorem 4.1

Let G be of Glauberman type for the prime p and let P be an S_p-subgroup of G. Then two subsets of P conjugate in G are already conjugate in $N_G(Z(J(P)))$.

Proof

Suppose $B = A^x$ with A, B subsets of P and $x \in G$. Set $N = N_G(Z(J(P)))$. Then $G = O_{p'}(G)N$ since G is of Glauberman type and consequently N maps onto $\bar{G} = G/O_{p'}(N)$. But the images $\bar{A}$, $\bar{B}$ of A, B in $\bar{G}$ are conjugate in $\bar{G}$ and hence the preimages C, D of $\bar{A}$, $\bar{B}$, respectively, in N are conjugate in N. Thus $C^y = D$ for some y in N, whence $A^y \subseteq D$.

On the other hand, by the third isomorphism theorem, $\langle D \rangle = (O_{p'}(G) \cap N)\langle B \rangle$ and so also $D = (O_{p'}(G) \cap N)B$. Furthermore, it is immediate that $\langle B \rangle \cap D = B$ and that elements of $O_{p'}(G) \cap N$ conjugate subsets of D into D. Now $\langle A^y \rangle$ and $\langle B \rangle$ have the same order since A^y and B are conjugate in G and hence each is an S_p-subgroup of $\langle D \rangle$. Thus $\langle A^{yz} \rangle = \langle B \rangle$ for some z in $O_{p'}(G) \cap N$. Since $A^y \subseteq D$, it follows that $A^{yz} \subseteq D$, whence $A^{yz} \subseteq \langle B \rangle \cap D = B$. Therefore $A^{yz} = B$. Since $z \in D \subseteq N$, we have $yz \in N$ and the theorem follows.

We shall express the conclusion of Theorem 4.1 by saying that the *functor Z(J) controls p-fusion in G*.

Suppose now that G denotes a group in which the normalizer of every nonidentity p-subgroup is of Glauberman type, so that by the preceding theorem the functor $Z(J)$ controls p-fusion in all such normalizers. These are "local" conditions; and it is natural to ask the "global" question whether $Z(J)$ controls p-fusion in G; that is, are any two subsets of an S_p-subgroup P of G that are conjugate in G already conjugate in $N_G(Z(J(P)))$? We emphasize that G itself need not be of Glauberman type—indeed, G may very well be simple.

The following theorem shows that the answer to this question is affirmative:

Theorem 4.2

If the normalizer of every nonidentity p-subgroup of G is of Glauberman type, then the functor Z(J) controls p-fusion in G.

Before turning to the proof of this theorem, we should like to derive two important consequences of it.

Theorem 4.3

If the normalizer of every nonidentity p-subgroup of G is of Glauberman type, then

$$P \cap G' = P \cap N',$$

where P is an S_p-subgroup of G and $N = N_G(Z(J(P)))$.

Proof

Obviously $P \cap N' \subseteq P \cap G'$. On the other hand, $P \cap G' = \langle x^{-1}x^u \mid x \in P,$ $u \in G,\ x^u \in P \rangle$ by Theorem 7.3.4. But by Theorem 4.2, if $x \in P$ and $x^u \in P$, $u \in G$, then $x^u = x^y,\ y \in N$, so $x^{-1}x^u = x^{-1}x^y \in N$. Thus $P \cap G' \subseteq P \cap N'$, proving the theorem.

Hence the largest abelian p-factor group of G is determined by that of N. In the particular case that N has a normal p-complement, we know this fact already by the Glauberman-Thompson normal p-complement theorem. For this reason Theorem 4.3 can be regarded as a generalization (under the given hypotheses) of the Glauberman-Thompson normal p-complement theorem.

Our next result will be needed in Section 6 in the proof of the Maximal Subgroup theorem.

Theorem 4.4

Assume that the normalizer of every nonidentity p-subgroup of G is p-constrained and p-stable. Let P be an S_p-subgroup of G, let A be an abelian normal subgroup of P, and set $N = N_G(Z(J(P)))$ and $V = V(\mathrm{ccl}_G(A); P)$. Then we have

$$N = O_{p'}(N)N_N(V).$$

Proof

Since N is p-constrained and p-stable, $A \subseteq O_{p',p}(N)$ by Theorem 1.3. Suppose $A^x \subseteq P$ for some x in G. By Glauberman's theorem the normalizer of every nonidentity p-subgroup of G is of Glauberman type, so Theorem 4.2 can be applied to yield that $A^x = A^y$ with $y \in N$. Since $A \subseteq O_{p',p}(N)$, it follows that also $A^x \subseteq O_{p',p}(N)$. Since V is generated by its subgroups A^x with $A^x \subseteq P$, we conclude that $V \subseteq Q = P \cap O_{p',p}(N)$. But $N = O_{p'}(N)N_N(Q)$ by Theorem 1.3.7. By the definition of V, $N_G(Q)$ normalizes V and so the desired conclusion $N = O_{p'}(N)N_N(V)$ follows.

The proof of Theorem 4.2 will be derived as a consequence of a generalization of Alperin's theorem. To state this result we need some preliminary definitions.

Let P be an S_p-subgroup of G. For any subgroup H of P, we set

$$W_1(H) = H \qquad P_1(H) = N_P(H) \qquad N_1(H) = N_G(H)$$

and define recursively

$$W_{i+1}(H) = Z(J(P_i(H))) \qquad P_{i+1}(H) = N_P(W_{i+1}(H))$$
$$N_{i+1}(H) = N_G(W_{i+1}(H)).$$

With this notation, we shall say that H is *well-placed* in P provided each $P_i(H)$ is an S_p-subgroup of $N_i(H)$. If H is not well-placed in P, we define the *height* of H to be the least positive integer d such that $P_d(H)$ is not an S_p-subgroup of $N_d(H)$.

Note that both P and 1 are well-placed in P, as follows readily from the definition.

Since $W_{i+1}(H) = Z(J(P_i(H)))$ char $P_i(H)$, $W_{i+1}(H) \lhd N_G(P_i(H))$ and so $P_{i+1}(H) = N_P(W_{i+1}(H)) \supseteq N_P(P_i(H))$. But $N_P(P_i(H)) \supseteq P_i(H)$ and, as P is a p-group, the inclusion is proper whenever $P_i(H) \subset P$. Hence $P_i(H) \subseteq P_j(H)$ for all $i \leqslant j$ and $P_i(H) \subset P_j(H)$ if $i < j$ and $P_i(H) \subset P$. Thus the sequence $P_i(H)$ is strictly increasing until it stabilizes at P. Note also that if $P_i(H) = P$, then $W_{i+1}(H) = Z(J(P))$, so that the sequence $W_i(H)$ stabilizes at $Z(J(P))$. On the other hand, no statement concerning inclusions can in general be made about the portion of the sequence $W_i(H)$ which precedes those terms equal to $Z(J(P))$.

Furthermore, if n is the least positive integer such that $P_n(H) = P$, then certainly $n \leqslant r$, where $|P| = p^r$. As a result, it follows, if H is not well-placed in P and has height d, that $d \leqslant r$. Thus the height of any non-well-placed subgroup of P is bounded by r. These observations will be used repeatedly in the ensuing discussion.

Alperin's theorem states, in effect, that the fusion of elements of P is completely determined by the normalizers of tame intersections $P \cap Q$, Q on S_p-subgroup of G. Our generalization of Alperin's theorem asserts that, in fact, it is completely determined by the normalizers of *well-placed* tame intersections. Thus we have

Theorem 4.5

If A and B are subsets of the S_p-subgroup P of G that are conjugate in G, then there exist S_p-subgroups Q_i of G with $P \cap Q_i$ a well-placed tame intersection, $1 \leqslant i \leqslant m$, and subsets $A = A_0, A_1, A_2, \ldots, A_m = B$ such that

(i) $A_{i-1} \subseteq P \cap Q_i$, $A_i \subseteq P \cap Q_i$.
(ii) $A_i = A_{i-1}^{y_i}$ *for some y_i in $N_G(P \cap Q_i)$, $1 \leqslant i \leqslant m$.*

Now both forms of Alperin's theorem (Theorems 7.2.6 and 7.2.7) were established as a direct consequence of Theorem 7.2.5, which asserted that for any S_p-subgroups P and Q of G, we have $Q \sim_P P$, where the definition of "$\sim$ with respect to P" is given in Section 7.2. To derive Theorem 4.5, we introduce a new relation among S_p-subgroups Q, R of G,

" $\approx$ with respect to P," which we denote by $\approx_P$ or simply by $\approx$, and which differs from the previous relation in the following regard only: Where the term "tame intersection" appears in condition (a) of the definition of $\sim$, the term "well-placed tame intersection" appears in condition (a) of $\approx$.

If we can establish the fact that $Q \approx_P P$ for any S_p-subgroups P and Q of G, then Theorem 4.5 above will follow in exactly the same way as Theorems 7.2.6 and 7.2.7 followed from Theorem 7.2.5. Thus Theorem 4.5 will be a consequence of

Theorem 4.6

For any S_p-subgroups P and Q of G, we have $Q \approx_P P$.

Now the proof of Theorem 4.6 is in turn entirely similar to that of Theorem 7.2.5, which was based upon Lemmas 7.2.1 to 7.2.4. The proofs of Lemmas 7.2.1 to 7.2.3 and the proof of Theorem 7.2.5 from Lemmas 7.2.1 to 7.2.4 are completely formal in nature and go through without change when the symbol $\sim$ is replaced by $\approx$. Thus the entire discussion hinges on Lemma 7.2.4, which we must generalize.

Therefore Theorem 4.6 and consequently also Theorem 4.5 will follow once we establish the following lemma:

Lemma 4.7

Let Q be an S_p-subgroup of G such that $P \cap Q$ is a tame intersection. If $S \approx_P P$ for all S_p-subgroups S of G with the property $|S \cap P| > |Q \cap P|$, then $Q \approx_P P$.

Proof

For convenience, we let $\mathscr{S} = \mathscr{S}(P \cap Q)$ be the set of S_p-subgroups S of G such that $|S \cap P| > |Q \cap P|$. Thus we are given that $S \approx P$ for all S in $\mathscr{S}$. It will suffice to prove the following statement:

$$(4.2) \qquad\qquad Q \approx S \qquad \text{for some } S \text{ in } \mathscr{S}.$$

Indeed, if this is the case, then both $Q \approx S$ and $S \approx P$ and the desired conclusion $Q \approx P$ will follow from the generalized form of Lemma 7.2.1. Clearly we need only consider the case $Q \neq P$.

Suppose first that $H = P \cap Q$ is a well-placed tame intersection. In this case, $N_P(H)$ and $N_Q(H)$ are S_p-subgroups of $N_G(H)$, whence $N_P(H) = N_Q(H)^x$ for some x in $N_G(H)$. Then $Q \approx Q^x$ by the meaning of the symbol $\approx$ (as this tame intersection is well-placed). But $Q^x \in \mathscr{S}$, since $P \cap Q^x \supseteq P \cap N_Q(H)^x = N_P(H) \supset H$, as H is a proper subgroup of P. Thus (4.2) holds.

Hence we may assume that H is not well-placed in P. Let its height be n. Our argument will be inductive and so we shall assume that (4.2) has been proved for all non-well-placed tame intersections whose heights exceed n.

By definition of the height, we have that $P_i(H)$ is an S_p-subgroup of $N_i(H)$ for $i < n$, but $P_n(H)$ is not an S_p-subgroup of $N_n(H)$. Let then T be an S_p-subgroup of $N_n(H)$ containing $P_n(H)$ and let R be an S_p-subgroup of G containing T. Since $P \cap R \supseteq P_n(H) \supset H$, $R \in \mathscr{S}$ and so $R \approx P$ via some element x of G by the hypothesis of the lemma.

We shall prove the lemma by establishing the following result:

Either $Q^x \in \mathscr{S}$ or we have:

   (i) $P \cap Q^x = (P \cap Q)^x$.

(4.3) (ii) $P \cap Q^x$ is a tame intersection.

   (iii) Either $P \cap Q^x$ is well-placed in P or has height exceeding n.

Indeed, assume that (4.3) holds. Since $P \cap R \supseteq P \cap Q$ and $R \approx P$ via x, it follows from the generalized form of Lemma 7.2.2 that $Q \approx Q^x$. Hence (4.2) holds if $Q^x \in \mathscr{S}$. On the other hand, assume (i), (ii), and (iii) hold. Set $K = P \cap Q^x$, so that $|K| = |H|$ by (i). Hence $\mathscr{S} = \mathscr{S}(H) = \mathscr{S}(K)$. Thus $S \approx P$ for all elements S of $\mathscr{S}(K)$ by the hypothesis of the lemma. Hence if the height of Q^x exceeds n, it follows from our induction assumption that $Q^x \approx S$ for some S in $\mathscr{S}(K)$, while if Q^x is well-placed in P, the same conclusion has been established at the beginning of the lemma. Since $Q \approx Q^x$, the generalized form of Lemma 7.2.1 now yields that $Q \approx S$. Since $S \in \mathscr{S}(K) = \mathscr{S}$, (4.2) will thus hold.

Finally we prove (4.3). We may assume that $Q^x \notin \mathscr{S}$ and then verify (i), (ii), and (iii). First, $(P \cap Q)^x \subseteq P \cap Q^x$ inasmuch as $(P \cap Q)^x \subset Q^x$ and $(P \cap Q)^x \subseteq R^x = P$. Since $Q^x \notin \mathscr{S}$, we have $|P \cap Q^x| \leqslant |P \cap Q|$, and so $|P \cap Q^x| \leqslant |(P \cap Q)^x|$, forcing $(P \cap Q)^x = P \cap Q^x$. Thus (i) holds.

Because of (i), we have

$$N_{Q^x}(P \cap Q^x) = N_{Q^x}((P \cap Q)^x) = (N_Q(P \cap Q))^x.$$

However, $N_Q(P \cap Q)$ is an S_p-subgroup of $N_G(P \cap Q)$ as $P \cap Q$ is tame, so $N_{Q^x}(P \cap Q^x)$ is an S_p-subgroup of $(N_G(P \cap Q))^x = N_G((P \cap Q)^x) = N_G(P \cap Q^x)$. Thus $P \cap Q^x$ is tame "on one side." Now observe that

(4.4) $(N_P(P \cap Q))^x = P_1(H)^x \subseteq P_n(H)^x \subseteq R^x = P$

by our choice of R and x. Furthermore, $N_P(P \cap Q)$ is an S_p-subgroup of $N_G(P \cap Q)$ as $P \cap Q$ is tame, so that $(N_P(P \cap Q))^x$ is an S_p-subgroup of $(N_G(P \cap Q))^x = N_G(P \cap Q^x)$. Since $(N_P(P \cap Q))^x \subseteq P$ by (4.4), we have $N_P(P \cap Q^x) = (N_P(P \cap Q))^x$ and is an S_p-subgroup of $N_G(P \cap Q^x)$. Thus

$P \cap Q^x$ is tame " on both sides," proving (ii). Note that we have also shown that $P_1(H)^x = P_1(H^x)$.

To prove (iii), it will suffice to prove

(4.5)
$$P_i(H)^x \text{ is an } S_p\text{-subgroup of } N_i(H^x) \qquad 1 \leqslant i \leqslant n$$
$$P_i(H)^x = P_i(H^x) \qquad\qquad\qquad 1 \leqslant i \leqslant n.$$

Indeed, since $H^x = P \cap Q^x$, the first statement of (4.5) will imply that either H^x is well-placed in P or else has height exceeding n. We prove (4.5) by induction on i, the case $i = 1$ having been established in the preceding paragraph. We thus assume (4.5) for $i - 1$ and verify it for i.

First consider the case $i < n$. Using induction and the fact that $Z(J(K^x)) = Z(J(K))^x$ for any subgroup K of P, we have

(4.6) $W_i(H^x) = Z(J(P_{i-1}(H^x))) = Z(J(P_{i-1}(H)))^x = W_i(H)^x.$

Furthermore, as $i < n$, $P_i(H)$ is an S_p-subgroup of $N_i(H)$, so using (4.6), $P_i(H)^x$ is an S_p-subgroup of

$$N_G(W_i(H))^x = N_G(W_i(H)^x) = N_G(W_i(H^x)).$$

But $P_i(H)^x \subseteq R^x = P$, so $P_i(H)^x = N_P(W_i(H^x)) = P_i(H^x)$, whence $P_i(H^x)$ is an S_p-subgroup of $N_i(H^x)$, giving the desired conclusions.

Now consider the case $i = n$. The same argument establishes (4.6) for $i = n$. Recall that $P_n(H) \subset T \subseteq R$ and that T is an S_p-subgroup of $N_n(H)$. Thus T^x is an S_p-subgroup of

$$N_G(W_n(H)^x) = N_G(W_n(H^x)) = N_n(H^x).$$

However, $T^x \subseteq R^x = P$, so

$$T^x = N_P(W_n(H^x)) = P_n(H^x)$$

and $P_n(H^x)$ is an S_p-subgroup of $N_n(H^x)$. Thus (4.5) holds in this case as well and the proof of the lemma is complete. This completes the proof of Theorems 4.5 and 4.6.

We are at last in a position to attain our main objective, which is to prove Theorem 4.2. We need the following lemma:

Lemma 4.8

Assume that the functor $Z(J)$ controls p-fusion in the normalizer of every nonidentity p-subgroup of G and let $P \cap Q$ be a well-placed tame intersection of S_p-subgroups P and Q of G. Then if A, B are subsets of $P \cap Q$ conjugate in $N_G(P \cap Q)$, they are conjugate in $N_G(Z(J(P)))$.

Proof

Set $W_i = W_i(P \cap Q)$, $P_i = P_i(P \cap Q)$, and $N_i = N_i(P \cap Q)$. We prove by induction on i that A and B are conjugate in N_i. Since $N_i = N_G(Z(J(P)))$ for all i sufficiently large, this will establish the lemma. Since $N_1 = N_G(P \cap Q)$, the desired conclusion holds for $i = 1$ by hypothesis.

Assume now that A and B are conjugate in N_i. First of all, A and B are contained in P_i since they are contained in $W_1 = P \cap Q$ and $W_1 \subseteq P_i$. Furthermore, since $P \cap Q$ is well-placed in P, P_i is an S_p-subgroup of N_i. But $Z(J)$ controls p-fusion in N_i and consequently A and B are conjugate in $N_{N_i}(Z(J(P_i))) = N_{N_i}(W_{i+1})$. Thus A and B are conjugate in $N_{i+1} = N_G(W_{i+1})$, completing the induction.

We can now quickly complete the proof of Theorem 4.2. Let the assumptions be as in that theorem and let A, B be two subsets of P conjugate in G. Then by Theorem 4.5 there exist subsets $A_1, A_2, \ldots, A_m$ of P with $A = A_1$ and $B = A_m$ such that for each i, $1 \leqslant i \leqslant m - 1$, A_i and A_{i+1} are contained in a well-placed tame intersection $P \cap Q_i$, Q_i an S_p-subgroup of G, and are conjugate by an element of $N_G(P \cap Q_i)$. But then each pair A_i, A_{i+1} are conjugate by an element y_i of $N_G(Z(J(P)))$ by the preceding lemma. Setting $y = y_1 y_2 \cdots y_{m-1}$, we have $A^y = B$ and $y \in N_G(Z(J(P)))$, thus completing the proof.

Remark We note that only the following two properties of $Z(J)$ have been used in the entire proof of Theorem 4.2:

(a) $Z(J(H)) \subseteq H$,

(b) $Z(J(H^x)) = (Z(J(H)))^x$,

for any p-subgroup H of G and any element x of G. This means that if W is any functor on the p-subgroups of G such that $W(H) \subseteq H$ and $W(H^x) = W(H)^x$ for all H and x, we can consider a group G in which the functor W controls p-fusion in the normalizer of every nonidentity p-subgroup (giving this term the obvious meaning) and can then conclude by the identical argument as in the case of $Z(J)$ that any two subsets of P conjugate in G are already conjugate in $N_G(W(P))$, P an S_p-subgroup of G.

This observation is of some interest, since other functors besides $Z(J)$, in particular J itself, are used in the study of simple groups.

5. THE THOMPSON TRANSITIVITY THEOREM

We have had occasion to consider maximal abelian normal subgroups of a p-group P. Since any such subgroup is self-centralizing, following Feit-Thompson, we denote the set of all such subgroups of P by $SCN(P)$.

Furthermore, if $A \in SCN(P)$ and $m(A) \geqslant t$ for some integer t, we write $A \in SCN_t(P)$. In general, for a particular t, $SCN_t(P)$ may be empty or nonempty. Clearly $SCN_t(P)$ is empty if and only if $d_n(P) < t$. In addition, for any group G, we say $A \in SCN(p)$ (in G) if $A \in SCN(P)$ for some S_p-subgroup P of G, with a similar meaning for $SCN_t(p)$. We also say that $SCN_t(p)$ is empty or nonempty in G according as $SCN_t(P)$ is empty or nonempty.

We observe that in this notation, Theorem 7.6.5 reads: If $A \in SCN(p)$, then $C_G(A) = A \times D$, where D is a p'-group.

Under the assumption that the normalizer of every nonidentity solvable subgroup of G is solvable, Thompson has shown that for any element A of $SCN_3(p)$ and any prime $q \neq p$, $C_G(A)$ permutes the set of all maximal A-invariant q-subgroups of G transitively under conjugation. It turns out that the proof of this theorem goes through with no essential changes under the weaker assumption that the normalizer of every nonidentity p-subgroup of G is p-constrained.

This transitivity theorem is of fundamental importance in the study of groups of odd order and in the study of simple groups in general. Because of it the subdivision of $\pi(G)$ into the sets of those primes p for which $SCN_3(p)$ is nonempty and those for which it is empty [equivalently $d_n(P) \geqslant 3$ and $d_n(P) \leqslant 2$, P an S_p-subgroup of G] is a significant one. We have seen in Section 5.4 that for odd p the structure of P is extremely restricted when $SCN_3(P)$ is empty and have remarked that all such p-groups have been completely classified for odd p.

To prove the transitivity theorem, we require a preliminary result of interest:

Theorem 5.1

Let G be a group in which the normalizer of every nonidentity p-subgroup of G is p-constrained. Let $A \in SCN_2(p)$ and let Q be an A-invariant q-subgroup of G, q a prime distinct from p. Then if H is any subgroup of G with $O_p(H) \neq 1$ which contains AQ, we have $Q \subseteq O_{p'}(H)$.

To establish this theorem, we first prove two preliminary lemmas:

Lemma 5.2

Let G be a p-constrained group, let P be an S_p-subgroup of G, and let $A \in SCN(P)$. Then every A-invariant p'-subgroup of G lies in $O_{p'}(G)$.

Proof

If K is an A-invariant p'-subgroup of G, it will suffice to show that the image $\bar{K}$ of K in $\bar{G} = G/O_{p'}(G)$ centralizes $O_p(\bar{G})$, for then $\bar{K} = \bar{1}$ by

Theorem 1.1(ii), whence $K \subseteq O_{p'}(G)$, as desired. Hence without loss we may assume that $O_{p'}(G) = 1$ and prove that K centralizes $Q = O_p(G)$.

Now $C_G(A) = A \times D$, where D is a p'-group. Since P normalizes $C_G(A)$, it normalizes D. Hence if K centralizes A, we have $K \subseteq D$ and $[K, Q] \subseteq D$, so $[K, Q]$ is both a p'-group and a p-group. Thus K centralizes Q in this case. Hence we can suppose that A does not centralize K. Let R be a subgroup of K of least order not centralized by A. Since A leaves invariant an S_r-subgroup of K for each prime r in $\pi(K)$ by Theorem 6.2.2(i), R is a special r-group for some prime r and A acts irreducibly and nontrivially on $R/\Phi(R)$ by Theorem 5.3.7. In particular, $[R, A] = R$.

We have $[R, Q \cap A] \subseteq R \cap Q = 1$, so R centralizes $A \cap Q$. On the other hand, $[A, Q] \subseteq A$ as $A \triangleleft P$ and $Q \subseteq P$. Hence $[A, Q] \subseteq A \cap Q$ and so A centralizes $\bar{Q} = Q/A \cap Q$. Since R centralizes $A \cap Q$, R also acts on $\bar{Q}$. Thus $C = C_{RA}(\bar{Q}) \triangleleft RA$ and $A \subseteq C$. But then $R = [R, A] \subseteq C$ and therefore R centralizes $\bar{Q}$. We conclude that R stabilizes the normal series $Q \supseteq A \cap Q \supseteq 1$ and consequently R centralizes Q by Theorem 5.3.2, completing the proof.

Lemma 5.3

Let G be a p-constrained group, let P be of index at most p in an S_p-subgroup of G, and let A be an abelian subgroup of P containing $Z(P)$. Then $O_{p'}(G)$ contains every A-invariant p'-subgroup K of G with the property $[K, B] = K$ for some subgroup B of $Z(P)$.

Proof

As in the preceding lemma, it will suffice to consider the case $O_{p'}(G) = 1$ and then to prove that K centralize $Q = O_p(G)$. Let S be an S_p-subgroup of G containing P, so that $|S : P| = 1$ or p by hypothesis. Then $P \triangleleft S$ and consequently $Z(P)$, being characteristic in S, is also normal in S. Since $B \subseteq Z(P)$, we have $[B, S] \subseteq Z(P)$, whence $[B, S] \subseteq A$. Since $Q \subseteq S$, it follows that $[Q, B, K] \subseteq [A, K] \cap Q \subseteq K \cap Q = 1$. Thus K centralizes $[Q, B]$. But now KB acts on $\bar{Q} = Q/[Q, B]$ and B centralizes $\bar{Q}$. Since $K = [K, B]$, we conclude at once as in the preceding lemma that K centralizes $\bar{Q}$, whence K centralizes the normal series $Q \supseteq [Q, B] \supseteq 1$. Thus K centralizes Q by another application of Theorem 5.3.2.

With these lemmas at our disposal, we turn now to the proof of Theorem 5.1. If $L = N_G(O_p(H))$, then $H \subseteq L$; so if $Q \subseteq O_{p'}(L)$, then $Q \subseteq H \cap O_{p'}(L) \subseteq O_{p'}(H)$. Thus it suffices to prove the theorem for L. By hypothesis, L is p-constrained.

Since $A \in SCN_2(p)$, $A \in SCN_2(P)$ for some S_p-subgroup P of G and, in particular, A is noncyclic. Since $C_P(A) \subseteq A$, A contains $Z(P)$. If $Z(P)$ is noncyclic, let B be a subgroup of $Z(P)$ of type (p, p). On the other hand, if $Z(P)$ is cyclic, let B be any normal abelian subgroup of P of type (p, p) contained in A. That A contains such a normal subgroup follows directly from Theorem 2.6.4. In either case, $B \lhd P$ and $B \cap Z(P) \neq 1$. Since B is a 2-dimensional vector space over Z_p, it contains exactly $p + 1$ distinct subgroups B_i of order p, $0 \leqslant i \leqslant p$; and we may assume that $B_0 \subseteq Z(P)$. For $1 \leqslant i \leqslant p$, set $Q_i = C_Q(B_i)$ and $R_i = [Q_i, B]$, while for $i = 0$, set $R_0 = C_Q(B_0)$.

We claim that $Q = \langle R_i \mid 0 \leqslant i \leqslant p \rangle$. Indeed, $Q = \langle R_0, Q_i \mid 1 \leqslant i \leqslant p \rangle$ by Theorem 5.3.16. But $Q_i = R_i C_{Q_i}(B) \subseteq R_i R_0$, $1 \leqslant i \leqslant$ p, by Theorem 5.3.5, and the desired conclusion follows. Thus it will suffice to prove that each $R_i \subseteq O_{p'}(L)$, $0 \leqslant i \leqslant p$. We note that $R_i = [R_i, B]$, $1 \leqslant i \leqslant p$, by Theorem 5.3.6 and also that each R_i is A-invariant as A is abelian and $B \subseteq A$.

Set $N_i = N_G(B_i)$, $0 \leqslant i \leqslant p$. We shall first argue that it is enough to prove that $R_i \subseteq O_{p'}(N_i)$. Indeed, assume this to be true and suppose that some $R_i \nsubseteq O_{p'}(L)$. For simplicity put $R = R_i$ and $N = N_i$. Set $\bar{L} = L/O_{p'}(L)$ and let $\bar{R}, \bar{A}, \bar{B}_i$ be the images of R, A, B_i in L. Then $\bar{R} \neq 1$. Since L is p-constrained, $\bar{R}$ does not centralize $O_p(\bar{L})$ by Theorem 1.1(ii). Let $\bar{D}$ be an $\bar{A}\bar{R}$-invariant subgroup of minimal order in $O_p(\bar{L})$ which is not centralized by $\bar{R}$. Now $\bar{B}_i$ centralizes $\bar{R}$ and hence $C_{\bar{D}}(\bar{B}_i)$ is also $\bar{R}\bar{A}$-invariant. But by Theorem 5.3.4, $\bar{R}$ does not centralize $C_{\bar{D}}(\bar{B}_i)$; otherwise $\bar{R}$ would centralize $\bar{D}$. Thus $C_{\bar{D}}(\bar{B}_i) = \bar{D}$ by our minimal choice of $\bar{D}$ and so $\bar{B}_i$ centralizes $\bar{D}$.

Now $B_i \subseteq S$ for some S_p-subgroup S of L and $T = S \cap O_{p',p}(L)$ is an S_p-subgroup of $O_{p',p}(L)$. Since TB_i maps isomorphically onto $O_p(\bar{L})\bar{B}_i$, T contains a subgroup D which is centralized by B_i and whose image is $\bar{D}$. Thus $D \subseteq N$. But by assumption $R \subseteq O_{p'}(N)$, so $[D, R]$ is a p'-group. Hence $[\bar{D}, \bar{R}]$ is both a p'-group and a p-group, forcing $\bar{R}$ to centralize $\bar{D}$, a contradiction. Thus it will suffice to show that each $R_i \subseteq O_{p'}(N_i)$, $0 \leqslant i \leqslant p$, as asserted.

Now R_i is an A-invariant p'-subgroup of the p-constrained group N_i. For $i = 0$, N_0 contains P and consequently $R_0 \subseteq O_{p'}(N_0)$ by Lemma 5.2. On the other hand, for $1 \leqslant i \leqslant p$, we have that $P^* = C_P(B) \subseteq N_i$, $A \subseteq P^*$, $Z(P^*) \subseteq A$, $B \subseteq Z(P^*)$, and $[R_i, B] = R_i$. Furthermore, since $B \lhd P$ and B is elementary abelian of type (p, p), $|P : P^*| = 1$ or p by Theorem 2.8.1. Since P is an S_p-subgroup of G, P^* thus has index at most p in an S_p-subgroup of N_i. But now all the hypotheses of Lemma 5.3 hold in N_i and we conclude that $R_i \subseteq O_{p'}(N_i)$, $1 \leqslant i \leqslant p$. This completes the proof of Theorem 5.1.

We now prove

Theorem 5.4 (Thompson Transitivity Theorem)

Let G be a group in which the normalizer of every nonidentity p-subgroup is p-constrained. Then if $A \in SCN_3(p)$, $C_G(A)$ permutes transitively under conjugation the set of all maximal A-invariant q-subgroups of G for any prime $q \neq p$.

For the proof we need the following elementary lemma, which will reveal how the assumption that $m(A) \geq 3$ is used in the proof of the theorem.

Lemma 5.5

Let A be an abelian p-group, p a prime, which acts as a group of automorphisms of each of two p'-groups R and S. If $m(A) \geq 3$, then there exists an element u in A^* such that both $C_R(u)$ and $C_S(u)$ are nontrivial.

Proof

Since $m(A) \geq 3$, A possesses an elementary abelian subgroup B of type (p, p, p). By Theorem 5.3.16 $R_0 = C_R(y) \neq 1$ for some y in B^*. Since R_0 is B-invariant and $B/\langle y \rangle$ is abelian of type (p, p), the same theorem yields that $R_1 = C_{R_0}(z) \neq 1$ for some z in $B - \langle y \rangle$. We see then that R_1 is a nontrivial B-invariant subgroup of R centralized by the elementary abelian subgroup $B_1 = \langle y, z \rangle$ of type (p, p). Hence by the same reasoning $S_1 = C_S(u) \neq 1$ for some u in $B_1^\#$. Since $u \in A^*$, and u centralizes R_1, the lemma follows.

We now prove Theorem 5.4. Let $\mathscr{S}_1, \mathscr{S}_2, \ldots, \mathscr{S}_t$ be the sets of transitivity of maximal A-invariant q-subgroups of G under the action of $C_G(A)$ and suppose by way of contradiction that $t > 1$. Clearly then 1 is not a maximal A-invariant q-subgroup of G.

We first argue that $Q_1 \cap Q_2 = 1$ whenever $Q_1 \in \mathscr{S}_i$, $Q_2 \in \mathscr{S}_j$, and $i \neq j$. Suppose false. Then among all choices of Q_1, Q_2 violating this conclusion, choose i, j with $1 \leq i, j \leq t$ and $i \neq j$ and $Q_1 \in \mathscr{S}_i$, $Q_2 \in \mathscr{S}_j$ in such a way that $D = Q_1 \cap Q_2$ has maximal order. Because Q_1, Q_2 are maximal A-invariant q-subgroups of G, certainly D is a proper subgroup of both Q_1 and Q_2. Set $N = N_G(D)$ and let $R_i = N_{Q_i}(D)$, $1 \leq i \leq 2$. Then A and R_i are contained in N, R_i is A-invariant, and $R_i \supset D, 1 \leq i \leq 2$. Set $\bar{R}_i = R_i/D$, so that A acts as a group of automorphisms of each $\bar{R}_i$. Since each $\bar{R}_i \neq 1$, it follows from Lemma 5.5 that $C_{\bar{R}_i}(u) \neq 1$ for some u in $A^\#, 1 \leq i \leq 2$. But then $S_i = C_{R_i}(u) \nsubseteq D$ by Theorem 5.3.15, whence $S_i D \supset D, 1 \leq i \leq 2$.

Now set $H = C_G(\langle u \rangle)$. Then H is p-constrained by hypothesis. Since each S_i is an A-invariant q-subgroup of H, Theorem 5.1 yields that $S_i \subseteq O_{p'}(H)$, $1 \leqslant i \leqslant 2$. Since also each $S_i \subseteq N$, we conclude at once that $S_i \subseteq O_{p'}(L)$, where $L = D(N \cap H)$. Since A normalizes $K = O_{p'}(L)$, it follows therefore from Theorem 6.2.2(ii) and (iii) that $S_i D$ is contained in an A-invariant S_q-subgroup T_i of K, $1 \leqslant i \leqslant 2$, and that $T_2 = T_1^x$ for some element x in $C_K(A)$. Finally, let Q be a maximal A-invariant q-subgroup of G containing Q_1. Then $Q_1 \cap Q \supseteq S_1 D \supset D$, whence $Q \in \mathscr{S}_i$ by our maximal choice of $D = Q_1 \cap Q_2$. However, Q^x contains T_2 and consequently $Q^x \cap Q_2 \supseteq S_2 D \supset D$, whence $Q^x \in \mathscr{S}_j$, again by our maximal choice of D. Since $x \in C_G(A)$, we conclude that $Q \in \mathscr{S}_j$, whence $i = j$, a contradiction.

Now choose Q_1 in $\mathscr{S}_1$ and Q_2 in $\mathscr{S}_2$. Applying Lemma 5.5 once again, it follows that there exists an element u in A^{*} such that $R_i = C_{Q_i}(u) \neq 1$, $1 \leqslant i \leqslant 2$. We set $H = N_G(\langle u \rangle)$ and apply Theorem 5.1 to obtain that both R_1 and R_2 lie in $O_{p'}(H)$. As in the preceding paragraph, there exists an A-invariant S_q-subgroup S_1 of $O_{p'}(H)$ containing R_1 and R_2^x for some element x in $C_G(A)$. But now if Q denotes a maximal A-invariant q-subgroup of G containing S_1, we have $Q \cap Q_1 \supseteq R_1 \neq 1$, so $Q \in \mathscr{S}_1$ by the argument of the preceding paragraph. Since $Q \cap Q_2^x \supseteq R_2^x \neq 1$, it follows for the same reason that $Q_2^x \in \mathscr{S}_1$. Since $x \in C_G(A)$, this yields $Q_2 \in \mathscr{S}_1$, contrary to our choice of Q_2. Theorem 5.4 is thus proved.

The transitivity theorem has the following important corollary.

Theorem 5.6

Let G be a group in which the normalizer of every nonidentity p-subgroup is p-constrained. Let P be an S_p-subgroup of G and let A be an element of $SCN_3(P)$. Then for any prime $q \neq p$, P normalizes some maximal A-invariant q-subgroup of G. In particular, if P normalizes no nontrivial p'-subgroups of G, then neither does A.

Proof

Let Q be a maximal A-invariant q-subgroup of G and set $K = N_G(Q)$. Also set $N = N_G(A)$ and $C = C_G(A)$. We shall argue that

$$(5.1) \qquad\qquad N = (N \cap K)C.$$

Indeed, suppose $x \in N$. Then Q^x is also clearly a maximal A-invariant q-subgroup of G, so $Q^x = Q^y$ for some y in C by the Thompson transitivity theorem. Thus $z = xy^{-1}$ normalizes Q and so lies in K. Since $C \subseteq N$, we also have $z \in N$. Hence $x = zy$ with $z \in N \cap K$ and $y \in C$, proving (5.1).

Now $A \subseteq N \cap K$ and so there exists an S_p-subgroup R of $N \cap K$ with

$A \subseteq R$. But A is an S_p-subgroup of C as $C = A \times D$, where D is a p'-group. Thus R contains an S_p-subgroup of C, while by (5.1) RC/C is an S_p-subgroup of N/C. It follows at once that R is an S_p-subgroup of N. But P is also an S_p-subgroup of N, so $P = R^u$ for some u in N. On the other hand, R normalizes Q, as $R \subseteq K$, and consequently P normalizes Q^u, which is also a maximal A-invariant q-subgroup of G.

Remark   If either the assumption of p-constraint or the assumption that $m(A) \geqslant 3$ is dropped, the transitivity theorem is in general false (see Exercises 7 and 8 below). We note, however, that the assumption of p-constraint is required only on the normalizers of those nonidentity p-subgroups of G which contain A.

6. THE MAXIMAL SUBGROUP THEOREM

Under what circumstances does the set $N(P)$ of normalizers of all nonidentity subgroups of a fixed S_p-subgroup P of G possess a *unique* maximal element? If P is disjoint from its conjugates, it is trivial to verify that $N_G(P)$ itself is the unique maximal element of $N(P)$. Thus there are at least some conditions under which this is the case.

The Maximal Subgroup theorem, which is concerned with this question, provides a sufficient condition for a suitable large subset of $N(P)$ to possess a unique maximal element in the case that $SCN_3(P)$ is nonempty. To define this subset of $N(P)$, we first introduce the following terminology:

Let P be a p-group in which $SCN_3(P)$ is nonempty. Then by definition:
$A_1(P) = \{Q \mid Q \subseteq P, \ Q \text{ contains an element of } SCN_3(P)\}$; and for $i > 1$,
$A_i(P) = \{Q \mid Q \subseteq P, \ Q \text{ contains an abelian subgroup } R \text{ of type } (p, p)$
$\qquad \text{such that } C_P(x) \in A_{i-1}(P) \text{ for all } x \text{ in } R^\#\}$.
In practice the sets $A_i(P)$ are needed only for $1 \leqslant i \leqslant 4$. That these constitute a fairly large collection of subsets of P can be seen by the following result:

Lemma 6.1
   If P is a p-group in which $SCN_3(P)$ is nonempty, then any subgroup Q of P which contains an abelian subgroup of type (p, p, p) lies in $A_3(P)$.

Proof
   Let $A \in SCN_3(P)$. Then $\Omega_1(A)$ is an elementary abelian normal subgroup of P of order at least p^3. By Theorem 2.6.4 there exists a subgroup B of order p^2 in $\Omega_1(A)$ with $B \vartriangleleft P$. Now if $x \in B^\#$, then $C_P(x) \supseteq A$ and so

$C_P(x) \in A_1(P)$. Hence by definition $B \in A_2(P)$. On the other hand, Q normalizes B, so $Q/C_Q(B)$ is isomorphic to a subgroup of Aut B. Since $|\text{Aut } B|_p = p$ by Theorem 2.8.1, we have $|Q : C_Q(B)| \leqslant p$. But Q contains an elementary abelian subgroup T of order p^3, so $T \cap C_Q(B)$ must contain an elementary abelian subgroup R of type (p, p). Then $C_P(y)$ contains B for each y in $R^\#$. Since $B \in A_2(P)$ and $R \subseteq Q$, we conclude that $Q \in A_3(P)$.

Since $Z(P) \subseteq A$ for any element A of $SCN_3(P)$, we note also, if $Z(P)$ is noncyclic, that $Z(P) \in A_2(P)$.

Now let P be an S_p-subgroup of the group G and assume that $SCN_3(P)$ is nonempty. Then by definition

$N^*(P) = \{H \subseteq G \mid H = N_G(Q), Q \subseteq P, Q \neq 1$, and H contains an element of $A_i(P)$ for some $i\}$.

Thus $N^*(P)$ is a subset of $N(P)$. By Lemma 6.1, if $Q \subseteq P$, $Q \neq 1$, and $N_P(Q)$ contains an abelian subgroup of type (p, p, p), then $N_G(Q) \in N^*(P)$. Moreover, since $N_P(Q) \supseteq Z(P)$, $N_G(Q)$ will always lie in $N^*(P)$ if $Z(P)$ is noncyclic. Hence in this case $N^*(P) = N(P)$. However, there do exist cases in which $N^*(P) \subset N(P)$, as the following lemma illustrates:

Lemma 6.2

Let P be a p-group in which $SCN_3(P)$ is nonempty which contains a subgroup Q of order p such that $N_P(Q)$ is elementary abelian of type (p, p). Then for no value of i does $N_P(Q) \in A_i(P)$.

Proof

Since $Q = \langle y \rangle$ has order p, $N = N_P(Q) = C_P(y)$. Since $|N| = p^2$, certainly $N \notin A_1(P)$. Suppose $N \in A_i(P)$ for some i and choose i minimal. Since $i > 1$, N must possess an abelian subgroup R of type (p, p) such that $C_P(x) \in A_{i-1}(P)$ for all x in $R^\#$. Since $|N| = p^2$, the only possibility is that $R = N$. Taking $y = x$, we see that $N = C_P(y) \in A_{i-1}(P)$, a contradiction.

One can easily verify that the symmetric group on p^2 letters has S_p-subgroups with this property, p odd. Furthermore, we leave as an exercise the fact that any p-group satisfying the hypothesis of the lemma is of maximal class. Blackburn [1] has shown that conversely, for odd p, any p-group P of maximal class contains a subgroup Q of order p such that $N_P(Q)$ is elementary abelian of type (p, p).

With these preliminaries, we can now state our main result:

Theorem 6.3 (The Maximal Subgroup Theorem)

Let P be an S_p-subgroup of G in which $SCN_3(P)$ is nonempty, p odd. Assume that the following conditions hold:

(a) Every element of $N^*(P)$ is p-constrained and p-stable.

(b) *P possesses a nontrivial normal subgroup which centralizes every P-invariant p'-subgroup of G.*

Then $N^*(P)$ has a unique maximal element.

For the sake of clarity, we break the proof into two parts.

Lemma 6.4

If $M^*(P)$ is the subset of $N^*(P)$ consisting of those elements which contain P, then $M^*(P)$ has a unique maximal element.

Proof

We first consider the case that P normalizes no nontrivial p'-subgroup of G. Then if $H \in M^*(P)$, we have $O_{p'}(H) = 1$. But now Glauberman's theorem implies that $Z(J(P)) \lhd H$, whence $H \subseteq N_G(Z(J(P)))$. Hence in this case $N_G(Z(J(P)))$ is the unique maximal element of $M^*(P)$.

Hence we may assume that P normalizes some nonidentity p'-subgroup of G. Let B be a normal subgroup of P which satisfies condition (b) and set $H = N_G(B)$, so that $H \in M^*(P)$ as $P \subseteq H$. We claim, first of all, that $K = O_{p'}(H)$ contains every p'-subgroup of G normalized by P. Indeed, let Y be such a subgroup. Then Y centralizes B and so $Y \subseteq H$. But H is p-constrained and Y is invariant under $P \cap O_{p',p}(H)$, which is an S_p-subgroup of $O_{p',p}(H)$. Hence $Y \subseteq K$ by Theorem 1.1(iii), proving the assertion. In particular, our conditions imply that $K \neq 1$.

Now let $A \in SCN_3(P)$. We next argue that K contains every A-invariant p'-subgroup of G. Indeed, if Y is such a subgroup, A leaves invariant an S_q-subgroup of Y for each q in $\pi(Y)$. Thus it suffices to prove that K contains any maximal A-invariant q-group Q, q any prime distinct from p. But by Theorems 5.4 and 5.6, Q^x is P-invariant for some x in $C_G(A)$. On the other hand, $C_G(A) = A \times D$, where D is a p'-group, and we can assume without loss that $x \in D$. But D char $C_G(A) \lhd N_G(A)$ and $N_G(A)$ contains P. Thus D is also P-invariant. Hence by the preceding paragraph both Q^x and D are contained in K. Since $x \in D$, we conclude that $Q \subseteq K$.

Now set $V = V(\mathrm{ccl}_G(A); P)$ and $L = N_G(V)$. We have that K is V-invariant. Hence for x in L, K^x is also V-invariant. But as $A \subseteq V$, K^x is thus an A-invariant p'-subgroup of G, whence $K^x = K$ by the preceding paragraph. Thus L normalizes K. But by Theorem 4.4, $N = O_{p'}(N)(N \cap L)$, where $N = N_G(Z(J(P)))$. Since $O_{p'}(N) \subseteq K$ while $N \cap L$ normalizes K, we conclude that N normalizes K.

Finally, observe that $B \cap Z(P) \neq 1$ as $B \lhd P$ and $B \neq 1$. Since $Z(J(P))$ contains $Z(P)$ and B centralizes K, it follows that $Q = C_{Z(J(P))}(K) \neq 1$. Now $Q \lhd N$ since $Z(J(P)) \lhd N$ and N normalizes K. Thus $M = N_G(Q)$ contains both K and N. In particular, $P \subseteq M$ and so $M \in M^*(P)$. But now if H is any element of $M^*(P)$, we have

$$H = O_{p'}(H)(H \cap N),$$

as H is of Glauberman type. Since $O_{p'}(H) \subseteq K \subset M$ and $N \subseteq M$, we conclude that $H \subseteq M$. Thus M is the unique maximal element of $M^*(P)$, completing the proof.

Now let M be the unique maximal element of $M^*(P)$. To prove Theorem 6.3, we must show that, in fact, M is the unique maximal element of $N^*(P)$. To this end, we now define:

$A_j^*(P) = \{Q \mid Q \subseteq P, Q$ contains A^y for some A in $SCN_3(P)$ and suitable y in $M\}$; and for $i > 1$,

$A_i^*(P) = \{Q \mid Q \subseteq P, Q$ contains an abelian subgroup R of type (p, p) such that $C_P(x)^y \in A_{i-1}^*(P)$ for all x in $R^\#$ and suitable y in $M\}$.

Clearly $A_i^*(P) \supseteq A_i(P)$ for all $i \geqslant 1$. Hence the desired conclusion will follow from the following stronger assertion:

Lemma 6.5

If H is the normalizer of a nontrivial p-subgroup of G and H contains an element of $A_i^*(P)$ for some i, then $H \subseteq M$.

Proof

Suppose false and let j be the least value of i for which there exists such a subgroup H of G which contains an element Q of $A_j^*(P)$ and is such that $H \nsubseteq M$. Furthermore, among all such subgroups, choose H so that $|Q|$ is maximal. Let T be an S_p-subgroup of H containing Q. Now $Q \neq P$, for then $H \subseteq M$ by the preceding lemma. Hence $Q \subset P$ and consequently $N_P(Q) \supset Q$ by Theorem 1.2.11(ii). Clearly $N_P(Q) \in A_j^*(P)$ since it contains Q, so $N_G(Q) \subseteq M$ by our choice of Q. In particular, $N_T(Q) \subseteq M$ and it follows therefore from the definition that $N_T(Q) \in A_j^*(P)$. But now our choice of Q implies that $N_T(Q) = Q$ and we conclude that $Q = T$ is an S_p-subgroup of H.

Applying Glauberman's theorem, we have $H = O_{p'}(H)N_H(Z(J(Q)))$. However, since $N_P(Z(J(Q))) \supset Q$, the same reasoning as in the preceding paragraph yields that $N_G(Z(J(Q))) \subseteq M$. Thus $K = O_{p'}(H) \nsubseteq M$.

Suppose now that $j > 1$. Let R be an abelian subgroup of Q of type (p, p) such that $C_P(x)^y \in A_{j-1}^*(P)$ for each x in $R^\#$ and suitable y in M. By our choice of j, it follows that $C_G(x) \subseteq M$ for each x in $R^\#$.

But $K = \langle C_K(x) \,|\, x \in R^* \rangle$ by Theorems 5.5.5 and 6.2.2(i) and consequently $K \subseteq M$, a contradiction. Thus $j = 1$.

Hence $Q \supseteq A^y$ for some element A of $SCN_3(P)$ and suitable y in M. To derive a contradiction, it will suffice to show that $L = K^{y-1} \subseteq M$. But L is A-invariant and in the course of the proof of Lemma 6.4 we have argued that M contains every A-invariant p'-subgroup of G. This completes the proof of the lemma and also of Theorem 6.3.

We note that condition (b) of the theorem is automatically fulfilled if P normalizes no nontrivial p'-subgroups of G. This is an important special case of the theorem.

Whenever $N^*(P)$ possesses a unique maximal element M, we shall say that G satisfies the *uniqueness condition for the prime* p. (By Sylow's theorem this property is independent of the particular S_p-subgroup P of G.) We shall also refer to M as *a uniqueness subgroup* for p.

EXERCISES

1. Let $p \in \pi(A_n)$, where $n \geqslant 2p$ if $p \geqslant 5$ and $n \geqslant p + 5$ if $p < 5$. Show that the normalizer of some nontrivial p-subgroup of A_n is not p-constrained.

2. Assume $SCN_3(p)$ is nonempty in A_n, let P be an S_p-subgroup of A_n, and let B be an element of $SCN_3(P)$. Prove that $N_G(B)$ is p-constrained.

3. Let P be a p-group, let $A^*(P)$ be the set of abelian subgroups A of P such that $m(A)$ is maximal, and set $J^*(P) = \langle A \,|\, A \in A^*(P) \rangle$. Show that the conclusions of Lemma 2.2 hold with $A^*(P)$ and $J^*(P)$ in place of $A(P)$ and $J(P)$.

4. Thompson has established the following theorem: Let G be strongly p-solvable with $O_{p'}(G) = 1$ and let P be an S_p-subgroup of G. Then

$$G = C_G(Z(P))N_G(J^*(P)).$$

On the basis of this result, show that a group G with S_p-subgroup P, p odd, possesses a normal p-complement provided $C_G(Z(P))$ and $N_G(J^*(P))$ both have normal p-complements (the *Thompson* normal p-complement theorem).

5. Show that Theorem 4.2 holds under the weaker assumption that $N_G(H)$ is of Glauberman type for every p-subgroup H of G such that $Z(P) \subseteq H$, where P is an S_p-subgroup of G containing H.

6. Let P be an S_p-subgroup of G and H a subgroup of P. Prove that some conjugate of H is well-placed in P.

7. Let $G = L_1 \times L_2 \times L_3$, where L_i is isomorphic to $L_2(7)$, $1 \leqslant i \leqslant 3$, and let A be an S_3-subgroup of G. Prove
   (i) A is elementary abelian of order 3^3 and $C_G(A) = A$.
   (ii) A normalizes eight distinct S_7-subgroups Q_i of G, $1 \leqslant i \leqslant 8$, no two of which are conjugate under the action of $C_G(A)$.
   (iii) The Q_i are all conjugate under the action of $N_G(A)$.
   (iv) The normalizer of some nontrivial 3-subgroup of G is not 3-constrained.

8. Let $G = L_2(13)$ and let A be an S_2-subgroup of G. Prove
   (i) A is abelian of type (2, 2) and $C_G(A) = A$.
   (ii) A normalizes three distinct S_3-subgroups Q_i of G, $1 \leqslant i \leqslant 3$, no two of which are conjugate under the action of $C_G(A)$.
   (iii) The Q_i are all conjugate under the action of $N_G(A)$.
   (iv) The normalizer of every nontrivial 2-subgroup of G is 2-constrained.

9. Let G be a group, let p and q be distinct primes, and let A be a p-subgroup of G such that $m(Z(A)) \geqslant 3$. If H is the normalizer of any nonidentity p- or q-subgroup of G and if $A \subseteq H$, assume that $C_H(A)$ permutes transitively under conjugation the set of all maximal A-invariant q-subgroups of H. Prove that $C_G(A)$ permutes transitively under conjugation the set of all maximal A-invariant q-subgroups of G.

10. Let P be an S_p-subgroup of G, set $Q = P \cap O_{p',p}(G)$, $N = N_G(Q)$, and $K = O_{p'}(G)$. Prove
   (i) If x is a p-element of N and $x^y \in N$ with $y \in K$, then $y = y_1 y_2$, where $y_1 \in C_K(y)$ and $y_2 \in C_K(Q)$.
   (ii) Two elements of P are conjugate in G if and only if they are conjugate in N.

11. Let G be a group in which the normalizer of every nonidentity p-subgroup is p-constrained, let P be an S_p-subgroup of G and A an element of $SCN_3(P)$, let Q be a maximal P-invariant q-subgroup of G, q a prime, $q \neq p$, and set $N = N_G(Q)$. Prove that

$$V(\mathrm{ccl}_G(A); P) = V(\mathrm{ccl}_N(A); P).$$

12. Let P be an S_p-subgroup of G in which $SCN_3(P)$ is nonempty, p odd. Assume that the following two conditions hold:
   (a) Every element of $N^*(P)$ is p-constrained and p-stable.
   (b) P possesses a noncyclic elementary abelian subgroup which centralizes every P-invariant $\{p, q\}'$-subgroup of G for some fixed prime q.
   (c) $O_q(G) = 1$.
   Prove that there exists a proper subgroup M of G which contains every element of $N^*(P)$.

CHAPTER 9

GROUPS OF EVEN ORDER

The global structure of a group of even order appears to be intimately connected with local properties of its involutions. A number of results and techniques have developed for studying and exploiting this relationship. We first establish some elementary properties of involutions and, on the basis of these, derive a striking result of Brauer and Fowler which bounds the order of a group (of even order) in terms of the orders of the centralizers of its real elements. In Section 3 we analyze a situation of great importance in the study of simple groups: a group G which possesses a proper subgroup M of even order containing the centralizer in G of each of its involutions as well as the normalizer in G of each of its Sylow 2-subgroups. In Section 4 we consider two fundamental applications of the results we derive concerning M. In the first of these, we assume in addition that G satisfies the uniqueness condition for some odd prime p and that M is a uniqueness subgroup for p. In Section 5 we discuss a procedure for determining the order of a group from information about its characters and carry this out in detail for a class of groups with a self-centralizing Sylow 2-subgroup of order 4.

1. ELEMENTARY PROPERTIES OF INVOLUTIONS

The following simple property of involutions is fundamental:

Theorem 1.1

If x and y are involutions of G, then x and y invert the product xy and so $\langle x, y \rangle$ is a dihedral group.

Proof

Since x and y are involutions, yx is the inverse of xy and consequently $x^{-1}(xy)x = yx = (xy)^{-1}$. Similarly, y inverts xy. Since $\langle x, y \rangle = \langle x, xy \rangle$, it follows at once that $\langle x, y \rangle$ is a dihedral group.

For elements x, y of odd prime order in G, no general statement concerning the structure of $\langle x, y \rangle$ can be made. It is largely because of this fact that the results we shall obtain concerning involutions have no general analogues for odd primes.

Theorem 1.1 has the following important corollary:

Theorem 1.2

If x, y are involutions of G, then either x and y are conjugate in $\langle x, y \rangle$ or there exists an involution z of $\langle x, y \rangle$ which commutes with both x and y.

Proof

Set $H = \langle x, y \rangle$, $u = xy$ and $m = |u|$. Since $H = \langle x, u \rangle$ and x inverts u, $|H| = 2m$. But then if m is odd, $\langle x \rangle$ and $\langle y \rangle$ are each S_2-subgroups of H, whence x and y are conjugate in H by Sylow's theorem. On the other hand, if $m = 2k$ is even, then $z = u^k$ is an involution. But x and y invert z, as they invert every power of u. Since $z = z^{-1}$, it follows that z centralizes both x and y, proving the theorem.

We illustrate the power of this last result by deriving the following bound for the order of a group with more than one class of involutions.

Theorem 1.3 (Brauer)

Let G be a group having at least two conjugate classes of involutions and let x be an involution of G whose centralizer has maximal order. Then

$$|G| < |C_G(x)|^3.$$

Proof

Set $C = C_G(x)$, $h = |C|$ and $m = |G : C|$. Since $|G| = mh$, we must show that $m < h^2$. By hypothesis, there exists an involution y of G which is not conjugate to x and we set $N = C_G(y)$. Let $y = y_1, y_2, \ldots, y_t$ be the distinct involutions of N and set $N_i = C_G(y_i)$, $1 \leqslant i \leqslant t$. By our choice of x, $|N_i| \leqslant h$, $1 \leqslant i \leqslant t$, and, in particular, $t \leqslant |N| \leqslant h$. Hence the number of distinct nonidentity elements in $\bigcup_{i=1}^{t} N_i$ is at most $-1 + \sum_{i=1}^{t} |N_i| \leqslant th - 1 < h^2$.

On the other hand, by Theorem 1.2.3(i), x has exactly m conjugates $x = x_1, x_2, \ldots, x_m$ in G. It will suffice to show that each x_j lies in $\bigcup_{i=1}^{t} N_i$, for then the desired conclusion $m < h^2$ will follow from the preceding paragraph (since each $x_j \neq 1$). But x_j is not conjugate to y since x is not; hence by the preceding theorem there exists an involution z_j in G which centralizes both y and x_j, $1 \leqslant j \leqslant m$. Then $z_j \in N = C_G(y)$, whence $z_j = y_{i_j}$ for some i_j. Since $x_j \in C_G(z_j) = N_{i_j}$, the theorem follows.

Theorem 1.3 may be false if G has only one class of involution, but the weaker assertion $|G| < |H|^3$ for some proper subgroup H of G is true. We shall prove this result, which is a little more delicate, shortly, but first we establish another interesting fact.

Theorem 1.4

   If an S_2-subgroup S of G is disjoint from its conjugates, then either $S \lhd G$ or G contains exactly one conjugate class of involutions.

Proof

   Suppose $S \ntriangleleft G$ and let T be an S_2-subgroup of G distinct from S. Let x, y be involutions of S, T, respectively. If x is not conjugate to y, then by Theorem 1.2 there exists an involution z in $\langle x, y \rangle$ which centralizes both x and y. Since the S_2-subgroup of G are disjoint from their conjugates, z lies in a unique S_2-subgroup R of G while S, T are the unique S_2-subgroups containing x and y, respectively. But $\langle z, x \rangle$ is a 2-group and so lies in an S_2-subgroup, which by the preceding assertion must, on the one hand, be R and, on the other hand, S. Thus $R = S$. Similarly, $R = T$ and so $S = T$, a contradiction. We conclude that every involution of S is conjugate to y. Hence all involutions of S are conjugate and so G has only one class of involutions.

   An important notion is that of the *extended centralizer* of an element x of G, which by definition is the set of all y in G such that x^y is either x or x^{-1}. We denote it by $C_G^*(x)$.

   It is immediate that $C_G^*(x)$ is a subgroup of G containing $C_G(x)$ as a subgroup of index at most 2. Furthermore, if x is an involution, this index is always 1, while if x is not an involution, it is 2 or 1 according as x is or is not inverted by an element of G.

   This concept is closely related to that of real and strongly real elements of G; $x \in G$ is called *real* if it is inverted by an element y of G and is called *strongly real* if y is an involution.

Obviously any involution is strongly real. If y is an involution inverting x, then y and yx are involutions (provided $y \neq x$), so x is a product of two involutions. Conversely, Theorem 1.1 shows that any element which is the product of two involutions is strongly real.

Lemma 1.5

For x in G, let $\beta(x)$ be the number of ordered pairs (u, v) of involutions of G such that $uv = x$. Then we have
  (i) If x is not strongly real, $\beta(x)$ is 0.
  (ii) If $x = 1$, $\beta(x)$ is the number of involutions of G.
  (iii) If x is an involution, $\beta(x) + 1$ is the number of involutions in $C_G(x)$.
  (iv) If $x \neq 1$ is not an involution, $\beta(x)$ is the number of involutions in $C_G^*(x) - C_G(x)$.
  (v) For any x, $\beta(x) \leqslant |C_G(x)|$.

Proof

If $x = uv$ with u, v involutions, then u inverts x and so x is strongly real. Thus $\beta(x) = 0$ if x is not strongly real. If $x = 1$, then $x = uu$ for any involution u of G and obviously x cannot be represented in any other way as a product of involutions. Thus (i) and (ii) hold.

Suppose next that x is an involution and let u be any involution of $C_G(x)$ except x. Then ux is also an involution and $x = u(ux)$. Conversely, if $x = uv$, where u, v are involutions of G, then $u \neq x$ and u inverts x. Thus $u \in C_G(x)$ and $v = ux$. This proves (iii).

Assume now that $x \neq 1$ is not an involution, and let u be any involution of $C_G^*(x) - C_G(x)$. Then ux is also an involution and $x = u(ux)$. Conversely, any representation of x as a product of involutions is of this form, so (iv) also holds.

Finally (v) is obvious in cases (i), (ii), or (iii), so assume x is a nontrivial strongly real element which is not an involution and set $C^* = C_G^*(x)$, $C = C_G(x)$. In this case $\beta(x) \leqslant |C^* - C|$ by (iv). Since $|C^*| = 2|C|$, it follows that $\beta(x) \leqslant |C|$, proving (v).

With the aid of Lemma 1.4, we now derive the following improvement of Theorem 1.3:

Theorem 1.6 (Brauer and Fowler)

If G is a group of even order greater than 2, then G possesses a proper subgroup H such that

$$|G| < |H|^3.$$

Furthermore, if $|Z(G)|$ is odd, we can take $H = C_G(x)$ for some strongly real element x of $G^{\#}$.

Let b be the maximum order of the centralizer of an involution of G and let c be the maximum order of the centralizer of a strongly real element of $G^{\#}$ that is not an involution, if such an element exists; otherwise set $c = 0$. The theorem depends upon the following lemma connecting b, c and $|G|$:

Lemma 1.7

The following inequality holds:

$$|G| \leqslant (c + 1)b(b - 1).$$

Proof

Let K_i, $1 \leqslant i \leqslant t$, be the distinct conjugate classes of strongly real elements of G with K_i, $1 \leqslant i \leqslant s$, being the classes of involutions and with $K_t = \{1\}$. Let x_i be a representative of K_i, set $c_i = |C_G(x_i)|$, and let a_i be the number of involutions of $C_G(x_i)$, $1 \leqslant i \leqslant t$. Furthermore, set $M = \bigcup_{i=1}^{s} K_i$ and $m = |M|$, so that m is the number of involutions of G. Finally set $g = |G|$ and $a = \max\{a_i \mid 1 \leqslant i \leqslant s\}$. Note that $c = \max\{c_i \mid s + 1 \leqslant i \leqslant t - 1\}$ if $t > s + 1$.

Since m is the number of involutions of G, m^2 is the number of ordered pairs (u, v) of involutions. Since each such pair (u, v) determines an element $x = uv$ of G, it follows from the definition of $\beta(x)$ that

$$(1.1) \qquad m^2 = \sum_{x \in G} \beta(x).$$

Furthermore, clearly $\beta(x) = \beta(y)$ if x and y are conjugate. Since $|K_i| = g/c_i$ by Theorem 1.2.3(i) and since $\beta(x) = 0$ if x is not strongly real, it follows from (1.1) that

$$(1.2) \qquad m^2 = \sum_{i=1}^{t} \frac{g}{c_i} \beta(x_i).$$

But now Lemma 1.5 yields

$$(1.3) \qquad m^2 \leqslant m + \sum_{i=1}^{s} (a_i - 1)\frac{g}{c_i} + (t - s - 1)g.$$

On the other hand, we also have

$$(1.4) \qquad m = \sum_{i=1}^{s} \frac{g}{c_i}.$$

Since $a_i \leqslant a$, $1 \leqslant i \leqslant s$, it follows that

$$(1.5) \qquad m + \sum_{i=1}^{s} (a_i - 1)g/c_i \leqslant am.$$

Furthermore, the number of strongly real elements of G is at most g, whence

$$(1.6) \qquad 1 + m + \sum_{i=s+1}^{t-1} \frac{g}{c_i} \leqslant g.$$

Since $c_i \leqslant c$ for $s + 1 \leqslant i \leqslant t - 1$, this yields

$$(1.7) \qquad (t - s - 1)g \leqslant c(g - m - 1).$$

It follows now from (1.3), (1.5), and (1.7) that

$$(1.8) \qquad m^2 \leqslant am + c(g - m) - c,$$

whence also

$$(1.9) \qquad m \leqslant \frac{cg}{m} + (a - c).$$

Setting $n = g/m$ and multiplying (1.9) by n, we obtain

$$(1.10) \qquad g \leqslant cn^2 + (a - c)n = cn(n - 1) + an.$$

Finally by (1.4), $1/n = m/g = \sum_{i=1}^{s} 1/c_i$, which implies that $n \leqslant c_i$ for all i, $1 \leqslant i \leqslant s$. But by its definition, $b = \max \{c_i \mid 1 \leqslant i \leqslant s\}$ and so $n \leqslant b$. Furthermore, we have $a = a_j$ for some j, $1 \leqslant j \leqslant s$. Since $a_j \leqslant c_j - 1 \leqslant b - 1$, it follows that $a \leqslant b - 1$. But now substituting the inequalities $n \leqslant b$ and $a \leqslant b - 1$ in (1.10), we obtain the conclusion of the lemma.

We can now easily establish the theorem. Suppose first that $b \leqslant c$. Then by the lemma $g < c^3$. But $c = |C_G(x_k)|$ for some k with $s + 1 \leqslant k \leqslant t - 1$. Since x_k is strongly real and is not an involution, $C_G^*(x_k) \supset C_G(x_k)$, so $C_G(x_k)$ is a proper subgroup of G. Hence the theorem follows in this case with $H = C_G(x_k)$.

Suppose, on the other hand, that $b > c$. Then again by the lemma, $g < b^3$. Now $b = |C_G(x_k)|$ for some k with $1 \leqslant k \leqslant s$. Hence the theorem follows with $H = C_G(x_k)$ if $C_G(x_k)$ is a proper subgroup of G. In the contrary case, the involution x_k lies in $Z(G)$. In particular, the theorem is proved if $|Z(G)|$ is odd.

Assume finally that $x_k \in Z(G)$. In this case, we proceed by induction on $|G|$. Set $\bar{G} = G/\langle x_k \rangle$. If $|\bar{G}|$ is odd, then an S_2-subgroup of G has order

2, so G possesses a normal 2-complement K by Theorem 7.6.1. Also $K \neq 1$ as $g = |G| > 2$. Since $g = 2|K|$, the theorem follows with $H = K$. If $|\bar{G}| = 2$, we can take $H = \langle x_k \rangle$. On the other hand, if $|\bar{G}| > 2$ and $|\bar{G}|$ is even, then by induction $\bar{G}$ possesses a proper subgroup $\bar{H}$ such that $|\bar{G}| < |\bar{H}|^3$. But then it is immediate that the inverse image of $\bar{H}$ in G can be taken as H. This completes the proof.

The calculations of Lemma 1.7 also yield the following result which we shall need in Chapter 13.

Theorem 1.8 (Brauer-Fowler)

If t is the number of strongly real conjugate classes of G and m is the number of involutions of G, then

$$t - 1 \geqslant \frac{m(m+1)}{|G|}.$$

Proof

We preserve the notation of Lemma 1.7. Since obviously $a_i \leqslant c_i - 1$, (1.3) and (1.5) yield

$$(1.11) \qquad m^2 \leqslant m + \sum_{i=1}^{s} (c_i - 2) \frac{g}{c_i} + (t - s - 1)g$$

$$= m + (t - 1)g - 2 \sum_{i=1}^{s} g/c_i = m + (t - 1)g - 2m.$$

Thus $m^2 + m \leqslant (t - 1)g$, and the theorem follows.

2. THE FEIT-SUZUKI-THOMPSON THEOREMS

The following two theorems combine results of each of the above authors. These theorems deal with a subgroup M of even order of a group G with the property that $C_G(x) \subseteq M$ for every involution x of M. They are of great importance in the study of simple groups.

Theorem 2.1

Let M be a subgroup of G of even order which satisfies the following three conditions:

(a) *$C_G(x) \subseteq M$ for any involution x of M.*
(b) *$N_G(S) \subseteq M$ for any S_2-subgroup S of M.*
(c) *Not every involution of G lies in M.*
Then we have
(i) *S is an S_2-subgroup of G.*

(ii) *G and M each have only one conjugate class of involutions.*

(iii) *If $C = C_G(x)$, x an involution of M, then $M = CK$ for some subgroup K of M of odd order.*

(iv) *If u is a strongly real element of $C^{\#}$, then $C_G^{*}(u) \subseteq M$.*

Proof

Let T be an S_2-subgroup of G containing S and let x, y be involutions of S and $Z(T)$, respectively. Note that x, y exist since $S \neq 1$ by hypothesis. We have $C_G(x) \subseteq M$ by condition (a), so $y \in M$. Hence $C_G(y) \subseteq M$ for the same reason and so $T \subseteq M$. Thus $S = T$ is an S_2-subgroup of G, proving (i).

We shall argue next that G has only one class of involutions. Let x, y now denote any involution of M and $G - M$, respectively. Such an involution y exists by condition (c). Suppose there exists an involution z in G which centralizes both x and y. Then $z \in C_G(x) \subseteq M$, whence $y \in C_G(z) \subseteq M$, a contradiction. Hence no such involution G exists and consequently x is conjugate to y (in $\langle x, y \rangle$) by Theorem 1.2. Our argument shows that any involution of M is conjugate to y and any involution of $G - M$ is conjugate to x and we conclude that all involutions of G are conjugate.

We note that the preceding argument did not require the hypothesis $N_G(S) \subseteq M$, which we now use to show that also M has only one class of involutions. Indeed, suppose $|M \cap M^u|$ is even for some u in G. Then for some S_2-subgroup of M, which without loss we may assume to be S, we have $S^u \cap M \neq 1$. Thus $S^u \cap M$ contains an involution. Arguing now as in (i), it follows first that $Z(S^u) \subseteq M$ and then that $S^u \subseteq M$. Hence $S^u = S^v$ for some v in M, whence $uv^{-1} \in N_G(S) \subseteq M$ and so $u \in M$. We conclude that $M \cap M^u$ has odd order whenever $u \notin M$. Now let x, y be involutions of M. Since G has only one class of involutions, $y = x^u$ for some u in G, whence $M \cap M^u$ contains y. Hence by the preceding argument $u \in M$ and so x, y are conjugate in M. Thus (ii) also holds.

Now let x be an involution of G, set $C = C_G(x)$, and define $m = |M : C|$, $r = |G : M|$. Then by (ii), m is the number of involutions in M and mr is the number in G. This implies that some coset Mu of M in G with $u \notin M$ contains $t \geq m$ involutions, which we denote by y_i, $1 \leq i \leq t$. Then no y_i is in M, $v_i = y_1 y_i^{-1} = y_1 y_i \in M$ for each i, and y_1 inverts each v_i, $1 \leq i \leq t$. Hence if $K = \langle v_i \mid 1 \leq i \leq t \rangle$, it follows that $K \subseteq M$ and that y_1 normalizes K (since it transforms the generators v_i of K into K). Set $L = \langle K, y_1 \rangle$ and let R be an S_2-subgroup of L containing y_1. Since $K \triangleleft L$, $R \cap K$ is an S_2-subgroup of K by Theorem 1.3.8. But then if $|K|$ were even, y_1 would centralize an involution x of $R \cap K$ by Theorem 2.6.4

and so $y_1 \in C_G(x) \subseteq M$, which is not the case. We conclude therefore that $|K|$ is odd.

Suppose next that v_i and v_j lie in the same coset of C for some $i \neq j$. Then $v = v_i^{-1} v_j = y_i y_1^{-1} y_1 y_j = y_i y_j$ lies in C, so that $x \in C_G(v)$. Furthermore, y_i inverts $v = y_i y_j$ and so lies in the extended centralizer $C_G^*(v)$. But v has odd order since $v \in K$ and consequently y_i does not centralize v. Since x does centralize v, it follows that x and y_i cannot be conjugate in $C_G^*(v)$ and so certainly not in $\langle x, y_i \rangle$. But then Theorem 1.2 implies that $\langle x, y_i \rangle$ contains an involution z which centralizes both x and y_i. Hence $z \in C_G(x) \subseteq M$ and so $y_i \in C_G(z) \subseteq M$, contrary to the fact that $y_i \notin M$. We conclude therefore that the t cosets $Cv_i, 1 \leqslant i \leqslant t$, of C in M are distinct. Since $t \geqslant m = |M:C|$, this is possible only if $M = \bigcup_{i=1}^{t} Cv_i$, whence $M = CK$, proving (iii).

Assume finally that u is a strongly real element of C^* and set $H = C_G^*(u)$. If u is an involution, then $H = C_G(u) \subseteq M$ by condition (a). Hence in proving (iv), we may assume that u is not an involution, in which case H contains an involution y not in $C_G(u)$. On the other hand, $x \in C_G(u)$, whence x and y are not conjugate in H. Hence they are not conjugate in the subgroup $\langle x, y \rangle$ of H and consequently there exists an involution z in $\langle x, y \rangle$ which commutes with both x and y. We conclude at once that $y \in M$. The same argument shows that $y^a \in M$ for any element a of H. But M has only one conjugate class of involutions by (ii), whence $y^a = y^b$ for some b in M. Therefore $ab^{-1} \in C_G(y) \subseteq M$ and it follows that $a = (ab^{-1})b \in M$. Thus $H \subseteq M$ and (iv) is proved.

It will be convenient to say that a subgroup M of G of even order which satisfies the hypotheses of Theorem 2.1 is *strongly embedded* in G.

Theorem 2.2

Let M be a strongly embedded subgroup of G, let x be an involution of M, and set $C = C_G(x)$. Then G satisfies the following conditions:

(i) *Every coset of C in G, not in M, contains exactly one involution.*

(ii) *If H is a subgroup of M containing C such that $C_G^*(u) \subseteq M$ for any strongly real element u of $H^\#$, then $H = C$.*

(iii) *If H is a subgroup of M containing C such that $C_G(u) \subseteq H$ for every strongly real element of $H^\#$, then either $H = C$ or*

$$|G:H| \leqslant |M:H| + |C|.$$

Proof

As in the proof of Theorem 2.1(iii), let $m = |M:C|$ and $r = |G:M|$, so that m and mr are the number of involutions of M and G, respectively.

Since the number of cosets of C in G, not contained in M, is exactly $mr - r$, which is also the number of involutions of $G - M$, (i) will follow if we can show that no coset Cu of C in G with $u \in G - M$ contains more than one involution. But if y_1, y_2 were two involutions of Cu, then $y_1 \notin M$, $y_1 y_2 = v \in C$, and y_1 inverts v. Then v is strongly real and consequently $y_1 \in C_G^*(v) \subseteq M$ by Theorem 2.1(iv), a contradiction. Thus (i) holds.

Now let $C \subseteq H \subseteq M$ satisfy (ii). Then the identical argument shows that any coset Hu of H is G with u in $G - M$ contains at most one involution. Hence if $h = |M : H|$, the number of involutions in G, not in M, is at most $hr - h$, whence

(2.1) $$mr \leqslant m + hr - h.$$

Equivalently, we have

(2.2) $$0 \leqslant (h - m)(r - 1).$$

But $M \subset G$ by condition (c) and so $r > 1$, whence $h \geqslant m$ by (2.2). However, $h \leqslant m$ since $C \subseteq H \subseteq M$, $h = |M : H|$, and $m = |M : C|$. Thus $h = m$ and $C = H$, proving (ii).

Next assume H satisfies (iii). Set $k = |H : C|$. Now each coset Hu of H in G is a union of k cosets of C in G. Hence if $u \in G - M$, it follows from (i) that Hu contains exactly k involutions y_i, $1 \leqslant i \leqslant k$. If Hv is another coset of H in G with $v \in G - M$, then also Hv contains exactly k involutions z_i, $1 \leqslant i \leqslant k$. Set $a_i = y_1 y_i$ and $b_i = z_1 z_i$, $2 \leqslant i \leqslant k$. We claim that $a_i \neq b_j$ if $i \neq j$. Indeed, if $a_i = b_j$, then a_i is inverted by both y_1 and z_1. In particular, a_i is a strongly real element of $H^\#$ and consequently $C_G(a_i) \subseteq H$ by the hypothesis of (iii). But $y_1 z_1$ centralizes a_i since y_1 and z_1 each invert it, whence $y_1 z_1 \in H$ and so $H y_1 = H z_1$, contrary to the fact that $H y_1 = Hu$ and $H z_1 = Hv$ are distinct cosets of H.

Thus each coset of H in $G - M$ determines $k - 1$ elements of $H^\#$ and all elements determined in this manner are distinct. In fact, these elements actually lie in $H - C$; for y_1 inverts a_i and if any $a_i \in C$, the argument of the first paragraph of the proof shows that $y_1 \in M$. But then $u \in H y_1 \subseteq M$, which is not the case. We conclude that

(2.3) $$|H| - |C| \geqslant (k - 1)(|G : H| - |M : H|).$$

Since $|H| = k|C|$, (2.3) yields

(2.4) $$0 \geqslant (k - 1)(|G : H| - |M : H| - |C|).$$

If $k = 1$, then $H = C$ and the first alternative of (iii) holds. On the other hand, if $k > 1$, then we must have $|G : H| \leqslant |M : H| + |C|$, and the second alternative of (iii) holds. The theorem is proved.

3. TWO APPLICATIONS

Since the statement of Theorem 2.2 is rather involved, we should like to clarify it now by giving two illustrations of how it is used in classification problems. As we shall see, part (ii) of the theorem applies in the "odd characteristic" case, while part (iii) applies in the "characteristic 2" case.

Our first result shows how to relate the Maximal Subgroup theorem and strongly embedded subgroups.

Theorem 3.1

Let G be a group which satisfies the uniqueness condition for the odd prime p and let M be a uniqueness subgroup for p. If M is strongly embedded in G, then one of the following holds:

(i) *An S_2-subgroup of G is cyclic or generalized quaternion.*

(ii) *$C_G(Z(O_p(M)))$ contains every involution of M.*

Proof

Let S be an S_2-subgroup of M, let x be an involution of S, and let $M \in N(P)$, P an S_p-subgroup of G. We shall establish (ii) under the assumption that S is not generalized quaternion or cyclic. Then by Theorem 5.4.10(ii), x is not the only involution of S. If $x \in Z(S)$, it centralizes every involution of S, while if $x \notin Z(S)$, it centralizes every involution of $Z(S)$, so in either case there exists a four subgroup T of S with $x \in T$.

Set $C = C_G(x)$, so that $C \subseteq M$ as M is strongly embedded in G. Assume by way of contradiction that (ii) is false. Since M has only one class of involutions, x does not centralize $Z(O_p(M))$ and consequently does not centralize $Z = \Omega_1(Z(O_p(M)))$ by Theorem 5.2.4, whence $Z \nsubseteq C$. Since $Z \lhd M$, $H = CZ$ is a group and $H \supset C$. We shall argue now that for any strongly real element u of $H^\#$, $C_G^*(u) \subseteq M$, which will contradict Theorem 2.2(ii) and thus establish the theorem. Since $C_G^*(u) \subseteq C_G^*(u^i)$ and u^i is strongly real for all i, it will suffice to prove the assertion when u has prime order q.

If $q \neq p$, then C contains an S_q-subgroup of H, whence $v = u^z \in C$ for some z in Z. Since v is also strongly real of order q, $C_G^*(v) \subseteq M$ by Theorem 2.1(iv). Since $z \in M$, $C_G^*(u) = C_G^*(v)^{z^{-1}} \subseteq M$.

Now assume that $q = p$. We can suppose without loss that $P \cap C$ is an S_p-subgroup of C. Then u is conjugate to an element v of $P \cap H = (P \cap C)Z$ and, as in the preceding paragraph, it will suffice to show that $C_G^*(v) \subseteq M$. We shall prove that $C_{P \cap H}(v)$ contains an abelian subgroup of type (p, p, p).

Since G satisfies the uniqueness condition for p, Lemma 8.6.1 will then yield that $C_G^*(v) \subseteq M$.

We first argue that $m(Z) \geqslant 3$. Indeed, let $x = x_1, x_2, x_3$ be the three involutions of T and set $Z_i = C_Z(x_i)$, $1 \leqslant i \leqslant 3$. Since $M \in N(P)$, $O_p(M) \neq 1$ and so $Z \neq 1$. Furthermore, since $Z \lhd M$ and M has only one class of involutions, Z_1, Z_2, Z_3 are all conjugate in M, whence $|Z_1| = |Z_2| = |Z_3|$. On the other hand, $Z = Z_1 Z_2 Z_3$ by Theorem 5.3.16 and consequently each $Z_i \neq 1$. Since $Z \nsubseteq C$, $Z_1 \subset Z$. Therefore, if $|Z_1| \geqslant p^2$, then $|Z| \geqslant p^3$ and hence $m(Z) \geqslant 3$. On the other hand, if $|Z_i| = p$, then x_i does not centralize Z_j for $i \neq j$, $1 \leqslant i, j \leqslant 3$, and consequently $Z = Z_1 \times Z_2 \times Z_3$, so that $m(Z) \geqslant 3$ in this case as well.

But now if $v \in Z$, then $C_{P \cap H}(v)$ contains Z and so contains an abelian subgroup of type (p, p, p), as required. Suppose then that $v \notin Z$. Since $P \cap H = (P \cap C)Z$, we can write $v = wz$, $w \in P \cap C$ and $z \in Z$. Now $C_Z(v) = C_Z(w)$, as Z is abelian. Since v is of order p and $v \notin Z$, $\langle v, C_Z(v) \rangle$ will thus contain an abelian subgroup of type (p, p, p) provided $|C_Z(w)| \geqslant p^2$. But $Z = Z_1 \times Z_0$, where Z_0 is inverted by x_1 by Theorem 5.2.3 and $Z_0 \neq 1$. Since w centralizes x_1, it leaves both Z_0 and Z_1 invariant, whence $C_{Z_j}(w) \neq 1$, $0 \leqslant j \leqslant 1$, and so $|C_Z(w)| \geqslant p^2$. This completes the proof of the theorem.

Remark   For most applications, one needs a stronger conclusion than (ii); namely, that $C_G(O_p(M))$ contains every involution of M. To prove this, one takes Z to be $\Omega_1(D)$, where D is a critical subgroup of $O_p(M)$ and reduces the problem by the same argument to showing that $C_{P \cap H}(v)$ contains an abelian subgroup of type (p, p, p), where v is of order p in $P \cap H$. If Z is abelian, the preceding proof applies without change. However if Z is of class 2, the argument is in general more subtle. For the particular case of groups with dihedral Sylow 2-subgroups that we shall analyze in Chapter 15, the present form of Theorem 3.1 will suffice.

Our second result which is an important result of Suzuki, utilizes Theorem 2.2(i) and (iii).

Theorem 3.2 (Suzuki)

Let K be a nilpotent subgroup of G of even order such that $C_G^*(u) \subseteq K$ for every element $u \neq 1$ of K. Then one of the following holds:

(i) *An S_2-subgroup of G is cyclic or generalized quaternion.*

(ii) *$\Omega_1(O_2(K)) \lhd G$.*

(iii) *Under the permutation representation of G on the right cosets of $N_G(K)$, G is a Zassenhaus group of degree $|K| + 1$.*

We first establish a preliminary lemma:

Lemma 3.3

If G does not satisfy conditions (i) *or* (ii) *of the theorem, then we have the following:*

    (i) K *is a Hall subgroup of* G.
    (ii) $M = N_G(O_2(K))$ *is strongly embedded in* G.
    (iii) $C_G(u) \subseteq M$ *for any element u of* $M^\#$.
    (iv) *For any x in G, either* $K^x \cap M = 1$ *or* $K^x = K$.

Proof

We may assume that G does not satisfy conditions (i) or (ii) of Theorem 3.2. Let P be an S_p-subgroup of G such that $P \cap K$ is an S_p-subgroup of K, $p \in \pi(K)$. If $u \in (P \cap K)^\#$, then $Z(P) \subseteq C_G(u) \subseteq K$ by our hypothesis. Hence if $v \in Z(P)^\#$, $P \subseteq C_G(v) \subseteq K$ for the same reason. Thus K is a Hall subgroup of G. In particular, (i) holds. Furthermore, an S_2-subgroup S of K is an S_2-subgroup of M and so all involutions of M lie in S. But then $C_G(u) \subseteq K \subseteq M$ for any involution u of M. By its definition, $M = N_G(S)$. Moreover, if all involutions of G were contained in M, they would lie in $\Omega_1(S)$ and it would follow that $\Omega_1(S) \vartriangleleft G$, contrary to assumption. Thus $G - M$ contains an involution. We conclude that M satisfies all the conditions in the definition of a strongly embedded subgroup, proving (ii).

By Theorem 2.1(ii), M has only one class of involutions and so any involution x of M lies in $Z(S)$, whence $K = C_G(x)$. But now Theorem 2.2(i) yields that every coset of K in $G - M$ contains exactly one involution. We shall use this fact to establish (iii). Indeed, suppose $u \in M^\#$ and $v \in C_G(u)$ with $v \notin M$. Let x be the unique involution of Kv, so that $v = yx$, $y \in K$. Since $uv = vu$, we have $uyx = yxu$, whence

$$(3.1) \qquad\qquad y^{-1}uy = xux^{-1} = xux.$$

Premultiplying by u^{-1}, we obtain

$$(3.2) \qquad\qquad [u, y] = u^{-1}xux.$$

But $K \vartriangleleft M$ since $K = C_G(Z(S))$ and $Z(S) \vartriangleleft M$. Since $u \in M$ and $y \in K$, it follows that $[u, y] \in K$. Thus $z = u^{-1}xux \in K$. On the other hand, z is the product of the two involutions $u^{-1}xu$ and x and so $x \in C_G^*(z)$. Hence if $z \neq 1$, $x \in M$ by our hypothesis on K, a contradiction. However, if $z = 1$, then u centralizes x. But $x \in S^w$ for some w in G, whence $u \in C_G(x) \subseteq K^w$. Then u is a π-element, where $\pi = \pi(K)$. Since K is a normal S_π-subgroup of M, it follows that $u \in K$, whence $C_G(u) \subseteq M$ by hypothesis and (iii) is proved.

Suppose finally that $K^x \cap M \neq 1$. Then $K^x \cap M = K^x \cap K$, as K is a normal S_π-subgroup of M. But if $y \in K^x \cap K$, $y \neq 1$, then $C = C_G(y) \subseteq K$ and C contains both Z and Z^x, where $Z = \Omega_1(Z(S))$. Since K is nilpotent, so is C. But Z contains all involutions of K and therefore $Z = Z^x$. Thus $x \in N_G(Z)$. Since $K = C_G(Z)$, $K \lhd N_G(Z)$ and so x normalizes K, whence $K^x = K$, proving (iv).

With these results at our disposal, we can now establish Theorem 3.2. We assume (i) and (ii) are false and verify condition (iii) of the theorem. First of all, by the preceding lemma an S_2-subgroup S of K is an S_2-subgroup of G and all involutions of S are conjugate in M, whence $\Omega_1(Z(S))$ contains all involutions u of M. Furthermore, the lemma shows that $C_G(u) \subseteq M$ for every strongly real element u of $M^\#$. This means that the hypotheses of Theorem 2.2(iii) are satisfied with K in the role of C and M in the role of H. Since $|M : H| = |M : M| = 1$ in the present case, we conclude that either

$$(3.3) \qquad\qquad M = K \qquad \text{or} \qquad |G : M| \leqslant |K| + 1.$$

If $M = K$, any involution of $Z(S)$ is conjugate only to itself in M and consequently S possesses a unique involution. But then S is either cyclic or generalized quaternion by Theorem 5.4.10(ii), contrary to our present assumption. Thus $|G : M| \leqslant |K| + 1$.

We shall prove next that equality holds. Since $\Omega_1(O_2(K))$ is not normal in G, but is characteristic in K, it follows that K is not normal in G. Hence $K^x \neq K$ for some x in G. But then $K^x \cap M = 1$ by Lemma 3.2(iv), whence $|G : M| \geqslant |K^x| = |K|$. Hence by (3.3), $|G : M| = |K| + 1$ or $|K|$. However, since $M \supseteq K \supseteq S$ and S is an S_2-subgroup of G, we have $|G : M|$ odd and $|K|$ even. We conclude at once that

$$(3.4) \qquad\qquad\qquad |G : M| = |K| + 1.$$

Set $m = |G : M|$ and consider the permutation representation of G on the m cosets $M = Mx_1, Mx_2, \ldots, Mx_m$ of M in G. By Theorem 2.7.3(i), this representation will be doubly transitive if M acts transitively on the cosets $Mx_i, 2 \leqslant i \leqslant m$. Since $|K| = m - 1$, either the elements of K transform Mx_2 successively into $Mx_i, 2 \leqslant i \leqslant m$, in which case M acts transitively on these cosets, or else two distinct elements of K transform Mx_2 into the same coset. However, in the latter case, $Mx_2 y = Mx_2$ for some y in $K^\#$, whence $y^{x_2^{-1}} \in K^{x_2^{-1}} \cap M$. But then $K^{x_2} = K$ by Lemma 3.3(iv) and so $x_2 \in M = N_G(K)$, which is not the case. Thus the representation of G is doubly transitive.

Now for x in G, let $\alpha(x)$ denote the number of cosets of M fixed by x. To show that G is a Zassenhaus group, we must prove that $\alpha(x) \leqslant 2$ if $x \neq 1$. Suppose $x \in G^\#$ and $\alpha(x) > 0$. Then x fixes a coset of M, so a conjugate of x fixes M. Since α takes the same value on all elements of a conjugate class, it will suffice to determine $\alpha(x)$ for $x \in M$. Consider M as a transitive permutation group of the $m - 1$ cosets of M in $G - M$ and let L be the subgroup of M fixing one of these cosets. Then $|M : L| = m - 1 = |K|$. On the other hand, no element of K fixes any of these cosets as we have shown in the preceding paragraph. Hence $L \cap K = 1$ and $M = KL$. Since $C_K(u) \subseteq K$ for all u in $K^\#$, it follows that L induces a regular group of automorphisms of K and therefore that M is a Frobenius group with kernel K and complement L. Thus every element x of M lies either in K or in a conjugate of L and in the latter case x fixes some coset of M in $G - M$. We conclude that

(3.5)
$$\begin{aligned} \alpha(1) &= m \\ \alpha(x) &= 1 \quad \text{if } x \text{ lies in a conjugate of } K^\# \\ \alpha(x) &\geqslant 2 \quad \text{if } x \text{ lies in a conjugate of } M - K \\ \alpha(x) &= 0 \quad \text{if } x \text{ does not lie in a conjugate of } M. \end{aligned}$$

Since K is disjoint from its conjugates, the conjugates of $K^\#$ contain precisely

(3.6) $(|K| - 1)|G : M| = (m - 2)m$

distinct elements [using (3.4)]. Hence if X denotes the set of those elements of G for which $\alpha(x) \geqslant 2$, it follows now from parts (i) and (ii) of Theorem 2.7.4 that

(3.7) $$m + (m - 2)m + \sum_{x \in X} \alpha(x) = |G|$$

(3.8) $$m^2 + (m - 2)m + \sum_{x \in X} \alpha(x)^2 = 2|G|$$

Multiplying (3.7) by 2 and subtracting from (3.8), we obtain

(3.9) $$\sum_{x \in X} \alpha(x)^2 - 2\alpha(x) = \sum_{x \in X} \alpha(x)(\alpha(x) - 2) = 0.$$

Since $\alpha(x) \geqslant 2$ for all x in X, (3.9) yields $\alpha(x) = 2$ for all x in X, whence $\alpha(x) \leqslant 2$ for all x in $G^\#$. Thus G is a Zassenhaus group of degree $m = |K| + 1$ and the theorem is proved.

Although we shall not present any applications of Theorem 2.1(iii), that result also has important uses in the study of simple groups.

4. GROUP ORDER FORMULAS

In Section 1 we obtained estimates for the order of a group G of even order using only elementary considerations. There exists an important method, due to Brauer, in which a knowledge of the characters of G can be used to give much more explicit expressions for $|G|$. The method depends upon a particular case of Theorem 4.2.12.

Let G be a group of even order, K a conjugate class of involutions, K' an arbitrary conjugate class, and x, y representatives of K, K', respectively. We write $\beta_K(y)$ for the number of ordered pairs of elements of K whose product is y. Thus $\beta_K(y)$ is precisely the integer λ_{ijk} of Theorem 4.2.12 with $K_i = K_j = K$ and $K_k = K'$. Moreover, if G has only one class of involutions, then all involutions of G lie in K and, in this case

$$(4.1) \qquad\qquad \beta_K(y) = \beta(y),$$

where $\beta(y)$ is the function considered in Lemma 1.5 above.

Now $|K| = |G : C_G(x)|$. Hence if χ_i, $1 \leqslant i \leqslant r$, denote the irreducible characters of G, Theorem 4.2.12 yields

$$(4.2) \qquad\qquad \beta_K(y) = \frac{|G|}{|C_G(x)|^2} \sum_{i=1}^{r} \frac{\chi_i(x)^2 \overline{\chi_i(y)}}{\deg \chi_i}.$$

Since $\chi_i(x)$ must be a sum of square roots of unity, it is an ordinary integer. Thus the function β_K from G to F is, in fact, a linear combination of the irreducible characters of G with rational coefficients.

If $\beta_K(y) \neq 0$, (4.2) gives an exact formula for $|G|$ in terms of $\beta_K(y)$, $|C_G(x)|$, and the values of the characters on the elements 1, x, and y. Approximate information concerning these various quantities will give an approximate expression for $|G|$. The important point about (4.2) is that $\beta_K(y)$ can often be evaluated from the subgroup structure of G, independently of a knowledge of the characters. This is especially true when $\beta_K(y) = \beta(y)$, in which case Lemma 1.5 shows that $\beta_K(y)$ is completely determined by the structure of $C_G(y)$.

Even when $\beta_K(y) = 0$ and, in particular, when y is not strongly real, (4.2) is useful. Although it does not then provide an expression for $|G|$, it nevertheless gives a relation between the values of the characters of G which can be exploited. We shall use (4.2) in this way in Chapters 12 in our analysis of groups with generalized quaternion Sylow 2-subgroups.

This method has been refined by Brauer and Suzuki with the aid of modular character theory, so that instead of requiring the values of all characters on the elements 1, x, and y, only the values of those characters belonging to particular 2-blocks are needed.

We shall now illustrate the method in a special case. The particular situation we intend to discuss arises in the course of the study of groups with a self-centralizing Sylow 2-subgroup of order 4, a complete classification of which will be given in Chapter 15. The group order formula and the values of the irreducible characters which we shall here derive represent a basic step in this classification. All the results we obtain appear in a joint paper of Brauer, Suzuki, and Wall.

We should like also to remark that the somewhat delicate arithmetic analysis that will be required at various points below is typical of this method.

We consider then a simple group G with an elementary abelian Sylow 2-subgroup of order 4 which contains a subgroup K of order $2n$, n odd, $n > 1$, that is disjoint from its conjugates and is such that $N = N_G(K)$ is the direct product of a group of order 2 and a Frobenius group with kernel U of order n and complement H of order 2. We preserve this notation throughout.

The analysis divides into three parts:

1. Using the theory of exceptional characters, determine the values of the irreducible characters of G on the elements of $K^\#$ and at the same time estimates for their degrees.

2. Using a count of the involutions of G together with Theorem 4.2.1(i), determine the exact degrees of the irreducible characters.

3. Use formula (4.2) to obtain an expression for $|G|$.

We have $N = (UH) \times T = KH$, where $T = \langle x_1 \rangle$ and $H = \langle x_2 \rangle$ are of order 2. By assumption, HT is an S_2-subgroup of G and, as G is simple, the three involutions x_1, x_2, and $x_1 x_2$ of HT are conjugate in G.

We again denote by $I(K)$ the module of characters of N induced by the nonprincipal irreducible characters of K. Since $|U|$ is odd, we can write the irreducible characters of U in the form ϕ_i, $\bar{\phi}_i$, where $\bar{\phi}_i = \phi_{i+(n-1/2)}$, $1 \leq i \leq n - 1/2$. We extend the definition of ϕ_i to K by defining ϕ_i to be trivial on T. Then by Theorem 4.5.3, the characters $\zeta_i = \tilde{\phi}_i$ induced on N by ϕ_i are distinct irreducible characters of N with support on K and $\zeta_i|_K = \phi_i + \bar{\phi}_i$, $1 \leq i \leq (n - 1/2)$. Moreover, $\bar{\phi}_i$ also induces ζ_i.

We next let η be the character of T taking the value -1 on x_1 and extend η to be trivial on UH. Then by Theorem 3.7.1, $\eta\zeta_i$ is an irreducible character of N for each i. One verifies directly that $\eta\zeta_i$ is induced from either of the characters $\eta\phi_i$ or $\eta\bar{\phi}_i$ and that $\eta\zeta_i|_K = \eta\phi_i + \eta\bar{\phi}_i, 1 \leqslant i \leqslant (n - 1/2)$. In particular, it follows that the $\eta\zeta_i$ are distinct from each other and from each ζ_j. We set $\zeta_{i+(n-1/2)} = \eta\zeta_i, 1 \leqslant i \leqslant (n - 1)/2$. We note that each ζ_i has degree 2, $1 \leqslant i \leqslant n - 1$.

Since K is abelian of order $2n$, it has $2n - 1$ nonprincipal characters, which are, in fact, the characters $\phi_i, \eta\bar{\phi}_i, 1 \leqslant i \leqslant n - 1$, and η. To determine $I(K)$, it thus remains to consider $\theta = \tilde{\eta}$. By Theorem 4.4.3(iii), θ is a character of N having U in its kernel. Since N/U is elementary abelian of type (2, 2), θ must therefore be the sum of two linear characters of N having U in their kernels. We shall denote these by α_3 and α_4 and shall also let α_1, α_2 be the remaining two characters of N having U in their kernels. Now a direct computation shows that $\theta(x_1) = -2$. Hence $\alpha_3(x_1) = \alpha_4(x_1) = -1$, so that, in particular, neither α_3 nor α_4 is the principal character of N. We choose the notation so that $\alpha_1 = 1_N$. Furthermore, since θ is 0 on $N - K$, we can order α_3, α_4 so that

$$(4.3) \qquad \begin{array}{lll} \alpha_3(x_1) = -1, \alpha_3(x_2) = -1, & \alpha_3(x_1 x_2) = +1 \\ \alpha_4(x_1) = -1, \alpha_4(x_2) = +1, & \alpha_4(x_1 x_2) = -1. \end{array}$$

In particular, we have proved

Lemma 4.1

The characters $\zeta_i, 1 \leqslant i \leqslant n - 1$, and θ form a basis of $I(K)$.

Here then we encounter a situation in which $I(K)$ does not possess a basis of irreducible characters. However, in the present case it will not be difficult to show that the induction map form $I_0(K)$ into $\mathrm{ch}_0(G)$ extends to an isometry of $I(K)$ into $\mathrm{ch}(G)$. Indeed, we have

Lemma 4.2

There exist distinct nonprincipal irreducible characters $\chi_i, 1 \leqslant i \leqslant n - 1$, and $\psi_j, 3 \leqslant j \leqslant 4$, and signs $\varepsilon = \pm 1, \delta_j = \pm 1, 3 \leqslant j \leqslant 4$, such that

$$(\zeta_i - \zeta_j)^* = \varepsilon(\chi_i - \chi_j) \qquad 1 \leqslant i, j \leqslant n - 1$$

$$(\zeta_i - \theta)^* = \varepsilon\chi_i - \delta_3\psi_3 - \delta_4\psi_4 \qquad 1 \leqslant i \leqslant n - 1.$$

Proof

Since $|U| = n$ is odd and $n > 1$, we have $n - 1 \geqslant 2$. Now

$$(\zeta_i^* - \zeta_j^*, \zeta_h^* - \zeta_k^*)_G = \delta_{ih} - \delta_{jh} - \delta_{ik} + \delta_{jk}$$

as in the derivation of equation (4.5.16). Hence by Theorem 4.5.4 there exist irreducible characters χ_i of G, $1 \leqslant i \leqslant n - 1$, and a sign $\varepsilon = \pm 1$ such that the first set of relations of the lemma holds. Moreover, by the Frobenius reciprocity theorem, $(\zeta_i^* - \zeta_j^*, 1_G)_G = (\zeta_i - \zeta_j, 1_N)_N = 0$, so each χ_j is nonprincipal. Hence it remains to treat the second set of relations.

Now $(\zeta_i - \theta, \zeta_i - \theta)_N = (\zeta_i, \zeta_i)_N + (\alpha_3, \alpha_3)_N + (\alpha_4, \alpha_4)_N = 3$. Since induction is an isometry on $I_0(K)$ by Theorem 4.4.6, also $(\zeta_i^* - \theta^*, \zeta_i^* - \theta^*)_G = 3$. Hence each $(\zeta_i - \theta)^*$ must be a sum of three distinct characters of norm 1. On the other hand,

(4.4) $(\zeta_i - \theta)^* - (\zeta_j - \theta)^* = (\zeta_i - \zeta_j)^* = \varepsilon\chi_i - \varepsilon\chi_j.$

This means that two of the characters appearing in $(\zeta_i - \theta)^*$ are the same as two appearing in $(\zeta_j - \theta)^*$ and that the remaining character is either $\varepsilon\chi_i$ or $-\varepsilon\chi_j$.

Consider first the case that $\varepsilon\chi_i$ appears in $(\zeta_i - \theta)^*$ for some i, say $i = 1$. Then we have

(4.5) $(\zeta_1 - \theta)^* = \varepsilon\chi_1 - \delta_3\psi_3 - \delta_4\psi_4$

for suitable irreducible characters ψ_j of G and signs $\delta_j = \pm 1, 3 \leqslant j \leqslant 4$. Moreover, since the χ_i are all of the same degree, $-\varepsilon\chi_j$ cannot appear in (4.5) for any j, for then the right side would not be of degree 0. But if $\varepsilon\chi_1$ appears in $(\zeta_j - \theta)^*$ for $j > 1$, the discussion of the preceding paragraph together with (4.4) would force $-\varepsilon\chi_j$ to appear in $(\zeta_1 - \theta)^*$. Hence $-\delta_3\psi_3$ and $-\delta_4\psi_4$ must appear in each $(\zeta_j - \theta)^*$ and we conclude from (4.4) that

(4.6) $(\zeta_j - \theta)^* = \varepsilon\chi_j - \delta_3\psi_3 - \delta_4\psi_4.$

In particular, the three characters χ_j, ψ_3, and ψ_4 are distinct. Furthermore, another application of the Frobenius reciprocity theorem shows that ψ_3 and ψ_4 are nonprincipal. Hence the lemma follows in this case.

On the other hand, if $\varepsilon\chi_1$ does not appear in $(\zeta_1 - \theta)^*$, our discussion shows that $-\varepsilon\chi_j$ must appear in it for each $j > 1$. Since n is odd and $(\zeta_1 - \theta)^*$ is a sum of three characters of norm 1, we must have $n = 3$ or 5. However, in the latter case $(\zeta_1 - \theta)^* = -\varepsilon(\chi_2 + \chi_3 + \chi_4)$ and so does not have degree 0, a contradiction. Thus $n = 3$. But in this case, ε is not uniquely determined since $n - 1 = 2$. In fact, we can replace ε by $-\varepsilon$ and interchange χ_1, χ_2. When we do this, the new $\varepsilon\chi_1$ does appear in $(\zeta_1 - \theta)^*$ and the proof is complete.

Because of Lemma 4.2, the mapping

(4.7) $\zeta_i^\tau = \varepsilon\chi_i \quad 1 \leqslant i \leqslant n - 1$ and $\alpha_j^\tau = \delta_j\psi_j \quad 3 \leqslant j \leqslant 4,$

is an isometry of $I(K)$ into ch (G) which extends the induction map of

$I_0(K)$ into ch_0 (G). With this information we can obtain results analogous to those of Theorem 4.6.6 in the Frobenius case and thereby obtain preliminary estimates for the values of the characters of G on $K^\#$. However, it will be simpler to show first that the isometry of the induction map can be extended to the larger module $\langle I(K), 1_N, \tilde{I}_K \rangle$, where $\tilde{I}_K = \rho_{N/K}$ is the character of the regular representation of N/K.

In the present case, $\tilde{I}_K = \alpha_1 + \alpha_2 + \alpha_3 + \alpha_4$ and, in particular, $\deg \tilde{I}_K = 4$. We now prove

Lemma 4.3

There exists a nonprincipal irreducible character ψ_2 of G distinct from χ_i, ψ_3, and ψ_4 and a sign $\delta_2 = \pm 1$ such that

$$(\tilde{I}_K - \theta - \zeta_i)^* = 1_G + \delta_2\psi_2 - \varepsilon\chi_i \qquad 1 \leqslant i \leqslant n - 1.$$

Proof

We have $\tilde{I}_K - \theta = (\alpha_1 + \alpha_2 + \alpha_3 + \alpha_4) - (\alpha_3 + \alpha_4) = \alpha_1 + \alpha_2$ and consequently $(\gamma_i, \gamma_i)_N = 3$, where $\gamma_i = \tilde{I}_K - \theta - \zeta_i$. Since γ_i is of degree 0, Theorem 4.4.6 implies that γ_i^* is a sum of three distinct characters of norm 1. Since $\gamma_i = 1_N + \alpha_2 - \zeta_i$, it follows from the Frobenius reciprocity theorem that

$$(\gamma_i^*, 1_G)_G = (\gamma_i, 1_N)_N = 1;$$

so 1_G is a constituent of γ_i^* of multiplicity 1.

Since $(\gamma_i - \gamma_j)^* = (\zeta_j - \zeta_i)^* = \varepsilon\chi_j - \varepsilon\chi_i$, two of the characters in γ_i^* are the same as two appearing in γ_j^* and the remaining character is either $-\varepsilon\chi_i$ or $\varepsilon\chi_j$. But now reasoning in the same manner as in the preceding lemma, we conclude easily that this character must be $-\varepsilon\chi_i$ and that there is an irreducible character ψ_2 of G and a sign $\delta_2 = \pm 1$ such that

(4.8) $\gamma_i^* = 1_G + \delta_2\psi_2 - \varepsilon\chi_i \qquad 1 \leqslant i \leqslant n - 1.$

In particular, it follows that ψ_2 is distinct from 1_G and $\chi_i, 1 \leqslant i \leqslant n - 1$.

Finally, we have

(4.9) $\gamma_i^* + (\zeta_i - \theta)^* = 1_G + \delta_2\psi_2 - \delta_3\psi_3 - \delta_4\psi_4.$

But $\gamma_i + (\zeta_i - \theta) = \tilde{I}_K - 2\theta = \alpha_1 + \alpha_2 - \alpha_3 - \alpha_4$. Since $\psi_j \neq 1_G, 2 \leqslant j \leqslant 4$, it follows that $\gamma_i^* + (\zeta_i - \theta)^*$ must be a sum of four distinct characters of norm 1. Hence $\psi_2 \neq \psi_3$ or ψ_4 and the lemma is proved.

We now extend the definition of ζ to $I'(K) = \langle I(K), 1_N, \tilde{I}_K \rangle$ by setting $\psi_1 = 1_G$ and defining

(4.10) $\alpha_1^\zeta = \psi_1 \qquad \text{and} \qquad \alpha_2^\zeta = \delta_2\psi_2.$

If $I_0'(K) = I'(K) \cap \mathrm{ch}_0(N)$, we conclude therefore from Lemmas 4.2 and 4.3 that the mapping τ of $I'(K)$ into $\mathrm{ch}(G)$ given by (4.7) and (4.10) extends the isometry of the induction map of $I_0'(K)$ into $\mathrm{ch}_0(G)$.

We now have sufficient information to determine the values of all the irreducible characters of G on $K^\#$. We denote the remaining irreducible characters of G (if any) by ψ_j, $5 \leqslant j \leqslant s$. We then have

Theorem 4.4
The irreducible characters of G have the following values on $K^\#$:

(i) $\qquad \chi_i(y) = \varepsilon(\phi_i(y) + \overline{\phi_i(y)}) \qquad\qquad y \in K^\#, \quad 1 \leqslant i \leqslant n - 1/2$

$\qquad \chi_{i+(n-1/2)}(y) = \varepsilon\eta(y)(\phi_i(y) + \overline{\phi_i(y)}) \qquad y \in K^\#, \quad 1 \leqslant i \leqslant n - 1/2$

(ii) $\qquad \psi_2(y) = \delta_2 \qquad\qquad\qquad\qquad\qquad y \in K^\#$

$\qquad \psi_j(y) = \begin{cases} \delta_j \\ -\delta_j \end{cases} \qquad\qquad\qquad \begin{array}{l} y \in U^\#, \quad 3 \leqslant j \leqslant 4 \\ y \in K - U, 3 \leqslant j \leqslant 4 \end{array}$

$\qquad \psi_j(y) = 0 \qquad\qquad\qquad\qquad\qquad y \in K^\#, \quad 5 \leqslant j \leqslant s.$

Proof
We can write

$$(4.11) \qquad \zeta_i^\tau|_N = \sum_{j=1}^{n-1} a_{ij}\zeta_j + \pi_i \qquad 1 \leqslant i \leqslant n - 1,$$

where the a_{ij} are nonnegative integers and π_i is a character of N having U in its kernel. But now the first calculation of Theorem 4.6.6 can be repeated verbatim. In the present case $|N:K| = 2$ and ζ_i, $1 \leqslant i \leqslant n - 1$, are all the irreducible characters of N not having U in their kernels. Hence setting $h_i = \frac{1}{2}(a_{i1} - \delta_{i1})$, we obtain

$$(4.12) \qquad \zeta_i^\tau|_N = \zeta_i + h_i(\rho_N - \rho_{N/U}) + \pi_i \qquad 1 \leqslant i \leqslant n - 1.$$

We now determine π_i. We can write

$$(4.13) \qquad \pi_i = b_{i1}\alpha_1 + b_{i2}\alpha_2 + b_{i3}\alpha_3 + b_{i4}\alpha_4.$$

By the Frobenius reciprocity theorem and the definition of τ, we obtain

$$(4.14) \qquad a_{i1} - b_{i3} - b_{i4} = (\zeta_i^\tau|_N, \zeta_1 - \alpha_3 - \alpha_4)_N$$
$$= (\zeta_i^\tau, \zeta_1^\tau - \alpha_3^\tau - \alpha_4^\tau)_G = \delta_{i1}$$

$$(4.15) \qquad a_{i1} - b_{i1} - b_{i2} = (\zeta_i^\tau|_N, \zeta_1 - \alpha_1 - \alpha_2)_N$$
$$= (\zeta_i^\tau, \zeta_1^\tau - \alpha_1^\tau - \alpha_2^\tau)_G = \delta_{i1}.$$

Thus

(4.16) $$2h_i = b_{i1} + b_{i2} = b_{i3} + b_{i4}.$$

We next evaluate ζ_i^τ on the three involutions x_1, x_2, and $x_1 x_2$, getting

(4.17) $$\zeta_i^\tau(x_1) = \zeta_i(x_1) + h_i \cdot 0 + b_{i1} + b_{i2} - b_{i3} - b_{i4} = \zeta_i(x_1)$$
$$\zeta_i^\tau(x_2) = b_{i1} - b_{i2} - b_{i3} + b_{i4}$$
$$\zeta_i^\tau(x_1 x_2) = b_{i1} - b_{i2} + b_{i3} - b_{i4}.$$

But $\zeta_i^\tau(x_1) = \zeta_i^\tau(x_2) = \zeta_i^\tau(x_1 x_2)$ since G has only one class of involutions. We conclude therefore from (4.16) and (4.17) that

(4.18) $$b_{i1} = h_i + \tfrac{1}{2}\zeta_i(x_1) \qquad b_{i2} = h_i - \tfrac{1}{2}\zeta_i(x_1) \qquad b_{i3} = b_{i4} = h_i.$$

Since $\rho_{N/U} = \alpha_1 + \alpha_2 + \alpha_3 + \alpha_4$, it follows that

$$\pi_i = h_i \rho_{N/U} + \tfrac{1}{2}\zeta_i(x_1)\alpha_1 - \tfrac{1}{2}\zeta_i(x_1)\alpha_2.$$

Combined with (4.12), this yields, finally,

(4.19) $$\zeta_i^\tau|_N = \zeta_i + h_i \rho_N + \tfrac{1}{2}\zeta_i(x_1)\alpha_1 - \tfrac{1}{2}\zeta_i(x_1)\alpha_2.$$

Since α_1 and α_2 are each 1 on $K^\#$, while ρ_N is 0 on $K^\#$, we conclude that

(4.20) $$\zeta_i^\tau(y) = \zeta_i(y) \qquad \text{for } y \text{ in } K^\#.$$

Since $\zeta_i^\tau = \varepsilon\chi_i$, (i) follows at once from (4.20) together with the definition of ζ_i.

Next put $\gamma_i = \alpha_i^\tau$, $2 \leqslant i \leqslant 4$, and $\gamma_i = \psi_i$ for $i > 4$. Then

(4.21) $$\gamma_i|_N = \sum_{j=1}^{n-1} c_{ij}\zeta_j + \sigma_i \qquad 2 \leqslant i \leqslant s,$$

where the c_{ij} are nonnegative integers and σ_i is a character of N having U in its kernel. This time we obtain, as in the derivation of (4.6.35),

(4.22) $$\gamma_i|_N = \frac{c_{i1}}{2}(\rho_N - \rho_{N/U}) + \sigma_i.$$

As above, we write $\sigma_i = d_{i1}\alpha_1 + d_{i2}\alpha_2 + d_{i3}\alpha_3 + d_{i4}\alpha_4$ and use the Frobenius reciprocity theorem as we did in (4.14) and (4.15) with $\gamma_i|_N$ in place of $\zeta_i^\tau|_N$ to obtain

(4.23)

$$c_{i1} - d_{i3} - d_{i4} = \begin{cases} 0 \\ -1 \\ 0 \end{cases} \quad \text{and} \quad c_{i1} - d_{i1} - d_{i2} = \begin{cases} -1 & \text{for } i = 2 \\ 0 & \text{for } i = 3, 4 \\ 0 & \text{for } i > 4. \end{cases}$$

Evaluating γ_i on x_1, x_2, and $x_1 x_2$ as we did in (4.17), this time we obtain upon simplification,

(4.24) $$d_{i2} = d_{i3} = d_{i4}.$$

Combining (4.23) and (4.24), it follows directly that

(4.25) $$\sigma_2 = \frac{c_{21}}{2} \rho_{N/U} + \alpha_1$$

$$\sigma_i = \frac{c_{i1}}{2} \rho_{N/U} + \frac{1}{2}(-\alpha_1 + \alpha_2 + \alpha_3 + \alpha_4) \qquad 3 \leqslant i \leqslant 4$$

$$\sigma_i = \frac{c_{i1}}{2} \rho_{N/U} \qquad\qquad\qquad\qquad 5 \leqslant i \leqslant s.$$

Using (4.22) and the definition of γ_i, we thus have

(4.26) $$\alpha_2^\tau|_N = \frac{c_{i1}}{2} \rho_N + \alpha_1$$

$$\alpha_i^\tau|_N = \frac{c_{i1}}{2} \rho_N + \frac{1}{2}(-\alpha_1 + \alpha_2 + \alpha_3 + \alpha_4) \qquad 3 \leqslant i \leqslant 4$$

$$\psi_i|_N = \frac{c_{i1}}{2} \rho_N \qquad\qquad\qquad\qquad 5 \leqslant i \leqslant s.$$

Since $\alpha_i^\tau = \delta_i \psi_i$, $2 \leqslant i \leqslant 4$, the values of ψ_i on $K^\#$ are determined from (4.26) and we obtain (ii).

We state one other direct consequence of our relations which we shall also need.

Lemma 4.5

If y is an element of G not in a conjugate of $K^\#$, then

$$1 + \delta_2 \psi_2(y) = \delta_3 \psi_3(y) + \delta_4 \psi_4(y) = \varepsilon \chi_i(y) \qquad 1 \leqslant i \leqslant n - 1.$$

Proof

This follows at once from Lemmas 4.2 and 4.3 together with the fact that $(\zeta_i - \theta)^*$ and $(\tilde{1}_K - \theta - \zeta_i)^*$ are 0 outside the conjugates of $K^\#$.

By Lemma 4.1, the characters χ_i have a common degree which we denote by f. We also define $f_j = \deg \psi_j$, $1 \leqslant j \leqslant s$, so that in particular, $f_1 = 1$. As a consequence of Theorem 4.4, we also have

Lemma 4.6

The following congruences hold:
   (i) $f \equiv 2\varepsilon \pmod{4n}$.

(ii) $f_2 \equiv \delta_2 \pmod{4n}$.

(iii) $f_j \equiv 2n + \delta_j \pmod{4n}$ $3 \leqslant j \leqslant 4$.

(iv) $f_j \equiv 0 \pmod{4n}$ $5 \leqslant j \leqslant s$.

Moreover, we have

(v) $1 + \delta_2 f_2 = \delta_3 f_3 + \delta_4 f_4 = \varepsilon f$.

Proof

If σ is any character of N, we know by Theorem 4.2.1(iii) that $\sum\limits_{y \in N} \sigma(y)$ is an integer divisible by $|N| = 4n$. Furthermore, the elements of $N - K$ lie in two distinct conjugate classes, represented by x_2 and $x_1 x_2$, each having n elements. Hence

$$(4.27) \qquad \sigma(1) + n\sigma(x_2) + n\sigma(x_1 x_2) + \sum_{y \in K^{\#}} \sigma(y) \equiv 0 \pmod{4n}.$$

Now we know that χ_i and ψ_j assume the same values on the three conjugate involutions x_1, x_2, and $x_1 x_2$. Hence if we take σ to be successively $\chi_1|_N, \psi_2|_N, \psi_j|_N, 3 \leqslant j \leqslant 4$, and $\psi_j|_N, 5 \leqslant j \leqslant s$, we can use the values given in Theorem 4.4 to evaluate (4.27). Thus in the first instance we obtain

$$(4.28) \qquad f + n(2\varepsilon) + n(2\varepsilon) + \varepsilon \sum_{y \in K^{\#}} (\phi_1(y) + \overline{\phi_1(y)}) \equiv 0 \pmod{4n},$$

since $\phi_1(x_1) = \overline{\phi_1(x_1)} = 1$. But as ϕ_1 and $\bar\phi_1$ are linear characters of K, the orthogonality relations on K give

$$(4.29) \qquad 2 + \sum_{y \in K^{\#}} (\phi_1(y) + \overline{\phi_1(y)}) = 0.$$

Now (4.28) and (4.29) yield the desired conclusion $f \equiv 2\varepsilon \pmod{4n}$.

Similarly, if $\sigma = \psi_2|_N$, we obtain

$$(4.30) \qquad f_2 + n\delta_2 + n\delta_2 + \sum_{y \in K^{\#}} \delta_2 \equiv 0 \pmod{4n}.$$

Since $\sum\limits_{y \in K^{\#}} \delta_2 = (2n - 1)\delta_2$, (4.30) reduces to $f_2 \equiv \delta_2 \pmod{4n}$. With $\sigma = \psi_j|_N$, $3 \leqslant j \leqslant 4$, we obtain (iii) in the same way, provided we note that $2n \equiv -2n \pmod{4n}$. Likewise (iv) follows in the same manner.

Finally, (v) is obtained by evaluating the relations of Lemma 4.5 on the element 1, which is not in a conjugate of $K^{\#}$.

This completes the first part of the analysis. We next determine the exact values of f and f_j.

Let K_j be the distinct conjugate classes of G and let y_j be a representative of $K_j, 1 \leqslant j \leqslant r$, with $y_1 = 1, y_2 = x_1$, and $y_j \in K - \langle x_1 \rangle, 3 \leqslant j \leqslant n + 1$. Moreover, we let $K_j, 1 \leqslant j \leqslant t$, be the real classes of G. In particular,

$r = (n - 1) + s$. We wish to obtain an expression for t in terms of g and n. To do this, we need the values of β on each y_j.

Lemma 4.7

   The values of β are given by

$$\beta(y_1) = g/4n$$

$$\beta(y_j) = 2n \qquad\qquad 2 \leqslant j \leqslant n + 1$$

$$\beta(y_j) = |C_G(y_j)| \qquad n + 2 \leqslant j \leqslant t$$

$$\beta(y_j) = 0 \qquad\qquad t + 1 \leqslant j \leqslant r.$$

Proof

   The number of involutions of G is $|G : N| = g/4n$. Hence by Lemma 1.5 and the structure of N, we obtain the given values of $\beta(y_j)$ for $1 \leqslant j \leqslant n + 1$. For $j > t$, we also have $\beta(y_j) = 0$, as y_j is not strongly real. In the remaining case, y_j is not conjugate to an element of N and so does not lie in a conjugate of N. Our conditions then imply that $C_G(y_j)$ contains no elements which lie in the centralizer of an involution. Hence $|C_G(y_j)|$ is odd and an involution of $C_G^*(y)$ inverts $C_G(y_j)$. But now Lemma 1.5 yields $\beta(y_j) = |C_G(y_j)|$.

Lemma 4.8

   If t is the number of real classes of G, then

$$t - 2 = \frac{g - 4n - 8n^2}{16n^2}.$$

Proof

   We consider the group algebra $A = A(G, F)$, where F is the complex field, and denote by z_j the sum in A of all the elements of K_j, $1 \leqslant j \leqslant r$. In particular, z_2 is the sum in A of the $g/4n$ involutions of G. Now the proof of Theorem 4.2.10 shows that $z_2^2 = c_1 z_1 + c_2 z_2 + \cdots + c_r z_r$, where c_j is the number of ordered pairs of elements of the class K_2 whose product is y_j. Thus, in fact, $c_j = \beta(y_j)$, $1 \leqslant j \leqslant r$, and therefore

(4.31) $$z_2^2 = \beta(y_1)z_1 + \beta(y_2)z_2 + \cdots + \beta(y_r)z_r.$$

   The number of elements of G appearing as summands of the left side is $(g/4n)^2$, while that appearing in z_j is $g/|C_G(y_j)|$. Hence (4.31) together with the preceding lemma yields

(4.32) $$\frac{g^2}{16n^2} = \frac{g}{4n} + 2n\frac{g}{4n} + \sum_{j=3}^{n+1} 2n\frac{g}{2n} + \sum_{j=n+2}^{t} |C_G(y_j)|\frac{g}{|C_G(y_j)|},$$

whence

(4.33) $$\frac{g^2}{16n^2} = \frac{g}{4n} + \frac{g}{2} + g(t - 2).$$

But now dividing by g and transposing, we obtain the desired expression for $t - 2$.

We can now prove

Theorem 4.9

One of the following two cases holds:
(i) $f = 4n + 2\varepsilon, f_2 = 4n + \varepsilon, f_3 = f_4 = 2n + \varepsilon, f_j = 4n, j \geqslant 5,$
$\delta_2 = \delta_3 = \delta_4 = \varepsilon,$ *and* $t = r - 1 + \varepsilon.$
(ii) $\varepsilon = -1,$ *and for a suitable ordering of* $\chi_3, \chi_4, f = 4n - 2,$
$f_2 = 4n - 1, \; f_3 = 6n - 1, \; f_4 = 2n + 1, \; f_j = 4n, \; j \geqslant 5,$
$\delta_2 = \delta_3 = -1, \delta_4 = +1,$ *and* $t = r.$

Remark   We shall show in a subsequent argument that case (ii) cannot arise.

Proof

We first treat the case $\varepsilon = 1$. By Lemma 4.6(v) this forces $\delta_2 = 1$ and δ_3 or $\delta_4 = 1$. Without loss we may assume that $\delta_3 = 1$.

Since G has $n - 1$ irreducible characters of degree f, Theorem 4.2.1(i) implies that

(4.34) $$g = (n - 1)f^2 + 1 + \sum_{j=2}^{r-n+1} f_j^2.$$

We use Lemma 4.6 to estimate f and f_j. Since G is simple, G has no nontrivial linear characters and so

(4.35)
$$f \geqslant 4n + 2 \quad f_2 \geqslant 4n + 1 \quad f_3 \geqslant 2n + 1 \quad f_4 \geqslant 2n + \delta_4 \quad f_j \geqslant 4n \quad j \geqslant 5.$$
Hence by (4.34),

(4.36) $g \geqslant (n - 1)(4n + 2)^2 + 1 + (4n + 1)^2$
$$+ (2n + 1)^2 + (2n + \delta_4)^2 + (r - n - 3)(4n)^2.$$

But $g = 16n^2(t - 2) + 4n + 8n^2$ by the preceding lemma. Substituting this value of g in (4.36) and simplifying, we obtain

(4.37) $$16n^2 t \geqslant 16n^2 r + 4\delta_4 n - 4n.$$

Now (4.37) forces $t \geqslant r$. But $t \leqslant r$ by definition of t and r, so $t = r$. If $\delta_4 = -1$, the left side of (4.37) exceeds the right by $8n$ and hence g exceeds the right side of (4.36) by $8n$. Setting $f_0 = f$, this means that for some $j, 0 \leqslant j \leqslant r$, the inequality (4.35) for f_j is strict. But then by Lemma 4.6, we have $f_j \geqslant f_j^* + 4n$, where f_j^* denotes the estimate used in (4.35). If we use the estimate $f_j^* + 4n$ in place of f_j^* in (4.36), we must still obtain an inequality for g. However, the new estimate adds $8nf_j^* + 16n^2$ to the right side of (4.36). Since this number exceeds $8n$, we have a contradiction. Thus $\delta_4 = 1$ and equality holds in (4.37) and (4.36). This in turn implies that equality holds throughout (4.35), and so (i) holds in the case $\varepsilon = 1$.

Assume next that $\varepsilon = -1$. In this case Lemma 4.6(v) forces $\delta_2 = -1$ and δ_3 or $\delta_4 = -1$. Without loss we may assume $\delta_3 = -1$. We consider the subcases $\delta_4 = -1$ and $+1$ independently. Suppose first that $\delta_4 = -1$. Then we have

(4.38)

$$f \geqslant 4n - 2 \qquad f_2 \geqslant 4n - 1 \qquad f_3 \geqslant 2n - 1 \qquad f_4 \geqslant 2n - 1 \qquad f_j \geqslant 4n \quad j \geqslant 5.$$

Hence by (4.34),

$$(4.39) \quad g \geqslant (n - 1)(4n - 2)^2 + 1 + (4n - 1)^2$$
$$+ (2n - 1)^2 + (2n - 1)^2 + (r - n - 3)(4n)^2.$$

Again using Lemma 4.8, this reduces to

$$(4.40) \qquad\qquad 16n^2 t \geqslant 16n^2 r - 32n^2.$$

If one of the f_j has a larger value than the estimate f_j^* which we have used, we can add a term $8nf_j^* + 16n^2$ to the right side of (4.40) and still preserve the inequality. If $j \geqslant 5$, this adds $48n^2$, which gives a contradiction as $t \leqslant r$. On the other hand, if $1 \leqslant j < 5$, it follows from Lemma 4.6(v) that $f = f_0 > f_0^*$. Since there are $n - 1$ characters of degree f, we again obtain a contradiction. Thus we must have equalities throughout (4.38), which implies equalities in (4.39) and (4.40). Hence $t = r - 2$ and (i) holds in this case.

Suppose finally that $\delta_4 = +1$. In this case $f \geqslant 4n - 2$, and $f_4 \geqslant 2n + 1$. But then Lemma 4.6(v) forces $f_3 > 2n - 1$, whence $f_3 \geqslant 6n - 1$. We also have $f_2 \geqslant 2n - 1$ and $f_j \geqslant 4n, j \geqslant 5$. We thus obtain

$$(4.41) \quad g \geqslant (n - 1)(4n - 2)^2 + 1 + (2n - 1)^2$$
$$+ (6n - 1)^2 + (2n + 1)^2 + (r - n - 3)(4n)^2.$$

Again using Lemma 4.8, (4.41) reduces to

$$(4.42) \qquad\qquad 16n^2 t \geqslant 16n^2 r.$$

Thus $t = r$ and the estimates used for f, f_j are exact. Hence (ii) holds and the theorem is proved.

We are at last in a position to compute our desired formula for g. At the same time we shall show that case (ii) above is excluded.

Theorem 4.10 (Brauer-Suzuki-Wall)

The order g of G is given by the following expression:

$$g = 4n(4n + \varepsilon)(2n + \varepsilon).$$

Proof

We can now evaluate (4.2) with y an element of $K - U$. The values of the irreducible characters of G on y as well as on the involution x of G are given in Theorems 4.4. Their degrees and the values of $\delta_2, \delta_3, \delta_4$, and ε are given in the preceding theorem. In addition, we have $\beta_K(y) = 2n$ by Lemma 4.7. We first use the degrees of case (i) and obtain

(4.43)

$$2n = \frac{g}{16n^2} \left(\sum_{i=1}^{\frac{n-1}{2}} \frac{(\pm 2)^2(\phi_i(y) + \bar{\phi}_i(y))}{4n + 2\varepsilon} + \sum_{i=1}^{\frac{n-1}{2}} \frac{(\pm 2)^2 \eta(y)(\phi_i(y) + \bar{\phi}_i(y))}{4n + 2\varepsilon} \right.$$

$$\left. + 1 + \frac{(\pm 1)^2 \varepsilon}{4n + \varepsilon} + 2\frac{(\pm 1)^2(-\varepsilon)}{2n + 2\varepsilon} \right).$$

But as $y \in K - U$, $\eta(y) = -1$, and hence the second sum is the negative of the first. Hence these two terms can be deleted. Now clearing denominators in (4.43), we get

(4.44)

$$32n^3(4n + \varepsilon)(2n + \varepsilon) = g((4n + \varepsilon)(2n + \varepsilon) + \varepsilon(2n + \varepsilon) - 2\varepsilon(4n + \varepsilon)) = 8gn^2,$$

which yields the desired formula for g.

Now use the degrees and values of $\delta_2, \delta_3, \delta_4$, and ε of case (ii). We obtain

(4.45)
$$2n = \frac{g}{16n^2} \left(1 + \frac{-1}{4n - 1} + \frac{1}{6n - 1} + \frac{-1}{2n + 1} \right).$$

But this time if we clear the denominator and reduce the resulting expression modulo $2n - 1$, we get

(4.46)
$$4 \equiv 0 \pmod{2n - 1},$$

which is impossible as $n = |U| > 1$ by assumption. Thus case (ii) is excluded.

Hence we also have

Theorem 4.11

Case (i) *of Theorem 4.9 holds. Moreover, $t = 2n + 3$ if $\varepsilon = +1$ and $t = 2n$ if $\varepsilon = -1$.*

Proof

The preceding theorem together with Lemma 4.8 yields

$$(4.47) \qquad 16n^2(t - 2) + 8n^2 + 4n = 4n(4n + \varepsilon)(2n + \varepsilon).$$

The given values of t follow at once from this equation.

In Chapter 15 we shall pursue further the analysis of groups satisfying the above conditions and shall classify them completely.

EXERCISES

1. Let G be a group in which an S_2-subgroup of $C_G(x)$ is normal in $C_G(x)$ for every involution x of G. Prove
    (i) If y is a real element of $G^{\#}$ of odd order, then y is strongly real and $C_G(y)$ has odd order.
    (ii) If $G/O_2(G)$ is a dihedral group of order $2n$, n odd, then $O_2(G)$ possesses a complement in G.
    (iii) If an S_2-subgroup P of G is neither cyclic nor generalized quaternion, then P centralizes $O_{2'}(G)$.
    (iv) If $O_2(G) = 1$, then G possesses S_2-subgroups P and Q such that $P \cap Q = 1$.
2. If x is an involution of the group G and $x \notin O_2(G)$, show that x must invert an element of $G^{\#}$ of odd order. (Use Theorem 3.8.2.)
3. Let x and y be nonconjugate involutions of the group G. For each nonempty *subset I* of involutions of $C_G(x)$, let $n(I)$ be the number of conjugates of y which lie in $C_G(I)$. Derive the following formula for the order of G:

$$|G| = |C_G(y)| \sum_I (-1)^{|I|+1} n(I).$$

4. Set $G = L_2(q)$, $q > 3$, $C = C_G(x)$, x an involution of G, and assume that $G = CH$, where H is of odd order. Prove that $q \equiv -1 \pmod 4$.
5. Let G be a simple group with a dihedral Sylow 2-subgroup S and assume G possesses a subgroup K with the following properties:

(a) $K = U \times (S \cap K)$, where U is abelian of odd order and $S \cap K$ is cyclic of index 2 in S.

(b) K is disjoint from its conjugates in G.

(c) $N_G(K) = KS$ and an involution of $S - (S \cap K)$ inverts K.

Note that if $|S| = 4$, the assumptions are identical to those of Section 4. Following the procedure of that section, derive an analogous formula for the order of G.

PART II APPLICATIONS

CHAPTER 10

FIXED-POINT-FREE
AUTOMORPHISMS

The single most important result concerning fixed-point-free auto-morphisms is Thompson's theorem on the nilpotency of a group which admits such an automorphism of prime order. On the basis of the Glauberman-Thompson normal p-complement theorem together with some general properties of fixed-point-free automorphisms established in the first section, we give a short proof of this result. Thompson's theorem is then applied to prove that the kernel of a Frobenius group is nilpotent and to show that a group with a nilpotent maximal subgroup of odd order is necessarily solvable. In Section 4 we give an elementary proof of the solvability of any group which possesses a fixed-point-free automorphism of order 4, and in Section 5 we obtain a similar result for groups which possess a fixed-point-free four-group of automorphisms.

1. ELEMENTARY PROPERTIES

An automorphism ϕ of a group G is said to be *fixed-point-free* if it leaves only the identity element of G fixed—equivalently, if $C_G(\phi) = 1$. Similarly, a group of automorphisms A of G is fixed-point-free if $C_G(A) = 1$. Obviously an automorphism ϕ is fixed-point-free if and only if $\langle \phi \rangle$

is. Furthermore, a regular group of automorphisms is fixed-point-free and so is each of its nonidentity elements. In general, of course, a group of automorphisms may be fixed-point-free without being regular. Likewise ϕ may be fixed-point-free, while ϕ^i may not for some i such that $\phi^i \neq 1$. On the other hand, if ϕ is of prime order, then it is immediate that ϕ is fixed-point-free if and only if $\langle \phi \rangle$ is a regular group of automorphisms.

In this section we shall establish a number of properties of fixed-point-free automorphisms.

Lemma 1.1

Let ϕ be a fixed-point-free automorphism of G of order n. Then
  (i) *Every element of G can be expressed in the form $x^{-1}(x\phi)$ and $(x\phi)x^{-1}$ for suitable x in G.*
  (ii) *For every x in G, we have*

$$x(x\phi) \cdots (x\phi^{n-1}) = (x\phi^{n-1}) \cdots (x\phi)x = 1.$$

Proof

If $x^{-1}(x\phi) = y^{-1}(y\phi)$ with x, y in G, then transposing we obtain $xy^{-1} = (xy^{-1})\phi$. But then $xy^{-1} = 1$ and $x = y$, as ϕ is fixed-point-free. Thus there are as many distinct elements of G of the form $x^{-1}(x\phi)$ as there are elements x of G and hence every element of G can be expressed in this form. Similarly, every element of G can be expressed in the form $(x\phi)x^{-1}$. Thus (i) holds.

Now if $x \in G$, $x = y^{-1}(y\phi)$ for some y in G by (i). Hence

$$(1.1) \qquad x(x\phi) \cdots (x\phi^{n-1}) = y^{-1}(y\phi)(y^{-1}(y\phi))\phi \cdots (y^{-1}(y\phi))\phi^{n-1}$$
$$= y^{-1}(y\phi^n) = y^{-1}y = 1.$$

The second relation of (ii) is proved similarly.

If n is not a prime power, then $|G|$ need not be prime to n. Indeed, if $G = G_1 \times G_2$, where G_1 is cyclic of order 3 and G_2 is a four-group, G possesses automorphisms ϕ_1, ϕ_2, where ϕ_1 inverts G_1 and is the identity on G_2, while ϕ_2 has order 3 on G_2 and is the identity on G_1. Then ϕ_1, ϕ_2 commute and consequently $\phi = \phi_1\phi_2$ is an automorphism of G of order $n = 6$, which one can verify is fixed-point-free. Since $|G| = 12$, $(|G|, n) \neq 1$.

If $(|\phi|, |G|) = 1$, then Theorem 6.2.2 tells us that for each p in $\pi(G)$, ϕ leaves invariant a unique S_p-subgroup of G. However, when $(|\phi|, |G|) \neq 1$, we can still derive the same conclusion with the aid of Lemma 1.1. Indeed, we have

Theorem 1.2

If ϕ is a fixed-point-free automorphism of G, then ϕ leaves invariant a unique S_p-subgroup P of G for each prime p in $\pi(G)$. Furthermore, P contains every ϕ-invariant p-subgroup of G.

Proof

Let Q be an S_p-subgroup of G. Then $(Q)\phi$ is also an S_p-subgroup of G and so $(Q)\phi = y^{-1}Qy$ for some y in G. But then $(z^{-1}Qz)\phi = (z\phi)^{-1}y^{-1}Qy(z\phi)$ for any z in G. By Lemma 1.1(i) we can choose z so that $(z\phi)z^{-1} = y^{-1}$, in which case $y(z\phi) = z$. For this choice of z, we then have $(z^{-1}Qz)\phi = z^{-1}Qz$, and so ϕ leaves invariant the S_p-subgroup $P = z^{-1}Qz$.

Suppose now that P and Q are two ϕ-invariant S_p-subgroups of G. Then $Q = x^{-1}Px$ for some x in G. Applying ϕ, it follows that also $Q = (x\phi)^{-1}P(x\phi)$, whence $y = (x\phi)x^{-1} \in N = N_G(P)$. Now N is ϕ-invariant by Theorem 2.1.1(i), and certainly ϕ fixes only the identity element of N. Hence by Lemma 1.1(i), applied to N, we have $y = (z\phi)z^{-1}$ for some z in N. But then $(x\phi)x^{-1} = (z\phi)z^{-1}$ and it follows that $x = z$. Thus $x \in N = N_G(P)$ and consequently $P = Q$. Thus P is unique.

Finally let H be a ϕ-invariant p-subgroup of G and let K be a maximal ϕ-invariant p-subgroup of G containing H. It will suffice to show that K is an S_p-subgroup of G, for then $K = P$ by the preceding argument and the desired conclusion $H \subseteq P$ will follow. Set $N = N_G(K)$, so that ϕ induces a fixed-point-free automorphism of N. Hence by the preceding argument, N possesses a unique ϕ-invariant S_p-subgroup Q. We have $Q \supseteq K$ and now our maximal choice of K implies that $Q = K$. Hence if R is an S_p-subgroup of G containing K, we have $K = N \cap R = N_R(K)$. But now it follows from Theorem 1.2.11(ii) that $R = K$. Thus K is an S_p-subgroup of G, as required.

The property of being fixed-point-free is also preserved under homomorphic images:

Lemma 1.3

Let ϕ be a fixed-point-free automorphism of G and let H be a ϕ-invariant normal subgroup of G. Then ϕ induces a fixed-point-free automorphism of G/H.

Proof

Set $\bar{G} = G/H$ and suppose that $\bar{x}\phi = \bar{x}$ for some $\bar{x}$ in $\bar{G}$. Then $\bar{x}^{-1}(\bar{x}\phi) = \bar{1}$ and so $y = x^{-1}(x\phi) \in H$ for any representative x of $\bar{x}$ in G. Since ϕ induces a fixed-point-free automorphism of H, we have $y = z^{-1}(z\phi)$ for some z in H and it follows that $x = z$. Hence $x \in H$ and so $\bar{x} = \bar{1}$. Thus ϕ induces a fixed-point-free automorphism of $\bar{G}$, as asserted.

With this information, we can easily analyze the cases that ϕ has order 2 or 3.

Theorem 1.4

If ϕ is a fixed-point-free automorphism of G of order 2, then G is abelian and $x\phi = x^{-1}$ for all x in G.

Proof

By Lemma 1.1(ii) we have $x(x\phi) = 1$, whence $x\phi = x^{-1}$ for all x in G. But now if $x, y \in G$, we have

$$(xy)^{-1} = (xy)\phi = (x\phi)(y\phi) = x^{-1}y^{-1}.$$

Thus $y^{-1}x^{-1} = x^{-1}y^{-1}$ and it follows at once that G is abelian.

Theorem 1.5

If ϕ is a fixed-point-free automorphism of G of order 3, then G is nilpotent and x commutes with $x\phi$ for all x in G.

Proof

Since $x(x\phi)(x\phi^2) = (x\phi)(x\phi)x$ by Lemma 1.1(ii), we have

$$x(x\phi) = (x\phi)x = (x\phi^2)^{-1},$$

so x commutes with $x\phi$ for all x in G.

Now let P be the unique ϕ-invariant S_p-subgroup of G for any p in $\pi(G)$. We shall argue that $P \lhd G$, which in view of Theorem 1.3.6 will suffice to show that G is nilpotent. Assume false, in which case there exists an S_p-subgroup Q of G with $Q \neq P$. Choose x in Q with $x \notin P$ and set $H = \langle x, x\phi \rangle$. By the preceding paragraph, x and $x\phi$ commute, so H is abelian. Since x is a p-element, so is $x\phi$, and it follows at once that H is a p-group. On the other hand, since $x\phi^2 = (x(x\phi))^{-1}$, ϕ transforms the generators x and $x\phi$ of H into elements of H and so leaves H invariant. Thus H is a ϕ-invariant p-subgroup of G and so $H \subseteq P$ by Theorem 1.2, contrary to the fact that $x \in H$, but $x \notin P$.

However, not every group admitting a fixed-point-free automorphism is nilpotent. Indeed, we have

Theorem 1.6

There exist solvable, nonnilpotent groups admitting fixed-point-free automorphisms of composite order.

Proof

Examples of such groups are easy to construct. We give one in which $|G| = 7^2 \cdot 3$ and $|\phi| = 4$. Here

(1.2) $G = \langle x_1, x_2, y \mid x_1^7 = x_2^7 = y^3 = 1, x_2 x_1 = x_1 x_2, x_1^y = x_1^2, x_2^y = x_2^4 \rangle.$

One verifies directly that G is the semidirect product of the abelian group $\langle x_1, x_2 \rangle$ of order 49 and the cyclic group $\langle y \rangle$ of order 3. Thus G is a group of order $7^2 \cdot 3$ whose elements are $x_1^i x_2^j y^k$, $0 \leqslant i \leqslant 6$, $0 \leqslant j \leqslant 6$, $0 \leqslant k \leqslant 2$. Since an S_3-subgroup of G is not normal, G is not nilpotent. But clearly G is solvable.

If ϕ is defined by the rule

(1.3) $(x_1^i x_2^j y^k)\phi = x_1^{-j} x_2^i y^{-k},$

(so that $x_1 \phi = x_2$, $x_2 \phi = x_1^{-1}$, and $y\phi = y^{-1}$), it is easy to check that ϕ is a fixed-point-free automorphism of G of order 4.

2. FIXED-POINT-FREE AUTOMORPHISMS OF PRIME ORDER

We have seen in the preceding section that a group G admitting a fixed-point-free automorphism ϕ of order 2 or 3 is necessarily nilpotent. These results were known at the turn of the century and at that time Frobenius conjectured that G had to be nilpotent whenever ϕ had prime order. This conjecture was first proved by Thompson in his doctoral thesis. We shall prove this result now with the aid of the Glauberman-Thompson normal p-complement theorem.

Theorem 2.1 (Thompson)
If G admits a fixed-point-free automorphism of prime order, then G is nilpotent.

Proof
Suppose false and let G be a minimal counterexample. Let ϕ be a fixed-point-free automorphism of G of prime order r. We first argue that G is, in fact, solvable. Indeed, suppose G possesses a proper ϕ-invariant normal subgroup $H \neq 1$. Then H is nilpotent by the minimality of G. Furthermore, ϕ induces a fixed-point-free automorphism of G/H by Lemma 1.3, which is necessarily of the same order r as r is a prime. Again by the minimality of G, it follows that G/H is nilpotent. So G is solvable in this case.

Suppose, on the other hand, that G has no nontrivial proper normal ϕ-invariant subgroups. Now G is not a 2-group, as G is not nilpotent. Let then P be the unique ϕ-invariant S_p-subgroup of G for some odd prime p in

$\pi(G)$ and set $N = N_G(Z(J(P)))$. Since $Z(J(P))$ char P, N is ϕ-invariant and consequently $N \subset G$ by our present assumption on G. But now N is nilpotent by the minimality of G. Clearly then N has a normal p-comple-ment. Since p is odd, the Glauberman-Thompson theorem now yields that G has a normal p-complement K. Since K char G, K is ϕ-invariant and so $K = 1$, again by our present assumption on G. Thus $G = P$ is nilpotent, which is not the case. This proves that G is solvable.

We see then that the effect of the Glauberman-Thompson theorem is to reduce the problem to establishing the theorem in the special case that G is solvable. In this case, we in turn reduce the problem to Theorem 3.4.4, which we obtained as a consequence of Clifford's theorem.

Suppose next that G possesses two nontrivial ϕ-invariant normal sub-groups H_1, H_2 such that $H_1 \cap H_2 = 1$. Then, as above, $\bar{G}_i = G/H_i$ is nilpotent, $1 \leqslant i \leqslant 2$, and consequently also $\bar{G}_1 \times \bar{G}_2$ is nilpotent. But for x in G, the mapping $x\psi = (H_1 x, H_2 x)$ clearly defines a homomorphism of G into $\bar{G}_1 \times \bar{G}_2$. Furthermore, since $H_1 \cap H_2 = 1$, $(H_1 x, H_2 x) = (H_1, H_2)$, the identity element of $\bar{G}_1 \times \bar{G}_2$, only if $x = 1$. Hence ψ is one-to-one and so ψ maps G isomorphically into $\bar{G}_1 \times \bar{G}_2$. Since $(G)\psi$ is nilpotent, so also is G, contrary to our choice of G. Thus G does not possess two such subgroups H_1, H_2.

Now let N be a minimal normal ϕ-invariant subgroup of G. Since G is solvable, N is an elementary abelian p-group for some prime p. Further-more, we again have that $\bar{G} = G/N$ is nilpotent. Also $\bar{G}$ is not a p-group; otherwise G would be nilpotent. Let $\bar{Q}$ be an S_q-subgroup of $\bar{G}$ with $q \neq p$ and let $\bar{M}$ be a minimal ϕ-invariant subgroup of $\Omega_1(Z(\bar{Q}))$. Then $\bar{M} \neq 1$ and $\bar{M} \lhd \bar{G}$ as $\bar{G}$ is nilpotent. If H denotes the inverse image of $\bar{M}$ in G, we have $H = NM$, where M is an elementary abelian q-group, $M \neq 1$, $H \lhd G$, and H is ϕ-invariant. We can assume that M is ϕ-invariant, in which case our minimal choice of M implies that ϕ acts irreducibly on M.

If $H \subset G$, then H is nilpotent, whence M char $H \lhd G$ and so M and N are two ϕ-invariant normal subgroups of G such that $M \cap N = 1$, contrary to what we have shown above. Thus $G = H = NM$. Furthermore, $C_M(N)$ is ϕ-invariant and, as ϕ acts irreducibly on M, either $C_M(N) = 1$ or M. However, in the latter case M centralizes N, so G is nilpotent, contrary to our choice of G. Thus $C_M(N) = 1$.

But now if G^* denotes the semidirect product of M by $\langle \phi \rangle$, G^* acts irreducibly on N as a vector space over Z_p and the representation is faithful inasmuch as $C_M(N) = 1$ and ϕ is fixed-point-free on N. But $G^* = M\langle \phi \rangle$ is a p'-group, $C_{G^*}(M) = M$, and G^*/M is of prime order.

Hence $C_N(\phi) \neq 1$ by Theorem 3.4.4. This contradiction completes the proof of the theorem.

3. FROBENIUS GROUPS AND GROUPS WITH NILPOTENT MAXIMAL SUBGROUPS

If G is a Frobenius group with kernel K and complement A, then we know that A induces a nontrivial regular group of automorphisms of K. But then A possesses an element x of prime order r and x induces by conjugation a fixed-point-free automorphism of K of order r. Hence K is nilpotent by Theorem 2.1. Thus as a corollary of the theorem we obtain the fundamental fact that the kernel of a Frobenius group is necessarily nilpotent.

We summarize now the basic structural properties of a Frobenius group that we have so far established:

Theorem 3.1

If G is a Frobenius group with kernel K and complement A, then the following conditions hold:
- (i) *A induces a regular group of automorphisms of K.*
- (ii) *$|A|$ divides $|K| - 1$.*
- (iii) *K is nilpotent and is abelian if $|A|$ is even.*
- (iv) *The S_p-subgroup of A are cyclic for odd p and are cyclic or generalized quaternion for $p = 2$.*
- (v) *Any subgroup of A of order pq, p and q primes, is cyclic.*
- (vi) *If $|A|$ is odd, A is metacyclic, while if $|A|$ is even, A possesses a unique involution which necessarily is contained in $Z(A)$.*

Proof

In view of the above remarks together with Theorems 2.7.6, 5.3.14, 5.4.11, 7.6.2, and 1.4 the theorem will be completely proved once we establish (vi) in the case that $|A|$ is even. Let x be an involution of A. Then if $y \in A$ and $z \in K^{\#}$, we have

$$z^{xy} = (z^{-1})^y \quad \text{and} \quad z^{yx} = (z^y)^x = (z^y)^{-1} = (z^{-1})^y.$$

Thus $z^{xy} = z^{yx}$ and consequently the element $[x, y]$ of A fixes the element z of $K^{\#}$. Since A acts regularly on K, this forces $[x, y] = 1$ and so x centralizes y for all y in A. Hence $x \in Z(A)$. In particular, x lies in every S_2-subgroup of A. But each S_2-subgroup of A, being cyclic or generalized quaternion, possesses a unique involution and therefore x is the unique involution of G.

Theorem 2.1 together with the Glauberman-Thompson theorem also has the following important consequence:

Theorem 3.2 (Thompson)

If a maximal subgroup of G is nilpotent of odd order, then G is solvable.

Proof

Let M be a maximal subgroup of G which is nilpotent of odd order. We proceed by induction on $|G|$. Suppose first that M contains a nontrivial subgroup H which is normal in G. Then M/H is a maximal subgroup of G/H and is nilpotent of odd order. Hence G/H is solvable by induction. Since H, being a subgroup of M, is nilpotent, it follows that G is solvable. Hence we may suppose that M contains no such subgroup H.

If $M = 1$, the maximality of M implies that G has prime order and so is solvable. Hence we may also assume that $M \neq 1$. Let P be an S_p-subgroup of M with $p \in \pi(M)$ and set $N = N_G(P)$. Then $M \subseteq N$ as M is nilpotent. But $N \subset G$ by the preceding paragraph and, as M is maximal, this forces $M = N$. In particular, P is an S_p-subgroup of its normalizer and so is an S_p-subgroup of G by Theorem 1.2.11(ii). Thus M is an S_π-subgroup of G, where $\pi = \pi(M)$. The same argument also shows that $M = N_G(Z(J(P)))$ and consequently $N_G(Z(J(P)))$ possesses a normal p-complement. Since p is odd, the Glauberman-Thompson theorem implies that G possesses a normal p-complement K_p. This argument holds for each p in π. We set $K = \bigcap_{p \in \pi} K_p$, so that $K \lhd G$. Now $G = PK_p$ with $P \cap K_p = 1$ and therefore K_p contains all p'-elements of G. We see then that K contains all π'-elements of G. But K, being a p'-group for each p in π, is a π'-group. Thus K is, in fact, an $S_{\pi'}$-subgroup of G. Since M is an S_π-subgroup of G, we conclude that $G = KM$ with $K \cap M = 1$ and $K \lhd G$.

Thus to complete the proof, it will suffice to show that K is nilpotent. Choose x of order p in $Z(P)$. Then $C = C_G(x)$ contains M as $x \in Z(M)$ and we conclude as above that $C = M$. Hence x centralizes no nontrivial π'-element, whence x induces by conjugation a fixed-point-free automorphism of K of prime order p. But then K is nilpotent by Theorem 2.1 and the theorem is proved.

4. FIXED-POINT-FREE AUTOMORPHISMS OF ORDER 4

We have seen in Theorem 1.6 that there exist solvable, nonnilpotent groups admitting fixed-point-free automorphisms of composite order. In view of Theorem 2.1 for the case of prime order, it is natural to ask whether a group G admitting a fixed-point-free automorphism ϕ of arbitrary order is necessarily solvable. If $|\phi| = 2^m$ for some m, then G must have odd order by Theorem 6.2.3 and so the conclusion is true in this case as a consequence of the Feit-Thompson theorem.

Without employing this result there is only one case when ϕ has composite order in which the desired conclusion has been directly obtained— namely, when $|\phi| = 4$. Since the proof in this case involves a lovely application of Philip Hall's characterization of solvable groups as well as properties of groups of odd order admitting an automorphism of order 2, we shall present it here.

We begin with the following general lemma:

Lemma 4.1

Let G be a group of odd order which admits an automorphism ϕ of order 2. Set $F = C_G(\phi)$ and let I be the subset of elements of G transformed into their inverses by ϕ. Then the following conditions hold:

(i) *$G = FI = IF$, $F \cap I = 1$, and $|I| = |G : F|$.*
(ii) *I is invariant under F.*
(iii) *If H is a subset of F such that $H^x \subseteq F$ for x in I, then x centralizes H.*
(iv) *Two elements of F conjugate in G are conjugate in F.*
(v) *If H is a subgroup of F, then $N_G(H) = C_G(H)N_F(H)$.*
(vi) *If H is a subgroup of I, then H is abelian.*

Proof

We note that I need not be a subgroup. Observe, first of all, that if $y = x^{-1}(x\phi)$, $x \in G$, then $y\phi = (x^{-1})\phi(x\phi^2) = (x\phi)^{-1}x = y^{-1}$, so every element y of this form lies in I. Now let x_i, $1 \leqslant i \leqslant n$, be a complete set of right coset representatives of F in G and set $y_i = x_i^{-1}(x_i\phi)$, so that $y_i \in I$, $1 \leqslant i \leqslant n$. We claim that the y_i are also a complete set of right coset representatives of F in G. Indeed, either this is the case or $y_j = zy_i$, $z \in F$, for some $i \neq j$. Applying ϕ gives $y_j^{-1} = zy_i^{-1}$, whence $y_j = y_i z^{-1}$. Thus

$$(4.1) \qquad\qquad zy_i = y_i z^{-1}$$

and consequently $z^{y_i} = z^{-1}$. But then $z^{y_i^2} = z$ and so y_i^2 centralizes z. Since $|G|$ is odd, it follows that y_i centralizes z. Hence (4.1) reduces to $z = z^{-1}$. Since also $|z|$ is odd, this forces $z = 1$ and $y_j = y_i$. But then $x_i^{-1}(x_i\phi) = x_j^{-1}(x_j\phi)$ and hence $(x_i x_j^{-1}) = (x_i x_j^{-1})\phi$. We conclude that $x_i x_j^{-1} \in F$, whence x_j and x_i determine the same coset of F, which is not the case as $i \neq j$. Thus the y_i are a complete set of coset representatives of F in G, as asserted.

Suppose next that $u = zy_i \in I$ for some z in F and some i. Then $u^{-1} = u\phi = (zy_i)\phi = zy_i^{-1}$, whence $zy_i = y_i z^{-1}$. We conclude now as in the preceding paragraph that $z = 1$. Thus $I = \{y_i | 1 \leqslant i \leqslant n\}$ and consequently $G = FI$ and $I = |G : F|$. Using left cosets we obtain similarly that $G = IF$. Finally, if $z \in F \cap I$, then $z = z^{-1}$ and so $z = 1$. Thus $F \cap I = 1$ and so all parts of (i) hold.

Now let $z \in F$ and $x \in I$. Then $(z^{-1}xz)\phi = z^{-1}x^{-1}z = (z^{-1}xz)^{-1}$, so $z^{-1}xz \in I$. Thus I is F-invariant, proving (ii).

Suppose next that $H^x \subseteq F$, H a subset of F, and $x \in I$. Let $z \in H$ and set $u = z^x$, so that also $u \in F$. Applying ϕ, we get $u = u\phi = (x^{-1}zx)\phi = xzx^{-1}$, whence $x^{-1}zx = xzx^{-1}$. Thus x^2 centralizes z and, as $|x|$ is odd, x centralizes z. Since z was arbitrary in H, (iii) follows.

Suppose now that $z_1, z_2 \in F$ and $z_2 = z_1^x$ for some x in G. Then by (i), $x = yz$, where $y \in I$ and $z \in F$, whence $z_1^y = z_2^{z^{-1}} \in F$. But then y centralizes z_1 by (iii) and consequently $z_2 = z_1^z$, proving (iv).

As for (v), set $N = N_G(H)$. Since H is ϕ-invariant, so is N, and consequently $N = (N \cap I)(N \cap F)$ by (i). But as $H^{N \cap I} = H \subseteq F$, (iii) implies that $N \cap I$ centralizes H. Since $N \cap F = N_F(H)$, (v) follows.

Finally if H is a subgroup of I, ϕ induces a fixed-point-free automorphism of H of order 2, so H is abelian by Theorem 1.4. Thus (vi) also holds.

With the aid of the preceding lemma we shall now establish our main result.

Theorem 4.2

If G admits a fixed-point-free automorphism of order 4, then G is solvable.

Proof

Let ψ be the given automorphism, let $\pi(G) = \{p_i | 1 \leqslant i \leqslant r\}$, and let P_i be the unique ψ-invariant S_{p_i}-subgroup of G. Our goal will be to show that $P_i P_j = P_j P_i$ is a group for each i and j. This will imply at once that $H_i = P_1 P_2 \cdots P_{i-1} P_{i+1} \cdots P_r$ is an S_{p_i}-subgroup of G for each i. But then Philip Hall's theorem will yield that G is solvable.

For the sake of clarity we shall carry out the argument in a sequence of lemmas. First of all, we set $\phi = \psi^2$, so that ϕ is an automorphism of G of order 2. Furthermore, $|G|$ is odd by Theorem 6.2.3 as $C_G(\psi) = 1$. Hence we can apply Lemma 4.1 to the action of ϕ on G. We set $F = C_G(\phi)$ and let I be the subset of G inverted by ϕ. We preserve this notation throughout the proof. If $F = 1$, then ϕ is a fixed-point-free automorphism of G of order 2 and so G is abelian. Since the theorem holds in this case, we can also assume that $F \neq 1$.

Lemma 4.3

The following conditions hold:
  (i) *ψ induces a fixed-point-free automorphism of F of order 2 and F is abelian.*
  (ii) *Two elements of F conjugate in G are equal.*
  (iii) *Any subgroup of F is in the center of its normalizer in G.*

Proof

Since ψ centralizes $\phi = \psi^2$, it leaves $F = C_G(\phi)$ invariant and so induces an automorphism of F of order 1 or 2. But $C_F(\psi) = 1$ and $F \neq 1$, whence ψ induces a fixed-point-free automorphism of F of order 2. In particular, F is abelian. Thus (i) holds. Since F is abelian, (ii) and (iii) follow at once from Lemma 4.1(iv) and (v), respectively.

The next lemma is crucial and, as in the case of automorphisms of order 2 and 3, it utilizes the equation

$$(4.2) \qquad\qquad x(x\psi)(x\psi^2)(x\psi^3) = 1$$

for x in G, which holds by Lemma 1.1(ii).

Lemma 4.4

If $x \in I$, then x and $x\psi$ commute.

Proof

Since $x\psi^2 = x\phi = x^{-1}$ and $x\psi^3 = x\phi\psi = (x^{-1})\psi$ for x in I, (4.2) reduces to $x(x\psi)x^{-1}(x\psi)^{-1} = 1$, from which the lemma follows.

With the aid of this result, we can prove

Lemma 4.5

If P is the unique ψ-invariant S_p-subgroup of G, $p \in \pi(G)$, then P is F-invariant.

Proof

We distinguish two cases. Suppose first that $F \cap P = 1$. Since $P = (P \cap F)(P \cap I)$, we have $P \subseteq I$. Since I is F-invariant by Lemma 4.1(ii), $Q = P^z \subseteq I$ for all z in F. But then if F does not normalize P, we can choose z so that $Q \neq P$, in which case there exists an element x of Q with $x \notin P$. Then x is a p-element of I and by the preceding lemma x commutes with $x\psi$. But then $H = \langle x, x\psi \rangle$ is an abelian p-group. On the other hand since $(x\psi)\psi = x\phi = x^{-1}$, ψ takes the generators of H into H and so leaves H invariant. But now Theorem 1.2 implies that $H \subseteq P$, contrary to the fact that $x \in H$, but $x \notin P$. Hence F normalizes P in this case.

Suppose next that $F \cap P \neq 1$. We proceed by induction on $|G|$. Since F is abelian, $F \cap P$ is a ψ-invariant p-subgroup of G normalized by F. Let Q now denote a maximal ψ-invariant p-subgroup of G containing $P \cap F$ and normalized by F. Then $Q \subseteq P$ and $Q \neq 1$. We may assume $Q \subset P$ or else the lemma is proved. Then if $N = N_G(Q)$, we have $P \cap N \supset Q$ and, as every ψ-invariant p-subgroup of G lies in P, $P \cap N$ is necessarily the unique ψ-invariant S_p-subgroup of N. Furthermore, $F \subseteq N$ and so if $N \subset G$, then F normalizes $P \cap N$ by induction, contrary to our maximal choice of Q.

Thus $G = N$. Set $\bar{G} = G/Q$ and let $\bar{P}, \bar{F}$ be the images of P, F in $\bar{G}$. By Lemma 1.3, ψ induces a fixed-point-free automorphism of $\bar{G}$. If ψ has order 1 or 2 on $\bar{G}$, then $\bar{G}$ is abelian and $\bar{F}$ normalizes $\bar{P}$, whence F normalizes P in this case. Suppose, finally, that ψ has order 4 on $\bar{G}$ and set $\bar{F}^* = C_{\bar{G}}(\phi)$, so that $\bar{F} \subseteq \bar{F}^*$. Now $\bar{P}$ is the unique ψ-invariant S_p-subgroup of $\bar{G}$. Hence if $\bar{F}^* \cap \bar{P} = 1$, then $\bar{F}^*$ normalizes $\bar{P}$ by the first case of the proof, while if $\bar{F}^* \cap \bar{P} \neq 1$, the same conclusion follows by induction. In either case $\bar{F}$ normalizes $\bar{P}$ and so F normalizes P.

The next lemma will enable us to exploit this last result.

Lemma 4.6

If A and B are two ψ-invariant subgroups of G that are normalized by F, then ABF is a group.

Proof

Since BF is a group, we need only show that $(BF)A = A(BF)$, which will follow if $BFA = BAF \subseteq ABF$. Thus it will suffice to prove that $BA \subseteq ABF$.

If $a \in A$, we can write $a = a_1 x$ with $a_1 \in A \cap I$ and $x \in A \cap F$; while if $b \in B$, we can write $b = y b_1$ with $b_1 \in B \cap I$ and $y \in B \cap F$. These results follow from Lemma 4.1(i) inasmuch as A and B are ϕ-invariant. We thus have $ba = y b_1 a_1 x$. Since A and B are F-invariant, we see that ba will lie in ABF provided $b_1 a_1$ does. But we can also write

(4.3) $$b_1 a_1 = uv$$

with $u \in F$ and $v \in I$. Applying ψ, we get $b_1^{-1} a_1^{-1} = uv^{-1}$, whence

(4.4) $$v = a_1 b_1 u,$$

which together with (4.3) yields

(4.5) $$b_1 a_1 = u a_1 b_1 u,$$

setting $a_2 = ua_1u^{-1}$ and $b_2 = ub_1u^{-1}$, (4.5) becomes

(4.6) $$b_1a_1 = a_2b_2u^2.$$

Since $a_2 \in A$, $b_2 \in B$, and $u \in F$, $b_1a_1 \in ABF$, and the lemma is proved.

The next lemma together with the first paragraph of the proof of Theorem 4.2 will suffice to complete its proof.

Lemma 4.7

If P, Q *are the unique* ψ-*invariant* S_p- *and* S_q-*subgroups of* G *for* p, q *in* $\pi(G)$, *then* $PQ = QP$ *is a group.*

Proof

We may clearly assume that $q \neq p$. By Lemma 4.5, F normalizes both P and Q. But then $K = PQF$ is a group by Lemma 4.6. Now $P \cap F$ and $Q \cap F$ are the S_p- and S_q-subgroups of F, so $F = (P \cap F) \times (Q \cap F) \times H$, where $H = O_{\pi'}(F)$ and $\pi = \{p, q\}$. Thus $K = PQH$ and, as QH is a p'-group, we also have $|K| = |P| |Q| |H|$. Hence H is an $S_{\pi'}$-subgroup of K.

Now let R be an S_r-subgroup of H and set $N = N_K(R)$. Then $R \subseteq Z(N)$ by Lemma 4.3(iii). Since R is an S_r-subgroup of K, Burnside's transfer theorem now yields that K possesses a normal r-complement L_r. Setting $L = \bigcap_{r \in \pi'} L_r$, we conclude at once that L is an S_π-subgroup of K. But P and Q lie in L_r for each r, whence $PQ \subseteq L$. Since L is an $S_{\{p,q\}}$-subgroup of K, it follows that $PQ = L$. Thus $PQ = QP$ is a group, completing the proof of the lemma and the theorem.

A variety of results concerning the structure of solvable groups admitting fixed-point-free automorphisms exist in the literature, but we shall not discuss them here.

5. FIXED-POINT-FREE FOUR-GROUPS OF AUTOMORPHISMS

So far we have dealt only with single automorphisms. Theorem 6.2.3 and the solvability of groups of odd order together show that any group which admits a fixed-point-free 2-group of automorphisms must be solvable. However, only in the case that A is a four-group has a direct proof of the solvability of the corresponding group G been obtained. Under the assumption that the Sylow subgroups of G are all abelian, it is not difficult to establish the solvability of G by applying P. Hall's theorem as we did in the preceding section. Using this result together with a theorem of Bauman on the structure of solvable groups admitting a fixed-point-free

four-group of automorphisms, Glauberman has given a beautiful proof
of the solvability of G in the general case. Since Glauberman's result will
be needed in Chapter 15 in our study of groups with a self-centralizing
Sylow 2-subgroup of order 4, we shall present a complete proof of it in
this section.

We begin with some general properties of groups which admit a fixed-
point-free four-group of automorphisms.

Lemma 5.1

Let A be a fixed-point-free four-group of automorphisms of G, let ϕ_i be
the involutions of A, and set $G_i = C_G(\phi_i)$, $1 \leqslant i \leqslant 3$. Then the following conditions hold:

(i) G_i is abelian, $1 \leqslant i \leqslant 3$.

(ii) $G = \langle G_1, G_2, G_3 \rangle$; and if G has prime power order, then
$G = G_1 G_2 G_3$.

(iii) If P_i is the S_p-subgroup of G_i, then $P = P_1 P_2 P_3$ is the unique
A-invariant S_p-subgroup of G.

(iv) If H_i is a subgroup of G_i, then $H_i \subseteq Z(N_G(H_i))$.

(v) If an S_p-subgroup of G_i is an S_p-subgroup of G, then G has a normal
p-complement.

(vi) If H is a normal A-invariant subgroup of G, then A induces a
fixed-point-free group of automorphisms of G/H.

Proof

Since $C_G(A) = 1$, $C_{G_i}(\phi_j) = 1$ for $j \neq i$. Thus ϕ_j inverts G_i and so G_i is
abelian by Theorem 1.4. Furthermore, (ii) follows from Theorems 6.2.4 and
5.3.16. Since G_i is abelian and A-invariant, each P_i is also A-invariant and
so lies in an A-invariant S_p-subgroup of G, by Theorem 6.2.2. But by the
same theorem, G possesses a unique A-invariant S_p-subgroup P since
$C_G(A) = 1$. Thus $P_i \subseteq P$, $1 \leqslant i \leqslant 3$. On the other hand, by (ii) we have
$P = (P \cap G_1)(P \cap G_2)(P \cap G_3)$. But $P \cap G_i \subseteq P_i$, as P_i is the unique
S_p-subgroup of G_i. We conclude that $P = P_1 P_2 P_3$, proving (iii).

Next let H_i be a subgroup of G_i, say $i = 1$, and set $N = N_G(H_1)$. Since ϕ_j
inverts H_1 for $j \neq 1$, H_1 is A-invariant, whence also N is A-invariant by
Theorem 2.1.1(i). Thus N is generated by its subgroups $N \cap G_i$, $1 \leqslant i \leqslant 3$,
by (ii). Since G_1 is abelian, $G_1 \subseteq N$ and G_1 centralizes H_1. Thus to prove
(iv), we need only show that $N \cap G_j$ centralizes H_1, $2 \leqslant j \leqslant 3$. But
$K_j = H_1(N \cap G_j)$ is a group of odd order acted on by the involution
ϕ_1. Furthermore, H_1 is the subgroup of K_j fixed by ϕ_1, while $N \cap G_j$ is the
subset inverted by ϕ_1. Since $H_1 \lhd K_j$, it follows therefore from Lemma
4.1(iii) that $N \cap G_j$ centralizes H_1, as required. Moreover, if P_i is an

S_p-subgroup of G_i, P_i is in the center of its normalizer, by (iv). Hence if P_i is an S_p-subgroup of G, then G possesses a normal p-complement by Burnside's transfer theorem. Thus (v) also holds. Finally, (vi) is a special case of Theorem 5.3.15.

Remark   A theorem of Brauer and Wielandt concerning the fixed points of automorphism groups (compare Wielandt [10]) implies under the above hypotheses that $|G| = |G_1| |G_2| |G_3|$. Using this formula, it is not difficult to show that $G = G_1 G_2 G_3$ for any group G which admits a fixed-point-free four-group of automorphisms. However, we do not require this stronger result for our applications.

Theorem 5.2

If G is a group with abelian Sylow subgroups which admits a fixed-point-free four-group of automorphisms, then G is solvable.

Proof

We use the same notation as above. Furthermore, if H is any A-invariant subgroup or homomorphic image of G, we shall write $H_i = C_H(\phi_i)$, $1 \leqslant i \leqslant 3$. Let $P = P_1 P_2 P_3$ be the unique A-invariant S_p-subgroup of G for p in $\pi(G)$. If $P = P_i$, then G has a normal p-complement K by the preceding lemma. Since K char G, K is A-invariant and so K is solvable by induction, whence also G is solvable. Hence we may assume that for each p in $\pi(G)$, $P_i \neq 1$, for at least two values of i, $1 \leqslant i \leqslant 3$. Let $Q = Q_1 Q_2 Q_3$ be the unique A-invariant S_q-subgroup of G, $q \in \pi(A)$. It will suffice to show that $PQ = QP$ is a group when $q \neq p$, for then it will follow from P. Hall's theorem as in the proof of Theorem 4.2 that G is solvable.

Consider first the case that $P_i \neq 1$ for all i. Set $C = C_G(P_1)$. Since P is abelian by hypothesis, $P \subseteq C$. Furthermore, $Q_1 \subseteq C$ since G_1 is abelian. Since C is A-invariant, it follows by induction, if $C \subset G$, that C is solvable. Hence also the semidirect product $C^* = CA$ is solvable. But then by Theorem 6.4.1(i), C^* possesses an S_π-subgroup H^* containing A, where $\pi = \{2, p, q\}$ and consequently $H = C \cap H^*$ is an A-invariant $S_{\{p,q\}}$-subgroup of C. On the other hand, if $C = G$, then $\bar{G} = G/P_1$ is solvable by induction since A acts fixed-point-free on $\bar{G}$ by Lemma 5.1(vi). But now the same reasoning on $\bar{G}A$ shows that $\bar{G}$ possesses an A-invariant $S_{\{p,q\}}$-subgroup $\bar{H}$. But then the inverse image H of $\bar{H}$ yields an A-invariant $S_{\{p,q\}}$-subgroup of C in this case as well.

Since P is the unique A-invariant S_p-subgroup of G, we have $H = PR = RP$, where R is the unique A-invariant S_q-subgroup of H and hence also of C. Since $Q_1 \subseteq C$, Lemma 5.1 implies that $Q_1 \subseteq R \subseteq Q$. Since $P_i \neq 1$ for $i = 2$ and 3, we can repeat this argument for P_2 and P_3 and we conclude that there exist A-invariant subgroups $R = R^{(1)}$, $R^{(2)}$, and $R^{(3)}$ of G such that

$$(5.1) \qquad PR^{(i)} = R^{(i)}P \qquad \text{and} \qquad Q_i \subseteq R^{(i)} \subseteq Q \quad 1 \leqslant i \leqslant 3.$$

Since P is permutable with each $R^{(i)}$, it follows at once that P is permutable with $R^* = \langle R^{(1)}, R^{(2)}, R^{(3)} \rangle$. But each $Q_i \subseteq R^*$ and $R^* \subseteq Q$ by (5.1). Since $Q = Q_1 Q_2 Q_3$, we conclude that $R^* = Q$, giving the desired conclusion that $PQ = QP$ is a group.

Finally, consider the case that $P_i \neq 1$ for just two values of i, say $i = 1$ and 2. Once again consider $C = C_G(P_1)$ and $H = PR$. In this case we shall argue that $R \lhd H$. Set $\bar{H} = H/P_1 = \bar{P}\bar{R}$. It will suffice to show that $\bar{R} \lhd \bar{H}$, for then $P_1 R \lhd H$. But $P_1 \subseteq Z(H)$ as $H \subseteq C$, so $P_1 R = P_1 \times R$ and R char $P_1 R \lhd H$, whence $R \lhd H$. Now A acts fixed-point-free on $\bar{H}$. Furthermore, $\bar{P} = C_P(\phi_2) = \bar{P}_2$ as $P = P_1 P_2$. Since $\bar{P}$ is an S_p-subgroup of $\bar{H}$, Lemma 5.1(v) now yields that $\bar{H}$ has a normal p-complement, which must clearly be $\bar{R}$. Thus $\bar{R} \lhd \bar{H}$ and so $R \lhd H$, as asserted.

But now set $N = N_G(R)$. Then N contains P and Q (as Q is abelian). If $R \neq 1$, we reason on N as we did above on C to conclude that N possesses an A-invariant $S_{\{p,q\}}$-subgroup K with $K = PQ = QP$. Since $Q_1 \subseteq R$, we see that the desired conclusion follows unless $Q_1 = 1$. Similarly, it holds unless also $Q_2 = 1$. But we know by the first paragraph of the proof that either $Q_1 \neq 1$ or $Q_2 \neq 1$. This completes the proof of the theorem.

To treat the case that G has arbitrary Sylow subgroups we require three preliminary results. We preserve the above notation for the balance of the section.

Theorem 5.3 (Bauman)

If G is a solvable group which admits a fixed-point-free four-group of automorphisms A, then G' is nilpotent.

Proof

We argue by induction on $|G|$. Suppose first that G possesses two distinct minimal normal A-invariant subgroups H and K. If H is disjoint from G', then G' and $(G/H)'$ are isomorphic. Since A acts fixed-point-free on G/H by Lemma 5.1, the theorem follows by induction. Hence we may assume that H, and similarly K, is contained in G'. Again by induction G'/H and G'/K are nilpotent. But $H \cap K = 1$ by the minimality of H and K and consequently G' is mapped isomorphically into the nilpotent group

$G'/H \times G'/K$ under the mapping $x \to (xH, xK)$, $x \in G'$. Thus G' is nilpotent. We may therefore assume that G possesses a unique minimal normal A-invariant subgroup H. Since the semidirect product of G by A is solvable, H is an elementary abelian p-group for some prime p by Theorem 2.4.1(v). Furthermore, clearly $O_{p'}(G) = 1$.

Set $P = O_p(G)$, let Q be a nontrivial A-invariant normal subgroup of G such that $\Phi(P) \subseteq Q \subseteq P$, and set $\bar{G} = G/Q$. By induction $\bar{G}'$ is nilpotent. In particular, $O_p(\bar{G}') \lhd \bar{G}$ and consequently $O_p(\bar{G}') \subseteq O_p(\bar{G}) = \bar{P}$, where $\bar{P}$ is the image of P in $\bar{G}$. Consider first the case that $Q = \Phi(P)$. Since $\bar{L} = O_{p'}(\bar{G}')$ and $\bar{P}$ are each normal in $\bar{G}$, $\bar{L}$ centralizes $\bar{P}$. But then by Theorem 5.1.4 every p'-element of the inverse image of $\bar{L}$ in G centralizes P. However, $C_G(P) \subseteq P$ by Theorem 6.3.2 and we conclude that $\bar{L} = \bar{1}$. Thus $\bar{G}' \subseteq \bar{P}$ and so $G' \subseteq P$, whence G' is nilpotent. This argument applies whenever $\Phi(P) \neq 1$ and therefore we may assume that $\Phi(P) = 1$.

Suppose next that $Q \subset P$. Since $\bar{L}$ centralizes $\bar{P} = P/Q$, we have $H = [P, \bar{L}] \subseteq Q$. Since $\bar{L}$ is a p'-group and P is abelian, it follows from Theorem 5.2.3 that $P = H \times C$, where $C = C_P(Q)$. But as $\bar{L}$ is an A-invariant normal subgroup of $\bar{G}$, both H and C are A-invariant normal subgroups of G. Since G possesses a unique such subgroup, the only possibility is $H = 1$ and $C = P$, whence $\bar{L} = \bar{1}$. Again $G' \subseteq P$ and so G' is nilpotent. Thus we may also assume that $P = Q$ is a minimal normal A-invariant subgroup of G.

In this case $O_p(\bar{G}') = \bar{1}$, so $\bar{G}' = \bar{L}$ is a p'-group. Let $\bar{N}$ be any A-invariant proper subgroup of $\bar{G}$ and let N be its inverse image in G. Then N' is nilpotent by induction. Since $P \lhd N$, it follows at once that P centralizes $O_{p'}(N')$, whence $O_{p'}(N') = 1$ as $C_G(P) \subseteq P$. Thus N' is a p-group and consequently $\bar{N}'$ is a p-group. But $\bar{N}' \subseteq \bar{G}'$ and $\bar{G}'$ is a p'-group. Hence $\bar{N}' = \bar{1}$ and we conclude that every proper A-invariant subgroup of $\bar{G}$ is abelian.

We shall argue next that for some i, j with $1 \leqslant i, j \leqslant 3$ and $i \neq j$, $\bar{G}_i \bar{G}_j$ is a normal abelian subgroup of $\bar{G}$. It will suffice to show that there exists a proper A-invariant normal subgroup $\bar{M}$ of $\bar{G}$ with $\bar{G}/\bar{M}$ cyclic of prime power order. Indeed, in that case some involution of A, say ϕ_3, acts trivially on $\bar{G}/\bar{M}$, whence $\bar{G} = \bar{M}\bar{G}_3$. Since A acts fixed-point-free on $\bar{G}/\bar{M}$, it follows that $\bar{G}_k \subseteq \bar{M}$, $1 \leqslant k \leqslant 2$. Since $\bar{M}$ is abelian, we conclude that $\bar{G}_1\bar{G}_2$ is an abelian group. But then $\bar{G}_1\bar{G}_2$ is precisely the subset of $\bar{G}$ inverted by ϕ_3 and so $\bar{G}_1\bar{G}_2 \lhd \bar{G}$ by Lemma 4.1(i) and (ii). If $\bar{G}/\bar{G}'$ is cyclic of prime power order, we can take $\bar{M} = \bar{G}'$. In the contrary case, it is easy to see that $\bar{G}$ possesses two proper A-invariant subgroups $\bar{X}$ and $\bar{Y}$, each containing $\bar{G}'$, such that $\bar{G} = \bar{X}\bar{Y}$. Since $\bar{X}$ and $\bar{Y}$ are abelian, it follows that $\bar{G}' \subseteq Z(\bar{G})$ and hence that $\bar{G}$ is nilpotent. However, in this case, it is immediate that $\bar{G}$ possesses an A-invariant normal subgroup $\bar{M}$ of prime index.

For definiteness, assume $\bar{G}_1\bar{G}_2 \lhd \bar{G}$. We may also assume that $\bar{G}$ is nonabelian, since otherwise $G' \subseteq P$ and G' would be nilpotent. Hence no ϕ_i induces a fixed-point-free automorphism of $\bar{G}$ and so $\bar{G}_i \neq \bar{1}$, $1 \leqslant i \leqslant 3$. In particular, it follows that the subset I_i of G inverted by ϕ_i is not contained in P for any i. If $P \subseteq I_i$, then I_i centralizes P by Lemma 4.1(vi), contrary to the fact that $C_G(P) \subseteq P$. Thus $P \nsubseteq I_i$ and we conclude that $P_i \neq 1$, $1 \leqslant i \leqslant 3$.

Finally we have $I_1 \cap P = P_2 P_3$ and consequently $P_2 P_3$ is invariant under G_1 by Lemma 4.1(ii). Since $\bar{G}_1\bar{G}_2$ is abelian, it follows that

$$K = \bigcap_{\bar{x} \in \bar{G}_2} (P_2 P_3)^{\bar{x}}$$

is invariant under $\bar{G}_1\bar{G}_2$ as well as under A. But $\bar{G}_2$ centralizes P_2 since G_2 is abelian and consequently $P_2 \subseteq K$. In particular, $K \neq 1$. If $K = P_2$, then G_1, being inverted by ϕ_2, centralizes K by Lemma 4.1(iii). Since G_2 also centralizes K in this case, we see that $K \subseteq C_P(\bar{G}_1\bar{G}_2)$. But this latter group is normal in G since $\bar{G}_1\bar{G}_2$ is normal in $\bar{G}$. Since P is a minimal A-invariant normal subgroup of G, we conclude that $\bar{G}_1\bar{G}_2$ centralizes P, a contradiction. Thus $K \supset P_2$ and therefore $K \cap P_3 \neq 1$. Setting

$$L = \bigcap_{\bar{y} \in \bar{G}_3} K^{\bar{y}},$$

it follows that $K \cap P_3 \subseteq L \subset P$ and that L is invariant under both $\bar{G}$ and A, again contradicting the fact that P is a minimal normal A-invariant subgroup of G, and the theorem is proved.

Lemma 5.4

Let G be a group in which G' is nilpotent and let P be an S_p-subgroup of G. Then $G = O_{p'}(G')N_G(P)$. In particular, if Q char P, then $Q \cap P' \lhd G$.

Proof

Since G/G' is abelian and G' is nilpotent, $O_{p'}(G')P = G'P$ and is normal in G. But then $G = O_{p'}(G')N_G(P)$ by Lemma 1.3.7. Furthermore, if Q char P, then $Q \cap P'$ char P and so $Q \cap P' \lhd N_G(P)$. But $Q \cap P'$ centralizes $O_{p'}(G')$ as G' is nilpotent and hence $Q \cap P' \lhd G$.

Lemma 5.5

Let P be a p-group which admits a fixed-point-free four-group of automorphisms A. Assume that the following conditions hold:

(a) $Z(P)$ *is cyclic.*

(b) $|\Omega_1(Z_2(P))| \geqslant p^3$.

(c) *If X is any A-invariant subgroup of $Z_2(P) - Z(P)$ of order p, then $C_P(X)$ is abelian.*

Then P *is the central product of a cyclic group and an extra-special group of order p^3 and exponent p.*

Proof

Conditions (a) and (b) imply that P is nonabelian. Set $Z = \Omega_1(Z(P))$ and $W = \Omega_1(Z_2(P))$, so that $|Z| = p$, $|W| \geqslant p^3$, and Z, W are each A-invariant. Since $W = W_1 W_2 W_3$, a subgroup X satisfying (c) exists. Since $ZX \lhd P$ and ZX is abelian of type (p, p), it follows from Theorem 2.8.1 that $|P : C| = p$, where $C = C_P(ZX)$. Moreover, C is abelian by (c).

We first argue that $W \cap C$ is not elementary abelian of order at least p^3, so assume the contrary. Choose y in $P - C$. Then y normalizes $W \cap C$ and $[W \cap C, y] \subseteq Z$. Since $|Z| = p$, this implies that $[W \cap C : V] \leqslant p$, where $V = C_{W \cap C}(y)$. But then V is noncyclic by our assumption. On the other hand, V centralizes both C and y, whence $V \subseteq Z(P)$, contrary to (a). This proves the assertion.

If $Z_2(P) \subseteq C$, then W would be abelian. Since $|W| \geqslant p^3$, this would contradict the preceding argument. Since C is abelian, it follows easily from this that $P/Z(P)$ is abelian. Hence cl $(P) = 2$, whence $P = Z_2(P)$ and $W = \Omega_1(P)$. Furthermore, W is of exponent p by Lemma 5.3.9 since p must be odd. Thus $W \cap C$ is elementary abelian and consequently $|W \cap C| \leqslant p^2$. We conclude that $|W| = p^3$ and that W is nonabelian, whence extra-special. Since $[P, W] = Z = Z(W)$, it follows now from Lemma 5.4.6 that $P = WC_P(W)$. But $C_P(W)$ is abelian by (c) and so $C_P(W) = Z(P)$ is cyclic, completing the proof.

With the aid of these results we shall now prove

Theorem 5.6 (Glauberman)

If G admits a fixed-point-free four-group of automorphisms A, then G is solvable.

The proof will be by contradiction and we let G denote a minimal counterexample to the theorem. Then G possesses no nontrivial proper A-invariant normal subgroups H. Indeed, since A acts fixed-point-free on G/H, the minimality of G implies that both H and G/H are solvable, whence G is solvable, contrary to our choice of G. Furthermore, by Theorem 5.2 the S_p-subgroups of G are nonabelian for some prime p.

Choose such a prime p and let P be the unique A-invariant S_p-subgroup of G.

The bulk of the proof consists of a detailed analysis of the structure of P and of $N = N_G(P')$. We preserve this notation throughout. Note that if K is any A-invariant proper subgroup of G, Lemma 5.1(ii) implies that $K \cap P$ is the unique A-invariant S_p-subgroup of K. Furthermore, K is solvable and hence K' is nilpotent by Theorem 5.3. We shall use these facts repeatedly. For the sake of clarity we break up the argument into a sequence of lemmas.

Lemma 5.7

Let M be a proper A-invariant subgroup of G and assume that one of the following two conditions holds:
   (a) *$M \cap P$ is nonabelian,*
   (b) *$M \cap Z(P) \cap G_i$ is noncyclic for some i, $1 \leqslant i \leqslant 3$. Then $M \subseteq N$.*

Proof

Suppose false and choose M to violate the desired conclusion in such a way that $Q = M \cap P$ has maximal order. Suppose first that Q is nonabelian, whence $K = N_G(Q')$ is a proper A-invariant subgroup of G. Since Q' char Q, Theorem 1.2.11(ii) implies that either $K \cap P \supset Q$ or that $Q = P$. In the first case $K \subseteq N$ by our maximal choice of M and in the second case $K = N$ by definition of N. But by Lemma 5.4 $Q' \lhd M$, whence $M \subseteq K \subseteq N$, a contradiction. Thus Q is abelian and hence (b) holds.

Since P is nonabelian, $Q \subset P$ and it follows now as in the preceding paragraph that $N_G(Q) \subseteq N$. But $M = L N_M(Q)$, where $L = O_{p'}(M')$ by Lemma 5.4. Hence to derive a contradiction and thus complete the proof, we need only show that $L \subseteq N$. By hypothesis $R = M \cap Z(P) \cap G_i$ is noncyclic for some i. Since $C_G(x)$ is a proper A-invariant subgroup of G containing P for each x in $R^{\#}$, it follows from the preceding paragraph that each $C_G(x) \subseteq N$. However, $L = \langle C_L(x) \mid x \in R^{\#} \rangle$ by Theorem 6.2.4 as R is noncyclic and we conclude that $L \subseteq N$.

Lemma 5.8

For $i \neq j$, $\langle G_i, G_j \rangle \nsubseteq N$.

Proof

Suppose, say, that $\langle G_2, G_3 \rangle \subseteq N$. We claim first that $G = G_1 N$, which will follow if we prove that $|G| = |G_1 N|$. It will clearly suffice to show that for any prime r in $\pi(G)$, if R is the unique A-invariant S_r-subgroup of G, then $|R|$ divides $|G_1 N|$. But $R = R_1 R_2 R_3$ and $R_i \subseteq G_i \subseteq N$, $2 \leqslant i \leqslant 3$, whence $R = R_1(R \cap N)$. Since G_1 is abelian, any r-element of $G_1 \cap N$ lies in $R_1 \cap N$ and the desired conclusion follows at once.

Now set $H = \bigcap_{x \in G} N^x$. Since $G = G_1 N = NG_1$, it follows that $H = \bigcap_{x \in G_1} N^x$. But G_1 is abelian and consequently $N_1 \subseteq H$. Furthermore, $N_1 \neq 1$, since otherwise N would be inverted by ϕ_1 and so N would be abelian, contrary to the fact that $P \subseteq N$ and P is nonabelian. Thus H is a nontrivial A-invariant normal subgroup of G contained in the proper subgroup N. However, G contains no such normal subgroup and the lemma is proved.

Since $Z(P)$ is A-invariant and nontrivial, $G_i \cap Z(P) \neq 1$ for some i, $1 \leq i \leq 3$. For definiteness, assume that $G_1 \cap Z(P) \neq 1$.

Lemma 5.9

The following conditions hold:
    (i) $Z(P)$ *is cyclic.*
    (ii) $\Omega_1(Z(P)) \subseteq Z(N)$.
    (iii) $Z(P) \subseteq G_1 \subseteq N$.

Proof

Set $M_i = N_G(G_i \cap Z(P))$, $1 \leq i \leq 3$. Then M_i is an A-invariant subgroup of G containing both G_i and P, $1 \leq i \leq 3$. Moreover, $M_1 \subset G$. But then $M_1 \subseteq N$ by Lemma 5.7(a) and hence $G_1 \subseteq N$. The same reasoning shows that $G_j \subseteq N$ if $M_j \subset G$, $j = 2$ or 3. However, Lemma 5.8 shows that $G_j \nsubseteq N$ for $j = 2$ or 3 as $G_1 \subseteq N$. Hence $G_j \cap Z(P) = 1$, $2 \leq j \leq 3$, and consequently $Z(P) \subseteq G_1$.

Suppose that $Z(P)$ is noncyclic. Since P is nonabelian, we must have $P_2 \neq 1$, whence $C_G(P_2)$ is a proper A-invariant subgroup of G containing both $Z(P)$ and G_2. But then $C_G(P_2) \subseteq N$ by Lemma 5.7(b), whence $G_2 \subseteq N$, contrary to Lemma 5.8. Thus $Z(P)$ is cyclic. Finally $P' \cap Z(P) \lhd N$ by Lemma 5.4. But $P' \cap Z(P) \neq 1$ as $P' \neq 1$. Since $Z(P)$ is cyclic, it follows that $Z = \Omega_1(Z(P))$ char $P' \cap Z(P)$ and hence that $Z \lhd N$. Lemma 5.1(iv) now yields that $Z \subseteq Z(N)$ and all parts of the lemma are proved.

Lemma 5.10

The following conditions hold:
    (i) $P_1 \cap Z_2(P) = Z(P)$.
    (ii) $N' \cap Z_2(P) \nsubseteq P_1$.
    (iii) N *does not possess a normal p-complement.*

Proof

Since $P_1 \cap Z_2(P) \supseteq Z(P)$ by the preceding lemma, we see that $P_1 \cap Z_2(P) \lhd P$. But then $P_1 \cap Z_2(P) = Z(P)$ by Lemma 5.1(iv), proving (i).

To establish (ii), it will suffice to show that $N' \cap P \nsubseteq P_1$. Indeed, if this is the case, then $N' \cap P \nsubseteq Z(P)$ and hence $N' \cap P/N' \cap Z(P)$ is a non-trivial normal subgroup of $P/N' \cap Z(P)$. Applying Theorem 2.6.4, it follows at once that $N' \cap Z_2(P) \nsubseteq Z(P)$. But now another application of Lemma 5.1(iv) yields that $N' \cap Z_2(P) \nsubseteq P_1$.

Suppose then that $Q = N' \cap P \subseteq P_1$. Since Q is an S_p-subgroup of N' and N/N' is abelian, we can clearly write $N = KP$, where K is A-invariant, $N' \subseteq K \lhd N$, and Q is an S_p-subgroup of K. Lemmas 5.1(iv) and 5.4 imply that $Q \subseteq Z(K)$ and consequently K possesses a normal p-complement by Burnside's transfer theorem. But then N also possesses a normal p-complement. We see then that (ii) will follow from (iii). But $N_G(Z(J(P))) \subseteq N$ by Lemma 5.7 and so $N_G(Z(J(P)))$ will have a normal p-complement whenever N does. Since p is odd, the Glauberman-Thompson normal p-complement theorem will then yield that G itself has a normal p-complement and it will follow that G is solvable, contrary to our choice of G. Thus (ii) and (iii) also hold.

We can now establish our main results on the structure of P and N.

Lemma 5.11

The following conditions hold:
   (i) *P is extra-special of order p^3 and exponent p.*
   (ii) *$P \subseteq N'$ and $P \lhd N$.*
   (iii) *$N = N_1 P$.*

Proof

Set $R = \Omega_1(Z_2(P))$. Since $Z_2(P)$ has class at most 2 and p is odd, R is of exponent p. In particular, $P_1 \cap R = Z$, where $Z = \Omega_1(Z(P))$, by Lemma 5.10(i). Furthermore, since $N' \cap Z_2(P) \nsubseteq P_1$ by Lemma 5.10(ii), also $S = N' \cap R \nsubseteq P_1$. Thus $|S| \geqslant p^2$, $Z \subseteq S$, and by Lemma 5.4, $S \lhd N$.

We shall argue that $|S| \geqslant p^3$, so assume by way of contradiction that $|S| = p^2$. We have $Z \subseteq Z(N)$ by Lemma 5.9(ii). Furthermore, since $|S/Z| = p$, Lemma 5.1(iv) implies that $S/Z \subseteq Z(N/Z)$. Hence N stabilizes the normal series $S \supset Z \supset 1$. Setting $C = C_N(S)$, it follows now from Corollary 5.3.3 that $N = CP$. On the other hand, if we choose $i = 2$ or 3 so that $P_i \cap S \neq 1$, then $G_i \subseteq M = C_G(P_i \cap S) \subset G$, whence $M \nsubseteq N$ by Lemma 5.8. But then $M \cap P$ must be abelian by Lemma 5.7. Since $S \subseteq M \cap P$, we see that $M \cap P = C \cap P$ and we conclude that the S_p-subgroup $C \cap P$ of C is abelian. Since $Z \subset S \subseteq Z(C)$, it follows now from Theorem 7.4.4(i) that $C' \cap Z = 1$. Since $C' \cap P \lhd P$ and $Z = \Omega_1(Z(P))$, Theorem 2.6.4 shows that this is possible only if $C' \cap P = 1$. But then C, and hence also

N, possesses a normal p-complement by another application of Theorem 7.4.4, contrary to Lemma 5.10(iii). Therefore $|S| \geqslant p^3$, as asserted.

Now let X be any A-invariant subgroup of $R - Z$ of order p. Then $X \subseteq G_j, j = 2$ or 3, and hence $G_j \subseteq C_G(X)$. As above, Lemmas 5.7 and 5.8 imply that $C_P(X)$ is abelian. Since $Z(P)$ is cyclic and $R = \Omega_1(Z_2(P))$ has order at least p^3 by the preceding paragraph, P satisfies all the hypotheses of Lemma 5.5 and we conclude that $P = RZ(P)$, where R is extra-special of order p^3 and exponent p. Since $S = R \cap N'$ has order at least p^3, this in turn implies that $R = S \subseteq N'$. Now Lemma 5.4 yields that $R \lhd N$.

Hence to complete the proof of (i) and (ii), it remains to show that $P = R$, or equivalently that $|Z(P)| = p$. Assume by way of contradiction that $|Z(P)| > p$. We shall argue that G is p-normal. First of all, it is immediate from the structure of P that if Y is any cyclic subgroup of P of order at least p^2, then $\Omega_1(Y) = Z$. Hence if $Z(P)$ is contained in an S_p-subgroup Q of G, it follows that $Z = \Omega_1(Z(Q))$, whence $Q \subseteq N$. However, $N = O_{p'}(N')N_N(P)$ by Lemma 5.4 and consequently $Q^x \subseteq P$ for some x in $O_{p'}(N')$. Since $Z(P)^x \subseteq P$, it follows that $[Z(P), x] \subseteq O_{p'}(N') \cap P = 1$, whence x centralizes $Z(P)$. But since $R \subseteq N'$ and N' is nilpotent, x also centralizes R. Hence x centralizes $P = RZ(P)$ and we conclude that $Q = P$. Thus G is p-normal, as asserted.

By Grün's second theorem, G will have a normal subgroup of index p if $N_G(Z(P))$ does and, as $N_G(Z(P)) \subseteq N$, if N does. Since $N = O_{p'}(N')K$, where $K = N_N(P)$, this will be the case if K has a normal subgroup of index p and hence if $\bar{K} = K/R$ has one. But the image $\bar{P}$ of P in $\bar{K}$ is the same as that of $Z(P)$ and so lies in $\bar{K}_1$. Moreover, $\bar{P} \neq \bar{1}$ as $Z(P) \cap R = Z \subset Z(P)$. By Lemma 5.1(v), $\bar{K}$ has a normal p-complement and we conclude that G possesses a normal subgroup of index p. But then the set of p'-elements of G generate a proper A-invariant normal subgroup of G, a contradiction. Thus $|Z(P)| = p$ and so (i) and (ii) hold.

Finally we prove (iii). Since $N = \langle N_1, N_2, N_3 \rangle$ and $P \lhd N$, it will clearly suffice to show that $N_i \subseteq P$ for $i = 2$ and 3. So assume, say, that $N_2 \nsubseteq P$, in which case the $S_{p'}$-subgroup L of N_2 is nontrivial. Since P is nonabelian, we also have $P_i \neq 1, 1 \leqslant i \leqslant 3$. Furthermore, L centralizes P_2 as well as $Z = Z(P)$. But then by Lemma 5.1(iv) L centralizes $P/P_2 Z$, since the latter group is centralized by ϕ_3. Thus L stabilizes the normal series $P \supset P_2 Z \supset 1$ of P and so centralizes P. It follows that $C_G(L)$ contains P as well as G_2, whence $G_2 \subseteq N$ by Lemma 5.7, contrary to Lemma 5.8. Thus (iii) also holds.

On the basis of these results we can now complete the proof of Theorem

5.6. We keep the same notation, but henceforth we choose p to be the *smallest* prime for which the S_p-subgroups of G are nonabelian. Since $P \subseteq N'$ by Lemma 5.11(ii), there exists a prime $q \neq p$ such that, if Q is the unique A-invariant S_q-subgroup of G, then $Q \cap N$ normalizes but does not centralize P. But then $Q \cap N$ does not centralize $P/\Phi(P)$, which is of order p^2, and hence by Theorem 2.8.1 we have either $q \mid (p-1)$ or $q \mid (p+1)$. Since q is odd, it follows that $q < p$. We conclude from our minimal choice of p that Q must be abelian.

We have $Q \cap N \subseteq N_1$ by Lemma 5.11(iii), whence $Q \cap N$ centralizes $Z(P)$ and is inverted by ϕ_2. Since $Q \cap N$ does not centralize P, it does not centralize $\bar{P} = P/Z(P)$. Since $|\bar{P}| = p^2$, this is possible only if $C\bar{P}(Q \cap N) = \bar{1}$, whence $C_P(Q \cap N) = Z(P)$. Hence if we set $C = C_G(Q \cap N)$, we have $Z(P) = P \cap C$. Since $Z(P) = P_1$, it follows from Lemma 5.1(v) that C possesses a normal p-complement K. However, $Q \subseteq C$ as Q is abelian and hence $Q \subseteq K$. By Theorem 6.2.2, Q must be the unique $AZ(P)$-invariant S_q-subgroup of K, whence $Z(P)$ normalizes Q.

Finally set $M = N_G(Q)$. Our minimal choice of G implies that G has no normal subgroups of index q and consequently $Q \subseteq M'$ by Theorem 7.3.1. Since M' is nilpotent, it follows that $Q \subseteq Z(M')$ and hence that $M/C_M(Q)$ is abelian. Since $Z(P) \subseteq M$, this in turn implies that $C_Q(Z(P)) \lhd M$. But $C_Q(Z(P)) = Q \cap N$ and so $Q \cap N \lhd M$. However, $Q \cap N \subseteq G_1$ by Lemma 5.11(iii) and therefore $Q \cap N \subseteq Z(M)$ by Lemma 5.1(iv). Theorem 7.4.4 now yields that G possesses a normal subgroup of index q. This contradiction completes the proof of Theorem 5.6.

EXERCISES

1. Let α be a fixed-point-free automorphism of G of order 4. Show that G' is nilpotent.

2. Construct a group G which possesses a fixed-point-free automorphism α of order 9 such that G' is not nilpotent. [Take $G = PQ$, P an elementary abelian p-group, $p \equiv 1 \pmod{3}$, $P \lhd G$, and Q an extra-special group of order q^3 and exponent q, where $q \equiv 1 \pmod{3}$.]

3. Let A be a four-group of automorphisms of the p-group P, p odd. Let Q be an A-invariant normal subgroup of P such that A acts trivially on P/Q. If A acts trivially on $Z(P)$, prove that A acts trivially on $Z(Q)$.

4. Let A be a four-group of automorphisms acting fixed-point-free on the group

G. Let ϕ_i, $1 \leqslant i \leqslant 3$, be the involutions of A and set $G_i = C_G(\phi_i)$, $1 \leqslant i \leqslant 3$. Assume $|G| = |G_1| \, |G_2| \, |G_3|$. Prove that $G = G_1 G_2 G_3$.

5. Let G be a solvable group of order prime to 6 which admits a fixed-point-free group of automorphisms A which is isomorphic to the symmetric group S_3. Prove that G' is nilpotent.

6. Let α be a fixed-point-free automorphism of the group G and assume that there exists a fixed element x of G such that every element of G is of the form $\alpha^i(x^j)$ for suitable i, j. Prove

   (i) G is nilpotent and $\pi(G) = \pi(\langle x \rangle)$.

   (ii) The Sylow subgroups of G are abelian, whence G itself is abelian.

7. Let $G = ABA$, where A and B are cyclic of relatively prime orders and $N_G(A) = A$. Show that A possesses a normal complement G_0 which satisfies the conditions of the preceding exercise relative to the automorphism α induced by conjugation by a generator of A. Hence show that G must be solvable.

CHAPTER 11

THE HALL-HIGMAN THEOREM

The theorem of P. Hall and G. Higman (Theorem B of [1]) has had a considerable influence on the study of simple groups and on certain problems concerning modular representations. In particular, it underlies Thompson's original proof of the nilpotency of groups admitting a fixed-point-free automorphism of prime order and is also used at various key points in the Odd Order paper. The Hall-Higman theorem deals with a p-solvable group G of linear transformations satisfying $O_{p'}(G) = 1$ and acting on a vector space over a field of the same characteristic p and provides a lower bound for the degree of the minimal polynomial of any p-element of G. Recent work has shown that its use can be avoided in a great many (but not all) places and that the same conclusions can be derived from the more elementary considerations of p-stability. However, its proof involves a large number of the results and techniques which we have developed in Part I as well as a deep and intriguing analysis of certain properties of extra-special p-groups. For these various reasons we present a complete proof of this theorem.

1. STATEMENT AND INITIAL REDUCTIONS

The precise formulation of the Hall-Higman theorem is as follows:

Theorem 1.1 (Hall-Higman)

Let G be a p-solvable group of linear transformations in which $O_p(G) = 1$ acting on a vector space V over a field F of characteristic p. Let x be an element of G of order p^n. Then the minimal polynomial of x on V is $(X - 1)^r$, where either

    (i) *$r = p^n$, or*

    (ii) *There exists an integer $n_0 \leqslant n$ such that $p^{n_0} - 1$ is a power of a prime q and the S_q-subgroups of G are nonabelian. In this case, if n_0 is the least such integer, then*

$$p^{n-n_0}(p^{n_0} - 1) \leqslant r \leqslant p^n.$$

As a corollary, we have

Corollary 1.2

Under the assumptions of the theorem, $r = p^n$, if either

    (i) *p is neither a Fermat prime nor 2.*

    (ii) *p is a Fermat prime and the S_2-subgroups of G are abelian.*

    (iii) *$p = 2$ and the S_q-subgroups of G are abelian for all Mersenne primes less than 2^n.*

Proof of Corollary

Suppose $p^{n_0} - 1 = q^m$ for some prime q. If p is odd, then $p^{n_0} - 1$ is even, so $q = 2$. Hence either p or q is 2. Furthermore, if $q = 2$, then $p - 1$ divides q^m, so $p - 1 = q^{m_0}$ and p is a Fermat prime. On the other hand, if $p = 2$, then $n_0 > 1$, whence $2^{n_0} - 1 \equiv 3 \pmod 4$. Thus $q^m \equiv 3 \pmod 4$. Since $q = 2t + 1$ for some integer t, this forces m to be odd since otherwise $q^m \equiv 1 \pmod 4$. But then $q + 1$ is a factor of $q^m + 1 = 2^{n_0}$ and so $q + 1 = 2^{n_1}$, whence q is a Mersenne prime. The various parts of the corollary now follow at once from the theorem.

We turn now to the proof of the theorem, which we establish by double induction on $|G|$ and $\dim_F V$. First of all, if K is an algebraic closure of F, then G can be regarded as group of linear transformations of $V_K = V \otimes_F K$. Since a basis of V is also a basis of V_K, x is represented by the same matrix on V_K as it is on V and consequently x has the same minimal polynomial on V_K as it does on V. Hence without loss we can assume that $K = F$ and hence that F is algebraically closed.

We shall reduce Theorem 1.1 to a minimal case; but to do so, we first prove a preliminary lemma.

Lemma 1.3

The $p^n \times p^n$ permutation matrix

$$A = \begin{pmatrix} 0 & 1 & 0 \cdots 0 \\ 0 & 0 & 1 \cdots 0 \\ \vdots & & \vdots \\ 0 & 0 & 0 \cdots 1 \\ 1 & 0 & 0 \cdots 0 \end{pmatrix}$$

with coefficients in Z_p has minimal polynomial $(X-1)^{p^n}$.

Proof

Let A act on W/Z_p with basis w_i, $1 \le i \le p^n$, such that

$$w_i A = w_{i+1} \pmod{p^n}.$$

We prove that

$$(1.1) \qquad w_1(A-I)^k = w_k + a_{k-1}w_{k-1} + \cdots + a_1 w_1$$

for suitable integers $a_1, a_2, \ldots, a_{k-1}$, $1 \le k \le p^n - 1$. Since

$$w_1(A-I) = w_2 - w_1,$$

(1.1) holds for $k = 1$. Assuming (1.1) for $1 \le i \le k$, we have

$$(1.2) \qquad w_1(A-I)^{k+1} = (w^k + a_{k-1}w_{k-1} + \cdots + a_1 w_1)(A-I)$$
$$= w_{k+1} + b_k w_k + \cdots + b_1 w_1$$

for suitable integers $b_1, b_2, \ldots, b_k$ and so (1.1) follows by induction.

But then $w_1(A-I)^{p^n-1} \ne 0$ and hence the minimal polynomial of A is $X^{p^n} - 1 = (X-1)^{p^n}$.

Theorem 1.4

Either Theorem 1.1 holds or the following conditions are satisfied:

    (i) $G = QP$, where Q is an extra-special q-group $q \ne p$, $P = \langle x \rangle$, P acts irreducibly on Q/Q', and trivially on Q'.

    (ii) The representation of Q on V is irreducible.

Proof

Set $H = O_{p'}(G)$ and $P = \langle x \rangle$. Since $O_p(G) = 1$ and G is p-solvable, $C_P(H) = 1$ by Theorem 6.3.2. Furthermore, for each q in $\pi(H)$, P leaves invariant an S_q-subgroup Q^* of H by Theorem 6.2.2. Since $\Omega_1(P)$ does not centralize H, it follows that $\Omega_1(P)$ does not centralize Q^* for some choice of q. But then $C_P(Q^*) = 1$ and so P is faithfully represented as a subgroup of Aut Q^*. Let Q be a minimal P-invariant subgroup of Q^* on which $y = x^{p^{n-1}}$ acts nontrivially. Then y acts trivially on every proper P-invariant subgroup of Q and now Theorem 5.3.7 implies that Q is a special q-group, that y acts trivially on Q', but nontrivially on Q/Q', and that P acts irreducibly on Q/Q'.

Set $G_1 = QP$. Since $O_p(G_1)$ is contained in every S_p-subgroup of G_1, the assumption that $O_p(G_1) \neq 1$ would imply that $\langle y \rangle = \Omega_1(P) \subseteq O_p(G_1)$, whence $[Q, y] \subseteq Q \cap P = 1$. But then y would centralize Q, which is not the case. Thus $O_p(G_1) = 1$. Hence if $G_1 \subset G$, Theorem 1.1 holds by induction. Thus we may suppose that $G_1 = G$.

Next let $0 = V_0 \subset V_1 \subset V_2 \cdots \subset V_m = V$ be a sequence of G-invariant subspaces of V such that G acts irreducibly on each $\bar{V}_i = V_i/V_{i-1}$, $1 \leq i \leq m$. Set $Q_i = C_Q(\bar{V}_i)$, $1 \leq i \leq m$. Since $Q_i \lhd G = PQ$ and since P acts irreducibly on Q/Q', it follows that either $Q_i \subseteq Q'$ or that $Q = Q'Q_i$. However, in the latter case $Q = Q_i$ by Theorem 5.1.1 inasmuch as $Q' = \Phi(Q)$. Since the characteristic p of F is prime to q, the representation of Q on V is completely reducible. Hence if each $Q_i = Q$, it would follow from Theorem 3.3.4 that Q acts trivially on V, whence $Q = 1$, which is not the case. We conclude that $Q_i \subseteq Q'$ for some i.

For such a choice of i, set $\bar{G} = G/Q_i = \bar{P}\bar{Q}$. Then it is immediate that $\bar{Q}$ is also a special q-group, that $\bar{Q}' = Q'/Q_i$, that the image $\bar{y}$ of $y = x^{p^{n-1}}$ acts nontrivially on $\bar{Q}/\bar{Q}'$ and trivially on $\bar{Q}'$, and that $\bar{P}$ acts irreducibly on $\bar{Q}/\bar{Q}'$. As above, this implies that $O_p(\bar{G}) = 1$. Hence $\bar{G}$ satisfies the same conditions as G. If $\dim_F \bar{V}_i < \dim_F V$, it follows therefore by induction that the image $\bar{x}$ of x in $\bar{G}$ has minimal polynomial $(X - 1)^r$, where r satisfies the conditions of Theorem 1.1. In particular, there exists a vector $\bar{v}$ in $\bar{V}_i$ such that $\bar{v}(\bar{x} - 1)^{r-1} \neq 0$. But then if v is a vector of V that maps on $\bar{v}$, we have $v(x - 1)^{r-1} \neq 0$. Hence the minimal polynomial of x on V is $(X - 1)^s$ with $s \geq r$ and the theorem follows in this case. Hence we may assume that $\dim_F V_i = \dim_F V$, which is possible only if $V_1 = V$ and G acts irreducibly on V.

Suppose Q is abelian and let $W_i, 1 \leq i \leq m$, be the Wedderburn components of V with respect to the normal subgroup Q of G. Since $C_G(Q) = Q$, we conclude from Theorem 3.4.3 that $m = p^n$. This means that if $v_i, 1 \leq i \leq h$, is a basis of W_1, then $(v) = \{v_i x^j \mid 1 \leq i \leq h, 1 \leq j \leq p^n\}$ is a basis of V. With respect to this basis (in the appropriate ordering) the matrix of x is

(1.3)
$$x_{(v)} = \begin{pmatrix} A_1 & & & & 0 \\ & A_2 & & & \\ & & \ddots & & \\ 0 & & & & A_h \end{pmatrix},$$

where each A_i is the $p^n \times p^n$ permutation matrix of Lemma 1.3. Hence by that lemma, the minimal polynomial of x on V is $(X - 1)^{p^n}$, so Theorem 1.1 holds in this case. Thus we may assume that Q is nonabelian.

Again let $W_i, 1 \leqslant i \leqslant m$, be the Wedderburn components of V with respect to Q. Suppose $m > 1$, in which case $m = p^a$ for some a with $1 \leqslant a \leqslant n$. If $a = n$, Theorem 1.1 follows as in the preceding paragraph, so we may assume that $a < n$. Then $\langle x^m \rangle = P_1$ leaves W_1 invariant and $P_1 \neq 1$. In particular, $G_1 = QP_1$ acts on W_1. Let $Q_1 = C_Q(W_1)$. Since P permutes the W_i transitively, the assumption $Q_1 = Q$ would imply that $Q = C_Q(V)$, contrary to the fact that $C_Q(V) = 1$. Hence $Q_1 \subset Q$ and, as $Q' = \Phi(Q)$, it follows that $Q_1 Q' \subset Q$.

Now set $\tilde{G}_1 = G_1/Q_1 = \tilde{P}_1 \tilde{Q}$. We claim that $O_p(\tilde{G}_1) = \tilde{1}$. Indeed, if not, then the image $\tilde{y}$ of y in $\tilde{G}_1$ centralizes $\tilde{Q}$. Since $Q_1 Q' \subset Q$, this implies that y has a nontrivial centralizer on $\bar{Q} = Q/Q'$. But $C_{\bar{Q}}(y)$ is invariant under $\langle x \rangle = P$ and P acts irreducibly on $\bar{Q}$, from which it follows that $\bar{Q} = C_{\bar{Q}}(y)$. This contradicts the fact that y acts nontrivially on $\bar{Q}$. Hence $O_p(\tilde{G}_1) = \tilde{1}$. Since $m > 1, |P_1| < |P|$, whence $|\tilde{G}_1| < |G|$. Since Theorem 1.1 is being proved by induction, we conclude that the minimal polynomial of x^m on W_1 is $(X - 1)^{r_0}$, where $r_0 = p^{n-a}$ if $\tilde{Q}$ is abelian or if no power p^b with $b \leqslant n - a$ is of the form $1 + q^c$, and where $r_0 \geqslant p^{n-a-b}(p^b - 1)$ if p^b is the least power of p which is of this form.

Now for any integer s, we have

$$(x - 1)^{sp^a - 1} = (x - 1)^{(s-1)p^a - 1}(x - 1)^{p^a}$$

$$= (x - 1)^{(s-1)p^a - 1}(x - 1)(1 + x + \cdots + x^{p^a - 1}),$$

whence

(1.4) $$(x - 1)^{sp^a - 1} = (x^{p^a} - 1)^{s-1}(1 + x + \cdots + x^{p^a - 1}).$$

Since the minimal polynomial of x^{p^a} on W_1 is $(X - 1)^{r_0}$, we can choose w_1 in W_1 such that $v_1 = w_1(x^{p^a} - 1)^{s-1} \neq 0$ provided $s \leqslant r_0$. Since $v_1 \in W_1$ and $W_1 x^i = W_i, 1 \leqslant i \leqslant p^a - 1$, also $v_1(1 + x + \cdots + x^{p^a - 1}) \neq 0$. It follows therefore from (1.4) that for $s \le r_0$

$$(1.5) \qquad\qquad w_1(x - 1)^{sp^{a-1}} \ne 0.$$

This means that the minimal polynomial of x on V is $(x - 1)^r$, where $r \ge r_0 p^a$. In the nonexceptional case $r_0 = p^{n-a}$ and so $r = p^n$. On the other hand, in the exceptional case, we get $r \ge p^{n-b}(p^b - 1)$. Thus in either case Theorem 1.1 follows.

Hence we may assume also that $m = p^a = 1$, in which case V is the direct sum of t isomorphic irreducible Q-submodules Y_i, $1 \le i \le t$. By Theorem 3.6.15 the representation of G on V can be written in a finite algebraic extension of Z_p contained in F and hence in $L = GF(p^e)$ for some e with $L \subseteq F$. Choosing an appropriate basis we can regard V as a vector space over the subfield L of F and the representation of G remains irreducible. Furthermore, the preceding analysis applies as well to V/L as to V/F, and consequently we can also assume that the Y_i are isomorphic irreducible Q-submodules over L. But now Theorem 3.5.6 shows that the total number d of irreducible Q-submodules of G is of the form $d = 1 + kp$ for some integer k since $\mathrm{Hom}_G(Y_1, Y_1)$ is a power of p. On the other hand, P permutes these d modules among themselves and the number of modules in each cycle under the action of P is a power of p. Since p does not divide d, some P-cycle consists of a single irreducible Q-submodule U. Thus U is invariant under P as well as Q and so U is G-invariant. The irreducibility of G on V now forces $U = V$. We conclude that Q acts irreducibly on V. But now Theorem 3.2.2 yields that $Z(Q)$ must be cyclic and consequently Q is extra-special.

Thus to complete the proof of the theorem, it remains only to show that P acts trivially on Q'. But as Q acts irreducibly on V, $Z(Q) = Q'$ is represented by scalar transformations. Since G acts faithfully on V, it follows that $Q' \subseteq Z(G)$, whence P acts trivially on Q'.

2. THE EXTRA-SPECIAL CASE

In this section we complete the proof of the Hall-Higman theorem by analyzing the special case to which Theorem 1.4 has reduced us. We shall follow the original argument of Hall-Higman, although an alternative, somewhat more conceptual, proof has recently been obtained by Thompson using properties of indecomposable and projective modules. However, the orginal proof is more closely related to the ideas which we have developed in Part I of the book.

In the present case, Theorem 1.1 can be stated in somewhat sharper form:

Theorem 2.1

Let G be a p-solvable group of linear transformations acting on a vector space V over an algebraically closed field F of characteristic p. Assume $G = QP$, where Q is extra-special of order q^{2t+1}, $P = \langle x \rangle$ is cyclic of order p^n, P acts irreducibly on Q/Q' and trivially on Q', $O_p(G) = 1$, and Q acts irreducibly on V. Then

(i) *$q^t = (p^n - 1) + ap^n$ for some integer $a \geqslant 0$.*

(ii) *If $x_{(v)}$ is in Jordan canonical form with respect to the basis (v) of V, then $x_{(v)}$ consists of $a + 1$ Jordan blocks, a of size p^n and 1 of size $p^n - 1$.*

(iii) *The minimal polynomial of x on V is $(X - 1)^r$, where $r = p^n$ if $a > 0$ and $r = p^n - 1$ if $a = 0$. In the latter case, $q^t = p^n - 1$.*

Part (iii) of the theorem will establish Theorem 1.1 in this case and so, together with Theorem 1.4, will complete its proof. We break up the proof into a sequence of lemmas.

Lemma 2.2

The following conditions hold:

(i) *$\dim_F V = q^t$.*

(ii) *The enveloping algebra E of Q is the algebra of all linear transformations of V into V.*

(iii) *Any complete set of coset representatives of Q' in Q forms a basis of E as a vector space over F.*

(iv) *$P \subseteq E$.*

Proof

Since Q is extra-special and F is algebraically closed of characteristic $p \neq q$, (i) and (ii) follow at once from Theorems 5.5.5 and 3.6.2. Since P is a group of linear transformations of V, (iv) is an immediate consequence of (ii).

To prove (iii), observe first of all that since $\dim_F V = q^t$, (ii) implies that $\dim_F E = q^{2t}$. Furthermore, since the elements of Q' are represented by scalar matrices, the elements of any coset $Q'u$ with u in Q all lie in a one-dimensional subspace of E/F. But as E is the enveloping algebra of Q, every element of E must be a linear combination of elements of Q with coefficients in F, so $q^{2t} = \dim_F E \leqslant |Q/Q'|$. However, $|Q/Q'| = q^{2t}$, which implies that any set of coset representatives of Q' in Q are linearly independent over F. Hence any complete set of coset representatives is a basis of E/F, so (iii) also holds.

With the aid of Lemma 2.2, we now compute $\dim_F C_E(x)$ in two distinct ways.

Lemma 2.3

Let (v) be a basis of V such that $x_{(v)}$ is in Jordan canonical form with Jordan blocks A_i of size $\alpha_i \times \alpha_i$, $1 \leqslant i \leqslant m$, where $p^n \geqslant \alpha_1 \geqslant \alpha_2 \geqslant \cdots \geqslant \alpha_m$. Then we have

(i) $q^t = \sum\limits_{i=1}^{m} \alpha_i$.

(ii) $\dim_F C_E(x) = \sum\limits_{i=1}^{m} (2i-1)\alpha_i$.

Proof

First of all, (i) is an immediate consequence of the fact that $\dim_F V = q^t$. With respect to the given basis (v), E is isomorphic to the algebra $E_{(v)}$ of all $q^t \times q^t$ matrices over F and so $\dim_F C_E(x) = \dim_F C_{E_{(v)}}(x_{(v)})$. Suppose $B \in E_{(v)}$ commutes with $x_{(v)}$, so that

$$(2.1) \qquad\qquad\qquad Bx_{(v)} = x_{(v)}B.$$

Since

$$(2.2) \qquad\qquad x_{(v)} = \begin{pmatrix} A_1 & & & & 0 \\ & A_2 & & & \\ & & \ddots & & \\ & & & \ddots & \\ 0 & & & & A_m \end{pmatrix},$$

we write

$$(2.3) \qquad\qquad B = \begin{pmatrix} B_{11} & \cdots & B_{1m} \\ \vdots & & \vdots \\ B_{m1} & \cdots & B_{mm} \end{pmatrix},$$

where B_{ij} is the appropriate size matrix. Substituting in (2.1), we find that (2.1) is equivalent to the set of equations.

$$(2.4) \qquad\qquad B_{ij} A_j = A_i B_{ij} \qquad 1 \leqslant i, j \leqslant m.$$

Thus $C = C_{E_{(v)}}(x_{(v)})$ consists of all matrices B which satisfy (2.4). Note that the possible choices for a particular B_{ij} are independent of the remaining entries i', j'. Hence if C_{ij} denotes the subspace of matrices consisting of 0's in all but the $\{i, j\}$th block and a matrix B_{ij} satisfying (2.4) in the

$\{i, j\}$th block, it follows that

(2.5)
$$C = \sum_{i,j=1}^{m} C_{ij}$$

and that this sum is direct. Hence

(2.6)
$$\dim_F C = \sum_{i,j=1}^{m} \dim_F C_{ij}.$$

We now compute $\dim_F C_{ij}$. Since x is a p-element, all its characteristic roots are 1 and consequently

(2.7)
$$A_i = \begin{pmatrix} 1\,1 & & & & \\ & 1\,1 & & 0 & \\ & & 1\,1 & & \\ & & & \ddots & \\ 0 & & & & 1 \end{pmatrix} \qquad 1 \leqslant i \leqslant m.$$

Thus we can write $A_i = I_i + N_i$, where I_i is the appropriate identity matrix and N_i is the appropriate nilpotent matrix. Then (2.4) reduces to

(2.8)
$$B_{ij} N_j = N_i B_{ij}.$$

Now $B_{ij} = (b_{rs})$ is an $\alpha_i \times \alpha_j$ matrix. For simplicity of notation set $\alpha = \alpha_j$ and $\beta = \alpha_i$. We shall treat the case $\alpha \leqslant \beta$. The remaining case is similar. From (2.8), we get

(2.9)
$$\begin{pmatrix} 0 & b_{11} & \cdots & b_{1\alpha-1} \\ & \vdots & & \vdots \\ 0 & b_{\beta 1} & \cdots & b_{\beta\alpha-1} \end{pmatrix} = \begin{pmatrix} b_{21} & \cdots & b_{2\alpha} \\ \vdots & & \vdots \\ b_{\beta 1} & \cdots & b_{\beta\alpha} \\ 0 & \cdots & 0 \end{pmatrix}.$$

Now (2.9) implies that $b_{k1} = 0, 2 \leqslant k \leqslant \beta$, whence also $b_{k2} = 0, 3 \leqslant k \leqslant \beta$, etc., and we conclude that B_{ij} must have the form

(2.10)
$$B_{ij} = \begin{pmatrix} b_{11} & b_{12} & \cdots & b_{1\alpha} \\ 0 & b_{22} & \cdots & b_{2\alpha} \\ \vdots & \vdots & & \vdots \\ 0 & 0 & \cdots & b_{\alpha\alpha} \\ & & 0 & \end{pmatrix}.$$

On the other hand, observe that (2.9) implies that the remaining entries b_{rs} are completely determined by the elements in the first row of B_{ij} and that each choice of this row leads to a matrix B_{ij} which satisfies (2.8) and hence also (2.4). We conclude that $\dim_F C_{ij} = \alpha_j$ if $\alpha = \alpha_j \leqslant \beta = \alpha_i$. Similarly, $\dim_F C_{ij} = \alpha_i$ if $\alpha_i \leqslant \alpha_j$. Hence

$$(2.11) \qquad\qquad \dim_F C_{ij} = \min(\alpha_i, \alpha_j),$$

and consequently

$$(2.12) \qquad\qquad \dim_F C = \sum_{i,j=1}^m \min(\alpha_i, \alpha_j).$$

Finally we have $\alpha_1 \geqslant \alpha_2 \geqslant \cdots \geqslant \alpha_m$ by assumption. Hence for a particular pair (α_i, α_j), we can thus always take the minimum to be α_i whenever $i \geqslant j$. Adopting this convention, we see that α_i will be the minimum precisely for the $2i - 1$ pairs:

$$(\alpha_1, \alpha_i), (\alpha_2, \alpha_i), \ldots, (\alpha_i, \alpha_i), (\alpha_i, \alpha_{i-1}), \ldots, (\alpha_i, \alpha_1);$$

$1 \leqslant i \leqslant m$. It follows that (2.12) can be rewritten

$$\dim_F C = \sum_{i=1}^m (2i - 1)\alpha_i,$$

which is the assertion of the lemma.

As our second expression for $\dim_F C_E(x)$, we prove

Lemma 2.4

$$\dim_F C_E(x) = \frac{q^{2t} - 1}{p^n} + 1.$$

Proof

Set $\bar{G} = G/Q' = \bar{Q}\bar{P}$ and $\bar{P} = \langle \bar{x} \rangle$. Now the $q^{2t} - 1$ elements of $\bar{Q}^{\#}$ are permuted among themselves by $\bar{x}$. We claim that each cycle consists of p^n elements. If not, then $\bar{x}^h$ must fix some element of $\bar{Q}^{\#}$, $1 \leqslant h < p^n$. But then $C_{\bar{Q}}(\bar{x}^h) \neq 1$. Since $\bar{P}$ leaves this subgroup invariant and acts irreducibly on $\bar{Q}$, it follows that $C_{\bar{Q}}(\bar{x}^h) = \bar{Q}$. Thus $\bar{x}^h$ centralizes $\bar{Q}$, whence x^h centralizes Q and hence $O_p(G) \neq 1$. Since $O_p(G) = 1$ by hypothesis, the desired assertion follows.

Thus $\bar{Q}^{\#}$ decomposes under $\bar{x}$ into $d = q^{2t} - 1/p^n$ cycles, each of length p^n. If u_i is a representative of a coset in the ith cycle, it follows that the elements $u_i^{x^j}$, $1 \leqslant i \leqslant d, 0 \leqslant j \leqslant p^n - 1$, form a set of coset representatives for the nonidentity cosets of Q/Q'. Taking u_0 as the identity element of Q, the augmented set of elements thus form a complete set of coset representatives of Q/Q'. But now Lemma 2.2(iii) implies that these q^{2t} elements form a basis of E/F.

Let E_0 be the subspace of E spanned by u_0 and for $1 \leqslant i \leqslant d$ let E_i the subspace spanned by $u_i^{x^j}$, $0 \leqslant j \leqslant p^n - 1$, so that x leaves each E_i invariant, $0 \leqslant i \leqslant d$. To prove the lemma we need only show that

$$(2.13) \qquad\qquad \dim_F C_{E_i}(x) = 1 \qquad 0 \leqslant i \leqslant d, \text{ and}$$

$$(2.14) \qquad\qquad C_E(x) = \sum_{i=0}^{d} C_{E_i}(x),$$

from which the desired conclusion

$$\dim_F C_E(x) = d + 1 = \frac{q^{2t} - 1}{p^n} + 1$$

will follow.

If $w \in C_E(x)$, then $w = \sum_{i=0}^{d} w_i$ with $w_i \in E_i$ and $w^x = w$. Since E is the direct sum of the E_i, each of which is x-invariant, it follows at once that $w_i^x = w_i$ for all i, which prove (2.14). Now $C_{E_0}(x) = E_0$ has dimension 1, so we can assume $i > 0$ in proving (2.13). Suppose then that $v \in C_{E_i}(x)$. We have

$$(2.15) \qquad\qquad v = \sum_{j=0}^{p^n - 1} a_i u_i^{x^j} \qquad a_i \in F.$$

Applying x to (2.15) and using the fact that $x^{p^n} = 1$ and that the $u_i^{x^j}$ are linearly independent, it follows easily that all a_i are equal. Hence the element $\sum_{j=0}^{p^n - 1} u_i^{x^j}$ is a basis of $C_{E_i}(x)$, which establish (2.13) and completes the proof.

To analyze the arithmetic relations of Lemmas 2.3 and 2.4, we need one further result:

Lemma 2.5
p^n *divides* $q^t + 1$.

Proof

By Lemma 2.4, we know that p^n divides $q^{2t} - 1$. Suppose first that p is odd, in which case p^n divides $q^t - 1$ or $q^t + 1$. If p^n divides $q^t - 1$, then the characteristic roots of x as a linear transformation of order p^n of $\bar{Q} = Q/Q'$, regarded as a vector space over Z_q, will all lie in $GF(q^t)$. But x acts irreducibly on $\bar{Q}$, which has dimension $2t$ over Z_q and consequently the characteristic polynomial of x is irreducible over Z_q and has degree $2t$. Hence $Z_q(\omega)$ is isomorphic to $GF(q^{2t})$ for any characteristic root ω of x, a contradiction. Thus p^n divides $q^t + 1$ in this case.

Assume next that $p = 2$. The argument of the preceding paragraph shows again that 2^n does not divide $q^t - 1$ and indeed that it does not divide $q^s - 1$ if $s < 2t$. However, since $q^t - 1$ and $q^t + 1$ are both even, we cannot draw the conclusion 2^n divides $q^t + 1$ directly from this fact. To complete the argument in this case we require Theorem 5.6.5. We have that Q is special and that x induces an automorphism of Q of order 2^n which acts irreducibly on $Q/\Phi(Q)$ and trivially on $Q' = \Phi(Q) = Z(Q)$. Thus that theorem is applicable and yields that 2^n divides $q^r + 1$ for some $r \leqslant t$.

But now 2^n divides $q^{2r} - 1 = (q^r + 1)(q^r - 1)$. By the preceding paragraph this is possible only if $2r \geqslant 2t$. Since $r \leqslant t$, we conclude that $r = t$ and the lemma follows.

Now combining Lemmas 2.3 and 2.4, we have

$$\frac{q^{2t} - 1}{p^n} + 1 = \sum_{i=1}^{m} (2i - 1)\alpha_i$$

(2.16)

$$q^t = \sum_{i=1}^{m} \alpha_i$$

$$p^n \geqslant \alpha_1 \geqslant \alpha_2 \geqslant \cdots \geqslant \alpha_m .$$

Our goal will be to show that the equations (2.16) have a unique solution in integers m and α_i, $1 \leqslant i \leqslant m$. By Lemma 2.5, $q^t + 1$ is divisible by p^n and consequently

(2.17) $q^t = ap^n + (p^n - 1)$

for some integer $a \geqslant 0$.

We shall prove

Lemma 2.6
The only solution of (2.16) *in integers* m *and* α_i, $1 \leqslant i \leqslant m$, *is*

$$m = a + 1 \qquad \alpha_i = p^n \quad 1 \leqslant i \leqslant m - 1 \qquad \alpha_m = p^n - 1.$$

Proof
First of all, with these values of m and α_i, we have

(2.18) $\sum_{i=1}^{m} \alpha_i = ap^n + (p^n - 1) = q^t$

by (2.17) and so the second equation of (2.16) holds. Furthermore,

(2.19)

$$\sum_{i=1}^{m} (2i - 1)\alpha_i = \sum_{i=1}^{a} (2i - 1)p^n + (2a + 1)(p^n - 1)$$

$$= a^2 p^n + (2ap^n + p^n - 2a - 1) = (a + 1)^2 p^n - (2a + 1).$$

On the other hand,

(2.20)

$$\frac{q^{2t} - 1}{p^n} + 1 = \frac{[(a + 1)p^n - 1]^2 - 1}{p^n} + 1$$

$$= \frac{[(a + 1)^2 p^{2n} - 2(a + 1)p^n + 1] - 1}{p^n} + 1 = (a + 1)^2 p^n - (2a + 1).$$

Combining (2.19) and (2.20) we obtain the first equation of (2.16). Since the third relation of (2.16) clearly holds, we see that these integers give a solution of (2.16).

To prove that this is the only solution of (2.16), we proceed as follows: Let β_i, $1 \leqslant i \leqslant h$, be an arbitrary sequence of integers such that

(2.21) $$q^t = \sum_{i=1}^{s} \beta_i \quad \text{and} \quad p^n \geqslant \beta_1 \geqslant \beta_2 \geqslant \cdots \geqslant \beta_s.$$

For brevity write $\beta = \{\beta_i | 1 \leqslant i \leqslant s\}$ and set

(2.22) $$f(\beta) = \sum_{i=1}^{s} (2i - 1)\beta_i.$$

Thus the integers s and β_i, $1 \leqslant i \leqslant s$, will represent a solution of (2.16) if and only if $f(\beta) = (q^{2t} - 1/p^n) + 1 = d + 1$. We shall now argue that, in fact, either $f(\beta) > d + 1$ or else

(2.23) $$s = a + 1 \qquad \beta_i = p^n \quad 1 \leqslant i < s \qquad \beta_s = p^n - 1,$$

which will prove the uniqueness of our solution of (2.16) and will establish the lemma.

Suppose then that s, β_i is not the solution (2.23). Then either $\beta_1 < p^n$ and $s > 1$ or $\beta_k = p^n$, $1 \leqslant k \leqslant j - 1 < s - 1$ and $\beta_j < p^n$. [Here we are using the fact that $q^t = ap^n + (p^n - 1)$.] In the first case, we consider the sequence β_i' defined by $\beta_1' = \beta_1 + 1$, $\beta_i' = \beta_i$, $2 \leqslant i \leqslant s - 1$, and $\beta_s' = \beta_s - 1$ if $\beta_s > 1$. On the other hand, if $\beta_s = 1$, we do not define β_s'. Correspondingly, we set $s' = s$ or $s' = s - 1$. In the second case, we consider the sequence β_i'

defined by $\beta'_k = \beta_k$, $1 \leqslant k \leqslant j-1$ and $j+1 \leqslant k \leqslant s-1$, $\beta'_j = \beta_j + 1$, and $\beta'_s = \beta_s - 1$ if $\beta_s > 1$, while again β'_s is undefined if $\beta_s = 1$. Again correspondingly we set $s' = s$ or $s - 1$. It follows at once in every case that the integers s' and β'_i, $1 \leqslant i \leqslant s'$, satisfy (2.21). Setting $\beta' = \{\beta'_i \mid 1 \leqslant i \leqslant s'\}$, we now compare $f(\beta')$ with $f(\beta)$. In the first case, we find by direct calculation that $f(\beta) - f(\beta') = (2s - 1) - 1$, while in the second that $f(\beta) - f(\beta') = (2s - 1) - (2j - 1)$. Hence, in either case,

$$(2.24) \qquad\qquad f(\beta) > f(\beta').$$

If β' is not the solution (2.23) we can repeat the argument on β', and can successively repeat it so long as we do not obtain the solution (2.23). On the other hand, it is clear from the definition of β' in terms of β that we must reach the solution (2.23) in a finite number of steps. Hence beginning with β we can determine a sequence $\beta = \beta^{(1)}$, $\beta' = \beta^{(2)}$, $\beta^{(3)}$, ..., $\beta^{(h)}$ of solutions of (2.21) with $\beta^{(h)}$ equal to the solution (2.23) with the property $f(\beta^{(i)}) > f(\beta^{(i+1)})$, $1 \leqslant i \leqslant h - 1$. But $f(\beta^{(h)}) = d + 1$ by the first part of the proof and so $f(\beta) > d + 1$, as asserted.

But now Lemma 2.6 together with Lemma 2.3 implies part (i) and (ii) of Theorem 2.1. Furthermore, part (iii) is an immediate consequence of (i) and (ii) and so the theorem is proved.

Remark It is not difficult to modify the proof of Theorem 2.1 to include the case that F is algebraically closed of characteristic 0 or prime to $|G|$, the minimal polynomial of x on V in this case being correspondingly $X^{p^n} - 1$ or $(X^{p^n} - 1)/(X - 1)$. This extension of the theorem, which we shall give in a sequence of exercises, is useful in the study of fixed-point-free automorphisms of solvable groups.

EXERCISES

Let G be a group of linear transformations acting irreducibly on a vector space V over an algebraically closed field F of characteristic 0 or prime to $|G|$. Assume $G = QP$, where $Q \lhd G$, Q is extra-special of order q^{2t+1}, $P = \langle x \rangle$ is cyclic of order p^n, and P acts faithfully and irreducibly on Q/Q' and trivially on Q'. Prove

1. $\dim_F V = q^t$; in particular, Q acts irreducibly on V.

2. Let λ_i be the distinct characteristic roots of x on V and let α_i be the multiplicity of λ_i, $1 \leqslant i \leqslant m$. If E denotes the enveloping algebra of Q, then $x \in E$ and

$$\dim_F C_E(x) = \sum_{i=1}^{m} \alpha_i^2.$$

3. Using Exercise 2 in place of Lemma 2.3(ii), show by an argument analogous to that of Lemma 2.6 that the minimal polynomial of x on V is either $X^{p^n} - 1$ or $(X^{p^n} - 1)/(X - 1)$, and in the latter case that $q' = p^n - 1$.

CHAPTER 12

GROUPS WITH GENERALIZED QUATERNION SYLOW 2-SUBGROUPS

In this short chapter we give a major application of exceptional character theory to prove the nonsimplicity of any group whose S_2-subgroups are generalized quaternion. Specifically we shall prove

Theorem 1.1 (Brauer-Suzuki)

Let G be a group with a generalized quaternion S_2-subgroup S of order at least 16 and let $K = O_{2'}(G)$ be the largest normal subgroup of G of odd order. Then the center of G/K is of order 2.

The same result holds when S is quaternion, but all known proofs require the theory of modular characters.

For convenience we break up the proof into a sequence of short lemmas, but first we introduce some notation. Let

$$S = \langle x, y \mid x^{2^n} = 1, \; y^2 = x^{2^{n-1}}, \; x^y = x^{-1} \rangle,$$

so that by assumption $n \geqslant 3$. Set $X = \langle x \rangle, T = \langle x^2 \rangle, R = \langle x^4 \rangle, C = C_G(T),$ and $N = N_G(T)$. Then we have

Lemma 1.2
   (i) $N = SH$, where $H \lhd N$ and $|H|$ is odd.
   (ii) $C = XH$.

Proof

We have $T = S' \lhd S$ and so $S \subseteq N$. On the other hand, since $n \geqslant 3$, S does not centralize T, so $S \cap C = X$. Since $C \lhd N$, X is an S_2-subgroup of N. But X is cyclic and hence C possesses a normal 2-complement H by Theorem 7.6.1. Since H char $C \lhd N$, also $H \lhd N$. Furthermore, by Lemma 5.4.1 any element of N of odd order centralizes T and so lies in H. Thus N/H is a 2-group and consequently $N = SH$, completing the proof.

Lemma 1.3

If $A = C - RH$, then A is disjoint from its conjugates in G and $N = N_G(A)$.

Proof

Note that if $z \in A$, then zH has order 2^n or 2^{n-1} in C/H. Correspondingly, $\langle z^2, H \rangle$ or $\langle z, H \rangle$ equals $TH = T \times H$. It follows at once that $\langle z^m \rangle = T$ for some integer m. But then if $z \in A \cap A^u$ for some u in G, our argument shows that $\langle z^m \rangle = T$ and T^u, so $u \in N_G(T) = N$. On the other hand, N normalizes both $C = XH$ and RH, as R char X, and so normalizes A. The lemma follows.

Now it is easily checked that the linear character of X which takes the value i on x has $R = \langle x^4 \rangle$ in its kernel and induces an irreducible character on S of degree 2. Hence there exists a linear character ψ of C having RH in its kernel which induces an irreducible character $\tilde{\psi}$ of N of degree 2. By definition of $\tilde{\psi}$, $\tilde{\psi}$ also has RH in its kernel. We next prove

Lemma 1.4

Set $\theta = \tilde{1}_C - \tilde{\psi}$. Then
  (i) $(\theta, \theta)_N = 3$.
  (ii) θ has degree 0 and has the value 0 on $N - A$.

Proof

Now $\tilde{1}_C$ is the character of the regular representation of N/C by Theorem 4.4.2. Since $|N/C| = 2$, $\tilde{1}_C$ has degree 2 and so is the sum of the two distinct linear characters of N having C in their kernels. Since $\tilde{\psi}$ is irreducible of degree 2, (i) follows from Theorem 4.2.4(i) since $\deg \theta = 0$. Furthermore, also $\tilde{1}_C$ has RH in its kernel, so θ is 0 on $RH = C - A$. By Theorem 4.4.3(ii), θ is 0 on $N - C$ as well and consequently θ is 0 on $N - A$.

Thus $\theta \in I_0(A)$. Since A is disjoint from its conjugates, Theorem 4.4.6 can now be applied to yield that $(\theta^*, \theta^*)_G = 3$. Since 1_N is a constituent of θ of multiplicity 1, the Frobenius reciprocity theorem implies that 1_G is a constituent of θ^* of the same multiplicity. Since $\deg \theta^* = \deg \theta = 0$ by Theorem 4.4.1, we must have

Lemma 1.5

There exist distinct nonprincipal irreducible characters χ_1, χ of G such that

$$\theta^* = 1_G + \chi_1 - \chi.$$

In particular,

$$\chi(1) = 1 + \chi_1(1).$$

The second statement follows from the first since $0 = \deg \theta^* = \theta^*(1)$.

By Theorem 4.4.3(ii), θ^* is 0 on any element not in a conjugate of A. But no element of A has odd order or is an involution. Hence by Lemma 1.5 we have

Lemma 1.6

If y is an involution or an element of odd order of G, then

$$\theta^*(y) = 0 \qquad and \qquad \chi(y) = 1 + \chi_1(y).$$

On the other hand, we have

Lemma 1.7

If $\beta(y)$ denotes the number of ordered pairs of involutions whose product is y, then $\beta(y) = 0$ if y is of even order.

Proof

Suppose $uv = y$ with u, v involutions, $y \in G^{\#}$ and $|y| = 2s$, s an integer. Then u and v invert y by Theorem 9.1.1 and so centralize $z = y^s$, which is also an involution. If $u \neq z$, then $\langle u, z \rangle$ is a four group and so lies in an S_2-subgroup of G. But each S_2-subgroup of G, being generalized quaternion, possesses a unique involution. Hence $u = z$. For the same reason $v = z$, so $u = v$ and $uv = 1$, a contradiction. Thus $\beta(y) = 0$, as asserted.

Since each S_2-subgroup of G has a unique involution, it follows from Sylow's theorem that G possesses only one class of involutions, which we denote by K. Now by equation (9.4.2),

$$(1.1) \qquad \beta(y) = \frac{|G|}{|C_G(u)|^2} \sum_{i=1}^{r} \frac{\zeta_i^2(u)}{\zeta_i(1)} \zeta_i(y),$$

where $\zeta_i, 1 \leqslant i \leqslant r$, are the irreducible characters of G, $u \in K$, and $y \in G$. By the preceding two lemmas $\beta(y)\overline{\theta^*(y)} = 0$ for every element y of G and consequently

$$(1.2) \qquad (\beta, \theta^*)_G = 0.$$

Since $\theta^* = 1_G + \chi_1 - \chi$ and χ_1, χ are irreducible characters of G, (1.1) and (1.2) together with Theorem 4.2.4(i) now yield

Lemma 1.8

For any involution u of G,

$$1 + \frac{\chi_1^2(u)}{\chi_1(u)} - \frac{\chi^2(u)}{\chi(1)} = 0.$$

Lemma 1.8 in turn gives

Lemma 1.9

The kernel of χ contains every involution of G.

Proof

Since $\chi_1(1) = \chi(1) - 1$ and $\chi_1(u) = \chi(u) - 1$ by Lemmas 1.5 and 1.6, we can substitute in the preceding equation and clear denominators to obtain

(1.3) $(\chi(1) - 1)\chi(1) + (\chi(u) - 1)^2\chi(1) + \chi(u)^2(\chi(1) - 1) = 0,$

which reduces upon expansion to

(1.4) $(\chi(u) - \chi(1))^2 = 0.$

Hence $\chi(u) = \chi(1)$ and the lemma follows.

Since $\chi(1) = 1 + \chi_1(1)$, we see that $\deg \chi \geqslant 2$. Our argument has thus shown that any group G with generalized quaternion S_2-subgroups possesses a nonlinear irreducible character whose kernel contains all the involutions of G. With this information we can now easily complete the proof of the theorem.

Let M be the normal subgroup of G generated by all its involutions and set $Q = S \cap M$, so that Q is an S_2-subgroup of M. We shall argue that Q is cyclic. Indeed, if not, then Q must be a generalized quaternion and so must contain yx^i for some i. Since $Q \lhd S$, also $(yx^i)^x = yx^{i+2} \in Q$, whence $x^2 \in Q$. Thus $|S : Q| \leqslant 2$ and, in particular, S/Q is abelian. On the other hand, consider the group $G_1 = SM$. The conclusion of the preceding paragraph implies that G_1 possesses a nonlinear irreducible character ϕ whose kernel K_1 contains all involutions of G_1. But every involution of G lies in G_1 and together they generate M, so $M \subseteq K_1$. But then G_1/K_1 is a homomorphic image of $G_1/M = SM/M$, which is isomorphic to S/Q. Since S/Q is abelian, so also is G_1/K_1. Since K_1 is the kernel of ϕ, it follows that ϕ is a linear character of G_1, which is not the case. We conclude that Q is cyclic, asserted.

But now M has a normal 2-complement L by Theorem 7.6.1. Since L char $M \lhd G$, we have $L \lhd G$ and so $L \subseteq K = O_{2'}(G)$. Since $M = LQ$ and $M \lhd G$, this yields $KQ \lhd G$. Setting $\bar{G} = G/K$, it follows that $\bar{Q}$, and hence also $\Omega_1(\bar{Q})$, is normal in $\bar{G}$, where $\bar{Q}$ is the image of Q in $\bar{G}$. But

$|\Omega_1(\bar{Q})| = 2$ as Q is cyclic and so $\Omega_1(\bar{Q}) \subseteq Z(\bar{G})$. On the other hand, $O_{2'}(\bar{G}) = 1$, whence $O_{2'}(Z(\bar{G})) = 1$ and therefore $Z(\bar{G})$ is a 2-group. But the center of S and hence also of an S_2-subgroup of $\bar{G}$ has order 2; so we conclude that $\Omega_1(\bar{Q}) = Z(\bar{G})$. This completes the proof of Theorem 1.1.

Remark If Z denotes the inverse image of $Z(G/O_{2'}(G))$ in G, the Brauer-Suzuki theorem asserts that $|Z|$ is twice an odd number. But then it follows directly that an S_2-subgroup of G/Z is dihedral. Hence once the classification of all groups with dihedral S_2-subgroups is established, it is possible to make a much stronger statement about the structure of $\bar{G} = G/O_{2'}(G)$. In fact, it can be shown that $\bar{G}$ is isomorphic to either an S_2-subgroup of G or to a uniquely determined extension of A_7 by a group of order 2 or else that $\bar{G}$ contains a normal subgroup $\bar{L}$ isomorphic to $SL(2, q)$, q odd, with $\bar{G}/\bar{L}$ cyclic of odd order.

CHAPTER 13

ZASSENHAUS GROUPS

A complete classification of Zassenhaus groups—doubly transitive groups in which only the identity fixes three letters—has been achieved by the combined efforts of Zassenhaus, Feit, Suzuki, and Ito. This is an extremely important class of groups, for it includes two of the families of simple groups " of rank 1 ": the groups $L_2(q), q > 3$, and the Suzuki groups. It thus bears directly on three major classification problems: groups with dihedral Sylow 2-subgroups, groups with abelian Sylow 2-subgroups, and groups in which the centralizer of every nonidentity element is nilpotent.

Here we shall present only some of the steps in the classification of Zassenhaus groups. Section 1 gives a number of their elementary properties. In Section 2 we shall derive Feit's key result, which asserts that the degree of a Zassenhaus group is necessarily of the form $1 + p^a$ for some prime p. The proof provides an excellent application of Feit's results on coherence which we established in Chapter 4.

Finally, in Section 3 we shall give a complete classification of a special class of Zassenhaus groups. The proof involves a fundamental, quite general, method—the characterization of a group in terms of a canonical set of generators and relations.

1. ELEMENTARY PROPERTIES

We first establish some basic properties of Zassenhaus groups.

Theorem 1.1

Let G be a Zassenhaus group of degree $n + 1$ and let N be the subgroup fixing a letter. Then we have

- (i)   *N is a Frobenius group with kernel K of order n and complement H.*
- (ii) *K is a Hall subgroup of G, K is disjoint from its conjugates, and $N = N_G(K)$. Moreover, $C_G(y) \subseteq K$ and $C^*(y) \subseteq N$ for all y in $K^\#$.*
- (iii) *H is a subgroup of G fixing two letters, H is disjoint from its conjugates in G, and $|N_G(H) : H| = 2$.*
- (iv) *$|G| = en(n + 1)$, where $e = |H|$ and e divides $n - 1$.*

Proof

Let G act on $S = \{1, 2, \ldots, n + 1\}$ and let N fix 1. Since G is doubly transitive and only the identity fixes three letters, N acts transitively on $T = S - \{1\}$ and only the identity of N fixes two letters. By definition of a Zassenhaus group, the subgroup fixing two letters of S, and hence fixing a letter of T, is nontrivial. Therefore, N is a Frobenius group in its action on T and so by Frobenius' theorem possesses a normal subgroup K of order $n = |T|$, where $K^\#$ consists of the set of elements of N fixing no letter of T. Moreover, a Frobenius complement H in N is the subgroup fixing a letter i of T, say $i = 2$. Thus H fixes 1 and 2 and so is a subgroup of G fixing two letters.

Let $y \in K^\#$ and $x \in G$. Since the elements of $K^\#$ fix only the letter 1, y^x fixes only the letter $(1)x$. But then if $y^x \in K$, we must have $(1)x = 1$, whence $x \in N$. It follows immediately from this that K is disjoint from its conjugates and that $N = N_G(K)$. In particular, if $y \in K^\#$ and $x \in C_G^*(y)$, then $K \cap K^x \neq 1$, so $x \in N$. Thus $C_G^*(y) \subseteq N$. Since N is a Frobenius group, it follows that $C_G(y) \subseteq K$.

Next let $y \in H^\#$ and $x \in G$. Since no element of $G^\#$ fixes three letters, y^x fixes only the letters $(1)x$ and $(2)x$. But then if $y^x \in H$, x must transform the set $\{1, 2\}$ into itself. This implies at once that H^x fixes 1 and 2, whence $x \in N_G(H)$. Thus also H is disjoint from its conjugates. Furthermore, the elements of $N_G(H)$ necessarily transform the set $\{1, 2\}$ into itself. Since G, being doubly transitive, contains an element which interchanges 1 and 2, we conclude that $|N_G(H) : H| = 2$.

Finally if $e = |H|$, we have $|G| = en(n + 1)$ by Theorem 2.7.3(iii). Since

N is a Frobenius group, e divides $n - 1$. In particular, n is prime to $e(n + 1)$ and so K is a Hall subgroup of G. All parts of the theorem are thus proved.

For convenience we shall say that G is of *type* (H, K) if K is the Frobenius kernel and H a Frobenius complement of a subgroup N of G fixing a letter.

Theorem 1.2

Let G be a Zassenhaus group of type (H, K) and let w be an element of $N_G(H) - H$. Then every element x of G, not in $N = HK$, has a unique representation in the form

$$x = y_1 w y_2 u,$$

where $u \in H$ and $y_i \in K$, $1 \leqslant i \leqslant 2$.

Proof

By Theorem 1.1(iii), such an element w of $N_G(H)$ exists and $w^2 \in H$. Furthermore, the proof of Theorem 2.7.3 shows that $G = N \cup NwN$. Hence any element x of $G - N$ can be written in the form $x = z_1 w z_2$ with z_1, z_2 in N. Now $z_1 = y_1 v$, where $v \in H$, $y_1 \in K$. Therefore, $x = y_1 v w z_2 = y_1 w (w^{-1} v w z_2)$ and $z_2' = w^{-1} v w z_2 \in N$ since $w \in N_G(H)$ and $H \subseteq N$. Hence $z_2' = y_2 u$ with $u \in H$, $y_2 \in K$, and consequently $x = y_1 w y_2 u$.

Suppose we also have $x = z_1 w z_2 v$ with $v \in H$ and $z_i \in K, 1 \leqslant i \leqslant 2$. Then $w^{-1} z_1^{-1} y_1 w = z_2 v u^{-1} y_2^{-1}$ and so lies in N. But $|w^{-1} z_1^{-1} y_1 w| = |z_1^{-1} y_1|$ and hence is a divisor of $|K|$. However, K is a Hall subgroup of G, whence $w^{-1} z_1^{-1} y_1 w$ lies in K as well as K^w. Since K is disjoint from its conjugates, either $z_1^{-1} y_1 = 1$ or $w \in N = N_G(K)$. However, in the latter case, $w \in N_N(H) = H$, contrary to our choice of w. Thus $y_1 = z_1$. But then also $y_2 u = z_2 v$. Since $H \cap K = 1$, this forces $u = v$ and $y_2 = z_2$. Therefore the expression for x is unique.

Theorem 1.3

Let G be a Zassenhaus group of type (H, K) with $|H| = e$ and $|K| = n$. Then we have

(i) *If e is even, K is abelian.*

(ii) *If $e \geqslant \frac{1}{2}(n - 1)$, K is an elementary abelian p-group for some prime p.*

Proof

If e is even, H contains an element u of order 2 and so u induces by conjugation a fixed-point-free automorphism of K of order 2. But then K is abelian by Theorem 10.1.4.

Now assume $e \geqslant \frac{1}{2}(n - 1)$. Since K is nilpotent, (ii) will follow from Theorem 2.1.4 if we can show that K is characteristically simple. If not, then K possesses a nontrivial proper H-invariant subgroup L. Since each orbit of L^{*} under the action of H contains e elements, $|L| \geqslant e + 1$, whence $|L| \geqslant \frac{1}{2}(n - 1) + 1 = \frac{1}{2}n + \frac{1}{2}$. However, this is impossible since $|L| < n$ and $|L|$ divides n.

Theorem 1.4

Let G be a simple Zassenhaus group of degree $n + 1$ and type (H, K) in which $e = |H|$ is odd. Then the following conditions hold:
  (i) H is cyclic and $N_G(H)$ is a Frobenius group.
  (ii) G has only one class of involutions.
  (iii) The only strongly real elements of K^{*} are involutions.
  (iv) The number of involutions of G is $e(n + 1)$ if n is even and is en if n is odd.
  (v) There are at least e conjugate classes of G not containing elements of K.

Proof

The Sylow subgroups of H are all cyclic by Theorem 10.3.1(iv). Let w be an element of order 2 in $L = N_G(H)$. If w inverts H, then H is abelian by Theorem 10.1.4. But then H is cyclic by Theorem 1.3.1(ii), as its Sylow subgroups are cyclic. In this case L is a Frobenius group (in fact, a dihedral group) and (i) holds.

Suppose then that w does not invert H, in which case $C = C_H(w) \neq 1$. We shall argue that $C \subseteq H'$. Since $|L : H| = 2$, and $|H|$ is odd, the Sylow subgroups of L are also cyclic, so L is metacyclic by Theorem 7.6.2. Thus L' and L/L' are each cyclic. But $L' \subseteq H$ as L/H is abelian and consequently w centralizes H/L'. Lemma 10.4.1(i) now yields that $CL' = H$. Since $H' \subseteq L'$, we have either $C \subseteq H'$ or $L' = H$. However, since L' is cyclic, it follows in the latter case that $H' = 1$, so $C \not\subseteq H'$ in this case as well.

Now w leaves an S_p-subgroup P of H invariant for each prime p by Theorem 6.2.2(i) and by the preceding paragraph we can choose P so that $P \cap C \neq 1$ and $P \not\subseteq H'$. By Theorem 5.2.4, w centralizes P. Let Q be an S_p-subgroup of G containing P. Since H is disjoint from its conjugates, $N_Q(P) \subseteq L$, whence $N_Q(P) = P$. But then $Q = P$ by Theorem 1.2.11(ii). Thus P is an S_p-subgroup of G. If $M = N_G(P)$, the same argument shows that $M \subseteq L$. However, as $P \not\subseteq H'$ and w centralizes P, L, and hence also M, possesses a normal subgroup of index p. Thus $P \cap M' \subset P$. But as P is abelian, $P \cap M' = P \cap G'$ by Theorem 7.4.4. Therefore G also possesses a normal subgroup of index p, contrary to the simplicity of G. Thus (i) holds.

Suppose next that n is even and let S be an S_2-subgroup of K. Then S is an S_2-subgroup of G and is disjoint from its conjugates by Theorem 1.1(ii). Therefore G has only one class of involutions by Theorem 9.1.4. Since K is nilpotent, there exists an involution y in $Z(K)$. Then $C_G(y) = K$ by Theorem 1.1(ii) and so $|G : C_G(y)| = e(n + 1)$. Thus G contains exactly $e(n + 1)$ involutions in this case. Furthermore, $N = HK$ contains both the centralizer of each of its involutions and $N_G(S)$. Since G is simple, also not every involution of G lies in N. Hence N has only one class of involutions by Theorem 9.2.1(ii) and therefore every involution of N lies in $Z(K)$. Now suppose $y \in K^\#$ and y is strongly real, so that $y = uv$, where u, v are involutions and u, v invert y. Then $u, v \in N$ by Theorem 1.1(ii) and consequently u, v lie in $Z(K)$. Thus $uv = vu$ and $y^2 = (uv)^2 = 1$. Hence (ii), (iii), and (iv) hold when n is even.

Now assume n is odd, whence $|N| = en$ is odd. Since $C_G^*(y) \subseteq N$ for all y in $K^\#$, it follows that $K^\#$ contains no strongly real elements. But then if $Ku = Kv$ for involutions u and v, we must have $u = v$, since otherwise uv would be a strongly real element of $K^\#$. Thus a right coset of K in $G - N$ contains at most one involution. Since N has no involutions, the number of involutions in G is therefore at most $e(n + 1) - e = en$. On the other hand, G contains an involution y as $|G|$ is even. To complete the proof of (ii), (iii), and (iv), it will suffice to show that $(en, |C_G(y)|) = 1$, for then $|C_G(y)|$ divides $n + 1$ and consequently the conjugate class containing y has $|G : C_G(y)| \geqslant en$ elements. But then G has exactly en involutions and they are all conjugate to y.

If $|C_G(y)|$ is not prime to en, then y centralizes an element x of prime order p with $p \mid en$. If $x \mid n$, x lies in a conjugate K_1 of K, whence $y \in C_G(x) \subseteq K_1$, a contradiction. Thus $x \mid e$. But as e is odd and $e \mid (n - 1)$, $(e, n(n + 1)) = 1$, so H is also a Hall subgroup of G. Thus x lies in a conjugate H_1 of H. But now it follows at once from (i) and Theorem 1.1(iii) that $C_G(x) \subseteq H_1$, giving the same contradiction.

Finally, let t be the number of strongly real conjugate classes of G. By (ii) and (iii), $t - 1$ of these classes do not contain involutions and of these only the class $\{1\}$ has an element in common with K. Thus there are at least $t - 2$ conjugate classes not consisting of involutions which have no elements in common with K.

If n is even, $e(n + 1)$ is the number of involutions of G by (iv). But then Theorem 9.1.8 yields

$$\text{(1.1)} \qquad t - 1 \geqslant \frac{e(n+1)(e(n+1)+1)}{en(n+1)} = \frac{e(n+1)+1}{n} > e,$$

whence $t - 2 \geqslant e$. Hence (v) follows from the preceding paragraph.

On the other hand, if n is odd, (iv) and Theorem 9.1.8 give

$$\text{(1.2)} \qquad t - 1 \geqslant \frac{en(en+1)}{en(n+1)} = \frac{en+1}{n+1} = e - \frac{e-1}{n+1}.$$

Since $e < n$, (1.2) implies that $t - 1 > e - 1$, whence $t - 2 \geqslant e - 1$. Since K has no involutions, (v) follows in this case as well.

Remark If G is a simple Zassenhaus group of type (H, K) in which $e = |H|$ is even, then an S_2-subgroup of H is either cyclic or generalized quaternion by Theorem 10.3.1(iv). It can be shown by studying the fusion of 2-elements in G that $N_G(H)$ contains an S_2-subgroup S of G and that S is dihedral or semidihedral according as $S \cap H$ is cyclic or generalized quaternion; however, we shall not need this result.

2. FEIT'S THEOREM

In this section we shall prove a key result needed for the classification of Zassenhaus groups, which will also provide an application of the concept of coherence developed in Section 4.6.

Theorem 2.1 (Feit)

Let G be a simple Zassenhaus group of degree $n + 1$ and type (H, K) in which $e = |H|$ is odd. Then

  (i) *K is a p-group for some prime p.*
  (ii) *Either $e \geqslant \frac{1}{2}(n-1)$ or K is nonabelian and $|K:K'| \leqslant 4e^2 + 1$.*

Proof

If $e \geqslant \frac{1}{2}(n-1)$, then K is an elementary abelian p-group by Theorem 1.3(ii). Hence we may assume that $e < \frac{1}{2}(n-1)$. Since K is nilpotent, disjoint from its conjugates, and $N = N_G(K)$ is a Frobenius group, Theorem 4.6.5 is applicable. Since $e \neq n - 1$, (ii) follows if $I(K)$ is not coherent. Hence we may also assume that $I(K)$ is coherent. We shall argue that the coherence of $I(K)$ forces $e \geqslant \frac{1}{2}(n-1)$ and this will suffice to complete the proof.

Let ζ_i, $1 \leqslant i \leqslant t$, be the irreducible characters of $I(K)$, so that the ζ_i are all the nonprincipal irreducible characters of N with support on K. The ζ_i are induced from the nonprincipal irreducible characters of K. Since K

is nilpotent, some ζ_i, say ζ_1, has degree e. Set $\zeta = \zeta_1$. Also let τ be the isometry of $I(K)$ into ch (G) which extends the induction map $*$ of $I_0(K)$ into $\mathrm{ch}_0(G)$. We shall prove in a sequence of lemmas that ζ^τ has degree e. Once this is accomplished, an argument of Brauer can be applied to yield the desired conclusion. (Compare the proof of Theorem 4.7.11, which employs a similar argument.)

Lemma 2.2

The following conditions hold:
 (i) $\zeta^*(y) = \zeta(y)$ for y in $K^\#$.
 (ii) $(\zeta^*, \zeta^*)_G = e + 1$.

Proof

First of all, (i) follows from Theorem 4.4.6(i). Now deg $\zeta^* = (n + 1)e$ as $|G : N| = n + 1$; also ζ^* is 0 outside of the conjugates of K. Since K is disjoint from its conjugates and K has $|G|/ne$ conjugates, it follows from (i) and the definition of $(\zeta^*, \zeta^*)_G$ that

$$(2.1) \qquad (\zeta^*, \zeta^*)_G = \frac{1}{|G|} \left\{ (n + 1)^2 e^2 + \frac{|G|}{ne} \sum_{y \in K^\#} \zeta(y) \overline{\zeta(y)} \right\}$$

$$= \frac{1}{|G|} \left\{ (n + 1)^2 e^2 - \frac{|G| e^2}{ne} + \frac{|G|}{ne} \sum_{y \in K} \zeta(y) \zeta(\bar{y}) \right\}.$$

However, as $\zeta(y) = 0$ for y in $N - K$, the final sum is the same as that over N and so equals $|N|(\zeta, \zeta)_N = ne$ as ζ is irreducible. Substituting this in (2.1) and using $|G| = ne(e + 1)$, (2.1) reduces to

$$(2.2) \qquad (\zeta^*, \zeta^*)_G = \left\{ \frac{(n + 1)e}{n} - \frac{e}{n} + 1 \right\} = e + 1,$$

proving (ii).

Lemma 2.3

The following conditions hold:
 (i) $\zeta_i^\tau(y) = \zeta_i(y)$ for all y in $K^\#$, $i \leqslant i \leqslant t$,
 (ii) $\zeta_i^* = \zeta_i^\tau + \dfrac{\deg \zeta_i}{e} \psi$, $i \leqslant i \leqslant t$,

  where ψ is a sum of e distinct irreducible characters of G, none of which is contained in $I(K)^\tau$.

Proof

We first argue that any nonprincipal irreducible character χ of G that is not in $I(K)^\tau$ is a constituent of ζ^*. Indeed, if not, then by the Frobenius reciprocity theorem, $(\zeta, \chi|_N)_N = 0$. But χ has a constant value a on $K^\#$ by Theorem 4.6.6 while ζ is 0 on $N - K$. Hence

$$(2.3) \qquad 0 = (\zeta, \chi|_N)_N = \frac{1}{|N|}\chi(1)e + \frac{1}{|N|}\sum_{y \in N^\#} a\zeta(y).$$

Since $\sum_{y \in N} \zeta(y) = 0$ by Theorem 4.2.1(iii) and $\zeta(1) = e$, (2.3) reduces to

$$(2.4) \qquad 0 = \frac{e}{|N|}(\chi(1) - a).$$

Thus $\chi(1) = a = \chi(y)$ for all y in $K^\#$ and K lies in the kernel of χ, contrary to the simplicity of G.

Now, $t = n - 1/e$ is the number of conjugate classes of elements of $K^\#$. Hence by Theorem 1.4(v), G has at least $t + 1 + e$ conjugate classes and so also at least $t + i + e$ irreducible characters. Since $I(K)$ contains exactly t irreducible characters, it follows from the preceding paragraph that there exist e distinct irreducible nonprincipal characters χ_j of G with no χ_j in $I(K)^\tau$, each of which is a constituent of ζ^*, $1 \leqslant j \leqslant e$. We set

$$(2.5) \qquad \psi = \sum_{j=1}^{e} \chi_j.$$

We next make a similar calculation with $\chi = \zeta_i^\tau$. By Theorem 4.6.6, we have for y in $K^\#$,

$$(2.6) \qquad \zeta_i^\tau(y) = \zeta_i(y) + \frac{\deg \zeta_i}{e}c \qquad 1 \leqslant i \leqslant t,$$

for some fixed integer c. But then as $\overline{\zeta(y)} = 0$ for y in $N - K$, we obtain

$$(2.7) \quad (\zeta_i^\tau, \zeta^*)_G = (\zeta_i^\tau|_N, \zeta)_N = \frac{1}{|N|}\left(e \deg \zeta_i + \sum_{y \in N^\#}\left(\zeta_i(y) + \frac{\deg \zeta_i}{e}c\right)\overline{\zeta(y)}\right).$$

Since $\sum_{y \in N}\overline{\zeta(y)} = 0$ and $\sum_{y \in N}\zeta_i(y)\overline{\zeta(y)} = |N|\delta_{i1}$ with $\delta_{i1} = 0$ or 1 according as $i \neq 1$ or $i = 1$, (2.7) reduces to

$$(2.8) \qquad (\zeta_i^\tau, \zeta^*)_G = \delta_{i1} - \frac{c \deg \zeta_i}{|N|}.$$

But $t = n - 1/e \geqslant 3$ as $e < \frac{1}{2}(n - 1)$. Hence if $c \neq 0$, $\pm\zeta_i^\tau$ would be a constituent of ζ^* for both $i = 2$ and 3. By the first part of the proof, ζ^* would then contain at least $e + 2$ distinct irreducible constituents, contrary to Lemma 2.2(ii). Thus $c = 0$ and, in particular, (i) follows from (2.6).

Moreover, $(\zeta^\tau, \zeta^*)_G = (\zeta_1^\tau, \zeta^*)_G = 1$ by (2.8). Thus ζ^τ is an irreducible character of G and we conclude from Lemma 2.2(ii) and (2.5) that

$$(2.9) \qquad\qquad \zeta^* = \zeta^\tau + \psi.$$

Finally, as ζ^τ is irreducible and $t \geqslant 3$, the coherence of $I(K)$ yields that ζ_i^τ is an irreducible character for all i and that

$$(2.10) \qquad\qquad \zeta_i^* - \frac{\deg \zeta_i}{e} \zeta^* = \zeta_i^\tau - \frac{\deg \zeta_1}{e} \zeta^\tau.$$

But now (2.9) and (2.10) together imply (ii).

We now bring the irreducible characters of N having K in their kernels into the argument. These are the same as the irreducible characters of the cyclic group N/K of order e. There are thus $e - 1$ such nonprincipal characters, each of degree 1, which we denote by η_j, $1 \leqslant j \leqslant e - 1$. If $H = \langle x \rangle$ and α is a primitive eth root of unity, we can choose the numbering so that $\eta_j(x) = \alpha^j$, $1 \leqslant j \leqslant e - 1$. Since $\bar{\eta}_j(x) = \overline{\eta_j(x)} = \eta_j(x^{-1}) = \alpha^{-1}$, we see that for $j \leqslant s = (e - 1)/2$, we have $\bar{\eta}_j = \eta_{j+s}$.

Lemma 2.4

The following conditions hold:

(i) $\eta_j^*(y) = \eta_j(y) + \overline{\eta_j(y)}$ *for y in $H^\#$, $1 \leqslant j \leqslant s$.*

(ii) $\eta_j^*(y) = 1$ *for y in $K^\#$, $1 \leqslant j \leqslant s$.*

(iii) *The η_j^* are distinct irreducible characters of G.*

(iv) $1_N^* = 1_G + \Theta$, *where Θ is an irreducible character of G which is 0 on $K^\#$.*

Proof

Set $L = N_G(H)$, so that by Theorem 1.4(i) L is a Frobenius group of order $2e$. Let w be an involution of L. Since H is disjoint from its conjugates and N is a Frobenius group, it follows that for y in $H^\#$, if $y^u \in N$, then either $u \in N$ or $u = wz$, where $z \in N$. But

$$\eta_j^*(y) = \frac{1}{|N|} \sum_{u \in G} \eta_j(y^u),$$

where η_j is defined to be 0 on $G - N$. But now using the fact that η_j is a class function on N, we conclude at once that $\eta_j^*(y) = \eta_j(y) + \eta_j(y^w)$. Since $y^w = y^{-1}$, we have $\eta_j(y^w) = \bar{\eta}_j(y)$, and (i) follows. We note that the same calculation also yields $1_N^*(y) = 2$ for y in $H^\#$.

Similarly, if $y \in K^\#$ and $y^u \in N$, then $y^u \in K$ and $u \in N$, as K is also disjoint from its conjugates. Since η_j is 1 on K, we compute directly that $\eta_j^*(y) = 1$ and that $1_N^*(y) = 1$ for y in $K^\#$. In particular, (ii) holds.

Now the given permutation representation of G is equivalent to that on the right cosets of N, as N is the subgroup fixing a letter. Since G is doubly transitive, Theorems 4.3.4(ii) and 4.4.2 imply that $1_N^* = 1_G + \theta$, where θ is an irreducible character of G. Since $1_N^*(y) = 1$ for y in $K^\#$, $\theta(y) = 0$ for y in $K^\#$, so (iv) also holds.

Finally, η_j^* and 1_N^* are each 0 outside of the conjugates of N, have the same value 1 on $K^\#$ and $|G:N| = n + 1$ on 1. Moreover, by (i), $\eta_j^*(y)\overline{\eta_j^*(y)} \le 2$ for all y in $H^\#$ and is strictly less than 2 on the generator x of $H^\#$. Since $1_N^*(y) = 2$ for y in $H^\#$, we conclude that

$$(2.11) \quad (\eta_j^*, \eta_j^*)_G = \frac{1}{|G|} \sum_{y \in G} \eta_j^*(y)\overline{\eta_j^*(y)} < \frac{1}{|G|} \sum_{y \in G} 1_N^*(y)\overline{1_N^*(y)} = (1_N^*, 1_N^*)_G.$$

But $(1_N^*, 1_N^*)_G = 2$ by (iv) and consequently $(\eta_j^*, \eta_j^*)_G = 1$, whence η_j^* is irreducible, $1 \le j \le s$. Furthermore, $\eta_j^* \neq \eta_k^*$ for $j \neq k, 1 \le j, k \le s$, since otherwise by (i) $\eta_j + \bar{\eta}_j$ and $\eta_k + \bar{\eta}_k$ would be the same characters of N/K, which is not the case. This establishes (iii) and completes the proof.

Finally we prove

Lemma 2.5

$$\deg \zeta^\tau = e.$$

Proof

We shall argue that $\zeta^\tau|_N = \zeta$. Since $\deg \zeta = \zeta(1) = e$, this will imply the lemma. First of all, no ζ_i is constant on $K^\#$, $1 \le i \le t$. But θ and each η_j^* is constant on $K^\#$ by Lemma 2.4(ii) and (iv). Since $\zeta_i^\tau = \zeta_i$ on $K^\#$ by Lemma 2.3(i), it follows that neither θ nor any $\eta_j^*, 1 \le j \le s$, is of the form ζ_i^τ.

Now clearly $\bar{\eta}_j$ also induces η_j^*. Hence by the Frobenius reciprocity theorem,

$$(2.12) \qquad 0 = (\zeta^\tau, \eta_j^*)_G = (\zeta^\tau|_N, \eta_j)_N = (\zeta^\tau|_N, \bar{\eta}_j)_N.$$

Thus no η_j nor $\bar{\eta}_j$ is a constituent of $\zeta^\tau|_N$. Furthermore, the representation $\tilde{1}_K$ induced by 1_K on N is the regular representation of N/K and consequently

$$(2.13) \qquad \tilde{1}_K = 1_N + \sum_{j=1}^s (\eta_j + \bar{\eta}_j)$$

by Theorem 3.6.14(iv). But $1_K^* = \tilde{1}_K^*$ by Theorem 4.4.4. Since η_j and $\bar{\eta}_j$ each induce η_j^*, we obtain from Lemma 2.4(iv) that

$$(2.14) \qquad\qquad 1_K^* = 1_G + \theta + 2 \sum_{j=1}^{s} \eta_j^*.$$

Hence ζ^τ is not a constituent of 1_K^* and so by the Frobenius reciprocity theorem 1_N is not a constituent of $\zeta^\tau|_N$.

Similarly by Lemma 2.3(ii), ζ^τ is not a constituent of ζ_i^* for all $i > 1$ and so ζ_i is not a constituent of $\zeta^\tau|_N$, $2 \leqslant i \leqslant t$. But $1_N, \eta_j, \bar{\eta}_j, \zeta_i, 1 \leqslant j \leqslant s$, $1 \leqslant i \leqslant t$, are all the irreducible characters of N. We conclude therefore that $\zeta^\tau|_N$ is a multiple of $\zeta = \zeta_1$. But ζ^τ and ζ take the same values on $K^\# \subseteq N$ by Lemma 2.3(i). Hence $\zeta^\tau|_N = \zeta$ and the lemma is proved.

We can now readily establish that $e \geqslant \frac{1}{2}(n-1)$. Indeed, we have for all y in G,

$$(2.15) \qquad \left(\frac{\deg \zeta_2}{e} \zeta^\tau(y) - \zeta_2^\tau(y) \right) (\eta_j^*(y) - 1_G(y)) = 0,$$

since the first factor is 0 outside of the conjugates of $K^\#$, while the second is 0 on the conjugates of $K^\#$ by Lemma 2.4(ii). But then for $1 \leqslant j \leqslant s$,

$$(2.16) \qquad \frac{\deg \zeta_2}{e} \zeta^\tau \eta_j^* + \zeta_2^\tau = \zeta_2^\tau \eta_j^* + \frac{\deg \zeta_2}{e} \zeta^\tau,$$

inasmuch as each side is a character of G taking the same values on each element of G by (2.15) and the definition of the product of two characters. It follows from (2.16) that ζ^τ, being distinct from ζ_2^τ, is a constituent of $\zeta^\tau \eta_j^*$. But now Theorem 4.2.6 yields that η_j^* is a constituent of $\zeta^\tau \overline{\zeta^\tau}$, $1 \leqslant j \leqslant s$.

Now $\deg \eta_j^* = |G:N| = n + 1$, $1 \leqslant j \leqslant s$, while $\deg \zeta^\tau \overline{\zeta^\tau} = e^2$ since ζ^τ has degree e by the preceding lemma. Furthermore, 1_G is also a constituent of $\zeta^\tau \overline{\zeta^\tau}$ by Theorem 4.2.6. Since $s = (e-1)/2$, we conclude that

$$(2.17) \qquad\qquad e^2 \geqslant 1 + \frac{e-1}{2}(n+1).$$

Subtracting 1 and then dividing by $e - 1$, it follows at once that $e \geqslant \frac{1}{2}(n-1)$. This completes the proof of Feit's theorem.

3. CLASSIFICATION OF CERTAIN ZASSENHAUS GROUPS

We have shown in Section 2.8 that the groups $L_2(p^r)$, $p^r > 3$, are simple Zassenhaus groups of degree $n + 1$ (with $n = p^r$) and type (H, K) with H cyclic, inverted by an involution, and of order $e = n - 1$ if n is even and of order $e = \frac{1}{2}(n - 1)$ if n is odd. Moreover, we shall prove in Section 15.1 that they are, in fact, simple. Our aim in the present section will be to show conversely that, up to isomorphism, these are the only Zassenhaus groups which satisfy these conditions.

The proof of this result will illustrate a fundamental method which underlies many classification problems and which stems from Zassenhaus's original paper on these groups. The idea is to show that any two Zassenhaus groups satisfying the given conditions and of the same degree $n + 1$ are necessarily isomorphic. Since $e \geqslant \frac{1}{2}(n - 1)$, n must be a prime power by Theorem 1.3(ii) and so the group $L_2(n)$ exists and satisfies the given conditions. It will thus follow that these are the only groups of this type. The existence of this isomorphism depends in turn upon constructing a *canonical* set of generators for each such Zassenhaus group of degree $n + 1$ and then showing that the mapping of the canonical set of one such group on that of another can be extended to an isomorphism of the two groups.

This approach can be viewed essentially as a uniqueness theorem, in which a given class of groups is characterized in terms of a set of *generators and relations*. Although this argument is implicit in Zassenhaus's paper [1], his procedure is actually more *geometric*. He identifies the underlying set S on which his group G is acting with the projective line coordinatized by the field $GF(n)$, in which case G becomes a group of transformations of this line. The content of his proof consists in showing that each element of G, in fact, induces a *projective* transformation of the line, which implies that G is a subgroup of $L_2(n)$. A comparison of orders then yields the desired conclusion $G = L_2(n)$.

Under the above assumptions Zassenhaus's geometric approach actually provides a shorter proof. However, the generator-relation method appears to have wider applicability in classification problems and for this reason we have chosen to follow it here.

We begin the discussion with a general result for an arbitrary Zassenhaus group G. Let its type be (H, K) and let w be an element of $N_G(H) - H$. Since w interchanges the two letters fixed by $N = HK$, $w \notin N$. Since K is disjoint from its conjugates, it follows that $w^{-1}xw \notin N$ for any $x \in K^{\#}$. But then, by Theorem 1.2, there exists uniquely determined elements u in H and y_1, y_2 in K such that

$$(3.1) \qquad w^{-1}xw = y_1 w y_2\, u,$$

Moreover, $y_1 \neq 1$, since otherwise $w = x^{-1}w^2 y_2 u$ would lie in N, which is not the case. Similarly, $y_2 \neq 1$.

Since u, y_1, and y_2 depend only upon x (once w is fixed), we can write $y_1 = \alpha(x)$, $y_2 = \beta(x)$, and $u = \gamma(x)$. Thus $\alpha(x)$, $\beta(x)$ are well-defined functions from $K^\#$ to $K^\#$ and $\gamma(x)$ is a well-defined function from $K^\#$ to H and we have for x in $K^\#$,

$$(3.2) \qquad w^{-1}xw = \alpha(x)w\beta(x)\gamma(x).$$

Furthermore, $\alpha(x)$ and $\beta(x)$ are one-to-one. Indeed, if $\alpha(x) = \alpha(x')$, then $w^{-1}x^{-1}x'w = (w^{-1}xw)^{-1}(w^{-1}x'w) = \gamma(x)^{-1}\beta(x)^{-1}\beta(x')\gamma(x') \in N$, which is possible only if $x^{-1}x' = 1$. Thus $\alpha(x) = \alpha(x')$ implies $x = x'$, so α is one-to-one. Similarly, β is one-to-one.

We shall call α, β, and γ the *multiplication functions* of G with respect to (H, K, w). The group laws in G imply that α, β, and γ satisfy a number of functional relations, some of which we shall derive in subsequent proofs. For the present we wish to show rather that the structure of G is entirely determined by these multiplication functions. Indeed, we have

Theorem 3.1

Let G_i be Zassenhaus groups of types (H_i, K_i), and let α_i, β_i, and γ_i be the multiplication functions of G_i with respect to (H_i, K_i, w_i) where $w_i \in N_{G_i}(H_i) - H_i$, $1 \leqslant i \leqslant 2$. Suppose there exists an isomorphism θ of $H_1 K_1$ on $H_2 K_2$ taking H_1 into H_2 such that

$$\theta\alpha_1 = \alpha_2\theta \qquad \theta\beta_1 = \beta_2\theta \qquad \theta\gamma_1 = \gamma_2\theta \qquad \theta(w_1^2) = w_2^2.$$

Then θ can be extended to an isomorphism of G_1 onto G_2.

Proof

We note first of all that as K_i is a Hall subgroup of $N_i = H_i K_i$, $1 \leqslant i \leqslant 2$, θ must also take K_1 into K_2. In addition, w_i normalizes H_i and $w_i^2 \in H_i$, $1 \leqslant i \leqslant 2$. Hence our conditions on θ are meaningful.

If $x \in G_1 - N_1$, we write $x = yw_1zu$ with u in H_1 and y, z in K_1 and set $\psi(x) = \theta(y)w_2\theta(z)\theta(u)$. Since u, y, and z are uniquely determined, ψ is a well-defined function from $G_1 - N_1$ to $G_2 - N_2$. Since θ is an isomorphism, it follows at once from Theorem 1.2 applied to G_2 that ψ is one-to-one. Hence ψ maps $G_1 - N_1$ onto $G_2 - N_2$. Finally, we set $\psi = \theta$ on N_1 and thus ψ is a one-to-one mapping of G_1 onto G_2 and ψ is an extension of θ.

We argue that ψ is a homomorphism, which will suffice to complete the proof. Since this is true on N_1, we need only show that $\psi(xx_1) = \psi(x)\psi(x_1)$ for $x \in G_1 - N_1$ and $x_1 \in G_1$. If $x_1 \in N_1$, write $x_1 = y_1u_1$, $u_1 \in H_1$, $y_1 \in K_1$. Then

$$(3.3) \qquad xx_1 = yw_1zuy_1u_1 = yw_1zy_1^{u^{-1}}uu_1.$$

Since θ is an isomorphism on N_1, we have

(3.4)
$$\psi(xx_1) = \theta(y)w_2\,\theta(z)\theta(y_1^{u^{-1}})\theta(uu_1)$$
$$= \theta(y)w_2\,\theta(z)\theta(y_1)^{\theta(u)^{-1}}\theta(u)\theta(u_1)$$
$$= \theta(y)w_2\,\theta(z)\theta(u)\theta(y_1u_1) = \psi(x)\psi(x_1).$$

Assume next that $z = w_1$ and $x_1 = y_1w_1$, $y_1 \in K_1$. If $y_1 = 1$, the desired conclusion is obvious, so assume $y_1 \neq 1$. Then

(3.5)
$$w_1y_1w_1 = w_1^2w_1^{-1}y_1w_1 = w_1^2\alpha_1(y_1)w_1\beta_1(y_1)\gamma_1(y_1)$$
$$= \alpha_1(y_1)^{w_1^{-2}}w_1\beta_1(y_1)^{w_1^{-2}}w_1^2\gamma(y_1).$$

Thus

(3.6) $\psi(xx_1) = \psi(w_1y_1w_1) = \theta(\alpha_1(y_1)^{w_1^{-2}})w_2\,\theta(\beta_1(y_1)^{w_1^{-2}})\theta(w_1^2y_1(y)).$

Now using our conditions on θ, we obtain

(3.7)
$$\psi(xx_1) = w_2^2\,\theta(\alpha_1(y_1))w_2\,\theta(\beta_1(y_1))\theta(\gamma_1(y_1))$$
$$= w_2^2\,\alpha_2(\theta(y_1))w_2\,\beta_2(\theta(y_1))\gamma_2\,\theta(y_1))$$
$$= w_2^2w_2^{-1}\theta(y_1)w_2 = w_2(\theta(y_1)w_2) = \psi(x)\psi(x_1).$$

It follows readily from this last case that also $\psi(xw_1) = \psi(x)\psi(w_1)$ for any x in $G_1 - N_1$. Clearly the same relation holds if $x \in N_1$.

Finally, let x, x_1 be arbitrary elements of $G_1 - N_1$ and write $x_1 = y_1wz_1u_1$ with $u_1 \in H_1$ and $y_1, z_1 \in H_1$. Then

(3.8) $\psi(x_1) = \theta(y_1)w_2\,\theta(z_1)\theta(u_1) = \psi(y_1)\psi(w_1)\psi(z_1u_1).$

Now by the first case of the proof, $\psi(xy_1) = \psi(x)\psi(y_1)$. But by the preceding paragraph, $\psi(xy_1w_1) = \psi(xy_1)\psi(w_1)$. Again by the first case $\psi(xy_1w_1z_1u_1) = \psi(xy_1w_1)\psi(z_1u_1)$. Combining these relations with (3.8) we obtain

(3.9) $\psi(xx_1) = \psi(xy_1w_1z_1u_1) = \psi(x)\psi(y_1)\psi(w_1)\psi(z_1u_1) = \psi(x)\psi(x_1).$

Thus ψ is a homomorphism and the proof is complete.

We turn now to the task of constructing a canonical set of generators for a Zassenhaus group G of type (H, K) and degree $n + 1$ in which H is cyclic, is inverted by an involution w of G, and has order $e = n - 1$ if n is even and order $e = \frac{1}{2}(n - 1)$ if n is odd. We assume G satisfies these conditions in our next two results.

We need a preliminary lemma.

Lemma 3.2

Suppose $e = \frac{1}{2}(n - 1)$ and let $x \in K^{\#}$. Then we have

   (i) *If e is odd, x and x^{-1} lie in distinct orbits under the action of H.*

   (ii) *There exists an element u in $H^{\#}$ such that x and $[x, u]$ lie in distinct orbits of $K^{\#}$ under the action of H.*

Proof

Assume e is odd and suppose $x^{v} = x^{-1}$, $v \in H$. Then $x^{v^2} = (x^{-1})^{v} = (x^{v})^{-1} = x$. Since H acts regularly on K, this forces $v^2 = 1$. But then $v = 1$ as $e = |H|$ is odd. Thus $x = x^{-1}$ and so $x^2 = 1$. However, $n = |K|$ is also odd since $e = \frac{1}{2}(n - 1)$, whence $x = 1$, contrary to $x \in K^{\#}$. Thus (i) holds.

Suppose next that (ii) is false and let $H = \langle v \rangle$. Then we have

$$(3.10) \qquad\qquad x^{-1}x^{v^i} = [x, v^i] = x^{v^j}$$

for all i, $1 \leqslant i \leqslant e$, where j is a function of i. Since K is an elementary abelian p-group for some prime p by Theorem 1.3(ii), we can regard K as a vector space over Z_p and H as a group of linear transformations of K. Because H is abelian and acts irreducibly on K, it follows from (3.10) that $-1 + v^i$ and v^j are the same linear transformations of K and so have the same characteristic roots.

Now if ω denotes a characteristic root of v on K, then $-1 + \omega^i$ is a characteristic root $-1 + v^i$, as is easily checked. Hence by Lemma 5.6.3,

$$(3.11) \qquad\qquad -1 + \omega^i = \omega^m$$

for some m, depending on i. Moreover, ω is a primitive eth root of unity over Z_p. But then multiplying by an arbitrary power of ω, we have the following relations for all i, j, $1 \leqslant i, j < e$, $i \neq j$:

$$(3.12) \qquad\qquad \omega^i - \omega^j = \omega^k,$$

where k depends on i and j. These relations assert that the e elements $\{0, \omega^i \mid 1 \leqslant i < e\}$ form an additive subgroup L of $Z_p(\omega)$. But as v acts irreducibly on K, we have $|Z_p(\omega)| = |K|$. However, this is impossible, as $\frac{1}{2}(n - 1) = e = |L|$ cannot divide $n = |K|$. Thus (ii) also holds.

The lemma tells us that when e is odd, every element of $K^{\#}$ is of the form $x^{\pm v}$ for some v in H. On the other hand, when e is even, H contains an element which inverts K, so x, x^{-1} both lie in the same orbit of $K^{\#}$ under H. Since $e = \frac{1}{2}(n - 1)$ in this case, the elements $x^{\pm v}$, $v \in H$, include only *half* the elements of $K^{\#}$. Part (ii) of the lemma gives a procedure for constructing the second H-orbit of $K^{\#}$ in this case.

We now prove

Theorem 3.3

Let α, β, and γ be the multiplication functions of G with respect to (H, K, w) and let $x \in K^*$. Then we have

(i) $\beta(x) = x^{-1}$ and $\alpha(x) = x^{-\gamma(x)}$.

(ii) There exists a unique pair of elements x_0, x_0^{-1} in K^* such that $(wx_0)^3 = (wx_0^{-1})^3 = 1$.

(iii) If e is odd, then $x = x_0^{\pm u}$ for some u in H and $\gamma(x) = u^{-2}$.

(iv) If e is even, then for some u_0 in H, $x_1 = [x_0, u_0]$ and x_0 lie in distinct orbits under H. We have $x = x_0^u$ or x_1^u for some u in H and correspondingly $\gamma(x) = u^{-2}$ or $\gamma(x) = \gamma(x_1)u^{-2}$. Moreover, $\gamma(x_1)$ is uniquely determined by the condition

$$x_1^{\gamma(x_1)} = x_0^{-1} x_1^{\gamma(x_1)u_0^{-1}}.$$

Proof

Let $x \in K^*$ and $u \in H$. Using (3.2) and the fact that w inverts H we obtain

$$(3.13) \qquad wx^u w = wu^{-1}xuw = uwxwu^{-1}$$

$$= u\alpha(x)w\beta(x)\gamma(x)u^{-1} = \alpha(x)^{u^{-1}}w\beta(x)^u\gamma(x)u^{-2}.$$

This gives

$$(3.14) \qquad\qquad\qquad \gamma(x^u) = \gamma(x)u^{-2}.$$

On the basis of this relation, we shall now prove the theorem in the case that $e = |H|$ is odd. Under this condition we can find an element a in H such that $a^2 = \gamma(x)$. But then $\gamma(x^a) = 1$ by (3.14). Hence setting $x_0 = x^a$, we obtain

$$(3.15) \qquad\qquad\qquad wx_0w = \alpha(x_0)w\beta(x_0).$$

Moreover, (3.13) with $x = x_0$ gives

$$(3.16) \qquad\qquad wx_0^u w = \alpha(x_0)^{u^{-1}}w\beta(x_0)^u u^{-2}.$$

Now if $e = n - 1$, then $x_0^v = \beta(x_0)^{-1}$ for some v in H, while if $e = \frac{1}{2}(n - 1)$, either $x_0^v = \beta(x_0)$ or $\beta(x_0)^{-1}$ for some v in H. We expand $wx_0w\beta(x_0)^{-1}w$ in two ways. First, using (3.15), we have

$$(3.17) \qquad (wx_0w)\beta(x_0)^{-1}w = \alpha(x_0)w\beta(x_0)\beta(x_0)^{-1}w = \alpha(x_0).$$

If $\beta(x_0)^{-1} = x_0^v$ for some v in H, we also have, using (3.16),

$$(3.18) \qquad wx_0(w\beta(x_0)^{-1}w) = wx_0\alpha(x_0)^{v^{-1}}w\beta(x_0)^v v^{-2}.$$

Together (3.17) and (3.18) yield

$$(3.19) \qquad\qquad w\alpha(x_0) = x_0\alpha(x_0)^{v^{-1}}w\beta(x_0)^v v^{-2}.$$

But now the uniqueness of expression forces $v^{-2} = 1$, $x_0 \alpha(x_0)^{v-1} = 1$, and $\alpha(x_0) = \beta(x_0)^v$. Hence $v = 1$ and, consequently,

(3.20) $\alpha(x_0) = \beta(x_0) = x_0^{-1}.$

On the other hand, if $\beta(x_0)^{-1}$ is not of this form, then $\beta(x_0) = x_0^v$ for some v in H. In this case, we put $u = v$ in (3.16) and take inverses of both sides to obtain an expression for $w\beta(x_0)^{-1}w$. Using it, we obtain

(3.21) $wx_0(w\beta(x_0)^{-1}w) = wx_0 \, v^2 \beta(x_0)^{-v} w\alpha(x_0)^{-v-1}.$

Comparing with (3.17) and using the uniqueness of expression, we obtain this time $v^2 = 1$ and $\alpha(x_0) = \alpha(x_0)^{-v}$. But then $v = 1$ and $\alpha(x_0)^2 = 1$. However, this case arises only if $e = \frac{1}{2}(n - 1)$, whence $n = |K|$ is odd. Thus $\alpha(x_0) = 1$, contrary to the fact that $\alpha(x_0) \in K^*$. Hence (3.20) must hold.
But now (3.16) reduces to

(3.22) $wx_0^u w = x_0^{-u^{-1}} wx_0^{-u} u^{-2}.$

In particular, $wx_0 w = x_0^{-1} wx_0^{-1}$, which yields upon taking inverses that $wx_0^{-1} w = x_0 wx_0$. Conjugating by u^{-1}, we obtain

(3.23) $wx_0^{-u} w = x_0^{u^{-1}} wx_0^u u^{-2}.$

Now if $x \in K^*$, we know that $x = x_0^u$ or x_0^{-u} for some u in H. It follows therefore correspondingly from (3.22) or (3.23) that $\beta(x) = x^{-1}$, $\gamma(x) = u^{-2}$, and $\alpha(x) = x^{-u^{-2}} = x^{-\gamma(x)}$. Thus (i) and (iii) hold. Moreover, the relations $wx_0 w = x_0^{-1} wx_0^{-1}$ and $wx_0^{-1} w = x_0 wx_0$ are equivalent to the assertions $(wx_0)^3 = (wx_0^{-1})^3 = 1$. On the other hand, (3.22) and (3.23) show that $(wx_0^{\pm u})^3 \neq 1$ if $u \neq 1$. Thus $\{x_0, x_0^{-1}\}$ is the unique pair in K^* satisfying (ii). Hence the theorem is proved when e is odd.
We turn now to the case e even, which is somewhat more delicate. In this case, H contains an element a of order 2 which inverts K, whence $x^a = x^{-1}$ for all x in K. Hence (3.16) with $u = a$ yields

(3.24) $\alpha(x^{-1}) = \alpha(x)^{-1}$ $\beta(x^{-1}) = \beta(x)^{-1}$ $\gamma(x^{-1}) = \gamma(x).$

We also have

$$\alpha(x^{-1}) w\beta(x^{-1})\gamma(x^{-1}) = wx^{-1}w = (wxw)^{-1}$$
$$= \gamma(x)^{-1}\beta(x)^{-1} w\alpha(x)^{-1} = \beta(x)^{-\gamma(x)} w\alpha(x)^{-\gamma(x)-1}\gamma(x).$$

The uniqueness of expression gives

(3.25) $\alpha(x^{-1}) = \beta(x)^{-\gamma(x)}.$

Furthermore, (3.2) gives

$$w\alpha(x)w = xw\gamma(x)^{-1}\beta(x)^{-1} = xw\beta(x)^{-\gamma(x)}\gamma(x)^{-1},$$

whence

(3.26) $$\beta(\alpha(x)) = \beta(x)^{-\gamma(x)}.$$

Combining (3.24), (3.25), and (3.26), we obtain

(3.27) $$\beta(\alpha(x)) = \alpha(x)^{-1}.$$

But $\alpha(x)$ runs over $K^{\#}$ as x does. Hence $\beta(x) = x^{-1}$ for all x in $K^{\#}$. It follows therefore from (3.24) and (3.25) that also $\alpha(x) = x^{-\gamma(x)}$. Thus (i) holds.

We next argue that $\gamma(x) = \gamma(y)$ if and only if $y = x^{\pm 1}$. Since $|H| = \frac{1}{2}|K^{\#}|$, this will prove the existence of a unique pair $\{x_0, x_0^{-1}\}$ in $K^{\#}$ such that $\gamma(z) = \gamma(z^{-1}) = 1$ and, as in the case e odd, this will establish (ii). In view of (3.24), we need only show that $\gamma(x) = \gamma(y)$ implies $y = x^{\pm 1}$.

Set $\gamma(x) = v$. Then we have by (i),

(3.28) $$wxw = x^{-v}wx^{-1}v \quad \text{and} \quad wyw = y^{-v}wy^{-1}v.$$

Now wxw and wyw lie in the same conjugate of K and so commute, as K is abelian. It follows therefore from (3.28) that

$$(x^{-v}wx^{-1}v)(y^{-v}wy^{-1}v) = (y^{-v}wy^{-1}v)(x^{-v}wx^{-1}v),$$

whence

(3.29) $$v^{-1}x^{-1}wx^{-v}y^{-v}wy^{-1}v = v^{-1}y^{-1}wy^{-v}x^{-v}wx^{-1}v.$$

If we set $b = wx^{-v}y^{-v}w$, then, as x, y commute, (3.29) yields

(3.30) $$b^{-1}yx^{-1}b = x^{-1}y = yx^{-1}.$$

But then, as K is disjoint from its conjugates, the assumption $y \neq x$ forces $b = w(xy)^{-v}w$ to lie in N. The uniqueness of expression shows that this is possible only if $xy = 1$, whence $y = x^{-1}$. Hence $y = x^{\pm 1}$ and (ii) is proved.

By the preceding lemma there is an element u_0 in H such that $x_1 = [x_0, u_0]$ does not lie in the same orbit as x_0 under H. Hence if $x \in K^{\#}$, we have $x = x_0^u$ or x_1^u for some u in H. Since $\gamma(x_0) = 1$, it follows from (3.14) that correspondingly $\gamma(x) = u^{-2}$ or $\gamma(x) = \gamma(x_1)u^{-2}$. Hence to complete the proof of (iv) it remains only to show that $\gamma(x_1)$ is uniquely determined by the stated condition.

Now $x_1 = x_0^{-1}x_0^{u_0}$, so also $x_1^{u_0^{-1}} = x_0^{-u_0^{-1}}x_0 = x_0x_0^{-u_0^{-1}}$. Using these relations together with (3.2), (3.13), and our knowledge of α and β, we have

$$(3.31) \quad x_1^{-\gamma(x_1)} \, wx_1^{-1}\gamma(x_1) = wx_1w = (wx_0^{-1}w)(wx_0^{u_0}w)$$

$$= x_0wx_0\,x_0^{-u_0-1}wx_0^{-1}u_0^{-2} = x_0(wx_1^{u_0}w)x_0^{-1}u_0^{-2}$$

$$= x_0(x_1^{-\gamma(x_1)u_0-1}wx_1^{-u_0}\gamma(x_1)u_0^{-2})x_0^{-1}u_0^{-2}.$$

Hence by the uniqueness of expression, we have $x_1^{-\gamma(x_1)} = x_0\,x_1^{-\gamma(x_1)u_0-1}$. Taking inverses, we get

$$(3.32) \qquad\qquad x_1^{\gamma(x_1)} = x_0^{-1}x_1^{\gamma(x_1)u_0-1}.$$

Suppose there were two values b and c of $\gamma(x_1)$ which satisfied (3.32), whence $x_1^b = x_0^{-1}x_1^{bu_0-1}$ and $x_1^c = x_0^{-1}x_1^{cu_0-1}$. Then

$$(3.33) \qquad\qquad x_0 = x_1^{bu_0-1}x_1^{-b} = x_1^{cu_0-1}x_1^{-c}.$$

However, it follows at once from this relation that u_0^{-1} centralizes $x_1^b x_1^{-c}$. Since $u_0 \in H^\#$, this forces $x_1^b x_1^{-c} = 1$, whence $x_1^b = x_1^c$ and $b = c$. Thus $\gamma(x_1)$ is uniquely determined by (3.32), which completes the proof of (iv) and of the theorem.

If $H = \langle v \rangle$ and w, x_0 are as in the theorem, the multiplication table of G can be completely described in terms of the elements v^i, $x_0^{\pm v^i}$, and w if e is odd and in terms of the elements v^i, $x_0^{v^i}$, $x_1^{v^i}$, and w if e is even. As the case may be, we call $\{v, w, x_0\}$ or $\{v, w, x_0, x_1\}$ a *canonical* set of generators of G. In particular, the relation $(wx_0)^3 = 1$ is equivalent to the equation

$$wx_0w = x_0^{-1}wx_0^{-1}.$$

Identities of this general form are of great importance in the study of doubly transitive groups and are termed *structure identities*.

To apply Theorem 3.3 in conjunction with Theorem 3.1, we need the following additional result:

Lemma 3.4

For $1 \leqslant i \leqslant 2$, let N_i be isomorphic Frobenius groups with cyclic complements H_i and elementary abelian kernels K_i of prime power order on which H_i acts irreducibly. Then if z_i are arbitrary elements of $K_i^\#$, $1 \leqslant i \leqslant 2$, there exists an isomorphism θ of N_1 onto N_2 such that $\theta(z_1) = z_2$ and $\theta(H_1) = H_2$.

Proof

Let $|K_i| = p^r$, $1 \leqslant i \leqslant 2$. If $H_1 = \langle u_1 \rangle$, the characteristic roots of u_1^j on K_1 as a vector space over Z_p are $(\omega^j)^{p^i}$, $0 \leqslant i \leqslant r - 1$, for some primitive $|H_1|$th root of unity ω by Lemma 5.6.3. As u_1^j runs through the generators of H_1, ω^j runs through all the primitive $|H_1|$th roots of unity in $Z_p(\omega)$. The same reasoning applies to H_2 and consequently we can write $H_2 = \langle u_2 \rangle$, where u_2 has the same characteristic roots ω^{p^i} on K_2 as u_1 has on K_1.

Now the elements $z_i, z_i^{u_i}, \ldots, z_i^{u_i^{r-1}}$ form a basis of K_i because of the irreducibility of H_i on K_i, and with respect to these bases the elements u_1, u_2 have identical companion matrices since they have the same characteristic roots on K_1, K_2, respectively. Hence if we define the linear transformation ψ of K_1 on K_2 by setting $\psi(z_1^{u_1^j}) = z_2^{u_2^j}$, $0 \leqslant j \leqslant r - 1$, and then define θ on the semidirect product $N_1 = H_1 K_1$ into $N_2 = H_2 K_2$ by the rule

$$\theta(u_1^k y_1) = u_2^k \psi(y_1)$$

for $y_1 \in K_1$ and $1 \leqslant k \leqslant |H_1|$, it follows directly that θ is an isomorphism of N_1 on N_2. Since $\theta(z_1) = \psi(z_1) = z_2$ and $\theta(u_1) = u_2$, the lemma holds.

We can now derive our main result:

Theorem 3.5 (Zassenhaus)

Let G be a Zassenhaus group of type (H, K) and degree $n + 1$ in which H is cyclic, H is inverted by an involution of G, and H has order $n - 1$ if n is even and order $\frac{1}{2}(n - 1)$ if n is odd. Then $n = p^r > 3$ for some prime p and G is isomorphic to $L_2(n)$.

Proof

In view of the discussion at the beginning of the section, we need only show that any two Zassenhaus groups G_i of the same degree $n + 1$ and satisfying the given conditions are isomorphic. Let G_i be of type (H_i, K_i) with $e = |H_i|$, $1 \leqslant i \leqslant 2$. If e is odd, let $\{v_i, w_i, x_{0i}\}$ be a set of canonical generators of G_i, while if e is even, let $\{v_i, w_i, x_{0i}, x_{1i}\}$ be a set of canonical generators of G_i, $1 \leqslant i \leqslant 2$.

Since the generators v_i of H_i can be taken arbitrarily, we can choose them, in view of the preceding lemma, so that there exists an isomorphism θ of $N_1 = H_1 K_1$ on $N_2 = H_2 K_2$ such that

$$(3.34) \qquad \theta(x_{01}) = x_{02} \qquad \text{and} \qquad \theta(v_1) = v_2.$$

Now if e is even, then $x_{11} = [x_{01}, v_1^k]$ for some integer k and x_{11} is not in the orbit of x_{01} under H_1. But then clearly $\theta(x_{11}) = [\theta(x_{01}), \theta(v_1^k)] = [x_{02}, v_2^k]$ is not in the orbit of x_{02} under H_2. Hence we can choose x_{12} to be $\theta(x_{11})$. Thus if e is even, we may also assume

$$(3.35) \qquad \theta(x_{11}) = x_{12}.$$

Next let α_i, β_i, and γ_i be the multiplication functions of G_i with respect to (H_i, K_i, w_i), $1 \leqslant i \leqslant 2$. The exact forms of α_i, β_i, and γ_i in terms of the canonical generators are given in Theorem 3.3. Using these results together with (3.35), it follows directly that $\theta\beta_1 = \beta_2\theta$ and that $\theta\gamma_1 = \gamma_2\theta$ and $\theta\alpha_1 = \alpha_2\theta$ on the orbits of x_{01} and x_{01}^{-1} under H_1. For example,

(3.36) $$\theta\gamma_1(x_{01}^{v_1^j}) = \theta(v_1^{-2_j}) = v_2^{-2_j} = \gamma_2(x_{02}^{v_2^j}) = \gamma_2\,\theta(x_{01}^{v_1^j}).$$

Furthermore, since w_1 and w_2 are involutions, we obviously have $\theta(w_1^2) = w_2^2$.

In particular, if e is odd, the hypothesis of Theorem 3.1 holds. On the other hand, if e is even, we apply θ to the equation of Theorem 3.3(iv) in the group G_1 and use (3.34) and (3.35) to obtain

(3.37) $$x_{12}^{\theta\gamma_1(x_{11})} = x_{02}^{-1}\,x_{12}^{\theta\gamma_1(x_{11})v_1^k}.$$

But then Theorem 3.3(iv) in G_2 yields

(3.38) $$\gamma_2(x_{12}) = \theta\gamma_1(x_{11}).$$

Combined with (3.35), this gives

(3.39) $$\gamma_2\theta(x_{11}) = \theta\gamma_1(x_{11}).$$

It follows at once from this that $\theta\gamma_1 = \gamma_2\theta$ and $\theta\alpha_1 = \alpha_2\theta$ on the orbit of x_{11} under H_1. Hence the hypothesis of Theorem 3.1 holds also in this case. We conclude therefore that G_1 and G_2 are isomorphic, thus completing the proof.

CHAPTER 14

GROUPS IN WHICH CENTRALIZERS ARE NILPOTENT

In this chapter we study the important class of groups in which the centralizer of every nonidentity element is nilpotent. For brevity such a group is called a *CN*-group. As in the case of Zassenhaus groups, *CN*-groups have been completely classified. In a major work Feit, M. Hall, and Thompson established the solvability of all *CN*-groups of odd order. The over-all conceptual outline of their proof followed that of Suzuki, who in a pioneering paper treated the special case in which the centralizers of every nonidentity element are assumed to be abelian. We shall present a complete proof of their result in Sections 2 and 3, after deriving a number of general properties of *CN*-groups. This special case of the general Odd-Order Paper, apart from its intrinsic value, is of great interest because of the light it sheds on a number of problems that arise in far more complex form in the general proof.

Suzuki has determined all nonsolvable *CN*-groups and in so doing discovered the family of simple groups which bears his name. Here we shall determine only those simple *CN*-groups which have abelian Sylow 2-subgroups, which will be done by showing that they are Zassenhaus groups which satisfy the hypothesis of Zassenhaus's theorem.

1. BASIC PROPERTIES OF *CN*-GROUPS

In this section we establish a number of basic properties of *CN*-groups which we shall need for the deeper analysis to be carried out in the succeeding sections.

The following lemma is obvious:

Lemma 1.1

If H is a nontrivial subgroup of the CN-group G, then H is a CN-group and $C_G(H)$ is nilpotent.

Lemma 1.2

Let P and Q be S_p- and S_q-subgroups of the CN-group G, where p and q are distinct primes. If an element of $P^\#$ centralizes an element of $Q^\#$, then P centralizes Q.

Proof

Suppose $x \in P^\#$, $y \in Q^\#$, and $[x, y] = 1$. Then $C_G(x)$ is nilpotent and contains $Z(P)$ as well as y. Then the S_p- and S_q-subgroups of $C_G(x)$ centralize each other and so y centralizes $Z(P)$. Choosing x_1 in $Z(P^\#)$, we have similarly that $C_G(x_1)$ contains both P and y and is nilpotent, so that P centralizes y. Consideration of $C_G(y)$ shows now that P centralizes $Z(Q)$. Choosing y_1 in $Z(Q^\#)$ and considering $C_G(y_1)$, we conclude that P centralizes Q.

Lemma 1.3

If G is a CN-group and H is a normal solvable subgroup of G, then G/H is a CN-group.

Proof

Suppose first that H is an elementary abelian p-group for some prime p. Set $\bar{G} = G/H$ and let $\bar{x} \in \bar{G}^\#$. We must show that $\bar{C} = C_{\bar{G}}(\bar{x})$ is nilpotent. If $\bar{y}$ is a power of $\bar{x}$, then clearly $G_{\bar{G}}(\bar{x}) \subseteq C_{\bar{G}}(\bar{y})$. Since subgroups of nilpotent groups are nilpotent, we need only show that $C_{\bar{G}}(\bar{y})$ is nilpotent. Since we can choose $\bar{y}$ of prime order q, it will suffice to prove that $\bar{C}$ is nilpotent in the case that $|\bar{x}| = q$.

Let C be the inverse image of $\bar{C}$ in G. If $q \neq p$, there exists an element x of C of order q which maps on $\bar{x}$. Setting $X = \langle x \rangle$, we have $HX \lhd C$ and X is an S_q-subgroup of HX, whence $C = HN$, where $N = N_C(X)$ by Theorem 1.3.7. Thus N maps onto $\bar{C}$. But then if $u \in N$, we have $x^u = xz$, $z \in H$, as $\bar{C}$ centralizes $\bar{x}$, and consequently $[x, u] = x^{-1}x^u = z \in H \cap X = 1$. Hence

$N \subseteq C_G(x)$ and so N is nilpotent. But then $\overline{C}$, being a homomorphic image of N, is nilpotent.

Suppose next $q = p$, in which case a representative x of $\bar{x}$ in C is a p-element and $K = HX$ is a p-group, where again $X = \langle x \rangle$. If C is a p-group, then so is $\overline{C}$ and hence $\overline{C}$ is nilpotent; so we may assume that C is not a p-group. Let R be an S_r-subgroup of C for some prime $r \neq p$ in $\pi(C)$. Our conditions imply that $[R, X] \subseteq H$ and hence that $[R, K] \subseteq H$. But by Theorem 5.3.5, $K = [R, K]C_K(R)$, whence $C_K(R) \neq 1$. Taking u in $R^\#$ and v in $C_K(R)^\#$, we conclude at once from Lemma 1.2 that R centralizes P, where P is an S_p-subgroup of C. Since this holds for each $r \neq p$ in C, it follows that $C = PC_C(P)$. But $C_C(P)$ is nilpotent by Lemma 1.1 and consequently also C is nilpotent. Thus $\overline{C}$ is nilpotent in this case as well.

Finally, if H is not an elementary abelian p-group, let L be a minimal characteristic subgroup of H, so that L is characteristically simple. Since H is solvable, L is an elementary abelian r-group for some prime r by Theorem 2.1.4. Hence G/L is a CN-group by the preceding case. But then it follows by induction on $|G|$ that $(G/L)/(H/L)$, which is isomorphic to G/H, is a CN-group.

In order to study an arbitrary CN-group, it is necessary first to determine the structure of all solvable CN-groups. For this purpose the following definition will be useful:

We shall call G a 3-*step* group (with respect to the prime p) provided:

(a) $O_{p,p'}(G)$ is a Frobenius group with kernel $O_p(G)$ and cyclic complement of odd order.
(b) $G = O_{p,p'p}(G)$ and $G \supset O_{p,p'}(G)$.
(c) $G/O_p(G)$ is a Frobenius group with kernel $O_{p,p'}(G)/O_p(G)$.

Lemma 1.4

A 3-step group is a solvable CN-group.

Proof

Let G be a 3-step group with respect to p and set $H = O_p(G)$, so that $O_{p,p'}(G) = HA$ is a Frobenius group with kernel H and cyclic complement A. Clearly HA is solvable and, as G/HA is a p-group, we see that G is solvable. Furthermore, if P is an S_p-subgroup of G, we have $G = PA$. Set $\overline{G} = G/H = \overline{P}\,\overline{A}$, so that also $\overline{G}$ is a Frobenius group with kernel $\overline{A}$ and complement $\overline{P}$.

Now any p'-element of G lies in HA and so lies in a conjugate of A. Hence to prove G is a CN-group, we need only show that $C_G(x)$ is nilpotent for x in $P^\#$ or $A^\#$. If $x \in H^\#$, then any p'-element of $C_G(x)$ lies in HA. But

$C_{HA}(x) \subseteq H$, as HA is a Frobenius group, so $C_G(x)$ is a p-group in this case. If $x \in P - H$, $C_{\bar{G}}(\bar{x}) \subseteq \bar{P}$, as $\bar{P}$ induces a regular group of automorphisms of $\bar{A}$, where $\bar{x}$ denotes the image of x in $\bar{G}$. Since $G_{\bar{G}}(\bar{x})$ contains the image of $C_G(x)$, we again have that $C_G(x)$ is a p-group. Finally, if $x \in A^*$, then $G_{\bar{G}}(\bar{x}) \subseteq \bar{A}$, as $\bar{G}$ is a Frobenius group, whence $C_G(x) \subseteq HA$. But $C_{HA}(x) = A$, as A is abelian and HA is a Frobenius group. Thus $C_G(x)$ is nilpotent in all cases and the lemma is proved.

Our main result on solvable CN-groups is:

Theorem 1.5

If G is a solvable CN-group, then one of the following holds:
   (i) *G is nilpotent.*
   (ii) *G is a Frobenius group whose complement is either cyclic or the direct product of a cyclic group of odd order and a generalized quarternion group.*
   (iii) *G is a 3-step group.*

Proof

Set $F = F(G)$. If $G = F$, then G is nilpotent and (i) holds; so we may assume that $G \supset F$. We have $C_G(F) \subseteq F$ by Theorem 6.1.3 and, in particular, $F \ne 1$. Set $\pi = \pi(F)$. Since G is solvable, G possesses an $S_{\pi'}$-subgroup A by Theorem 6.4.1(i). Suppose a q-element y of A^* centralizes a p-element x of F^*. Since $q \in \pi'$ and $p \in \pi$, $q \ne p$. Hence by Lemma 1.2, y centralizes an S_p-subgroup of G and so centralizes $O_p(G)$. Furthermore, $y \in C_G(x)$, which is nilpotent and contains $O_{p'}(F)$. Since q is prime to $|O_{p'}(F)|$, it follows that y centralizes $O_{p'}(F)$. Thus y centralizes $F = O_p(G) \times O_{p'}(F)$. Since $C_G(F) \subseteq F$, we conclude that $y \in F$, contrary to the fact that y is a π'-element. Hence no q-element of A^* centralizes any p-element of F^*, which implies at once that no element of A^* centralizes any element of F^*. Thus A induces a regular group of automorphisms of F and so FA is a Frobenius group if $A \ne 1$.

We claim next that A is nilpotent. If $|A|$ is even, then A possesses a unique involution y and $y \in Z(A)$ by Theorem 10.3.1(vi). Then $A \subseteq C_G(y)$ and so A is nilpotent. If $|A|$ is odd, then A has cyclic Sylow subgroups and is metacyclic by Theorem 10.3.1(iv) and 7.6.2. But then $\Omega_1(Q) \lhd A$ for some S_q-subgroup Q of A. Hence if R is an S_r-subgroup of A for any $r \ne q$ in $\pi(A) = \pi'$, $\Omega_1(Q)\Omega_1(R)$ is a group of order qr and so is cyclic by Theorem 10.3.1(v). Thus $\Omega_1(Q)$ centralizes $\Omega_1(R)$ and so Q centralizes R by Lemma 1.2 for any r in $\pi(A) - q$. It follows that $Q \subseteq Z(A)$, whence A is contained in the nilpotent group $C_G(Q)$. Hence A is nilpotent in this case as well.

Since the Sylow subgroups of A are cyclic for odd primes and cyclic or generalized quaternion for the prime 2, A has the structure given in (ii), by Theorem 1.3.1(ii). Hence (ii) holds if $G = FA$.

Assume finally that $G \supset FA$. We first argue that $\pi = \pi(F)$ consists of a single prime. Suppose false. Let P be an S_p-subgroup of G for p in π. Then $O_p(G)$ centralizes $O_{p'}(F)$ which by our assumption is nontrivial, and so P centralizes $O_{p'}(F)$ by Lemma 1.2. But then $P \subseteq C = C_G(O_{p'}(F))$, which is nilpotent and normal in G. Since P char $C, P \lhd G$, whence $P = O_p(G)$. Since this argument applies for each p in π, we conclude that F is an S_π-subgroup of G. Since A is an $S_{\pi'}$-subgroup of G, we have $G = FA$, contrary to our present assumption. Thus $\pi = p$ for some prime p and so $G = PA$ and $F \subseteq P$, where P is an S_p-subgroup of G. In particular, $A \neq 1$.

Now set $\bar{G} = \bar{P}\bar{A} = G/F$. We have $\bar{A} = O_2(\bar{A}) \times O_{2'}(\bar{A})$, where $O_{2'}(\bar{A})$ is cyclic and $O_2(\bar{A})$ is cyclic or generalized quaternion. We shall argue now that $\bar{P}$ induces a regular group of automorphisms of $\bar{A}$ and hence that $\bar{P}\bar{A}$ is a Frobenius group. This will force $O_2(\bar{A}) = 1$, since otherwise $\bar{P}$ would have to centralize the unique involution of $O_2(\bar{A})$. Thus $\bar{A}$ will be cyclic of odd order and G will be a 3-step group with respect to p, so that (iii) will hold.

Suppose $\bar{y}$ in $\bar{P}^{*}$ centralizes $\bar{x}$ in $\bar{A}^{*}$. Let K be the inverse image of $\langle \bar{y} \rangle$ in P and let x be a representative of $\bar{x}$ in A. Then x normalizes the p-group K and x does not centralize $F \cap K$. Hence by Lemma 1.2, x induces a fixed-point-free automorphism of K. But then x induces a fixed-point-free automorphism of $K/F = \langle \bar{y} \rangle$ by Lemma 10.1.3, which is not the case. This proves the assertion and completes the proof of the theorem.

As an immediate corollary, we have

Corollary 1.6

If G is a solvable CN-group and $O_p(G) \neq 1$, then either $O_p(G)$ is an S_p-subgroup of G or G is a 3-step group with respect to p.

We can also establish the following general property of *CN*-groups:

Theorem 1.7

Let G be a CN-group and let H be a subgroup of G maximal subject to being nilpotent. Then we have
   (i)   *H is a Hall subgroup of G.*
   (ii) *If H is not of prime power order, then H is disjoint from its conjugates.*
   (iii) *If H is disjoint from its conjugates, then $C_G(x) \subseteq H^{*}$ for any x in H^{*}.*

(iv) *If H is disjoint from its conjugates and H is of even order, then $C_G^*(x) \subseteq H$ for any x in H^*.*

Proof

Let P be an S_p-subgroup of G such that $P \cap H$ is an S_p-subgroup of H for p in $\pi(H)$. Then if $x \in Z(P \cap H)^*$, $C = C_G(x)$ is nilpotent and contains both H and $Z(P)$. But then $C = H$ by the maximality of H. This means that we can choose x in $Z(P)$, whence $P \subseteq C = H$. Since this holds for each p in $\pi(H)$, H is thus a Hall subgroup of G.

Assume next that H is not of prime power order and suppose $H \cap H^y \neq 1$ for some y in G. Since H is nilpotent, it follows that $P \cap P^y \neq 1$ for some S_p-subgroup P of H. But then if $u \in P \cap P^y$, $u \neq 1$, $C_G(u)$ contains both $O_{p'}(H)$ and $O_{p'}(H)^y$. Since $C_G(u)$ is nilpotent and $O_{p'}(H)$ is a Hall subgroup of G, it follows that $O_{p'}(H) = O_{p'}(H)^y$. But then y normalizes $O_{p'}(H)$ and so also normalizes $K = C_G(O_{p'}(H))$, which is nilpotent and contains P. Since P is an S_p-subgroup of G, P char K and so y normalizes P. Thus y normalizes $H = P \times O_{p'}(H)$ and therefore H is disjoint from its conjugates.

Suppose next that H is disjoint from its conjugates. Since $C_G(x) \subseteq C_G(x^i)$ for all i, we need only prove that $C_G(x) \subseteq H$ in the case that x is an element of prime order p of H. Since $C_G(x)$ is generated by its elements of prime power order, it will suffice to show that any q-element y of $C_G(x)$ lies in H. Since y centralizes x, $x \in H \cap H^y$, whence $H^y = H$ by our assumption. But then y normalizes $P = O_p(H)$, which is an S_p-subgroup of G. Hence if $q = p$, $\langle P, y \rangle$ is a p-group and so $y \in P \subseteq H$. On the other hand, if $q \neq p$, y centralizes P by Lemma 1.2 and so $y \in C_G(Z(P))$, which is nilpotent and contains H. Maximality of H forces $H = C_G(Z(P))$ and again we have $y \in H$.

Assume finally that $|H|$ is even and that H is disjoint from its conjugates. Let S be an S_2-subgroup of H and hence of G. By the preceding paragraph, $C_G(x) \subseteq H$ for any x in H^*. Thus to prove that $C_G^*(x) \subseteq H$, we need only show that an S_2-subgroup of $C_G^*(x)$ lies in H since $|C_G^*(x) : C_G(x)| \leqslant 2$. Let then y be a 2-element of $C_G^*(x)$. It follows that $H \cap H^y$ contains x, whence $H^y = H$ and consequently $\langle S, y \rangle$ is a 2-group, forcing $y \in S \subseteq H$. This completes the proof of the theorem.

We remark that (ii) is false if H is not of prime power order. Indeed, if G is a 3-step group with respect to p, it is immediate that an S_p-subgroup P of G is maximal subject to being nilpotent. Furthermore, $P \cap P^y \supseteq O_p(G) \neq 1$ for every y in G. Since $P \supset O_p(G)$, P is not the only

S_p-subgroup of G and hence we can choose y so that $P \neq P^y$. Thus P is not disjoint from its conjugates.

2. *CN*-GROUPS OF ODD ORDER

In the next two sections we shall prove that every *CN*-group of odd order is solvable. In the present section we analyze the subgroup structure of a minimal counterexample to the theorem and in the following section, using exceptional character theory, we show that no such counterexample exists.

Lemma 2.1

If G is a nonsolvable CN-group of least order, then G is simple and all proper subgroups of G are solvable.

Proof

Since all proper subgroups of G are *CN*-groups, they are all solvable by the minimality of G. If N is a nontrivial normal subgroup of G, then G/N is a *CN*-group by Lemma 1.3, so G/N is solvable, again by the minimality of G. Since N is also solvable, so is G, which is not the case. Thus G is simple.

A simple group G of composite order in which all proper subgroups are solvable is called a *minimal simple* group. Lemma 2.1 shows that to prove that all *CN*-groups of odd order are solvable is equivalent to proving that there are no minimal simple *CN*-groups of odd order. With the ultimate aim of proving their nonexistence, we now investigate properties of such minimal simple groups.

Theorem 2.2

If G is a minimal simple CN-group of odd order, then no subgroup of G is a 3-step group.

Proof

Assume false and let H be a 3-step subgroup of G of maximal order (with respect to the prime p). Let P be an S_p-subgroup of H. Since $O_{p,p'}(H)$ is a Frobenius group with kernel $O_p(H)$ and contains all p'-elements of H, obviously $O_{p'}(H) = 1$. Since H is strongly p-solvable (being solvable of odd order), Glauberman's theorem implies that $Z(J(P)) \triangleleft H$. Thus $H \subseteq N = N_G(Z(J(P)))$ and $N \subset G$. Since $O_p(N) \neq 1$, either N is a 3-step group with respect to p or else $O_p(N)$ is an S_p-subgroup of N by Corollary

1.6. However, in the latter case, $P \subseteq O_p(N) \cap H$, whence $P \subseteq O_p(H)$, which is not the case. Thus N is a 3-step group and so $H = N$ by our maximal choice of H. But if Q is an S_p-subgroup of G containing P, $N_Q(P) \subset N$, as $Z(J(P))$ char P. Since $N = H$, it follows that $N_Q(P) = P$, whence $P = Q$ by Theorem 1.2.11(ii) and so P is an S_p-subgroup of G.

Since the normalizer of every nonidentity p-subgroup of G is strongly p-solvable and hence of Glauberman type, we can apply Theorem 8.4.3 to obtain that $P \cap G' = P \cap N' = P \cap H'$. But H has a nontrivial p-factor group, as $H/O_{p,p'}(H)$ is a nontrivial p-group and consequently $P \cap H' \subset P$. Hence by Theorem 7.3.1, G has a nontrivial p-factor group, contrary to the simplicity of G.

It will be convenient to introduce the symbol $\mathscr{H}$ for the set of all subgroups H of G which are maximal subject to being nilpotent. The elements of $\mathscr{H}$ have the following properties:

Theorem 2.3

Let G be a minimal simple CN-group of odd order and let $H \in \mathscr{H}$. Then we have

    (i) *H is a Hall subgroup of G and is disjoint from its conjugates.*

    (ii) *$N_G(H)$ is a Frobenius group with kernel H and is a maximal subgroup of G.*

Conversely, every maximal subgroup of G is a Frobenius group whose kernel is an element of $\mathscr{H}$.

Proof

By Theorem 1.7, H is a Hall subgroup of G and, if H is not of prime power order, H is disjoint from its conjugates. Consider then the case that $H = P$ is an S_p-subgroup of G. Suppose $P \cap Q \neq 1$ for some S_p-subgroup Q of G distinct from P and choose Q so that $D = P \cap Q$ has maximal order. Then $D \subset P$ and $D \subset Q$. Set $N = N_G(D)$. Since N is not a 3-step group by Theorem 2.2 and since N is solvable, $O_p(N)$ is the unique S_p-subgroup of N by Corollary 1.6. Let R be an S_p-subgroup of G containing $O_p(N)$. Since $N_P(D) \subseteq O_p(N)$, we have $P \cap R \supseteq N_P(D) \supset D$, whence $R = P$ by our maximal choice of Q. Thus $O_p(N) \subseteq P$. But also $N_Q(D) \subseteq O_p(N)$, so $P \cap Q \supseteq N_Q(D) \supset D$, contrary to the definition of D. Thus $H = P$ is disjoint from its conjugates in this case as well, proving (i).

Now let P be an S_p-subgroup of H and set $N = N_G(Z(J(P)))$. Since G is simple and p is odd, N does not have a normal p-complement by the Glauberman-Thompson normal p-complement theorem and so N is not nilpotent. Since N is solvable and is not a 3-step group, N must be a

Frobenius group by Theorem 1.5. By Corollary 1.6, P is contained in the kernel K of N. Since $O_{p'}(H)$ centralizes P and since the Frobenius complement of N induces a regular group of automorphisms of K, we must have $O_{p'}(H) \subseteq K$, whence $H \subseteq K$. But K is nilpotent by Theorem 10.3.1(iii) and so $H = K$ by the maximality of H. Thus $H \lhd N$ and so $N \subseteq N_G(H)$. But $Z(J(P))$ char H and so $N_G(H) \subseteq N$. Hence $N_G(H) = N$ is a Frobenius group.

Let M be a maximal subgroup of G containing N. Since N is not nilpotent, neither is M and so M is also a Frobenius group with kernel, say, R. If $R \cap H \neq 1$, then $R \cap Z(H) \neq 1$ as $R \cap H \lhd H$ and H is nilpotent. Thus no element of H induces a regular automorphism of R and consequently $H \subseteq R$, whence $H = R$ and $M = N$. Suppose, on the other hand, that $R \cap H = 1$. Since M/R is cyclic by Theorem 1.5(ii), $M' \subseteq R$ and hence $M' \cap H = 1$. But $N \subseteq M$ and $H = N'$, so $H \subseteq M'$, a contradiction. Thus N is a maximal subgroup of G and (ii) is proved.

Conversely, let M now denote an arbitrary maximal subgroup of G. If M is nilpotent, it is certainly an element of $\mathscr{H}$. But then $N_G(M)$ is a Frobenius group by the preceding argument, so $N_G(M) \supset M$, contrary to the maximality of M. Hence M is a Frobenius group. Let K be its kernel, which we know is nilpotent, and let H be an element of $\mathscr{H}$ containing K. Now $M = N_G(K)$ by the maximality of M. Since K is a maximal nilpotent subgroup of M and $N_H(K)$ is a nilpotent subgroup of M, we must have $N_H(K) = K$, whence $H = K$ by Theorem 2.3.4. Thus $K = H$ and the theorem is proved.

We now relate distinct elements of $\mathscr{H}$.

Theorem 2.4

Let G be a minimal simple CN-group of odd order. If H_1, H_2 are in $\mathscr{H}$, either H_1 and H_2 are conjugate in G or H_1, H_2 have relatively prime orders.

Proof

We know that H_1, H_2 are Hall subgroups of G. Suppose $p \in \pi(H_1) \cap \pi(H_2)$. Then replacing H_2 by a suitable conjugate, we can assume that H_1 and H_2 contain the same S_p-subgroup P of G. But then $C = C_G(Z(P))$ contains both H_1 and H_2. Since C is nilpotent, the maximality of H_1, H_2 forces $C = H_1 = H_2$ and the theorem is proved.

Thus the elements of $\mathscr{H}$ are distributed into disjoint conjugate class $\mathscr{H}_i$, $1 \leqslant i \leqslant r$, such that H_i, H_j have relatively prime orders for $i \neq j$. Now every element of $G^\#$ generates a cyclic, and hence nilpotent, subgroup and so lies in some element of $\mathscr{H}$, whence in an element of some $\mathscr{H}_i$.

Hence if H_i is an element of $\mathscr{H}_i$ and $\pi_i = \pi(H_i)$, $1 \leqslant i \leqslant r$, we have

$$\pi(G) = \bigcup_{i=1}^{r} \pi_i \quad \text{and} \quad \pi_i \cap \pi_j = \varnothing \quad \text{if } i \neq j.$$

We see also that p, q in $\pi(G)$ lie in the same π_i if and only if a p-element of G^* centralizes a q-element of G^*.

Hence if we define the relation $p \sim q$ for p, q in $\pi(G)$ by the condition that a p-element and q-element of G^* commute, we have the following alternative description of our results:

Theorem 2.5

Let G be a minimal simple CN-group of odd order. Then we have
  (i) *The relation $p \sim q$ for p, q in $\pi(G)$ is an equivalence relation on $\pi(G)$.*
  (ii) *If π_i, $1 \leqslant i \leqslant r$, denote the equivalence classes in $\pi(G)$ under $\sim$, then G possesses nilpotent S_{π_i}-subgroups H_i with H_i in $\mathscr{H}_i$ which are disjoint from their conjugates and whose normalizers are Frobenius groups and are maximal subgroups of G.*
  (iii) *Every maximal subgroup of G is conjugate to $N_G(H_i)$ for some i, $1 \leqslant i \leqslant r$.*
  (iv) *Every element of G lies in a conjugate of H_i for some i, $1 \leqslant i \leqslant r$.*

Theorem 2.5 gives a quite precise statement concerning the subgroup structure of G. As a corollary, we have the following arithmetic result.

Theorem 2.6

Let G be a minimal simple CN-group of odd order and let H_i be representatives of the conjugate classes of elements of $\mathscr{H}$, $1 \leqslant i \leqslant r$. Set $h_i = |H_i|$ and $N_G(H_i) = h_i n_i$, $1 \leqslant i \leqslant r$. Then we have
  (i) *$n_i > 1$, n_i divides $h_i - 1$, $n_i h_i$ divides $|G|$, $1 \leqslant i \leqslant r$, and $(h_i, h_j) = 1$ if $i \neq j$.*

  (ii)
$$\sum_{i=1}^{r} \frac{h_i - 1}{h_i n_i} = 1 - \frac{1}{|G|}.$$

Proof

Since $N_i = N_G(H_i)$ is a Frobenius group, $n_i > 1$ and $n_i \mid (h_i - 1)$; and since N_i is a subgroup of G, obviously $n_i h_i$ divides $|G|$. Also $(h_i, h_j) = 1$ for $i \neq j$ by Theorem 2.4. Furthermore, if $g = |G|$, then H_i possesses exactly $g/h_i n_i$ distinct conjugates. Since these conjugates are disjoint, they contain exactly $(h_i - 1)(g/h_i n_i)$ distinct elements of G^*. Since the elements of H_i are π_i-elements and $\pi_i \cap \pi_j = \varnothing$ for $i \neq j$, the elements of G^* in a conjugate of H_i are distinct from those in a conjugate of H_j for $i \neq j$. But every element of $G^\#$ lies in a conjugate of some H_i by Theorem 2.5(iv). We conclude that

$$|G^\#| = g - 1 = \sum_{i=1}^{r} (h_i - 1)\frac{g}{h_i n_i},$$

from which (ii) follows at once.

3. SOLVABILITY OF CN-GROUPS OF ODD ORDER

Theorems 2.5 and 2.6 represent the maximum information that it appears possible to obtain by purely internal group-theoretic methods concerning the structure of a minimal simple CN-group G of odd order. To show that no such group exists, we shall now apply our results from character theory to obtain delicate estimates on the size of $|G|$ and thereby derive a contradiction.

Theorem 3.1 (Feit, M. Hall, Thompson)
All CN-groups of odd order are solvable.

To establish the theorem, we need only show that no minimal simple CN-group of odd order exists. So let G be a minimal simple CN-group of odd order, in which case G satisfies the conditions of Theorems 2.5 and 2.6. We preserve the notation of those theorems and also set $M_i = N_G(H_i), 1 \leqslant i \leqslant r$. Our first aim will be to describe the irreducible characters of each M_i and in terms of them to describe the irreducible characters of G. Throughout we shall use the symbol $\bar{\chi}$ (rather than χ') for the contragredient character of a character χ.

We denote by C_i the set of irreducible characters of M_i which do not have H_i in their kernels. Since M_i is a Frobenius group, deg ζ is divisible by n_i for any ζ in C_i by Theorem 4.5.3. We let $d_{ij}, 1 \leqslant j \leqslant t_i$, be the set of integers such that $n_i d_{ij}$ is the degree of some element of C_i and choose the notation such that

(3.1) $$d_{i1} < d_{i2} < \cdots < d_{it_i} \qquad 1 \leqslant i \leqslant r.$$

Also define C_{ij} to be the subset of C_i consisting of the characters of degree $n_i d_{ij}, 1 \leqslant i \leqslant r, 1 \leqslant j \leqslant t_i$, and set $w_{ij} = |C_{ij}|$. Since $|M_i|$ is odd, $\bar{\zeta} \neq \zeta$ for any ζ in C_{ij} by Theorem 4.3.6(i). But $\bar{\zeta}$ has the same degree and same kernel as ζ by Theorem 4.1.5(ii), so also $\bar{\zeta} \in C_{ij}$. Hence

(3.2) $$w_{ij} = |C_{ij}| \text{ is a positive even integer for all } i, j.$$

Since H_i is nilpotent, H_i/H_i' is a nontrivial abelian group and $|H_i : H_i'| - 1$ is the number of distinct nonprincipal linear characters of H_i. If N_i is a Frobenius complement in M_i, these characters are permuted among themselves by N_i in orbits of size $n_i = |N_i|$. But now Theorem 4.5.3 implies that there are exactly $(1/n_i)(|H_i : H_i'| - 1)$ irreducible characters of M_i of degree n_i which do not have H_i in their kernels. Hence $d_{i1} = 1$ and

$$(3.3) \qquad w_{i1} = \frac{1}{n_i}(|H_i : H_i'| - 1) \qquad 1 \leqslant i \leqslant r.$$

Note that since $|H_i|$ and $|H_j|$ have coprime orders, the assumption $n_i = n_j$ forces $w_{i1} \neq w_{j1}$. Hence we can number the H_i so that

$$(3.4) \qquad n_1 \leqslant n_2 \leqslant \cdots \leqslant n_r \qquad \text{and either} \qquad n_1 < n_2 \text{ or } w_{11} > w_{21}.$$

Next let $C_{ij} = \{\zeta_{ijk} \mid 1 \leqslant k \leqslant w_{ij}\}$ for all i, j. We set

$$(3.5) \qquad \theta_{ijkm} = (\zeta_{ijk} - \zeta_{ijm})^*.$$

Now the generalized character $\alpha_{ijkm} = \zeta_{ijk} - \zeta_{ijm}$ has degree 0 and, by Theorem 4.5.3, is 0 on $M_i - H_i$ and so lies in $I_0(H_i)$. Since H_i is disjoint from its conjugates, we conclude from Theorem 4.4.6 that

$$(3.6) \qquad (\theta_{ijkm}, \theta_{ijk'm'})_G = (\alpha_{ijkm}, \alpha_{ijk'm'})_{M_i} = \delta_{kk'} - \delta_{km'} - \delta_{mk'} + \delta_{m'k'},$$

where $\delta_{st} = 0$ or 1 according as $s \neq t$ or $s = t$. By (3.2) each $w_{ij} \geqslant 2$ and so it follows from Theorem 4.5.4 that there exists a sign $\varepsilon_{ij} = \pm 1$ and a set $D_{ij} = \{\chi_{ijk} \mid 1 \leqslant k \leqslant w_{ij}\}$ of irreducible characters χ_{ijk} of G with $\chi_{ijk} \neq \chi_{ijm}$ if $k \neq m$ such that

$$(3.7) \qquad \theta_{ijkm} = \varepsilon_{ij}(\chi_{ijk} - \chi_{ijm}) \qquad \text{all } i, j.$$

We shall now determine some basic properties of the χ_{ijk} which, for the sake of clarity, we state as separate lemmas.

Lemma 3.2

For $i' \neq i$, $\chi_{ijk}|_{H_{i'}}$ is integral-valued.

Proof

By Theorem 4.5.5, χ_{ijk} is integral-valued on all elements of G not in a conjugate of H_i. Since H_i and $H_{i'}$ have relatively prime orders for $i \neq i'$, the lemma follows.

Lemma 3.3

$\chi_{ijk} \neq \chi_{i'j'k'}$ unless $i' = i, j' = j$, and $k' = k$. Moreover, $\chi_{ijk} \neq 1_G$ for all i, j, k.

Proof

By the Frobenius reciprocity theorem and Theorem 4.2.4(i), $(1_G, \theta_{ijkm})_G = (1_{M_i}, \zeta_{ijk} - \zeta_{ijm})_{M_i} = 0$. Since $\chi_{ijk} \neq \chi_{ijm}$ for $k \neq m$, it follows therefore from (3.7) that 1_G is not a constituent of θ_{ijkm}, whence $\chi_{ijk} \neq 1_G$ for all i, j, k.

Suppose now that $\chi_{ijk} = \chi_{i'j'k'}$. If $i \neq i'$, Lemma 3.2 implies that χ_{ijk} is integral-valued on each H_m, $1 \leqslant m \leqslant r$. But every element of G lies in a conjugate of some H_m, so χ_{ijk} is integral-valued on G. However, as $|G|$ is odd, χ_{ijk} must be nonreal by Theorem 4.3.6, a contradiction. Hence $i = i'$.

Observe next that by equation (4.5.22)

$$(3.8) \qquad \bar{\chi}_{ijk} - \chi_{ijk} = \varepsilon_{ij}(\bar{\zeta}_{ijk} - \zeta_{ijk})^* \qquad \text{for all } i, j, k;$$

while by Theorem 4.3.6, $\bar{\chi}_{ijk} \neq \chi_{ijk}$. Assume now that $j \neq j'$ or $k \neq k'$. Then either the four characters $\zeta_{ijk}, \bar{\zeta}_{ijk}, \zeta_{ij'k'}, \bar{\zeta}_{ij'k'}$ are all distinct or $j = j'$ and $\zeta_{ijk'} = \bar{\zeta}_{ijk}$ and $\bar{\zeta}_{ijk'} = \zeta_{ijk}$. Correspondingly, we have

$$(3.9) \qquad (\bar{\zeta}_{ijk} - \zeta_{ijk}, \bar{\zeta}_{ij'k'} - \zeta_{ij'k'})_{M_i} = 0 \text{ or } -2.$$

But then, by Theorem 4.5.4, we have

$$(3.10) \qquad (\bar{\chi}_{ijk} - \chi_{ijk}, \bar{\chi}_{ij'k'} - \chi_{ijk})_G = 0 \text{ or } -2.$$

However, if $\chi_{ijk} = \chi_{ij'k'}$, then also $\bar{\chi}_{ijk} = \bar{\chi}_{ij'k'}$ and the inner product (3.10) would be 2. Thus $\chi_{ijk} \neq \chi_{ij'k'}$, completing the proof.

This gives

Lemma 3.4

The characters 1_G and χ_{ijk}, $1 \leqslant i \leqslant r$, $1 \leqslant j \leqslant t_i$, $1 \leqslant k \leqslant w_{ij}$, are all the irreducible characters of G.

Proof

By definition of t_i and w_{ij}, $\sum_{j=1}^{t_i} w_{ij}$ is the number of irreducible characters of M_i not having H_i in their kernels, which by the proof of Theorem 4.5.3 is the same as the number of conjugate classes of elements of $H_i^\#$ in M_i. However, by Theorem 2.5, any π_i-element of G is conjugate to one in H_i and two elements of H_i are conjugate in G if and only if they are conjugate in M_i. Since every element of G lies in some H_i, we conclude that $1 + \sum_{i,j} w_{ij}$ is the total number of conjugate classes of G as well as the number of characters in the set $\{1_G, \chi_{ijk}\}$. Since the number of irreducible characters of G is the same as the number of conjugate classes of G, the lemma follows.

To simplify notation, we now put

$$H = H_1, M = M_1, h = h_1, n = n_1, w = w_1, \zeta = \zeta_{11k}, \chi_k = \chi_{11k},$$

and set

(3.11) $$\Delta = \sum_{i=1}^{w} \chi_i.$$

We note that each χ_k has degree n and has the form $\chi_k = \tilde{\phi}_k$ for some linear character ϕ_k of H, $1 \leqslant k \leqslant w$, where $\tilde{\phi}_k$ denotes the character of M induced by ϕ_k. In particular, $1_H - \phi_1 \in \mathrm{ch}_0(H)$. We next examine the constituents of $(1_H - \phi_1)^*$.

Lemma 3.5

If $\beta = (1_H - \phi_1)^*$, then
$$\beta = 1_G - \varepsilon_{11}\chi_1 + a\Delta + \psi,$$

where a is a nonnegative integer and ψ is a real-valued character of G with the property

$$(\psi, \psi)_G \leqslant n - 1 \qquad and \qquad (1_G, \psi)_G = (\chi_k, \psi)_G = 0, 1 \leqslant k \leqslant w.$$

Proof

By Theorem 4.4.4, $\beta = \sigma^*$, where σ is the character of M induced by $1_H - \phi_1$. But $\tilde{\phi}_1 = \zeta_1$ is irreducible, while $\tilde{1}_H$ is the regular representation of M/H by Theorem 4.4.2. But then all the constituents of $\tilde{1}_H$ have H in their kernel and by Theorem 4.2.7(i) we have $(\tilde{1}_H, \tilde{1}_H)_M = n$. Since ζ_1 does not have H in its kernel, it follows therefore from Theorem 4.2.4(i) that $(\sigma, \sigma)_M = n + 1$. However, $\sigma \in I_0(H)$ and we conclude therefore from Theorem 4.4.6 that

(3.12) $$(\beta, \beta)_G = n + 1.$$

But now we see that the inequality $(\psi, \psi)_G \leqslant n - 1$ will follow from the remaining parts of the lemma.

By Theorem 4.4.3(ii), β is 0 outside of the conjugates of $H^\#$. On the other hand, for $i > 1$, χ_{ijk} is integral-valued on H and so $\bar{\chi}_{ijk} - \chi_{ijk}$ is 0 on H. But then it follows at once from the definition of the inner product that

(3.13) $$(\beta, \bar{\chi}_{ijk} - \chi_{ijk})_G = 0 \qquad \text{for all } j, k \text{ and all } i > 1.$$

For $i = 1$ we can use Theorem 4.4.6 to obtain

$$(\beta, \theta_{1jkm})_G = (\sigma, \zeta_{1jk} - \zeta_{1jm})_M,$$

which yields in the usual way

$$(3.14) \qquad (\beta, \chi_{1jk} - \chi_{1jm})_G = \begin{cases} 0 & \text{if } j > 1; \\ \varepsilon_{11}(\delta_{1m} - \delta_{1k}) & \text{if } j = 1. \end{cases}$$

Let ψ be the sum of all χ_{ijk} appearing in β for which either $i > 1$ or $j > 1$. Then (3.13) and (3.14) tell us that any such χ_{ijk} appears in β with the same multiplicity as $\bar{\chi}_{ijk}$ and so ψ is real. Moreover, $(1_G, \psi)_G = (\chi_k, \psi)_G = 0$ as neither 1_G nor any χ_k is a constituent of ψ.

By the Frobenius reciprocity theorem, 1_G has multiplicity 1 in β. Since 1_G and the χ_{ijk} are all the irreducible characters of G, it follows therefore from the second relation of (3.14) that $\beta - 1_G - \psi = -\varepsilon_{11}\chi_1 + a\Delta$ for some nonnegative integer a, thus completing the proof of the lemma.

With this information we shall now obtain some numerical estimates for the sum in Theorem 2.6(ii). To this end, we subdivide the indices $2 \leqslant i \leqslant r$ into two disjoint subsets Y, Z, as follows: If χ_{ijk} is not a constituent of ψ for a given i and all j, k, we put i in Y; in the contrary case, we put i in Z. We now prove

Lemma 3.6

The following inequalities hold:

$$(i) \quad \sum_{i \in Y} \frac{h_i - 1}{h_i n_i} \leqslant \frac{1}{w}.$$

$$(ii) \quad \sum_{i \in Z} \frac{h_i - 1}{h_i n_i} \leqslant \frac{n - 1}{2n_2}.$$

Proof

We first prove (ii). Suppose χ_{ijk} is a constituent of ψ. Then so is $\bar{\chi}_{ijk}$, as ψ is real. Since $\bar{\chi}_{ijk} \neq \chi_{ijk}$ and $(\psi, \psi)_G \leqslant n - 1$, we see that there are at most $(n - 1)/2$ distinct such indices i. Thus

$$(3.15) \qquad\qquad |Z| \leqslant \frac{n-1}{2}.$$

Furthermore,

$$(3.16) \qquad\qquad \frac{h_i - 1}{h_i n_i} \leqslant \frac{1}{n_i} \leqslant \frac{1}{n_2} \qquad \text{for } i > 1$$

by (3.4). But now (ii) follows at once from (3.15) and (3.16).

Next let $m \in Y$ and $y \in H_m$. Then for χ_{ijk} a constituent of $\psi + a\Delta$, we have $i \neq m$, whence χ_{ijk} is integral-valued on y. But then $\bar{\chi}_{ijk}(y) = \chi_{ijk}(y)$. But as ψ is real, it is immediate that $\bar{\chi}_{ijk}$ and χ_{ijk} have the same multiplicities in $\psi + a\Delta$. Thus the value of $\psi + a\Delta$ on y is an even integer. On the other hand, by Theorem 4.4.3 and the definition of β, β is 0 on H_m. Hence

(3.17) $0 = \beta(y) \equiv 1 - \varepsilon_{11}\chi_1(y) \,(\text{mod } 2),$

which forces $\chi_1(y) \neq 0$. Since χ_1 is integral-valued on H_m, it follows that $|\chi_1(y)| \geq 1$. Furthermore, as with β, $\chi_1 - \chi_k$ is 0 on H_m, so $\chi_k(y) = \chi_1(y)$. We conclude from (3.11) that

(3.18) $|\Delta(y)| = w\,|\chi_1(y)| \geq w$ for all y in H_m and all m in Y.

Finally, let G_0 be the subset of elements of G conjugate to an element of $H_i^{\#}$ for i in Y. Then by Theorem 2.5 and 2.6 we have

(3.19) $$|G_0| = |G| \sum_{i \in Y} \frac{h_i - 1}{h_i n_i}.$$

But as $\Delta(y)\overline{\Delta(y)}$ is a nonnegative real number for all y in G and $\Delta(y)$ is integral-valued on G_0, we have

(3.20) $$w = (\Delta, \Delta)_G \geq \frac{1}{|G|} \sum_{y \in G_0} |\Delta(y)|^2 \geq \frac{1}{|G|} \, w^2 |G_0|.$$

Hence $1/w \geq |G_0|/|G|$ and now (i) follows from (3.19).

Combining Lemma 3.6 with Theorem 2.6 we obtain the fundamental inequality:

Lemma 3.7

$$1 \leq \frac{1}{|G|} + \frac{h-1}{hn} + \frac{1}{w} + \frac{n-1}{2n_2}.$$

On the strength of this inequality we can now easily complete the proof of Theorem 3.1. Suppose first that $w > 2$, in which case $w \geq 4$, as w is even. Moreover, $n_2 \geq n \geq 3$ as n is odd and $n > 1$. But now the preceding inequality reduces to

(3.21) $$1 \leq \frac{1}{|G|} + \frac{1}{n} + \frac{1}{4} + \frac{1}{2} - \frac{1}{2n} = \frac{1}{|G|} + \frac{3}{4} + \frac{1}{2n} \leq \frac{1}{|G|} + \frac{11}{12},$$

whence $|G| \leq 12$. Since $|G|$ is odd, it therefore has prime power order and so is solvable, a contradiction. Hence $w = 2$.

Since $w = w_{11}$, we have $w_{11} = 2$ and it follows now from (3.4) that $n = n_1 < n_2$. Thus $n_2 \geq n + 2$, as n_2 is also odd. This time we obtain

(3.22) $$1 \leq \frac{1}{|G|} + \frac{h - 1}{hn} + \frac{1}{2} + \frac{n - 1}{2(n + 2)}.$$

Since

$$\frac{n-1}{2(n+2)} = \frac{1}{2} - \frac{3}{2(n+2)} \quad \text{and} \quad \frac{h-1}{hn} = \frac{1}{n} - \frac{1}{hn},$$

(3.22) reduces directly to

(3.23) $$0 \geqslant \frac{1}{|G|} - \frac{1}{hn} + \frac{-n+4}{2n(n+2)}.$$

If $n \geqslant 5$, this yields $|G| \leqslant hn$, contrary to the fact that M is a proper subgroup of G of order hn. Thus $n = 3$. Since $w = 2$, (3.3) now implies that $|H:H'| = wn + 1 = 7$. But then H/H' is cyclic and so H is cyclic by Lemma 1.3.4, whence $H' = 1$ and $|H| = 7$. Substituting in (3.23), we conclude that $|G| \leqslant 70$. In this case the oddness of $|G|$ forces $|G| = p^a q^b$ for some primes p and q and so G is solvable by Burnside's theorem. This contradiction completes the proof of the theorem.

4. CN-GROUPS WITH ABELIAN SYLOW 2-SUBGROUPS

As our final result we shall classify all simple CN-groups which have abelian S_2-subgroups. We prove

Theorem 4.1

If G is a simple CN-group of composite order with abelian Sylow 2-subgroup S, then G is isomorphic to $L_2(2^n)$, where $|S| = 2^n$ and $n \geqslant 2$.

We first establish two short lemmas.

Lemma 4.2

If H is a maximal nilpotent subgroup of G containing S, then $C_G^*(x) \subseteq H$ for any x in $H^\#$.

Proof

In view of Theorem 1.7(iv), we need only show that H is disjoint from its conjugates. If $H \supset S$, this follows from Theorem 1.7(ii). So assume $H = S$. If $S \cap S^y \neq 1$, and $x \in S \cap S^y$, $x \neq 1$, then $C_G(x) \supseteq S$ and S^y, as each is abelian. Since $C_G(x)$ is nilpotent, the maximality of $H = S$ implies that $C_G(x) = S = S^y$, so S is disjoint from its conjugates in this case as well.

Lemma 4.3

If $M = N_G(H)$, then G is a Zassenhaus group of degree $|H| + 1$ acting on the right cosets of M.

Proof

By Theorem 9.3.2, either the lemma holds or S is cyclic (as S is abelian) or else $\Omega_1(S) \lhd G$. If S is cyclic, G possesses a normal 2-complement K, which is thus a CN-group of odd order. But then K, and hence G, is solvable by Theorem 3.1. On the other hand, if $\Omega_1(S) \lhd G$, so also is $C = C_G(\Omega_1(S))$. But C is nilpotent and contains S. In particular, $|G/C|$ is odd. Since G/C is a CN-group by Lemma 1.3, G/C is therefore solvable and hence so is G. The lemma follows.

Since G is a Zassenhaus group and $|M:H|$ is odd, we can apply Feit's theorem (Theorem 13.2.1) to conclude that $S = H$. Moreover, as S is abelian, the same theorem yields that a Frobenius complement L in M has order $|S| - 1$. But L is cyclic and is inverted by an involution by Theorem 13.1.4(i). Thus the hypotheses of Zassenhaus's theorem are satisfied and it follows that G is isomorphic to $L_2(2^n)$, where $2^n = |S|$, and $n \geqslant 2$.

Remark   When S is not abelian, S need not be disjoint from its conjugate and so G need not be a Zassenhaus group. Suzuki [9] has shown in general that, if G is a nonsolvable CN-group, then either

    (a) G is a Zassenhaus group of degree $|S| + 1$ with $S = H$.

    (b) G is isomorphic to one of the groups $L_2(p)$, p a Fermat or Mersenne prime, $L_2(9)$, or $L_3(4)$.

In a fundamental separate work he has proved that the only nonsolvable Zassenhaus groups of degree $2^n + 1$ are the group $L_2(2^n)$ and the Suzuki groups $Sz(2^n)$, thus completing the classification of all nonsolvable CN-groups.

In the same connection, Ito [3] has shown that the only nonsolvable Zassenhaus groups of degree $p^n + 1$, p odd, are the groups $L_2(p^n)$. The combined work of Suzuki and Ito, together with the earlier results of Zassenhaus and Feit, provide a complete classification of Zassenhaus groups.

CHAPTER 15

GROUPS WITH SELF-CENTRALIZING SYLOW 2-SUBGROUPS OF ORDER 4

In this chapter we shall determine in detail the structure of a group G which has an S_2-subgroup of order 4 which is its own centralizer in G. In particular, we shall prove that the groups $L_2(q)$, $q \equiv 3, 5 \pmod{8}$ and $q > 3$ are the only simple groups with this property. In the course of our analysis we shall present a typical application of the Maximal Subgroup theorem in the study of simple groups. Under the present hypotheses, the effect of this theorem is to reduce our problem to the special case in which the given group G satisfies precisely those conditions which we investigated in Section 9.4 and on the basis of which we established the Brauer-Suzuki-Wall theorem. In Section 4 we continue the analysis begun in Chapter 9 and establish the main result of the paper of Brauer, Suzuki, and Wall [1] —that such a group G is necessarily a Zassenhaus group in which the hypotheses of Zassenhaus's theorem hold. Application of that theorem then enables us to complete our classification theorem.

This special case of the dihedral Sylow 2-subgroup problem embodies in simpler form the essential structure of the general proof.

Unfortunately at one point our argument will require the fact that all groups of odd order are solvable (Lemma 3.9 below). Although it is possible to avoid this deep result by means of group order formulas derived by character theory, we prefer to assume this result, where needed, and to use the Maximal Subgroup theorem approach because of its importance in classification problems. We shall present the character-theoretic alternative in a series of exercises.

1. SOME PROPERTIES OF $L_2(q)$

For the proof we shall require several properties of the groups $L_2(q)$. Although these properties are needed only for the case $q \equiv 3, 5 \,(\text{mod } 8)$, the proofs are the same for all values of q.

Lemma 1.1

Let $G = L_2(q)$ with $q = p^r$, p a prime. Then we have
  (i) An S_p-subgroup P of G is elementary abelian of order p^r, P is disjoint from its conjugates, and $N_G(P)$ is a Frobenius group with a cyclic complement which acts irreducibly on P.
  (ii) If t is a prime distinct from p or 2, then an S_t-subgroup of G is cyclic.
  (iii) If p is odd, an S_2-subgroup of G is dihedral and has order 4 if and only if $q \equiv 3, 5 \,(\text{mod } 8)$.
  (iv) If p is odd and R is a four-subgroup of G, then $C_G(R) = R$.
  (v) If Q is a nontrivial subgroup of G of odd prime power order, then $N_G(Q)$ does not contain a subgroup isomorphic to A_4. Moreover, if $N_G(Q)$ contains a four-subgroup, then Q is cyclic.

Proof

By Theorem 2.8.2, G is a Zassenhaus group of degree $q + 1$ of type (H, K), where K is an elementary abelian p-group disjoint from its conjugates and H is cyclic of order $\varepsilon(q - 1)$, where $\varepsilon = 1$ if $p = 2$ and $\varepsilon = \frac{1}{2}$ if $p > 2$. In particular, $K = P$ is an S_p-subgroup of G. Since G is doubly transitive, $N = HP$ is maximal by Theorem 2.7.3(iii). Hence $N = N_G(P)$ and so $N_G(P)$ has the given properties. Thus (i) holds.

As for (ii), we know by Theorem 2.8.3(i) that $SL(2, q)$ contains cyclic subgroups of order $q - 1$ and $q + 1$. Since $|SL(2, q)| = q(q - 1)(q + 1)$, the S_t-subgroups of $SL(2, q)$ are cyclic for $t \neq 2$ or p. Since G is a homomorphic image of $SL(2, q)$, (ii) follows. Furthermore, an S_2-subgroup S of $SL(2, q)$ is generalized quaternion for odd p by Theorem 2.8.3(ii). Since $Z(S) = \langle -I \rangle$, where I is the 2×2 identity matrix, an S_2-subgroup of G is isomorphic to $S/Z(S)$ and so is dihedral. Since $|G| = \frac{1}{2}q(q - 1)(q + 1)$, $|S/Z(S)| = 4$ if and only if $q^2 - 1 \not\equiv 0 \,(\text{mod } 16)$ and hence if and only if $q \equiv 3$ or $5 \,(\text{mod } 8)$. Thus (iii) also holds.

Again assume p is odd and let R be a four-subgroup of G. Set $C = C_G(R)$ and let t be an odd prime in $\pi(C)$. If $t = p$, R lies in a conjugate of $N_G(P)$ by (i). But also by (i), an S_2-subgroup of $N_G(P)$ is cyclic when p is odd. Thus $t \neq p$. If t divides $q - 1$, then a conjugate of R lies in $C_G(H)$. But G is a Zassenhaus group and H is inverted by an involution of G, so $C_G(H) = H$ and the cyclicity of H is contradicted.

Suppose, finally, that t divides $q + 1$. Let $y \in C$ and let x be an element of order t in $SL(2, q)$ which maps on y. Then it is immediate that the inverse image R_1 of R in $SL(2, q)$ centralizes x. On the other hand, as t divides $q + 1$, the characteristic roots of x do not lie in $GF(q)$, so x acts irreducibly on the natural vector space V on which $SL(2, q)$ acts. But then by Theorem 3.5.2, $D = \text{Hom}_{\langle x \rangle} (V, V)$ is a finite division algebra and so by Wedderburn's theorem is a field. Since $D \cap SL(2, q)$ is a multiplicative subgroup of this field, it is cyclic, contrary to the fact that $R_1 \subseteq D$ and R_1 is noncyclic. Since t divides neither $q, q - 1$, nor $q + 1$, C must be a 2-group. But then C is contained in a conjugate of the dihedral group S and so $C = R$ by Lemma 7.7.2(iv), proving (iv).

Finally, let Q be a nontrivial t-subgroup of G, t an odd prime, and set $M = N_G(Q)$. If M contains a four-subgroup R, then $t \neq p$, for otherwise R would lie in a conjugate of $N_G(P)$ which has cyclic S_2-subgroups by (i). Hence Q is cyclic by (ii). Now assume M contains a subgroup L isomorphic to A_4, in which case L' is a four group. By what we have just shown Q must be cyclic, whence Aut Q is abelian by Theorem 1.3.10(i). Hence L' centralizes Q, contrary to (iv). Thus (v) also holds.

We next prove

Theorem 1.2

The groups $L_2(q)$ are simple for $q > 3$. Moreover, $L_2(4)$, $L_2(5)$, and A_5 are all isomorphic.

Proof

Set $G = L_2(q)$, $q = p^r > 3$. Suppose by way of contradiction that G contains a nontrivial proper normal subgroup H. Consider first the case that $p \in \pi(H)$. Then $P \cap H \neq 1$ for some S_p-subgroup P of G. Now $N_G(P)$ normalizes both P and H and so leaves $P \cap H$ invariant. But by the preceding lemma, $N_G(P)$ leaves no nontrivial proper subgroup of P invariant. Hence $P = P \cap H$ and so $P \subseteq H$. We can assume P is the image of the S_p-subgroup $Q = \left\{ \begin{pmatrix} 1 & 0 \\ \lambda & 1 \end{pmatrix} \middle| \lambda \in GF(q) \right\}$ of $SL(2, q)$. Now Q is conjugate in $SL(2, q)$ to $Q_1 = \left\{ \begin{pmatrix} 1 & \lambda \\ 0 & 1 \end{pmatrix} \middle| \lambda \in GF(q) \right\}$ by the element $\begin{pmatrix} 0 & 1 \\ -1 & 0 \end{pmatrix}$, as can be directly checked. Hence P is conjugate in G to the image P_1 of Q_1. Since $H \lhd G$ it follows, that $P_1 \subseteq H$. But $SL(2, q) = \langle Q, Q_1 \rangle$ by Theorem 2.8.4 as $q > 3$, whence $\langle P, P_1 \rangle = G$. We conclude that $H = G$, a contradiction.

Hence H is a p'-group. Let T be an S_t-subgroup of H for t in $\pi(H)$. Then $G = HN_G(T)$ by Theorem 1.3.7 and so $N_G(T)$ contains an S_p-subgroup of G, which we may again denote by P. Let $x \in P^\#$. Since P is disjoint from its conjugates, it follows that $C_T(x) \subseteq N_G(P)$. But then $[C_T(x), P] \subseteq P \cap T = 1$ and so $C_T(x)$ centralizes P. Since $C_G(P) = P$, we conclude that $C_T(x) = 1$ for all x in $P^\#$ and hence that P induces a regular group of automorphisms of T. Since P is abelian, Theorem 5.4.11 now forces P to be cyclic. Hence $|P| = p = q$ and, in particular, $p \geqslant 5$.

If t is odd, then T is cyclic by the preceding lemma. Moreover, $|T| = t^m$ divides $p - 1$ or $p + 1$ and so p does not divide $t - 1$. However, the proof of Lemma 5.4.1 shows that $|\operatorname{Aut} T| = t^{m-1}(t - 1)$. Hence T does not admit an automorphism of order p and so P centralizes T contrary to $C_G(P) = P$. Thus H is a 2-group. Since an S_2-subgroup of G is dihedral, H is either cyclic or dihedral. But then $|\bar{H}| \leqslant 4$, where $\bar{H} = H/\Phi(H)$ and so $|\operatorname{Aut} \bar{H}|$ is not divisible by p as $p \geqslant 5$. Thus P centralizes $\bar{H}$ and hence also centralizes H, giving the same contradiction. Thus G is simple.

Finally, let $q = 4$ or 5, in which cases $|G| = 60$ by Theorem 2.8.1. It will suffice to show that G possesses a subgroup H of order 12, for then, as in the proof of Lemma 2.8.14, the permutation representation π of G on the right cosets of H will map G isomorphically onto A_5 inasmuch as G is simple.

If $q = 4$, then the subgroup fixing a letter has order 12. Suppose then that $q = 5$. In this case an S_2-subgroup S of G is abelian of type $(2, 2)$ and $C_G(S) = S$ by the preceding theorem. Moreover, $N_G(S) \supset S$ by Burnside's theorem as G is simple. Since $|\operatorname{Aut} S| = 6$, we conclude that $N_G(S)$ is a subgroup of the required order.

The preceding theorem together with Lemma 1.1(iii) and (iv) show that the groups $L_2(q)$ with $q \equiv 3, 5 \pmod 8$ and $q > 3$ are, in fact, simple groups with self-centralizing Sylow 2-subgroups of order 4. Our goal will be to show that these are the only such simple groups.

2. STATEMENT OF THE THEOREM AND INITIAL REDUCTION

It will be simpler to use the symbol $O(G)$ in place of $O_{2'}(G)$. Thus $O(G)$ is the largest normal subgroup of *odd* order in the group G. Our aim in the balance of the chapter will be to establish the following theorem:

Theorem 2.1

Let G be a group with a self-centralizing Sylow 2-subgroup of order 4. Then one of the following holds:

    (i) G has a normal 2-complement, or

    (ii) $G/O(G)$ is isomorphic to $L_2(q)$, $q \equiv 3, 5 \pmod 8$.

In particular, if G is simple, then G is isomorphic to $L_2(q)$ with $q \equiv 3, 5 \pmod 8$ and $q > 3$.

We first prove

Lemma 2.2

Let G be a counterexample to Theorem 2.1 of lowest possible order. Then we have

    (i) G is simple.

    (ii) An S_2-subgroup S of G is a four-group.

    (iii) Every proper subgroup of G satisfies the conclusion of Theorem 2.1.

Proof

If S is cyclic, then G possesses a normal 2-complement by Theorem 7.6.1 and consequently S must be a four-group. Let H be a proper subgroup of G. If an S_2-subgroup of H is cyclic, then H has a normal 2-complement by the same theorem. In the contrary case, H contains an S_2-subgroup of G and hence H satisfies the conclusion of Theorem 2.1 by our minimal choice of G. Thus (ii) and (iii) hold.

Finally, suppose G is not simple and let N be a minimal normal subgroup of G, so that $1 \subset N \subset G$. Since $O(N)$ char $N \lhd G$, either $N = O(N)$ or $O(N) = 1$. In the first case, set $\bar{G} = G/N$ and let $\bar{S}$ be the image of S in $\bar{G}$. By Burnside's transfer theorem, $C_{\bar{G}}(\bar{S}) = \bar{S} \times \bar{D}$, where $|\bar{D}|$ is odd. But then if D is the inverse image of $\bar{D}$ in G, $C_D(S) = 1$ since S is self-centralizing in G and consequently $C_D(\bar{S}) = 1$ by Lemma 10.5.2(vi). Thus $\bar{D} = \bar{1}$ and so $C_{\bar{G}}(\bar{S}) = \bar{S}$. Since $|\bar{G}| < |G|$, Theorem 2.1 holds for $\bar{G}$ and hence follows at once for G, contrary to our choice of G. We conclude that $O(N) = 1$.

Assume next that N is a 2-group. If $N = \langle x \rangle$ is of order 2, then x is conjugate only to itself in G and so G has a normal 2-complement by Theorem 7.7.1. On the other hand, if $|N| = 4$, we have $N = S$. Since $C_G(S) = S$, G/S must be isomorphic to a subgroup of Aut S of odd order. Hence $|G/S| = 1$ or 3 and therefore either $G = S$ or G is isomorphic to $L_2(3)$, again contradicting our choice of G.

By (iii), the only other possibility is that N be isomorphic to $L_2(q)$, $q \equiv 3, 5 \pmod 8$. In particular, $S \subseteq N$ and consequently $G = NK$, where

$K = N_G(S)$, by Theorem 1.3.7. Since $C_G(S) = S$, it follows as in the preceding paragraph that $|K| \leqslant 12$. But as N has no normal subgroups of index 2 by Theorem 1.2, $N_N(S) \supset S$ by Theorem 7.7.1, whence $|N_N(S)| = 12$. Thus $K \subseteq N$ and hence $G = N$, a contradiction. Therefore G is simple and the lemma is proved.

To prove Theorem 2.1, we must obviously show that no counterexample to the theorem exists. Hence, by Lemma 1.2, we must prove that a minimal counterexample is, in fact, isomorphic to $L_2(q)$ with $q \equiv 3, 5 \pmod 8$ and $q > 3$. Thus it will suffice to establish the following result:

Theorem 2.3

Let G be a simple group with an elementary abelian S_2-subgroup S of order 4 such that $C_G(S) = S$, and assume that for any proper subgroup H of G, either H has a normal 2-complement or $H/O(H)$ is isomorphic to $L_2(r)$, $r \equiv 3, 5 \pmod 8$. Then G is isomorphic to $L_2(q)$, $q \equiv 3, 5 \pmod 8$ and $q > 3$.

The remainder of the chapter will be devoted to a proof of Theorem 2.3. We note also that the proof of Lemma 2.2 shows that Theorem 7.7.1 reduces under the assumption $C_G(S) = S$ to:

Lemma 2.4

Let G be an arbitrary group with a self-centralizing elementary abelian S_2-subgroup S of order 4. Then one of the following holds:

    (i) *$N_G(S) = S$ and G has a normal 2-complement.*

    (ii) *$N_G(S)$ is isomorphic to $L_2(3)$ and G has no normal subgroups of index 2 and only one class of involutions.*

Finally, we establish Theorem 2.3 in a degenerate case.

Theorem 2.5

Let G be a simple group with a self-centralizing elementary abelian S_2-subgroup S of order 4 and assume that $C_G(x) \subseteq S$ for some involution x of S. Then G is isomorphic to $L_2(5)$.

Proof

Our conditions imply that all involutions of S are conjugate in $N = N_G(S)$, that N has order 12, and that $C_G(y) = S$ for every involution y of S. Since G has no nontrivial normal 2-subgroups, it follows therefore from Theorem 9.3.2 that G is a Zassenhaus group of degree $5 = |S| + 1$ with N the subgroup fixing a letter. Thus N is a Frobenius group with complement H of order $e = 3$ and kernel S of order $n = 4$. Since e is odd and $e \geqslant \frac{1}{2}(n - 1)$, Theorem 13.3.5 now yields that G is isomorphic to $L_2(4)$.

But $L_2(4)$ and $L_2(5)$ are isomorphic by Theorem 1.2 and the theorem is proved.

For brevity we shall call a simple group G an L_2-*group* if it satisfies the hypothesis of Theorem 2.3 and if $C_G(x) \nsubseteq S$ for any x in $S^\#$. To prove Theorem 2.3 we must therefore show that an L_2-group is necessarily isomorphic to $L_2(q)$, $q \equiv 3, 5 \pmod 8$ with $q > 5$.

3. THE STRUCTURE OF THE CENTRALIZER OF AN INVOLUTION

With the aid of the Maximal Subgroup theorem we shall now establish the following basic result, which represents a major step in the proof of Theorem 2.3.

Theorem 3.1

If G is an L_2-group, then G possesses an abelian subgroup K of order $2n$, n odd, $n > 1$, which is disjoint from its conjugates and such that $N_G(K)$ is the direct product of a group $\langle x \rangle$ of order 2 and a Frobenius group with kernel of order n and complement of order 2. In particular, $N_G(K)$ is the centralizer of the involution x.

Thus the effect of Theorem 3.1 will be to reduce the study of L_2-groups to the precise situation which we discussed in Section 9.4.

In this section we adopt the following notation: S an S_2-subgroup of G, x_i, $1 \leqslant i \leqslant 3$, the three involutions of S, $N = N_G(S)$, $N_i = C_G(x_i)$, $1 \leqslant i \leqslant 3$, and y an element of order 3 in N with the property

$$(3.1) \qquad x_1^y = x_2 \qquad x_2^y = x_3 \qquad x_3^y = x_1.$$

By Theorem 7.7.1, each N_i has a normal 2-complement U_i; so $N_i = SU_i$, $1 \leqslant i \leqslant 3$. Furthermore, the element y cyclically permutes N_1, N_2, and N_3 and so we also have

$$(3.2) \qquad U_1^y = U_2 \qquad U_2^y = U_3 \qquad U_3^y = U_1.$$

Since $C_{U_i}(S) = 1$, x_j inverts U_i for $j \neq i$ and consequently each U_i is abelian.

If H is any S-invariant subgroup of G of odd order, we shall write $H_i = C_H(x_i)$, $1 \leqslant i \leqslant 3$. Then by Lemma 10.5.1 each H_i is abelian, $H = \langle H_1, H_2, H_3 \rangle$, and for any p in $\pi(H)$, H possesses a unique S-invariant S_p-subgroup P and $P = P_1 P_2 P_3$, where P_i is the unique S_p-subgroup of H_i, $1 \leqslant i \leqslant 3$.

Finally we divide $\pi(U_1)$ into two disjoint subsets α and β as follows:

(3.3)
$$p \in \alpha \quad \text{if } U_1 \text{ contains an } S_p\text{-subgroup of } G;$$
$$p \in \beta \quad \text{if } U_1 \text{ does not contain an } S_p\text{-subgroup of } G.$$

Since G has only one class of involutions, the definition of α and β depends only upon G and not upon the particular involution x_1.

The following lemma shows the importance of this subdivision:

Lemma 3.2

Theorem 3.1 *holds if* β *is empty.*

Proof

Assume β is empty, in which case U_1 is an S_α-subgroup of G. Moreover, $n = |U_1| > 1$ by definition of an L_2-group. Now x_2 inverts U_1 as $C_{U_1}(S) = 1$ and consequently $\langle U_1, x_2 \rangle$ is a Frobenius group with kernel U_1 and complement $\langle x_2 \rangle$. Furthermore, $N_1 = \langle U_1, x_2 \rangle \times \langle x_1 \rangle$. Hence if we set $K = U_1 \times \langle x_1 \rangle$, it will suffice to show that K is disjoint from its conjugates and that $N_1 = N_G(K)$.

To prove this, we first show that U_1 is a maximal S-invariant subgroup of G of odd order. Indeed, suppose R is S-invariant of odd order and contains U_1. Then S normalizes an S_p-subgroup P of R for any prime p in $\pi(R)$. Since $P = P_1 P_2 P_3$, it follows that $p \in \alpha$, whence R is an α-group. But U_1 is an S_α-subgroup of G and consequently $R = U_1$.

Now set $M = N_G(U_1)$ and $C = C_G(U_1)$. Then $S \subset M$ and $S \cap C = \langle x_1 \rangle$. Since $C \lhd M$, x_1 cannot be conjugate to x_2 or x_3 in M and consequently M possesses a normal 2-complement R. Thus $C = SR$ and $R \supseteq U_1$. But then $R = U_1$ by the preceding paragraph and so $M = SU_1 = N_1$. Since U_1 char K, $N_G(K) \subseteq N_G(U_1)$ and we conclude that $N_G(K) = N_1$.

Next let $z \in K \cap K^v$, $z \neq 1$, $v \in G$. If z has even order, then $z^i = x_1 = x_1^v$, as x_1, x_1^v are the unique involutions of K, K^v, respectively. But then $v \in C_G(x_1) = N_1 = N_G(K)$, so $K^v = K$. Suppose, on the other hand, that z has odd order. In this case, set $C = C_G(z)$ and $M = C_G^*(z)$. Since x_2 inverts z, it follows that $S \subseteq M$ and that $S \cap C = \langle x_1 \rangle$. Since $C \lhd M$ and $U_1 \subseteq M$, we conclude as in the preceding paragraph that $M = SU_1$. But U_1^v is also contained in M. Since $|U_1^v| = |U_1|$ it follows that $U_1^v = U_1$, whence $v \in N_1 = N_G(U_1)$, again by the preceding paragraph. Hence K is disjoint from its conjugates and the lemma is proved.

We therefore assume for the balance of the proof of Theorem 3.1 that β is nonempty.

Lemma 3.3

If H_i is a nontrivial subset of U_i, then $N_G(H_i)$ contains S and possesses a normal 2-complement which centralizes H_i.

Proof

Setting $C = C_G(H_i)$ and $C^* = N_G(H_i)$, we again have $S \subseteq C^*$ and $S \cap C = \langle x_i \rangle$, so that C^* possesses a normal 2-complement K by Lemma 2.4. Since $|K|$ is odd, Lemma 10.5.1(iv) now yields that $H_i \subseteq Z(K)$.

Lemma 3.4

There exists a unique maximal S-invariant p-subgroup of G containing the S_p-subgroup of U_1 for any p in $\pi(U_1)$.

Proof

Let P_i be the S_p-subgroup of U_i, $1 \leqslant i \leqslant 3$, and note that any S-invariant p-subgroup X of G has the form $X = X_1 X_2 X_3$ with $X_i = X \cap P_i$, $1 \leqslant i \leqslant 3$. Suppose now that P and Q are distinct maximal S-invariant p-subgroups of G containing P_1 and choose Q so that $D = P \cap Q$ has maximal order. We have $D \subset P$ and $D \subset Q$. Set $L = N_G(D)$. Then $P \cap L \supset D$ and $Q \cap L \supset D$ by Theorem 1.2.11(ii). If L has a normal 2-complement K, then K possesses a unique S-invariant S_p-subgroup R which must therefore contain both $P \cap L$ and $Q \cap L$. But then if T is a maximal S-invariant p-subgroup of G containing R, we have $P \cap T \supseteq P \cap L \supset D \supset P_1$, whence $P = T$ by our maximal choice of Q. But now $P \cap Q = T \cap Q \supseteq L \cap Q \supset D$, contrary to the definition of D. We conclude that L does not have a normal 2-complement.

It follows now from Lemma 2.4 that $N = N_G(S) \subseteq L$ and hence that $y \in L$. On the other hand, $D = D_1 D_2 D_3$ with $D_1 = P_1$ and $D_i \subseteq P_i$, $2 \leqslant i \leqslant 3$. But as D is y-invariant, y must cyclically permute the subgroups D_i, $1 \leqslant i \leqslant 3$. Since the P_i all have the same order and $D_1 = P_1$, it follows that $D_i = P_i$ for all i, whence $D = P_1 P_2 P_3$. But then clearly P and Q are each contained in D, whence $P = Q = D$, a contradiction.

The next lemma is critical.

Lemma 3.5

If P_i is the S_p-subgroup of U_i for p in β, $1 \leqslant i \leqslant 3$, then $P = \langle P_1, P_2, P_3 \rangle = P_1 P_2 P_3$ is a p-group.

Proof

By Lemma 3.3, $L = N_G(P_1) = SK$, where $K \vartriangleleft L$, $|K|$ is odd, and $P_1 \subseteq Z(K)$. Let Q be the unique S-invariant S_p-subgroup of K, so that Q

is also an S_p-subgroup of L. Since $p \in \beta$, P_1 is not an S_p-subgroup of G and hence $P_1 \subset Q$. But $Q = P_1(P_2 \cap Q)(P_3 \cap Q)$, whence $P_i \cap Q \neq 1$ for $i = 2$ or 3, say, $i = 2$. Furthermore, P_1 centralizes $P_2 \cap Q$.

We now repeat the same argument on $N_G(P_2 \cap Q)$, which we see contains both P_1 and P_2 and possesses a normal 2-complement. But then if R is the unique S-invariant S_p-subgroup of $N_G(P_2 \cap Q)$, we have $R = P_1 P_2(P_3 \cap R)$. Thus the unique maximal S-invariant p-subgroup P of G containing P_1 has the form

$$(3.4) \qquad\qquad P = P_1 P_2(P_3 \cap P),$$

in which $P_3 \cap P$ has maximal order. The lemma will be proved if we can show that $P_3 = P_3 \cap P$. Consider first the case $P_3 \cap P = 1$, so that $P = P_1 P_2$. Then x_3 inverts P and consequently $P = P_1 \times P_2$ is abelian. On the other hand, since P_i is the unique S_p-subgroup of U_i, $1 \leqslant i \leqslant 3$, it follows from (3.2) that y cyclically permutes P_1, P_2, and P_3. But then we see that $P^y = P_2 \times P_3$. Thus P_2 centralizes both P_1 and P_3 and consequently $N_G(P_2)$ contains each P_i, $1 \leqslant i \leqslant 3$. But then the unique S-invariant S_p-subgroup of the normal 2-complement in $N_G(P_2)$ has the form $P_1 P_2 P_3$. We conclude that $P_3 \cap P \neq 1$.

Next set $D_3 = P_3 \cap P$, $D_1 = D_3^y$, and $D_2 = D_1^y$. Then $D_1 \subseteq P_1$ and $D_2 \subseteq P_2$, so that $D = \langle D_1, D_2, D_3 \rangle = D_1 D_2 D_3$ is a p-subgroup of P. By construction D is invariant under y as well as S and so is invariant under N. We may assume by way of contradiction that $D_3 \subset P_3$, whence $D \subset P$. We shall argue that D is not a maximal N-invariant p-subgroup of G. Indeed, set $H = N_G(D)$ and let E be the unique S-invariant S_p-subgroup of $O(H)$, so that $D \subseteq E$. Since $N \subseteq H$, E^y is also an S-invariant S_p-subgroup of $O(H)$, so $E^y = E$ and consequently E is also N-invariant. If $E \supset D$, the desired assertion follows, so assume $E = D$.

On the other hand, $B = N_P(D) \supset D$ as $P \supset D$. Thus $B = B_1 B_2 B_3$ with $B_i \supset D_i$, $i = 1$ or 2, say $i = 1$, and $B_3 = D_3$. Since D is y-invariant and $B_1^y \subseteq P_2 \subseteq P$, it follows that $B_1^y \subseteq B$, which implies that also $B_2 = B \cap P_2 \supset D_2$. Now $O(H)$ is not a normal 2-complement in H, otherwise $D = E$ would be an S_p-subgroup of H, contrary to the fact that $B \subseteq H$ and $B \supset D$. Since G is an L_2-group, this implies that $\bar{H} = H/O(H)$ is isomorphic to $L_2(r)$, $r \equiv 3, 5 \pmod 8$. We use superscripts for images in $\bar{H}$. Since D is an S_p-subgroup of $O(H)$ and $B_i \supset D_i$ for both $i = 1$ and 2, it follows from Lemma 10.5.1(vi) that $\bar{B} = \bar{B}_1 \bar{B}_2$, where $\bar{B}_i = C_{\bar{B}}(\bar{x}_i) \neq 1$, $1 \leqslant i \leqslant 2$. However, this contradicts Lemma 1.1(v). Thus $E \supset D$ and the assertion is proved.

Finally, consider $E = E_1 E_2 E_3$. Since y normalizes E, it cyclically permutes the E_i and as $E \supset D$, we have $E_i \supset D_i$, $1 \le i \le 3$. In particular, $E_3 \supset D_3$. Furthermore, $Z(E)$ is also y-invariant and $Z(E) \ne 1$, which implies that $Z(E) \cap E_1 \ne 1$. But now we see that the unique S-invariant S_p-subgroup F of $N_G(Z(E) \cap E_1)$ contains both P_1 and E. Since $P_1 \subseteq F$, it follows therefore from Lemma 3.4 that $F \subseteq P$. Hence $P \cap P_3 \supseteq F \cap P_3 \supseteq E_3 \supset D_3$, contrary to the definition of D_3 as $P \cap P_3$. This completes the proof of the lemma.

Lemma 3.5 shows, in particular, that for p in β, G possesses a unique maximal S-invariant p-subgroup.

So far we have not used the fact that a group of odd order admitting a fixed-point-free four-group of automorphisms is solvable. The next lemma is the one place in the proof of Theorem 2.1 that we need this result.

Lemma 3.6

If P and Q are, respectively, the unique maximal S-invariant p- and q-subgroups of G, for p and q in β, then $PQ = QP$ is a group.

Proof

By the preceding lemma, we have $P = P_1 P_2 P_3$ and $Q = Q_1 Q_2 Q_3$, where $P_i Q_i$ are the S_p- and S_q-subgroups of U_i, $1 \le i \le 3$. We shall argue that, for $1 \le i \le 3$, P is permutable with a subgroup $R^{(i)}$ of Q containing Q_i. But then P will be permutable with the subgroup $R = \langle R^{(1)}, R^{(2)}, R^{(3)} \rangle$ of Q. Since $Q_i \subseteq R$, $1 \le i \le 3$, $R = Q$ and the lemma will follow. It will suffice to prove the existence of $R^{(1)}$.

Since y cyclically permutes the P_i and since $Z(P) \ne 1$, it follows that $Z_1 = Z(P) \cap P_1 \ne 1$. By Lemma 3.3, $N_G(Z_1)$ has a normal 2-complement K. Since $Z_1 \subseteq Z(P)$ and U_1 is abelian, K contains both P and Q_1. But K is solvable by Theorem 10.5.6 and therefore possesses an S-invariant $S_{\{p,q\}}$-subgroup H (compare Theorem 10.5.2). We then have $H = PR$, where R is the unique S-invariant S_q-subgroup of H and hence of K. Since $Q_1 \subseteq R$ by Lemma 10.5.1(iii), $R = R^{(1)}$ has the required properties.

Lemma 3.7

If W_i denotes the S_β-subgroup of U, then $W = \langle W_1, W_2, W_3 \rangle$ is a solvable β-group.

Proof

Let $\beta = \{p_i \mid 1 \le i \le r\}$ and let $P^{(i)}$ be the unique maximal S-invariant p_i-subgroup of G, $1 \le i \le r$. Since $P^{(i)}$ and $P^{(j)}$ are permutable for all i, j, it follows that $W = P^{(1)} P^{(2)} \cdots P^{(r)}$ is a β-group containing each

W_i, $1 \leqslant i \leqslant 3$. Hence $W = \langle W_1, W_2, W_3 \rangle$ as W is S-invariant. Finally, W is solvable by P. Hall's theorem.

This entire line of argument culminates in the following result:

Lemma 3.8

$M = N_G(W)$ is strongly embedded in G.

Proof

We must verify conditions (a), (b), and (c) of Theorems 9.2.1. First of all, since y permutes the W_i cyclically, W is invariant under y as well as S and so $N \subseteq M$. Thus (b) holds and, in particular, M has only one class of involutions. Hence to prove (a), we need only show $N_1 = SU_1 \subseteq M$. Let V_1 be the S_α-subgroup of U_1, so that $U_1 = V_1 \times W_1$. Since S and W_1 lie in M, we must therefore prove that $V_1 \subset M$. We shall, in fact, argue that V_1 normalizes the unique maximal S-invariant p-sub-group P of G for each p in β and this will suffice to prove the assertion.

Set $Z_1 = Z(P) \cap P_1$. Then, as usual, $Z_1 \neq 1$, $N_G(Z_1)$ has a normal 2-complement K, and $\langle U_1, P \rangle \subseteq K$. Let Q be the unique S-invariant S_q-sub-group of K for q in α. Then $Q \supseteq Q_1$ and so $Q = Q_1$ as Q_1 is an S_q-subgroup of G by definition of α. But then K has a normal q-complement H_q by Lemma 10.1.5(v). Setting $H = \bigcap_{q \in \alpha} H_q$, we see that H is a normal $S_{\alpha'}$-subgroup of K and that $P \subseteq H$. Now $V_1 S$ induces a group of automorphisms of H of order relatively prime to $|H|$, so $V_1 S$ leaves some S_p-subgroup R of H invariant by Theorem 6.2.2(i). Since R is S-invariant, we must have $R = P$ and so P is V_1 invariant, as required.

Now M is a proper subgroup. Since the set of all involutions of G generates a normal subgroup, the simplicity of G shows that some involution of G is not in M. Thus (c) also holds, completing the proof of the lemma.

Since W is a nontrivial solvable group, we have $O_p(M) \neq 1$ for some p in β. The procedure for completing the proof of Theorem 3.1 should now become apparent. Indeed, we need only argue that G satisfies the unique-ness condition for p with corresponding uniqueness subgroup M. For if we establish this fact, we can then apply Theorem 9.3.1 to obtain that S centralizes $Z(O_p(M))$, which is not the case. Thus the assumption β non-empty will yield a contradiction, as required.

We carry this out in several steps. Throughout the discussion P will denote the unique maximal S-invariant p-subgroup of G. We note also that if H is any S-invariant subgroup of G of odd order, then $H = \langle H_1, H_2, H_3 \rangle$, so $H \subseteq M$ inasmuch as $H_i \subseteq U_i \subseteq M$, $1 \leqslant i \leqslant 3$.

Lemma 3.9

The following conditions hold:
  (i) $SCN_3(p)$ *is nonempty.*
  (ii) *The normalizer of every nonidentity p-subgroup of G is p-stable and p-constrained.*

Proof

Let Q be a nontrivial p-subgroup of G, set $H = N_G(Q)$, let R be an S_p-subgroup of $O_{p',p}(H)$, and set $C = C_H(R)$. To prove that H is p-constrained, we must show that $C \subseteq O_{p',p}(H)$. First of all, C must have a normal 2-complement, otherwise $C/O(C)$ would be isomorphic to $L_2(r)$ for some $r \equiv 3, 5 \pmod 8$ and consequently $S^z \subseteq C$ for some z in G. But then S would centralize a conjugate of R, a contradiction. Since we are *assuming* the fact that groups of odd order are solvable, it follows that $O(C)$, and therefore also C, is solvable. Since $O_{p'}(H)C \lhd H$ by Theorem 1.3.7, this implies that $C = C_K(R)$, where K is the maximal normal p-solvable subgroup of H. But $C_K(R) \subseteq O_{p',p}(K)$ by Theorem 6.3.3. Since $O_{p',p}(K)$ char $K \lhd H$, $O_{p',p}(K) \subseteq O_{p',p}(H)$ and the desired conclusion $C \subseteq O_{p',p}(H)$ follows. That H is p-stable follows at once from Theorem 8.1.2. Hence (ii) holds.

Next set $L = N_G(P)$. Then $y \in L$ by Lemma 3.5. Since $O_{p'}(L)$ centralizes P, this implies that $|O_{p'}(L)|$ must be odd; otherwise P would centralize S. Thus $O_{p',p}(L) \subseteq O(L)$ and now the maximality of P implies that P is an S_p-subgroup of $O_{p',p}(L)$. Next let Q be an S_p-subgroup of G such that $Q \cap L$ is an S_p-subgroup of L and let $A \in SCN(Q)$. Since L is p-constrained and p-stable, it follows now from Corollary 8.1.4 that $A \subseteq P$. Since $C_P(A) = A$, this gives $Z = Z(P) \subseteq A$. But $Z = Z_1 \times Z_2 \times Z_3$ with y cyclically permuting the Z_i. Hence each $Z_i \neq 1$, whence $m(A) \geqslant m(Z) \geqslant 3$, proving (i).

We have thus verified two of the three hypotheses of the Maximal Subgroup theorem. To establish the third, we need two preliminary results:

Lemma 3.10

The following conditions hold:
  (i) $O_{p'}(M)$ *contains every P-invariant p'-subgroup of M of odd order.*
  (ii) *M is a maximal subgroup of G.*
  (iii) *There exists an S_p-subgroup R of G with $P \lhd R$ such that $N_G(Z(J(R)))$ contains $N = N_G(S)$.*
  (iv) *P contains every element of $SCN_3(R)$.*

Proof

We make a preliminary observation: If H is a proper subgroup of G containing N and Q is an N-invariant q-subgroup of H, q odd, then $Q \subseteq O(H)$. Indeed, set $\bar{H} = H/O(H)$ and use superscripts for images in $\bar{H}$.

Then $\bar{Q} = \bar{Q}_1 \bar{Q}_2 \bar{Q}_3$, where $\bar{Q}_i = C_{\bar{Q}}(\bar{x}_i)$, $1 \leqslant i \leqslant 3$, and $\bar{y}$ cyclically permutes the $\bar{Q}_i$. Since $\bar{H}$ is isomorphic to $L_2(r)$ for suitable r, Lemma 1.1(v) forces $\bar{Q} = 1$, proving the assertion.

Now let K be a maximal subgroup of G containing M. Then $N \subset K$. If Q is the unique S-invariant S_q-subgroup of W for q in $\beta = \pi(W)$, then Q is y-invariant and so $Q \subseteq O(K)$ by the preceding argument. Thus $W \subseteq O(K)$. Since Q is the unique maximal S-invariant q-subgroup of G, Q is necessarily an S_q-subgroup of $O(K)$. Since this holds for each q in β, W is thus an S_β-subgroup of $O(K)$. Suppose $W \subset O(K)$, in which case $O(K)$ possesses an N-invariant S_t-subgroup $T \neq 1$ for some prime $t \notin \beta$. Since $T = T_1 T_2 T_3$ with $T_i \subseteq U_i$, we must have $t \in \alpha$. But now $Z(T) \cap T_1 \neq 1$, and if we consider $N_G(Z(T) \cap T_1)$, which we know has a normal 2-complement, and let Y be its unique S-invariant S_p-subgroup, we see that Y contains T and that $Y_1 = C_Y(x_1)$ is the S_t-subgroup of U_1. But $Y = Y_1$, as $t \in \alpha$, forcing $T_2 = T_3 = 1$. Since N normalizes T, also $T_1 = 1$, whence $T = 1$, a contradiction. We conclude that $W = O(K)$. Thus $K \subseteq N_G(W) = M$, so $K = M$ is a maximal subgroup of G, proving (ii).

Since $M \subseteq N_G(O_p(M))$, equality holds by (ii) and so M is p-constrained by Lemma 3.9. But now (i) follows from Theorem 8.1.1(iii).

To prove (iii), it will suffice to show that $N_G(Z(J(Q)))$ contains a conjugate of N for some S_p-subgroup Q of G. Indeed, if this is the case, then there is a conjugate R of Q such that $K = N_G(Z(J(R)))$ contains N. Since $D = R \cap O(K)$ is an S_p-subgroup of $O(K)$, we can choose R so that D is S-invariant, whence also D is N-invariant. Setting $H = N_G(D)$, we have $\langle R, N \rangle \subseteq H$ and, by Theorem 1.3.7, $K = O(K)(H \cap K)$. This last condition implies that D is an S_p-subgroup of $O(H)$. On the other hand, $D \subseteq P$ by Lemma 3.5 and since $N_P(D)$ is N-invariant, we have $N_P(D) \subseteq O(H)$ by the first paragraph of the proof. Thus $N_P(D) = D$ and now Theorem 1.2.11(ii) yields that $P = D$, whence $P \lhd R$, as required.

Finally, there exists a nontrivial p-subgroup E of G such that $L = N_G(E)$ contains a conjugate of N. Indeed, P itself is such a p-subgroup. Among all such subgroups, choose E so that an S_p-subgroup Q of L has maximal order. Without loss we can assume that $N \subset L$. By Lemma 3.9(ii) and Glauberman's theorem, we then have $L = O_{p'}(L)(L \cap K)$, where $K = N_G(Z(J(Q)))$. Since $S \subset L$, it follows that $S^u \subseteq L \cap K$ for some u in $O_{p'}(L)$. Furthermore, as $N \subset L$, L has only one class of involutions. Since $|O_{p'}(L)|$ is necessarily odd, $L \cap K$ must also have only one class of involutions, whence $N_{L \cap K}(S^u) \supset S^u$. We conclude that $N^u \subseteq L \cap K \subseteq K$. But now our choice of E implies that Q is an S_p-subgroup of $K = N_G(Z(J(Q)))$. Since

$Z(J(Q))$ char Q, it follows from Theorem 1.2.11(ii) that Q is an S_p-subgroup G, proving (iii).

To prove (iv), let R be as in (iii) and now set $K = N_G(Z(J(R)))$, $Q = R \cap O_{p',p}(K)$, and $H = N_G(Q)$. Since $K = O_{p'}(K)(H \cap K)$ by Theorem 1.3.7 and R is an S_p-subgroup of both H and K, it follows that Q is an S_p-subgroup of $O_{p',p}(H)$. But now Corollary 8.1.4 implies that Q contains every element of $SCN_3(R)$. However, P is an S_p-subgroup of $O(K)$ by the first paragraph of the proof, so $Q \subseteq P$ and (iv) follows.

Lemma 3.11

$O_{p'}(M)$ *contains every P-invariant p'-subgroup of G.*

Proof

If P normalizes the p'-subgroup Y of G, it normalizes an S_q-subgroup of Y for each q in $\pi(Y)$ by Theorem 6.2.2(i). Thus we see that it suffices to prove the following assertion: If Q is a nontrivial maximal P-invariant q-subgroup of G, for any prime $q \neq p$, then $Q \subseteq O_{p'}(M)$.

If $q = 2$, then $|Q| = 2$ or 4. In the first case P centralizes Q. However, as N normalizes P and S is self-centralizing, clearly $|C_G(P)|$ is odd. On the other hand, if $|Q| = 4$, Q is a conjugate of S and so is also self-centralizing. But $C_P(Q) \neq 1$ as P is noncyclic. Thus q is odd.

Now let A be an element of $SCN_3(R)$, so that $A \subseteq P$ by Lemma 3.10(iv). Since $Z(P) \subseteq A$, we have $C_G(A) \subseteq C = C_G(Z(P))$ and, as C is N-invariant, it follows as in the preceding paragraph that $|C|$ is odd. Thus $C \subseteq O_{p'}(M)$ and hence also $C_G(A) \subseteq O_{p'}(M)$.

Set $H = N_G(Q)$. We shall argue that $S^v \subseteq H$ for some v in M. Indeed, we have $S^\# = \{x_i \mid 1 \leq i \leq 3\}$ and Q^{x_i} is P-invariant for each i. Since $A \subseteq P$, it follows from the Thompson transitivity theorem and its corollary Theorem 8.5.6 that $Q^{x_i} = Q^{u_i}$ for some u_i in $C_G(A)$, $1 \leq i \leq 3$. Setting $K = \langle x_i u_i^{-1} \mid 1 \leq i \leq 3 \rangle$, we have $K \subseteq H$. But also $K \subseteq O_{p'}(M)S$, as $C_G(A) \subseteq O_{p'}(M)$. Since K clearly maps onto $O_{p'}(M)S/O_{p'}(M)$, we conclude that $|K|$ is divisible by 4. Hence by Sylow's theorem $S^v \subseteq K \subseteq H$ for some v in $O_{p'}(M)$, as asserted.

But then $Q^{v^{-1}}$ is S-invariant and consequently is contained in M. Since $v \in M$, it follows that $Q \subseteq M$. But now $Q \subseteq O_{p'}(M)$ by Lemma 3.10(i).

Our desired conclusion now follows:

Lemma 3.12

G *satisfies the uniqueness condition for the prime p and M is a uniqueness subgroup for p.*

Proof

Set $H = O_{p'}(M)$. By Lemma 3.10(iii) $P \lhd R$ for some S_p-subgroup R of G. Then for u in R, $P^u = P$, so P normalizes H^u, whence $H^u = H$ by the preceding lemma. Thus R normalizes H and H contains every R-invariant p'-subgroup of G. But H centralizes $O_p(M)$, whence $O_p(M) \subseteq B = O_p(HR)$ and so $B \neq 1$. Now $B \lhd R$ and since B centralizes H, it follows that B centralizes every R-invariant p'-subgroup of G. In view of Lemma 3.9, the hypotheses of the Maximal Subgroup theorem are all satisfied and so the uniqueness condition holds for p.

Let K be the corresponding uniqueness subgroup containing R. Since $O_p(M) \neq 1$ and $O_p(M)$ contains an abelian subgroup of type (p, p, p), we have $M \subseteq K$. But then $M = K$ by Lemma 3.10(ii).

Lemmas 3.8 and 3.12 together with Theorem 9.3.1 now yield the desired contradiction that S centralizes $Z(O_p(M))$. This completes the proof of Theorem 3.1.

Remark   Once it is known that G contains a strongly embedded subgroup M (Lemma 3.8 above), an alternate proof of Theorem 3.1 can be given which does not require the solvability of groups of odd order. Indeed, Brauer has shown by means of modular character theory that there exists an approximate formula for the order of an arbitrary group H with an S_2-subgroup S of order 4 and having no normal subgroups of index 2. In fact, if x is an involution of S,

$$(3.5) \qquad |H| = 8 \frac{|C_H(x)|^3}{|C_H(S)|^2} a_H, \text{ where } \frac{3}{8} \leqslant a_H \leqslant \frac{15}{8}.$$

In the present situation, (3.5) can be applied to both G and M. Since $C_G(x) = C_M(x) = N$ and $C_G(S) = C_M(S) = S$, it follows that $|G : M| = a_G/a_M$. Since $a_G \leqslant 15/8$ and $a_M \geqslant 3/8$, we conclude that

$$(3.6) \qquad\qquad |G : M| \leqslant 5.$$

But now if we consider the permutation representation π_M of G on the cosets of M, we see that $\pi_M(G)$ is a subgroup of the symmetric group S_5. Since G is simple, we conclude that G is isomorphic to a subgroup of S_5. However, this is impossible as $M \subset G$ and $|M|$ is divisible by p^3 for any p in β by Lemma 3.5.

In the case that S is self-centralizing, Glauberman has observed that the inequality $|G : M| \leqslant 5$ can be derived using solely results from ordinary character theory. We shall outline the argument in a series of exercises.

4. THE BRAUER-SUZUKI-WALL THEOREM

We shall now complete the proof of Theorem 2.3 and thereby also the proof of Theorem 2.1 by establishing the following fundamental result:

Theorem 4.1 (Brauer-Suzuki-Wall)

If G is a simple group containing an abelian subgroup K of order 2n which satisfies the hypothesis of Theorem 3.1, then G is isomorphic to $L_2(q)$, where $q \equiv 3, 5 \pmod 8$, $q > 5$, and $q = 4n + \varepsilon$ with $\varepsilon = \pm 1$.

We preserve the notation introduced in Section 9.4. Thus $K = U \times \langle x \rangle$, where $|U| = n$ and $|x| = 2$, $N = N_G(K)$, $g = |G|$, t is the number of conjugate classes of strongly real elements of G, and r is the total number of conjugate classes of G. In Section 9.4 we established the following results, which for the sake of clarity we summarize here:

(4.1) $\quad g = 4n(4n + \varepsilon)(2n + \varepsilon)$ $\quad$ where $\varepsilon = \pm 1$.

(4.2) $\quad t = 2n + 3$ if $\varepsilon = +1$ $\quad$ and $\quad t = 2n$ $\quad$ if $\varepsilon = -1$.

(4.3) $\quad r = t$ $\quad$ if $\varepsilon = +1$ $\quad$ and $\quad r = t + 2$ if $\varepsilon = -1$.

The irreducible characters of G are $\chi_i, 1 \le i \le n - 1$, and ψ_j, $1 \le j \le r - n + 1$, and we have

(4.4) $\quad \deg \chi_i = 4n + 2\varepsilon, 1 \le i \le n - 1, \deg \psi_1 = 1, \deg \psi_2 = 4n + \varepsilon$,

$\qquad \deg \psi_3 = \deg \psi_4 = 2n + \varepsilon, \deg \psi_j = 4n$ for $j \ge 5$.

If $\phi_i, 1 \le i \le n - 1$, are the nonprincipal irreducible characters of K having x in their kernels and η is the nonprincipal irreducible character of K having U in its kernel, then for a suitable ordering of the indices we have

(4.5) $\qquad \chi_i(y) = \varepsilon(\phi_i(y) + \bar\phi_i(y))$ $\qquad$ if $y \in K^\#, 1 \le i \le \frac{1}{2}(n - 1)$

$\qquad\qquad \chi_{i + \frac{1}{2}(n-1)}(y) = \varepsilon\eta(y)(\phi_i(y) + \bar\phi_i(y))$ $\qquad$ if $y \in K^\#, 1 \le i \le \frac{1}{2}(n - 1)$

(4.6) $\qquad \psi_2(y) = \varepsilon$ $\qquad$ if $y \in K^\#$

(4.7) $\qquad \begin{aligned} \psi_j(y) &= \varepsilon \\ \psi_j(y) &= -\varepsilon \end{aligned}$ $\qquad \begin{aligned} &\text{if } y \in U^\# \\ &\text{if } y \in K - U, 3 \le j \le 4 \end{aligned}$

(4.8) $\qquad \psi_j(y) = 0$ $\qquad$ if $y \in K^\#, j \ge 5$.

In addition, we have for y not in a conjugate of K and $1 \le i \le n - 1$,

(4.9) $\qquad\qquad\qquad 1 + \varepsilon\psi_2(y) = \varepsilon\chi_i(y)$

(4.10) $\psi_3(y) + \psi_4(y) = \chi_i(y).$

On the basis of this information we shall argue in a sequence of lemmas that G is a Zassenhaus group of degree $(4n + \varepsilon) + 1$ to which Theorem 13.3.5 is applicable. Theorem 4.1 will then follow at once. To accomplish this objective we investigate the structure of the subgroups of G whose orders are divisible by primes in $(2n + \varepsilon)(4n + \varepsilon)$. Note that the three odd numbers n, $2n + \varepsilon$, and $4n + \varepsilon$ are pairwise relatively prime.

Let π_k be the set of primes dividing $2kn + \varepsilon$, $1 \leqslant k \leqslant 2$. It will be convenient to call an element of G π_k-singular if its order is divisible by a prime in π_k, $1 \leqslant k \leqslant 2$.

We first prove

Lemma 4.2

The characters of G have the following values on π_k-singular elements:
  (i) $\chi_i(y) = 0$ *if y is π_1-singular*
                   $\chi_i(y) = \varepsilon$ *if y is π_2-singular, $1 \leqslant i \leqslant n - 1$.*
  (ii) $\psi_2(y) = -\varepsilon$ *if y is π_1-singular*
                   $\psi_2(y) = 0$ *if y is π_2-singular.*
  (iii) $\psi_j(y) = 0$ *if y is π_1-singular, $3 \leqslant j \leqslant 4$*
                   $\psi_3(y) + \psi_4(y) = \varepsilon$ *if y is π_2-singular.*

Proof

By (4.4), $\deg \psi_2 = 4n + \varepsilon$. Since $4n + \varepsilon$ and $g/(4n + \varepsilon)$ are relatively prime, we see that $\deg \psi_2$ is divisible by the full power of p dividing g for any prime p in π_2. But then by Theorem 4.7.13, $\psi_2(y) = 0$ for any element y of G of order divisible by p and so ψ_2 is 0 on any π_2-singular element of G. Similarly, ψ_3 and ψ_4, being of degree $2n + \varepsilon$, are 0 on any π_1-singular element of G.

But now (4.9) implies that $\chi_i(y) = \varepsilon$ if y is π_2-singular, while (4.10) implies that $\chi_i(y) = 0$ if y is π_1-singular. Using these values of χ_i, it follows now from (4.9) that $\psi_2(y) = -\varepsilon$ if y is π_1-singular and from (4.10) that $\psi_3(y) + \psi_4(y) = \varepsilon$ if y is π_2-singular and the lemma is proved.

We can now prove

Lemma 4.3

G contains an abelian S_{π_1}-subgroup R of order $2n + \varepsilon$ which is disjoint from its conjugates and such that $N_G(R)$ is a Frobenius group of order $2(2n + \varepsilon)$.

Proof

We evaluate formula (9.4.2) with y a π_1-singular element. We have $\chi_i(y) = 0$, $1 \leqslant i \leqslant n - 1$, and $\psi_j(y) = 0$, $3 \leqslant j \leqslant 4$, by Lemma 4.2(i) and (iii).

Moreover, $\psi_j(x) = 0$, where x is the involution of $K, j \geqslant 5$, by (4.8). Hence only the characters $1_G = \psi_1$ and ψ_2 contribute to the sum. Using (4.4), (4.6), and Lemma 4.2(ii) to evaluate $\deg \psi_2$, $\psi_2(x)$, and $\psi_2(y)$, and also using the value of g given in (4.1), we obtain

$$(4.11) \qquad \beta(y) = \frac{g}{16n^2}\left(1 - \frac{\varepsilon}{4n + \varepsilon}\right) = 2n + \varepsilon.$$

In particular, $\beta(y) > 0$, which means that y is a strongly real element. But then, by Lemma 9.4.7, we have $\beta(y) = |C_G(y)|$, whence

$$(4.12) \qquad |C_G(y)| = 2n + \varepsilon$$

for any π_1-singular element y of G.

Set $R = C_G(y)$. Since y is strongly real, R is normalized by some involution x' of G. Since $|R| = 2n + \varepsilon$, x' must invert R, whence R is abelian. Suppose now that $z \in R \cap R^v$, $z \neq 1, v \in G$. Then z is π_1-singular, so $|C_G(z)| = 2n + \varepsilon$. But as R and R^v are abelian, $C_G(z) \supseteq \langle R, R^v \rangle$. Since $|R| = |R^v| = 2n + \varepsilon$, it follows that $R = R^v = C_G(z)$. Thus R is disjoint from its conjugates. Since $|G : R| = 4n(4n + \varepsilon)$, we see also that R is an S_{π_1}-subgroup of G. Hence to complete the proof it will suffice to show that $|N_G(R) : R| = 2$, for then $N_G(R)$ will be a Frobenius group of the required order.

To prove this we use the fact that $\sum_{z \in G} \psi_2(z) = 0$. Now the elements of $K^\# - \langle x \rangle$ have $g/2n$ conjugates and include $n - 1$ conjugate classes of G, while x has $g/4n$ conjugates. Hence using our values for ψ_2, we obtain

$$(4.13) \qquad 4n + \varepsilon + \frac{g}{4n}\varepsilon + \frac{g}{2n}(n - 1)\varepsilon + \sum{}' (-\varepsilon) = 0,$$

where the summation is over the m_1 distinct π_1-singular elements of G. Transposing and dividing by ε, we conclude upon simplification that

$$(4.14) \qquad m_1 = (4n + \varepsilon)2n(2n + \varepsilon - 1).$$

On the other hand, by what we have shown above, every π_1-singular element lies in a conjugate of $R^\#$. Let $h = |N_G(R) : R|$. Since R is disjoint from its conjugates, it follows therefore that

$$(4.15) \qquad m_1 = \frac{g}{h(2n + \varepsilon)}(2n + \varepsilon - 1).$$

Comparing (4.14), (4.15), and using (4.1), we conclude that $h = 2$, as required.

As a consequence, we have

Lemma 4.4

There are precisely two conjugate classes of π_2-singular elements in G.

Proof

By the preceding lemma, two elements y, z of $R^\#$ are conjugate in G if and only if they are conjugate in $N_G(R)$ and hence if and only if $z = y^{\pm 1}$. Thus there are exactly $\frac{1}{2}(2n + \varepsilon - 1)$ conjugate classes of π_1-singular elements in G. Furthermore, there are $n + 1$ conjugate classes of G coming from elements of N. But by (4.2) and (4.3), $r = 2n + 3$ if $\varepsilon = +1$ and $r = 2n + 2$ if $\varepsilon = -1$. Thus in either case we have counted all but two of the conjugate classes of G. Since the remaining two classes necessarily consist of π_2-singular elements, the lemma follows.

We next prove

Lemma 4.5

$4n + \varepsilon = p^a$ *for some prime p and an S_p-subgroup P of G is abelian with $N_G(P)$ of order $\frac{1}{2}(4n + \varepsilon - 1)(4n + \varepsilon)$.*

Proof

We now evaluate formula (9.4.2) with y a π_2-singular element as we did in Lemma 4.3. Using the given values of our characters, we obtain, similarly,

$$(4.16) \qquad \beta(y) = \frac{g}{16n^2}\left(\frac{4(n-1)}{4n + 2\varepsilon}\varepsilon + \frac{1}{2n + \varepsilon}(\psi_3(y) + \psi_4(y)) + 1\right).$$

But $\psi_3(y) + \psi_4(y) = \varepsilon$ by Lemma 4.2(iii) and now (4.16) reduces to

$$(4.17) \qquad\qquad \beta(y) = \tfrac{1}{2}(4n + \varepsilon)(1 + \varepsilon).$$

If $\varepsilon = +1$, y is strongly real and $|C_G(y)| = 4n + \varepsilon$ for every π_2-singular element. But now if we set $P = C_G(y)$, it follows as in Lemma 4.3 that P is abelian, P is disjoint from its conjugates, P is an S_{π_2}-subgroup of G of order $4n + \varepsilon$, and $M = N_G(P)$ is a Frobenius group. Hence every π_2-singular element of G is conjugate to one in $P^\#$ and two elements of $P^\#$ are conjugate if and only if they are conjugate in M. Since G has exactly two conjugate classes of π_2-singular elements, we conclude that $|M : P| = \frac{1}{2}(4n + 1 - 1) = 2n$ and the lemma follows in this case.

Assume then that $\varepsilon = -1$. In this case (4.17) gives $\beta(y) = 0$ and so any π_2-singular element y of G is not strongly real and hence is nonreal. In particular, y is not conjugate to y^{-1}. Since there are only two classes of π_2-singular elements, we must have $\pi_2 = \{p\}$ for some prime p; otherwise there would exist elements y_i of G of order p_i with $p_i \in \pi_2$, $1 \leqslant i \leqslant 2$, and $p_1 \neq p_2$, in which case y_1, y_1^{-1}, y_2, y_2^{-1} would be representatives of distinct conjugate classes of π_2-singular elements. Thus $4n + \varepsilon = p^a$ for some a.

Let P be an S_p-subgroup of G. We shall argue next that P is disjoint from its conjugates. If not, let D be a maximal intersection of P with a conjugate P_1. Then $D \neq 1$ and $D \subset P$, $D \subset P_1$. Set $T = N_G(D)$. If $O_p(T)$ were an S_p-subgroup of T, then an S_p-subgroup P_2 of G containing $O_p(T)$ would contain both $N_P(D)$ and $N_{P_1}(D)$. Since $N_P(D) \supset D$, maximality of D would force $P_2 = P$, whence $N_{P_1}(D) \subseteq P$, which is not the case. Thus $O_p(T)$ is not an S_p-subgroup of T.

We shall now contradict this fact. Let L be the smallest normal subgroup of T containing D such that $O_p(L)$ is not an S_p-subgroup of L. Then certainly L is not a p-group. Let q be the smallest prime in $\pi(L)$ with $q \neq p$ and let Q be an S_q-subgroup of L. Now q divides $4n$ or $2n + \varepsilon$ and so our preceding results show that $N_G(Q)$ and $C_G(y)$ are p'-groups for all y in $Q^{\#}$. Hence Q induces a regular group of automorphisms of D and therefore Q is cyclic by Theorem 5.4.11. Since $H = N_L(Q)$ is a p'-group, q is the smallest prime in $\pi(H)$, so H has a normal q-complement by Theorem 7.6.1. Since $Q \lhd H$, we have $H = Q \times O_{q'}(H)$ and consequently $Q \subseteq Z(H)$. But now Burnside's transfer theorem yields that L has a normal q-complement L_1. Minimality of L implies that $O_p(L_1)$ is an S_p-subgroup of L_1. But $O_p(L_1)$ char $L_1 \lhd L$, so $O_p(L_1) \subseteq O_p(L)$. However, $O_p(L_1)$ is an S_p-subgroup of L as $L = QL_1$. Hence $O_p(L_1) = O_p(L)$ is a normal S_p-subgroup of L, contrary to our choice of L. We conclude that P is disjoint from its conjugates.

But now by Theorem 7.4.6, two elements of $P^{\#}$ conjugate in G are conjugate in $M = N_G(P)$. Furthermore, our conditions imply that M is a Frobenius group with kernel P, and, as in the case $\varepsilon = +1$, it follows that $|M : P| = \frac{1}{2}(4n - 1 - 1) = 2n - 1$. Also the argument of Theorem 13.1.3(ii) shows that P is abelian.

Finally, we prove

Lemma 4.6

G is a Zassenhaus group of degree $4n + \varepsilon + 1$ in its action on the right cosets of $N_G(P)$.

Proof

Set $M = N_G(P)$ and consider the transitive permutation representation of G on the right cosets of M. Let θ be its character. It follows at once from the preceding lemma that $|G : M| = 4n + \varepsilon + 1$. Hence

(4.18) $\deg \theta = 4n + \varepsilon + 1.$

Now by Theorem 4.3.4(i), $\theta = 1_G + \psi$, where ψ is a character of G which does not have 1_G as a constituent. Thus $\deg \psi = 4n + \varepsilon$. Examining the degrees of the nonprincipal irreducible characters of G as given in (4.4), we see that there is only one possibility for ψ: $\psi = \psi_2$. Therefore,

(4.19) $\theta = 1_G + \psi_2.$

Hence, by Theorem 4.3.4(ii), G acts doubly transitively. To prove that G is a Zassenhaus group, we must show that only the identity element fixes three cosets of M, or equivalently that $\theta(y) \leqslant 2$ for all y in $G^\#$, which will follow if ψ_2 takes on only the values 0, $+1$, and -1 on $G^\#$. But (4.6) and Lemma 4.2(ii) show that this is indeed the case. Thus G is a Zassenhaus group of the given degree.

We can now easily establish Theorem 4.1. Setting $4n + \varepsilon = p^a = q$ and $e = \frac{1}{2}(4n + \varepsilon - 1) = \frac{1}{2}(q - 1)$, we can then write $g = eq(q + 1)$. Let X be a Frobenius complement in M and set $Y = N_G(X)$. Then $|X| = e$ and $|Y| = 2e$. Replacing P by a conjugate, if necessary, we can assume without loss that $S \cap Y$ is an S_2-subgroup of Y. Now if $\varepsilon = +1$, then $e = 2n$, so $S \cap X \neq 1$. Thus $x_i \in S \cap X$ for some i, $1 \leqslant i \leqslant 3$. Since X is disjoint from its conjugates, it follows that $N_i = C_G(x_i) \subseteq Y$. But $|N_i| = 2e$ and hence $N_i = Y$. Thus $X = U_i \times \langle x_i \rangle$ is abelian and is inverted by an involution of Y. Since $M = XP$ is a Frobenius group, the Sylow subgroups of X are cyclic by Theorem 10.3.1(iv) and hence X is cyclic. On the other hand, if $\varepsilon = -1$, then $e = 2n - 1$ is odd. In this case the same conclusions follow from Theorem 13.1.4(i), in view of the simplicity of G (alternatively from the preceding analysis). Thus the hypotheses of Zassenhaus's theorem are satisfied and we conclude that G is isomorphic to $L_2(q)$ with $q > 5$ (as $n > 1$). That $q \equiv 3, 5 \pmod 8$ follows from the fact that g is not divisible by 8. This completes the proof of Theorem 4.1 and with it the proof of Theorems 2.3 and 2.1.

EXERCISES

In the following exercises, G will denote a simple group with a self-centralizing S_2-subgroup S of order 4, $x = x_1$, x_2, x_3 are the involutions of S, and $N = C_G(x)$. We assume that there exists a subgroup M of G containing N such that $M/O(M)$ is isomorphic to $L_2(q)$, $q \equiv 3, 5 \pmod 8$, $q > 3$. Prove

1. There exist irreducible characters ϕ_i, $0 \leqslant i \leqslant 3$, of M with $\phi_0 = 1_M$ such that

(i) $O(M) \subseteq \ker \phi_i$, $0 \leqslant i \leqslant 3$.

(ii) $\phi_i(xy) = \phi_i(x)$ for y in $O(N)$, $0 \leqslant i \leqslant 3$.

(iii) $\deg \phi_1 = q$ and $\deg \phi_2 = \deg \phi_3 = \frac{1}{2}(q + \delta)$, where $q \equiv \delta \pmod 4$.

(iv) $\theta = \sum\limits_{i=0}^{3} \phi_i(x)\phi_i$ vanishes on all elements of M of odd order.

2. N possesses $n - 1$ distinct irreducible characters ζ_i, $1 \leqslant i \leqslant n - 1$, where $|N| = 4n$, such that

(i) $\zeta_{i+\frac{1}{2}(n-1)} = \eta\zeta_i$, where η is the nontrivial linear character of N having $O(N)$, x_2, and x_3 in its kernel, $1 \leqslant i \leqslant \frac{1}{2}(n - 1)$.

(ii) $\deg \zeta_i = 2$, $1 \leqslant i \leqslant n - 1$.

(iii) $\zeta_i(x) = 2$, $1 \leqslant i \leqslant \frac{1}{2}(n - 1)$.

3. There exist distinct irreducible characters ψ_i, $0 \leqslant i \leqslant 3$, and χ_i, $1 \leqslant i \leqslant n - 1$, of G with $\psi_0 = 1_G$ and signs ε and δ_i, $0 \leqslant i \leqslant 3$, such that

(i) $\theta^* = \sum\limits_{i=0}^{3} \delta_i \psi_i$.

(ii) $(\zeta_i - \zeta_j)^* = \varepsilon(\chi_i - \chi_j)$, $1 \leqslant i, j \leqslant n$.

4. Set $\theta_i = \zeta_i - \zeta_{i+\frac{1}{2}(n-1)}$, $1 \leqslant i \leqslant \frac{1}{2}(n - 1)$. Show that

$$\chi_i(x)^2 + \chi_{i+\frac{1}{2}(n-1)}(x)^2 \geqslant \frac{1}{2}\theta_i^*(x)^2 = 8.$$

5. Use Exercise 4 and Theorem 4.2.8 to show

(i) $\sum\limits_{i=0}^{3} \psi_i(x)^2 \leqslant 4$.

(ii) $\psi_0(x) = 1$, $\psi_i(x) = 0, 1$, or -1, $1 \leqslant i \leqslant 3$.

6. Set $\gamma_G = \sum \dfrac{\chi(x)^2}{\deg \chi} \chi$ and $\gamma_M = \sum \dfrac{\zeta(x)^2}{\deg \zeta} \zeta$, where χ, ζ range over the irreducible characters of G and M, respectively. Use (9.4.2) and Lemma 9.1.5 to show

(i) $\gamma_G(xy) = |G : M| \gamma_M(xy)$ for all y in $O(N)$.

(ii) $(\gamma_G, \theta^*)_G = (\gamma_M, \theta)_M$.

(iii) $\sum\limits_{i=0}^{3} \dfrac{\psi_i(x)^2}{\psi_i(1)} \delta_i = |G : M| \sum\limits_{i=0}^{3} \dfrac{\phi_i(x)^2}{\phi_i(1)} \phi_i(x) = |G : M| \dfrac{(q - \delta)^2}{q(q + \delta)}$.

7. Finally use Exercises 5 and 6 to prove

$$|G : M| \leqslant 5.$$

PART **III** GENERAL CLASSIFICATION PROBLEMS

CHAPTER 16

SIMPLE GROUPS OF LOW RANK

In Part II we have considered, among other questions, particular cases of three major problems of finite group theory: groups of odd order, groups with dihedral Sylow 2-subgroups, and *CN*-groups of even order. Through these special cases we have tried to provide insight into the nature of the general solutions of these problems. However, special cases often hide as much as they reveal, and they may fail to convey the degree of technical difficulty involved in passing to the general case. This is especially true of the problems at hand, the complete solutions of which are long and intricate.

We should like therefore to present in this chapter a conceptual picture, without proofs, of the content of these theorems and of some of the difficulties they involve. At the same time we hope to be able to show how the methods we have developed in the book are used in these and other problems.

Each of our three problems is closely linked to certain other classification problems that it will be valuable to discuss at the same time. For example, in dealing with groups of odd order, one studies a simple group (of odd order) all of whose proper subgroups are solvable. Clearly this is a particular case of the class of simple groups (of arbitrary order) in which the normalizer of every nontrivial solvable subgroup is solvable (for brevity, a simple *N-group*). In a major work Thompson has determined all simple *N*-groups. In particular, he obtains a complete classification of all minimal simple groups. The proof of this result has great significance for the study of simple groups.

Clearly a *CN*-group G satisfies the following condition: For any involution x of G, $C_G(x)$ is *2-closed*; that is, the Sylow 2-subgroup of $C_G(x)$ is normal in $C_G(x)$. For brevity, we shall call an arbitrary group G satisfying this condition a *C-group*. As the culminating step in a long series of papers, Suzuki has determined all simple *C*-groups.

Finally, both the general *C*-group and dihedral Sylow 2-subgroup problems include, as special cases, certain groups with abelian Sylow 2-subgroups. They thus impinge directly upon this additional basic classification problem, which we also wish to discuss briefly.

These classification problems may appear to be somewhat disparate in character despite the preceding remarks. However, it turns out that they can be regarded as part of a single classification problem. Indeed, each of the known simple groups can be assigned a *rank* in a fairly natural way. For example, the linear groups in dimension n over $GF(q)$ have rank $n - 1$. From this point of view, groups of prime order have rank 0, while groups of rank 1 are identical to certain types of doubly transitive groups. In these terms the odd-order problem becomes that of classifying all simple groups of rank 0, while our other problems become part of that of determining all simple groups of rank 1.

Among the set of known simple groups, those of rank 1 have the most elementary subgroup structure—their proper subgroups being either solvable or, at worst, involving other simple groups of rank 1. Thus we would expect conversely that our classification of these groups be made in terms relating to the nature of their proper subgroups. In practice these conditions do not involve all proper subgroups, but only what we may call the *local subgroups*—that is, the normalizers of the nonidentity solvable subgroups, equivalently the nonidentity subgroups of prime power order. (For a specific prime p, we shall refer to the normalizers of the nonidentity *p*-subgroups as the *p-local subgroups*). No matter how each of our classification problems above is initially stated, it quickly reduces to the study of a simple group whose local subgroups are either solvable or involve simple groups of the type $L_2(q)$ (occasionally certain other rank 1 groups must be allowed). In precise terms, the classification of the simple groups of rank 1 means just this: determination of all finite simple groups whose local subgroups are of this special form.

It turns out, in fact, that the members of certain families of simple groups of rank 2 possess local subgroups of exactly the same type; in particular, this is true of the groups $L_3(q)$ [by definition, $SL(3, q)$ modulo its center]. Thus the most general classification problem for simple groups of rank 1 will involve a partial classification of those of rank 2.

The techniques we have developed in this book (together with certain methods of modular character theory not treated here) provide the appropriate tools for investigating this enormous classification problem, large parts of which have been successfully completed at the time of this writing.

1. GENERAL METHODS AND OBJECTIVES

As we have just indicated, each of our classification problems involves the study of a simple group G whose proper subgroups are of some suitably restricted form. Except in the odd-order problem, the goal in each case is to show that G is isomorphic to one of the known simple groups. Thus, for example, in Theorem 15.2.3, the classification of groups with self-centralizing S_2-subgroups of order four was reduced to showing that a simple group G satisfying appropriate conditions was necessarily isomorphic to $L_2(q)$, $q \equiv 3, 5 \pmod 8$, $q > 3$. In the odd order case, of course, the task is rather to derive a contradiction. However, despite this apparent distinction, the methods of proof are essentially the same in all cases. Thus the following discussion will be pertinent in large part to the odd order problem as well.

To prove that G is isomorphic to some known simple group G^*, it is obviously necessary that the proper subgroups of G be isomorphic to corresponding proper subgroups of G^*. We may ask conversely whether this condition will be sufficient for G and G^* to be isomorphic. Zassenhaus' theorem of Chapter 13 provides an example in which this is indeed the case. There we considered an "unknown" Zassenhaus group G, on the one hand, and a suitable known group $G^* = L_2(q)$, on the other, with the property that their respective subgroups N, N^* fixing a letter were isomorphic. Using the method of generators and relations, we were able to deduce that G and G^* themselves were isomorphic. This proof did not involve the complete subgroup structure of G or even its complete local structure. The precise information we required concerned the structure of N, the intersection of N with its conjugates, and the action of G on the cosets of N. For reasons that we shall explain in a moment, we shall speak of this as the *generalized Bruhat structure* of G.

This suggests a fairly natural approach to our general classification problem:

(1) Prove that G possesses a generalized Bruhat structure identical to that of some known simple group G^*.

(2) Under assumption 1, prove that G and G^* are isomorphic.

Two questions immediately arise in connection with (1): First, what do we mean by the generalized Bruhat structure of a known simple group G^* and, second, how shall we prove that our unknown simple group G has such a structure at all?

A considerable amount of work has been done on the first question and the situation is now well understood. Apart from certain specific exceptions (the five simple groups of Mathieu, Janko's group, and the alternating groups A_n, $n \geqslant 7$), all the remaining known simple groups have natural descriptions which are very similar to that of $L_2(q)$: They are homomorphic images of certain matrix groups (modulo their centers) which are defined over a finite field $GF(q)$. Let us write $G^*(q)$ rather than G^* for one of these groups.

In the case of the Zassenhaus group $G^*(q) = L_2(q)$, the subgroup N^* above is the normalizer of a Sylow p-subgroup of $G^*(q)$, where $q = p^r$ and its generalized Bruhat structure is expressed in terms of conditions on this normalizer N^*. The same general situation prevails for arbitrary $G^*(q)$. The normalizer of an S_p-subgroup of $G^*(q)$ for $q = p^r$ is called a *Borel* subgroup and accordingly is denoted by B. The structure of B, the intersection of B with its conjugates, and the action of $G^*(q)$ on the cosets of B determine the generalized Bruhat structure of $G^*(q)$. In fact, the precise conditions which describe this structure is called the *Bruhat decomposition* of $G^*(q)$. (A fuller discussion appears in Section 17.1.) We have added the qualifying objective " generalized " so as to be able to include those simple groups which are not of matrix type and also for the reasons discussed in the next two paragraphs. However, we wish to remark first that Tits, abstracting from the conditions appearing in a Bruhat decomposition, has introduced the general notion of a (B, N)-*pair*. Groups with a (B, N)-pair structure have been extensively studied by him and several other authors.

Actually, (1) turns out in many cases to be more than one is able to prove. In the first place, there may yet remain some indeterminacy in the structure of B; that is, B may have the same general form as that of some known simple group, but its exact structure may depend upon certain parameters, only certain possibilities for which correspond to actual known simple groups. This indeterminacy is resolved only in the process of answering the second question.

Second, for most groups of rank higher than 1, it seems that it is not G which must be shown to have a generalized Bruhat structure but rather a well-specified homomorphic image $\bar{G}_1$ of a subgroup G_1 of G (possibly proper) that is shown to have such a structure. Under these circumstances, we must answer question (2) for $\bar{G}_1$ and, in addition, must prove that $G_1 \lhd G$. The simplicity of G will then yield that G is isomorphic to $\bar{G}_1$. The procedure for accomplishing this final step is already available to us. Indeed, if $M = N_G(G_1)$ is a proper subgroup of G, one is able to show that M satisfies the hypotheses of Theorem 9.2.1. Part (iii) of that theorem (which we have not previously used) can then be invoked to produce a contradiction. It will be understood when we say that G has a generalized Bruhat structure that these indeterminacies are permitted.

We turn now to question (2), which asks, in effect, whether a group having a generalized Bruhat structure is uniquely determined by that structure. Equivalently whether a (B, N)-pair is completely characterized by its (B, N)-structure. This problem has been the subject of much investigation. The methods for treating it are either those of generators and relations or that of geometry, which was mentioned briefly in Chapter 13.

No matter how difficult it may be in a particular case to settle this question, once we have shown that our given group G has a generalized Bruhat structure, we can be sure that we have reached the final stage of our classification problem. By far the largest portion of our work will be involved in establishing that G, in fact, has such a Bruhat structure. In Part II we have accomplished this goal for two distinct problems: for CN-groups with abelian S_2-subgroups and for groups with self-centralizing S_2-subgroups of order four.

A careful examination of the proofs of these results will reveal that the arguments divide into two major parts:

(a) First, we constructed a strongly embedded subgroup M of G to which we applied the theorems of Section 9.3. This gave precise information concerning the maximal local subgroups that contained an S_2-subgroup of G and how they intersected their conjugates.

(b) On the basis of this information, we employed character-theoretic methods to deduce the fact that G had a generalized Bruhat structure.

More specifically, in the case of CN-groups, part (a) already yielded the conclusion that G was a Zassenhaus group. We then used Feit's theorem to show that G had a Bruhat structure identical to that of some $L_2(2^n)$. In the case of groups with self-centralizing S_2-subgroups of order four, part (a) involved a basic application of the Maximal Subgroup theorem and gave strong information on how the centralizer N of an involution intersected its conjugates. It is not difficult to see that these conditions imply that N is a maximal local subgroup containing an S_2-subgroup of G. For part (b) we applied the Brauer-Suzuki-Wall theorem to deduce that G had a Bruhat structure identical to that of some $L_2(q)$, $q \equiv 3, 5 \pmod 8$.

The kind of arguments that we used in each case in part (a) may be called *local group-theoretic*. They have also been referred to as Sylow-type arguments. In this kind of analysis we study the interrelations between the various local subgroups of G. We try to piece together our information to obtain conclusions concerning the maximal p-local subgroups of G and how they intersect each other for appropriate primes p. In its most general form, the entire approach has its origins in Chapter IV of the Odd Order paper, where many of the basic ideas were first introduced. Our Chapter 8 represents a synthesis as well as an extension of many, but by no means all, of these ideas. In carrying out this analysis our hypotheses on the local subgroups of G enter in a crucial way. The arguments depend critically upon basic properties of solvable groups and, if the local subgroups involve various $L_2(q)$'s, also upon properties of these groups.

On the other hand, the methods of character theory treat primarily the relation between the characters of G and those of some subgroup N of G. To be effective we must have fairly exact information on N and on its embedding in G. In the various situations studied in this book, N has always been a Frobenius group (or at worst the direct product of a Frobenius group with a group of order 2) whose kernel is disjoint from its conjugates. For more general problems, some weakening of these conditions must be allowed.

The objective of the local group-theoretic analysis should now be clear: to force conditions on the local structure of G sufficient to permit the effective use of character-theoretic methods.

At first glance it would appear that the odd order problem does not fit the over-all conceptual approach just outlined. For a simple (nonabelian) group of odd order cannot possibly possess a generalized Bruhat structure in the above sense, inasmuch as there exists no known simple group to which that structure could be identical. However, if we think rather of a generalized Bruhat structure as a set of conditions on certain local subgroups of a simple group G, on the basis of which the structure of G can be uniquely characterized by means of generators and relations, then there comes a point in the proof of the solvability of groups of odd order in which just such a situation is reached (to be described in the next section). Hence it is reasonable to say that the general simple group G of odd order (if it existed) has a generalized Bruhat structure. This point is completely camouflaged in the special case that G is a CN-group, which we studied in Sections 14.2 and 14.3. There the character-theoretic methods led directly to a contradiction and so the generator-relations method never entered into the arguments. In other words, a simple CN-group of odd order does not possess such a Bruhat structure.

In other respects the analysis of CN-groups of odd order has the same spirit as that for the general group of odd order. First, we apply local group-theoretic methods to obtain precise information concerning the maximal local subgroups and their embedding. This analysis differs in one fundamental respect from the corresponding analysis in all other classi-fication problems. Indeed, in the study of simple groups of even order, the focus is on the maximal local subgroups containing a Sylow 2-subgroup or suitable "large" subgroups thereof. Because of this, only p-local subgroups for those p "in the neighborhood" of the prime 2 enter into the arguments. Thus, for example, in the case of groups with self-centralizing S_2-subgroups of order 4, our attention was limited to odd primes dividing the order of the centralizer of an involution. By contrast, the odd-order problem requires information on *all* the maximal local subgroups (com-pare Theorem 14.2.5 for CN-groups of odd order). In part at least, this accounts for its intrinsic complexity.

The methods of character theory are then applied to the various con-figurations of maximal local subgroups to which the local group-theoretic analysis leads. Contradictions similar in nature to that derived in Section 14.3 are obtained for all but one of these configurations. It is this last configuration which defines the Bruhat structure of the general simple group of odd order.

We must still say a few words in the case of groups of even order about the passage from a knowledge of the set $\mathscr{M}$ of maximal local subgroups of G "in the neighborhood" of the prime 2 to the existence of a Bruhat structure in G. For an important distinction between the classification of groups of rank 1 and most of those of higher rank appears to be emerging from the work of Thompson and Suzuki. Observe that the generalized Bruhat structure of G is expressed in terms of an S_p-subgroup of G for a distinguished prime p, which we may call the *characteristic* of G. Now this characteristic may or may not appear directly in properties of the elements of $\mathcal{M}$ derived by our initial local group-theoretic analysis. Of course, this will always be the case if G happens to have characteristic 2, but not necessarily if G has odd characteristic. For example, for groups with self-centralizing S_2-subgroups of order four, the characteristic prime p is not in the neighborhood of 2 and so does not enter in any way into the elements of $\mathcal{M}$. It emerges for the first time only after an expression for the order of G has been established by a long character-theoretic argument. On the other hand, in certain cases in the study of N-groups, the elements of $\mathcal{M}$ include 3-local subgroups, and in these cases the characteristic of G turns out to be 3 (the corresponding simple groups being of rank 2).

We have raised this specific point for the following reason: When the elements of $\mathcal{M}$ include p-local groups for the odd characteristic p, the appropriate method for proving that G has a generalized Bruhat structure appears to be again the local group-theoretic rather than that of character theory. The same remark applies in characteristic 2 for groups of rank greater than 1. Since we have noted above that the classification of all simple groups of rank 1 includes that of some groups of rank 2, these remarks are pertinent to our over-all classification problem.

We conclude now with a short table of methods and objectives in the study of simple groups which summarizes the preceding discussion. The reader will do well to keep it in mind when studying the succeeding sections. With appropriate modifications also discussed above, this summary applies equally well to the odd order problem:

Method	*Objective*
I. Local group-theoretic	Properties of the maximal local subgroups of G in the neighborhood of the prime 2
II. Character-theoretic or local group-theoretic	The existence of a generalized Bruhat structure in G identical to that of a known simple group G^*
III. Generators and relations or geometric	A proof that G and G^* are isomorphic

2. GROUPS OF ODD ORDER

The Feit-Thompson theorem on the solvability of groups of odd order will here be referred to as O. The over-all organization of the paper is as follows: Chapters I, II, and III are in a sense preliminary, providing definitions of a number of important general concepts along with a great many specialized results that are needed for the proof itself. In Chapter IV a minimal counterexample G to the theorem is considered. G is, in fact, minimal simple: a nonabelian simple group of odd order whose proper subgroups are all solvable. Chapter IV presents the local group-theoretic analysis of the maximal subgroups of G, Chapter V utilizes the methods of character theory to show that G has a generalized Bruhat structure, and Chapter VI derives a final contradiction by the method of generators and relations.

We shall present an outline of the proof, which we hope will clarify some of our preceding remarks and at the same time give the reader an understanding of its great achievement. First, we note that a minimal normal subgroup of a solvable group is a p-group for some prime p. Hence every proper subgroup of G is contained in a p-local subgroup of G for an appropriate prime p. In particular, the set of maximal subgroups of G is the same as that of the maximal local subgroups.

In the case that G is a CN-group, Theorem 14.2.5 gives the exact structure and embedding of all the maximal subgroups of G, each being a Frobenius group whose kernel is a Hall subgroup of G and is disjoint from its conjugates. The key point in the proof of this result is the fact that no maximal subgroup of G is a three-step group as this term was defined in Section 14.1. Underlying the entire argument was a natural equivalence relation that exists among the primes of $\pi(G)$: $p \sim q$, provided some nontrivial p- and q-elements of G commute. Lemma 14.1.2 showed that this condition is in turn equivalent to the fact that an S_p- and S_q-subgroup of G commute elementwise. The spirit of this equivalence relation is that the existence of a "small" $\{p, q\}$-subgroup implies the existence of an $S_{\{p,q\}}$-subgroup in G. As a direct consequence, it followed that for each equivalence class ω of $\pi(G)$ under $\sim$, G possesses a nilpotent S_ω-subgroup.

In the general case, the analysis of the structure and embedding of the maximal subgroups of G follows a similar pattern; however, the difficulties involved are of a different order of magnitude. A key tool throughout is the Thompson transitivity theorem (Theorem 8.5.4). Roughly speaking, it enables one to reduce certain problems about arbitrary p-groups to questions concerning abelian p-groups. However, this theorem was proved only under the assumption that $SCN_3(p)$ is nonempty. This forces a subdivision of the argument: One first studies the set σ of primes in $\pi(G)$

for which $SCN_3(p)$ is nonempty. Only after this long analysis is completed can one effectively investigate the remaining primes.

The notion of equivalence is restricted to the set σ and, moreover, is not quite the same as that in the CN-case:

If $p, q \in \sigma$, we write $p \sim q$ provided there exists a $\{p, q\}$-subgroup D of G which contains elementary abelian subgroups of both order p^3 and q^3.

Thus p and q "mesh" in a "small," but not "too small," subgroup of G. We note that if G is a CN-group, this definition implies that p and q are equivalent in our earlier sense, as is easily verified.

It is by no means obvious that $\sim$ is an equivalence relation; in fact, a large portion of Chapter IV of O is taken up with this problem and the related task of showing that G possesses an S_ω-subgroup for each equivalence class ω in σ. The Maximal Subgroup theorem (Theorem 8.6.3) enters into this argument and into the subsequent analysis of the structure and embedding of the maximal subgroups of G in a crucial way. Note that the proper subgroups of G, being solvable of odd order, are all p-constrained and p-stable for any p in $\pi(G)$ by Theorems 6.3.2 and 8.1.2. Hence the first condition of Theorem 8.6.3 automatically holds for every prime in σ. Once one knows that G possesses an S_ω-subgroup, it is possible to show that ω necessarily contains a prime p for which the critical second condition of that theorem is satisfied. Ultimately it is shown that G satisfies the uniqueness condition for each prime in σ.

That the uniqueness condition gives strong information concerning the intersection of subgroups and their conjugates should be fairly clear. Indeed, let P be an S_p-subgroup of G with corresponding uniqueness subgroup M. Then if $P \cap P^x$ contains an element of $A_i(P)$ for some i, the uniqueness condition for p forces P^x to lie in M. Since M contains $N_G(P)$, this in turn implies that $x \in M$. Thus whenever $x \notin M$, the intersection of P^x with P is "very small." However, we emphasize that it need not be trivial.

We wish to point out also that Glauberman's theorem (Theorem 8.2.11) enables one to simplify the proofs of some of the preceding assertions as they appear in O.

Only when this stage is reached are the primes in $\pi(G)$ for which $SCN_3(p)$ is empty considered in detail (Section 26 of O). For such a prime, Theorem 5.4.15 shows that G contains no elementary abelian p-group of order p^3 whatsoever. Despite the strong restriction that this places on the p-subgroups of G, the complete analysis of the p-local subgroups of G for such primes is very long. In flavor, the argument is similar to that carried out at a certain point in the analysis of groups with dihedral Sylow 2-subgroups, which will be discussed in Section 3. Actually the analysis involves a slightly larger set of primes than those in which $SCN_3(p)$ is empty. Indeed, we define π^* to be the set of primes p in $\pi(G)$ such that either $SCN_3(p)$ is empty or an S_p-subgroup P of G possesses a subgroup A of order p such that $C_P(A) = A \times B$, where B is cyclic.

The precise set of possibilities for the structure and embedding of the maximal subgroups of G is extremely complicated to state. To convey the nature of the results without going into elaborate detail, we shall suppress some of the more delicate conditions in our summary.

We first introduce the concept of a three-step group, which differs from the one we used in the case of CN-groups. However, they do have in common the property of possessing a normal series of length three whose respective factor groups are nilpotent (equivalently, their "Fitting length" is at most three).

We shall say that X is a *three-step group* provided the following conditions hold:

(a) $X = X'Q$, where $X' \cap Q = 1$ and Q is a cyclic Hall subgroup of X.

(b) If $K = F(X)$, then $(X')' \subseteq K \subseteq X'$.

(c) If H is the maximal Hall subgroup of X contained in K, then H is noncyclic and $K = C_X(H)H$.

(d) H contains a cyclic subgroup R such that $C_{X'}(y) = R$ for all y in $Q^{\#}$.

For convenience, let us call K the *kernel* of X and Q a *complement* of X. Note that Q and R have relatively prime orders by (a). Since each is cyclic, it follows that $W = QR$ is a cyclic subgroup of X. Observe also that the possibility of X' being nilpotent is not excluded, so that X may have Fitting length 2.

We also need the notion of a group X of *Frobenius type*, which is a slight generalization of that of Frobenius group: It has a *kernel* K which is the maximal normal nilpotent subgroup of X, a complement of K in X has a restricted structure, and the nonprincipal irreducible characters of K, when induced to X, have properties similar to those that hold when X is a Frobenius group.

With the aid of these terms we shall now define subgroups of our minimal simple group G of odd order of types I and II. A maximal subgroup M of G will be said to be:

Of type I provided:

(a) M is of Frobenius type.

(b) Either the kernel K of M is disjoint from its conjugates or $\pi(K) \subseteq \pi^*$.

Of type II provided:

(a) M is a three-step group.

(b) Either the kernel K of M is disjoint from its conjugates or $\pi(K) \subseteq \pi^*$.

(In actuality, Feit and Thompson consider four different types of three-step groups: types II, III, IV, and V, which we have combined under our type II by ignoring various additional requirements. We note only that those of type II, III, or IV have Fitting length three, while those of type V has fitting length two. Moreover, the set π^* should, in fact, be replaced by a certain, fairly involved, proper subset π^* of it.)

The first main result of Chapter IV of O can now be stated:

Theorem 1

Let G be a minimal simple group of odd order. Two elements of a nilpotent Hall subgroup H of G are conjugate in G if and only if they are conjugate in $N_G(H)$. Moreover, either (i) *or* (ii) *holds:*

(i) *Every maximal subgroup of G is of type I.*

(ii) (a) *G contains a cyclic subgroup $W = W_1 \times W_2$ with the property $N_G(W_0) = W$ for every nonempty subset W_0 of $W - W_1 - W_2$. In addition, $W_i \neq 1$, $1 \leqslant i \leqslant 2$.*

(b) *There exist maximal subgroups X_1 and X_2 of G of type II with X_1 of Fitting length 3 having the respective complements W_1, W_2 and such that $X_1 \cap X_2 = W$.*

(c) *Every maximal subgroup of G is either of type I or is conjugate to X_1 or X_2.*

This theorem reveals the inherent complication of the general odd-order problem in comparison with the special case of CN-groups. Indeed, if (i) holds, we are essentially back to the conditions of the CN-case. Note also that the subgroup W of (ii) is self-normalizing. Thus (ii) is directly related to the general problem of determining all simple groups, if any, which possess a self-normalizing cyclic subgroup. Considering the work entailed in resolving (ii) in the case of groups of odd order, this general question is obviously a very difficult one.

If M is a maximal subgroup of G and x is a nonidentity element of the kernel of M, Theorem 1 does not necessarily give any information concerning the structure of $C_G(x)$. Without some restriction on $C_G(x)$, one cannot obtain adequate relations between the character ring of M and that of G. In particular, one cannot establish the coherence of suitable subsets of ch (M) which is needed to carry out a character-theoretic and arithmetic analysis of G along the lines of Section 14.3 in the CN-case. The second theorem of Chapter IV of O provides this required information. Unfortunately it involves still another rather complicated concept, which we shall define in only a general sort of way.

Roughly speaking, a subset $\hat{L}$ of a group G is said to be *tamely embedded* in G if either $C_G(x) \subseteq L = N_G(\hat{L})$ for all x in $\hat{L}^*$ or else if there exists a set of subgroups H_i of G with normalizers $N_i = N_G(H_i)$, $1 \leqslant i \leqslant n$, such that

(a) $N_i = H_i(L \cap N_i)$ and $H_i \cap L = 1$, $1 \leqslant i \leqslant n$.

(b) For any x in $\hat{L}^*$, there is a conjugate y of x in $\hat{L}$ and an index i such that

$$C_G(y) = C_{H_i}(y)C_L(y) \subseteq N_i.$$

(In addition, a number of other small conditions must be satisfied, but we shall not list them here.)

The point of this definition is that, even though the centralizers of the elements of $\hat{L}^*$ do not lie in $L = N_G(\hat{L})$, we are given very specific information about the structure of these centralizers. In our present situation, the subset $\hat{L}$ will be an appropriate subset of a maximal subgroup L of G. Indeed, if L is of type I, we set.

$$\hat{L} = \bigcup_{x \in K^*} C_L(x) \qquad \text{where } K \text{ is the kernel of } L,$$

while if L is of type II, we set either

$$\hat{L} = L' \qquad \text{or} \qquad \hat{L} = \bigcup_{x \in H^*} C_L(x),$$

where H is the maximal nilpotent normal Hall subgroup of L (according to the actual type of L in the terminology of O).

The second major result of Chapter IV of O is:

Theorem 2

If L is a maximal subgroup of G, then $\hat{L}$ is a tamely embedded subset of G with $L = N_G(\hat{L})$.

(In the case that L is of type II, the actual theorem also asserts that a certain subset $\hat{L}_1$ of L with $\hat{L} \subseteq \hat{L}_1$ is also tamely embedded, $\hat{L}_1$ being defined in terms of $\hat{L}$ and the set $W - W_1 - W_2$.)

Now the stage is set for character theory. The aim is identical with that of the CN-case: to rule out the various possibilities for the configurations of maximal subgroups of G by arithmetic estimates for $|G|$. Ultimately all but a single such configuration is eliminated by this procedure. But compare the general situation we encounter here with the special case of a Frobenius group L whose kernel K is disjoint from its conjugates, which we treated in detail in Sections 4.4, 4.5, and 4.6. Obviously it requires a technical accomplishment of great magnitude to extend the results obtained there concerning coherence to our present configurations of subgroups.

In the Frobenius group case, the problem divided into two distinct parts. We considered the submodule $I(K)$ of the character ring $\operatorname{ch}(L)$ of L generated by the characters of L induced from the nonprincipal irreducible characters of K and showed first that the induction map * from $\operatorname{ch}(L)$ into $\operatorname{ch}(G)$ was an isometry on the submodule $I_0(K)$ of $I(K)$ consisting of those elements which had the value 0 at the identity (Theorem 4.5.4). At the same time Theorem 4.4.6 provided information on the values of appropriate induced characters on the elements of $K^\#$. We note that these particular results could equally well have been obtained for the larger module $I'(K)$ consisting of *all* generalized characters of N vanishing outside K and the corresponding submodule $I_0'(K)$. Second, we derived Feit's theorems (Theorems 4.6.3, 4.6.4, and 4.6.5) which gave sufficient conditions for the isometry * to extend to an isometry τ of the larger module $I(K)$ into $\operatorname{ch}(G)$, which in turn yielded sharper information on the values of appropriate characters of G on $K^\#$. [This part of the argument was definitely restricted to $I(K)$ and does not apply to $I'(K)$.]

In the general case even the induction map turns out to be inadequate for obtaining the corresponding initial isometry. Indeed, with the terminology as above, denote by $I'(\hat{L})$ the set of all generalized characters of L which vanish outside of $\hat{L}$ and by $I_0'(\hat{L})$ its submodule whose elements vanish on the identity. For ζ in $I_0'(\hat{L})$, let $\zeta_i = \zeta|_{L \cap N_i}$, $1 \leqslant i \leqslant n$. Since $N_i = H_i(L \cap N_i)$ and $H_i \cap L = 1$, there exists a generalized character ζ_{i1} of N_i which is the difference of two characters of N_i each having H_i in its kernel with the property $\zeta_{i1}|_{L \cap N_i} = \zeta_i$. We can regard ζ_{i1} as the difference of two characters of N_i having H_i in their kernels. Also let ζ_{i2} be the generalized character of N_i induced from the character ζ_i of the subgroup $L \cap N_i$. Finally, define the mapping τ from $I_0'(\hat{L})$ into $\operatorname{ch}(G)$ by the rule

$$(2.1) \qquad\qquad \zeta^\tau = \zeta^* + \sum_{i=1}^{n} (\zeta_{i1} - \zeta_{i2})^*$$

for all ζ in $I_0'(\hat{L})$. It is this map τ which is shown by Feit and Thompson to be an isometry from $I_0'(\hat{L})$ into $\operatorname{ch}(G)$. Moreover, by analogy with Theorem 4.4.6 they determine the values of ζ^τ on suitable elements of G. This portion of their character theory development has subsequently been given a very elegant treatment by Dade [1].

The problem of coherence is equally complex. As in the Frobenius case we wish to extend the isometry τ of a certain submodule $I_0(\hat{L})$ of $I_0'(\hat{L})$ into ch (G) to an isometry τ^* of a larger module $I(\hat{L})$ into ch (G). Once again $I(\hat{L})$ is defined to be generated essentially by characters of L induced from nonprincipal characters of an appropriate subgroup of L. The fact that $I(\hat{L})$ does not necessarily possess a basis of irreducible characters of L adds to the difficulties. In the end, results analogous to those of Section 4.6 are obtained. Remarkably enough, and despite the enormous complexity of the situation, these results are strong enough for the arithmetic estimates which Feit and Thompson must make on the basis of them. We shall not attempt to state explicitly any of their results on coherence. These can be found in Chapter III of O.

As for the arithmetic estimates themselves, which are carried out in Chapter V of O, one will hardly be surprised to find that they are far more elaborate than in the CN-case. For one thing, the general notion of coherence was not even needed in the CN-group problem, since all our estimates were based on information obtained from appropriate characters of our maximal subgroups of a given degree, which automatically formed a coherent set. In fact, a great portion of Chapter V concerns itself with showing, under the assumption of case (ii) of Theorem 1, that the modules $I_0(\hat{X}_1)$ and $I_0(\hat{X}_2)$ are, in fact, coherent.

The argument is divided into two major parts. The following intermediate result is first proved:

Theorem 3

Assume $I_0(\hat{X}_1)$ is not coherent. Then we have
  (i) The kernel K of X_1 is the direct product of a group C and a non-abelian 3-group H which is the maximal Hall subgroup of X_1 contained in K.
 (ii) X_1'/C is a Frobenius group with kernel K/C.
(iii) The complement W_1 of X_1 has prime order q.
 (iv) $|H : H'| = 3^q$.
  (v) $|X_1' : H| < 3^{q/2}$.
       Moreover, the maximal subgroup X_2 has the following structure:
 (vi) X_2' is the kernel of X_2 and either X_2' is disjoint from its conjugates or X_2' is the direct product of a cyclic group and an S_p-subgroup P of X_2 with $p \in \pi_1^*$. (X_2 is of type V in the terminology of O.)

This theorem should convey the degree of precision which the analysis requires. Its proof is very difficult and depends upon a number of the general results on coherence established in Chapter III of O.

The coherence of $I_0(X_1)$ and $I_0(X_2)$ is now established on the basis of the following independent result:

Theorem 4

X_2 *does not satisfy condition* (vi) *of Theorem* 3.

The proof of this theorem is very lovely and very delicate. Under the assumption that X_2 satisfies the given condition, it is first shown that $I_0(X_2)$ is coherent. The argument utilizes all the information already known about X_1: that either $I_0(X_1)$ is coherent or that X_1 has an extremely limited structure. Once this is established, a contradiction is derived by estimating the number of elements of G contained in the conjugates of (1) $W - W_1 - W_2$, (2) the centralizers of the elements of $\hat{X}_1$, and (3) the maximal nilpotent normal Hall subgroup of X_1.

Theorems 3 and 4 yield as a corollary that $I_0(X_i)$ is coherent and that X_i has Fitting length three, $1 \leqslant i \leqslant 2$. Moreover, Theorem 4 in turn is used to establish the next key result:

Theorem 5

Every maximal subgroup of G of type I is a Frobenius group.

If false for some maximal subgroup M of type I, then there is associated with M a second maximal subgronp L of G. A certain irreducible character λ of L is constructed and estimates for λ^{τ} on particular elements of $M^{\#}$ are obtained, where λ^{τ} is defined as in (2.1) above. By choosing M properly, it is shown ultimately that an S_3-subgroup of G has order 3 and hence that G has a normal 3-complement, by Burnside's transfer theorem, a contradiction.

Now Feit and Thompson are at last in a position to obtain estimates for $|G|$ using all the maximal subgroups of G, on the basis of which they can force still further restrictions on X_1 and X_2. The arguments, which we shall not attempt to summarize, are by far the most intricate of the entire chapter, several cases involving small primes having to be treated individually. They finally yield the main objective of the chapter, which is to obtain the exact structure of X_1 and X_2. To present this in the most symmetric form, we alter the notation, conforming to that of O.

Theorem 6

If G is a minimal simple group of odd order, then G satisfies the following conditions:

(i) *There exist odd primes p and q with p > q such that an S_p-subgroup*

> P of G is elementary abelian of order p^q, an S_q-subgroup Q of G is elementary abelian of order q^p, and P, Q are each disjoint from their conjugates.
> (ii) $N_G(P) = PUQ^*$, where PU and UQ^* are Frobenius groups with kernels P and U, respectively, $|Q^*| = q$, $|U| = (p^q - 1)/(p - 1)$, and $Q^* \subseteq Q$. Moreover, $p - 1$ and $|U|$ are relatively prime.
> (iii) If $P^* = C_P(Q^*)$, then $|P^*| = p$ and P^*Q^* is a self-normalizing cyclic subgroup of G. Furthermore, $C_G(P^*) = PQ^*$, $C_G(Q^*) = QP^*$, and $P^* \subseteq N_G(Q)$.
> (iv) $C_G(U)$ is a cyclic group which is disjoint from its conjugates. Furthermore, $Q^* \subseteq N_G(U) = N_G(C_G(U))$, $N_G(U)/C_G(U)$ is a cyclic group of order pq, and $N_G(U)$ is a Frobenius group with Frobenius kernel $C_G(U)$.

One could also list analogous properties of $N_G(Q)$, but these are not needed for the subsequent argument. We should also like to point out that this configuration of subgroups can occur even if all the Sylow subgroups of G are, by assumption, abelian. Hence even this special case of the odd order problem does not avoid this residual case.

Chapter VI of O is taken up with the proof of the following result:

Theorem 7

There are no groups G which satisfy conditions (i) to (iv) of Theorem 6.

Once this is established, the solvability of all groups of odd order is proved. Since the proof of Theorem 7 is based on the method of generators and relations, it is entirely reasonable to say that the conditions of Theorem 6 represent the generalized Bruhat structure of the general minimal simple group of odd order.

The only way to describe the proof of Theorem 7 is as an absolute tour de force. We shall try to convey the gist of the argument, so assume G is a group which satisfies the given conditions. Let u and v be generators of U and P^*, respectively, and set $h = |U|$, so that $h = (p^q - 1)/(p - 1)$. Then u acts irreducibly on P as a vector space of dimension q over Z_p. If ω is a characteristic root of u on P, then $Z_p(\omega) = GF(p^q)$. The proof involves an investigation of the set of relations of a certain form satisfied by the elements u and v. A purely local analysis of the group PU establishes the following two lemmas:

Lemma 1

Let a_1, a_2, and a_3 be elements of Z_h, not all 0. Then we have

$$vu^{a_1}v^{-2}u^{a_2}vu^{a_3} = 1$$

if and only if the following conditions hold:
  (i) $a_i \neq 0, 1 \leqslant i \leqslant 3$.
  (ii) $a_1 + a_2 + a_3 = 0$.
  (iii) $\omega^{a_1} + \omega^{a_1 + a_3} - 2 = 0$.

Denote by $\mathscr{A}$ the set of triples (a_1, a_2, a_3) which satisfy (i), (ii), and (iii).

Lemma 2
  The following conditions hold:
   (i) $\mathscr{A}$ *is nonempty.*
   (ii) *If* $(a_1, a_2, a_3) \in \mathscr{A}$, *then* $(-a_2, -a_1, -a_3) \in \mathscr{A}$.

The bulk of the proof consists in the derivation of a single additional property of $\mathscr{A}$, using our complete configuration of subgroups of G. To state it, let us denote by $\mathscr{B}$ the set of first components a_1 of all triples (a_1, a_2, a_3) of $\mathscr{A}$. Then $\mathscr{B}$ has the following fundamental property:

Lemma 3
  If $a \in \mathscr{B}$, *then* $-a \in \mathscr{B}$.

In other words, if $(a_1, a_2, a_3) \in \mathscr{A}$, then also $(-a_1, a_2', a_3') \in \mathscr{A}$ for suitable elements a_2', a_3' of Z_h. Once Lemma 3 is established, a contradiction can be derived by the following procedure. First, define

$$\mathscr{C} = \{\omega^a \mid a \in \mathscr{B}\}.$$

A direct consequence of these lemmas is

Lemma 4
  $\mathscr{C}$ *has the following properties:*
   (i) $\mathscr{C}$ *is nonempty and every element of* $\mathscr{C}$ *lies in* $GF(p^q) - GF(p)$.
   (ii) *If* $\gamma \in \mathscr{C}$, *then* $N(\gamma) = \gamma^{1 + p + \cdots + p^{q-1}} = 1$.
   (iii) *If* $\gamma \in \mathscr{C}$, *then* $1/(2 - \gamma) \in \mathscr{C}$.

Proof
  The critical property is (iii), which we prove first. If $\gamma \in \mathscr{C}$, Lemmas 1(iii) and 2(ii) imply that $2 - \gamma \in \mathscr{C}$. But then Lemma 3 yields that $(2 - \gamma)^{-1} = 1/(2 - \gamma) \in \mathscr{C}$.
  Now $\mathscr{C}$ is nonempty, by Lemma 2(i). If $\gamma \in \mathscr{C}$, $\gamma = \omega^a$ with $a \in \mathscr{B}$ and $a \neq 0$ by Lemma 1(i). Since ω is a primitive hth root of unity and $(h, p - 1) = 1$ by assumption, it follows that $\gamma \notin GF(p)$. On the other hand, γ is in $GF(p^q)$ since ω is. Finally $h = (p^q - 1)/(p - 1) = 1 + p + \cdots + p^{q-1}$. Since $\omega^h = 1$, we have $N(\gamma) = 1$. Thus (i) and (ii) also hold.

But the conclusions of Lemma 4 are in direct contradiction to the following purely field-theoretic fact:

Lemma 5

For x in $GF(p^q)$, define $N(x) = x^{1+p+\cdots+p^{q-1}}$, and for $x \neq 2$, define $x^\sigma = 1/(2 - x)$. Let $\gamma \in GF(p^q) - GF(p)$. Then for some positive integer i we have

$$N(\gamma^{\sigma^i}) \neq 1.$$

Indeed, by Lemma 4, there is such an element γ with the property $N(\gamma^{\sigma^i}) = 1$ for all i.

In conclusion, we comment briefly on the proof of Lemma 3, which involves a stunning display of virtuosity in the manipulation of highly complex words in the elements u and v and certain of their conjugates. At the base of the argument lies the following fact, which is essentially an immediate consequence of our over-all hypothesis on G.

Lemma 6

There exists an element y in Q^* such that $P^* = \langle v \rangle$ normalizes $yC_G(U)y^{-1}$.

Thus we have for some integer d of Z_h,

(2.2) $(yuy^{-1})^v = (yuy^{-1})^d$.

Now for b in Z_p, define

(2.3) $y_b = [y, v^b]$.

Then the elements u, v, and y are connected by the following identities:

Lemma 7

$v^{-b}uv^b = y_b^{-1}u^{v^b}y_b$ for all b in Z_p.

This lemma enables one to obtain a relation between u, v, and y involving the elements of $\mathscr{A}$:

Lemma 8

Set $z = yuy^{-1}$. If $(a_1, a_2, a_2) \in \mathscr{A}$, then we have

$$y_2 z^{a_1 d} y_3^{-1} y_1 z^{a_2 d^3} y_2^{-1} = y_1 z^{-a_3 d^2} y_3^{-1}.$$

It is this very unwieldy identity that has to be exploited. A series of long and extremely difficult generator-relation calculations establish Lemma 3.

We hope this summary has adequately conveyed the magnitude of Feit and Thompson's accomplishment in proving that all groups of odd order are solvable.

3. GROUPS WITH DIHEDRAL SYLOW 2-SUBGROUPS

In discussing the general dihedral problem, we use the notation $PSL(2, q)$ rather than $L_2(q)$ and denote by $P\Gamma L(2, q)$ the automorphism group of $PSL(2, q)$. The structure of $P\Gamma L(2, q)$ is well known; it is isomorphic to the semidirect product of $PGL(2, q)$ by a cyclic group A of order n, where $q = p^n$, p a prime. The automorphisms determined by A arise from corresponding ones of $SL(2, q)$ that are induced from automorphisms of the field $GF(q)$. The complete classification of groups with dihedral Sylow 2-subgroups can now be stated:

Theorem
   If G is a group with dihedral Sylow 2-subgroups, then $G/O(G)$ is isomorphic to either
      (i) *a subgroup of $P\Gamma L(2, q)$ containing $PSL(2, q)$, q odd,*
      (ii) *the alternating group A_7, or*
      (iii) *a Sylow 2-subgroup of G.*
In particular, if G is simple, it is isomorphic to either $PSL(2, q)$, q odd, $q > 3$, or to A_7.

For convenience we say that a group H is a *D-group* if it has a dihedral S_2-subgroup and if $H/O(H)$ satisfies (i) or (ii) above. In these terms the theorem asserts that any group with a dihedral S_2-subgroup is either a *D*-group or possesses a normal 2-complement. We shall refer to the three papers by the author and J. H. Walter comprising the proof of this theorem as D.

As in the proof of Lemma 15.2.2, a minimal counterexample to the theorem is a simple group G with dihedral S_2-subgroups such that every proper subgroup of G is either a *D*-group or has a normal 2-complement. To establish the classification theorem, we must show, under these hypotheses, that G is isomorphic to either $PSL(2, q)$, q odd, $q > 3$, or to A_7.

By Theorem 7.7.3, G has only one conjugate class of involutions and if x is an involution in the center of an S_2-subgroup S of G, then $N = C_G(x)$ possesses a normal 2-complement U. Thus $N = SU$, $U \lhd N$ and $|U|$ odd, exactly the conditions that prevailed in the special case of Chapter 15 in which S was a self-centralizing four group. Under that hypothesis the involutions of $S - \langle x \rangle$ inverted U and, in particular, U was abelian. Moreover, the aim of the local group-theoretic analysis (Theorem 15.3.1) was to show that U was disjoint from its conjugates. At that point the character-theoretic argument of Brauer-Suzuki-Wall took over to establish that G had a generalized Bruhat structure, and then Zassenhaus's theorem was applied to complete the classification.

In the general case, the pattern of the proof is entirely similar in nature, but, as one would expect, involves many significant complications. First, the structure of the centralizer of an involution in $PSL(2, q)$ differs in one important respect from that in A_7. Indeed, if G is $PSL(2, q)$, then every involution of $S - \langle x \rangle$ inverts U, whereas if G is A_7 (in which case $|S| = 8$ and $|U| = 3$), two of the involutions of $S - \langle x \rangle$ invert U while the remaining two centralize U. Hence the analysis must allow for both these possibilities. In fact, the ultimate goal of D is to establish the following result:

Proposition
One of the following two sets of conditions holds:
    I. (i) *Every involution of $S - \langle x \rangle$ inverts U and*
         (ii) *U is disjoint from its conjugates; or*
    II. *The centralizer of an involution in G is isomorphic to that of an involution in A_7.*

Although we have proved the Brauer-Suzuki-Wall theorem only in the case that $|S|$ is four, it holds for arbitrary dihedral 2-group S under assumption I (compare Exercise 9.5) and leads to the conclusion that G has a Bruhat structure identical to that in $PSL(2, q)$ for some odd $q > 3$, and again Zassenhaus's theorem can be applied to show that G is isomorphic to $PSL(2, q)$.

On the other hand, condition II can be regarded for our purposes as the assertion that G has a generalized Bruhat structure identical to that of A_7, for Suzuki has shown in [6] under this hypothesis that G is, in fact, isomorphic to A_7. The proof is not difficult: One obtains group order formulas for $|G|$ with the aid of modular character theory which yield the conclusion $|G| = |A_7|$; then one shows that G has the appropriate transitive permutation representation.

The proof of the above proposition is considerably more complicated than in the special case that S is a self-centralizing four group. Indeed, the local group-theoretic analysis alone does not yield it, but instead gives conclusion of the same general nature as those reached at the end of Chapter IV of O. Here we obtain rather detailed possibilities for the structure of $N = C_G(x)$ which are divided into nine cases of four distinct types (see Proposition 18 of D). To establish our proposition, seven of these cases must be eliminated by deriving suitable contradictions. The methods for accomplishing this utilize various group order formulas for $|G|$, established by means of modular character theory, in conjunction with delicate arithmetic analyses. These arguments have the same flavor as those of Section 14.3.

We turn now to a description of the local group-theoretic analysis which leads to these nine cases for the structure of N. In the self-centralizing four group case we divided the primes p in $\pi(U)$ into two subsets α, β, setting $p \in \alpha$ if U contains an S_p-subgroup of G and $p \in \beta$ in the contrary case. This simple subdivision was possible since for any S_p-subgroup P of U, $N_G(P)$ always possessed a normal 2-complement. However, the general situation is much more complicated, because $N_G(P)$ may either be a D-group or have a normal 2-complement. We are led to subdivide $\pi(U)$ into four disjoint subsets $\sigma_1, \sigma_2, \sigma_3$, and σ_4 as follows:

Let P be an S_p-subgroup of U for p in $\pi(U)$. Then
1. $p \in \sigma_1$ if P is an S_p-subgroup of $O(N_G(P))$ and $N_G(P)$ possesses a normal 2-complement.
2. $p \in \sigma_2$ if P is an S_p-subgroup of $O(N_G(P))$ and $N_G(P)$ is a D-group.
3. $P \in \sigma_3$ if P is cyclic and P is not an S_p-subgroup of $O(N_G(P))$.
4. $p \in \sigma_4$ if P is noncyclic and P is not an S_p-subgroup of $O(N_G(P))$.

In the self-centralizing four-group case, $\alpha = \sigma_1$, σ_2 is empty, and $\beta = \sigma_3 \cup \sigma_4$. In that case the local group-theoretic analysis consisted in proving that β was empty, which implied immediately that U was disjoint from its conjugates (Lemma 15.3.2). In the general situation, the object of the first part of this analysis is again to show that $\sigma_3 \cup \sigma_4$ is empty. Such a result is clearly called for, inasmuch as this holds for both $PSL(2, q)$ and A_7. Indeed, if G is $PSL(2, q)$, then $\pi(U) = \sigma_1$, while if G is A_7, then $\pi(U) = \sigma_2 = \{3\}$.

The reason for breaking β up in the general case into two subsets σ_3, σ_4 is a technical one. For two odd primes p and q in $\pi(G)$, we have the same notion, $p \sim q$, as in O. The point is that we can establish rather easily the fact $SCN_3(p)$ is nonempty for p in σ_4 and that all primes in σ_4 lie in a single equivalence class under $\sim$. Although it is also easy to show that $SCN_3(p)$ is nonempty for p in σ_3, one does not seem to be able to establish directly that the primes in $\sigma_3 \cup \sigma_4$ lie in a single equivalence class. The procedure we follow is to argue first that σ_4 is empty and only after that to prove that σ_3 is also empty.

Now it is not difficult to prove that the p-local subgroups of G are p-constrained for all p in $\sigma_3 \cup \sigma_4$. Moreover, Theorem 8.1.2 shows that every proper subgroup of G is p-stable for any odd prime p. Once again the conditions are favorable for application of the Maximal Subgroup theorem. Since all the primes in σ_4 are equivalent, one can prove essentially, as in O, that G possesses a proper subgroup H which contains an S_p-subgroup of G for each p in σ_4. (Since H may be a nonsolvable D-group, we cannot infer from this that G possesses an S_{σ_4}-subgroup.) Again as in O, this enables us to show that G satisfies the uniqueness condition for some prime p in σ_4.

We remark that Glauberman's theorem also effects a considerable simplification of the published version of the proofs of these results.

At this point one can derive a contradiction by either of two methods. Let M be a uniqueness subgroup in G for p. First, we can follow the procedure of the self-centralizing order four case: We show, on the one hand, that M is strongly embedded in G and, on the other hand, that $|C_G(O_p(M))|$ is odd. An appropriate extension of Theorem 9.3.1 gives a contradiction. Second, we can follow the procedure of D which is to derive expressions for $|G|$ and $|M|$ by means of modular character theory, which upon comparison yield the conclusion $|G : M| \leqslant 5$. But then G is isomorphic to a subgroup of S_5, which is clearly impossible with σ_4 nonempty.

The proof that σ_3 is empty and the subsequent reduction to the nine possibilities for the structure of N are both similar in character. Once we know that σ_4 is empty, a very severe restriction becomes placed upon the structure of the p-subgroups of G for p in $\pi(U)$. In deriving these restrictions, fairly detailed properties of the groups $L_2(q)$ and A_7 come into play. This is in sharp contrast to the previous analysis of σ_4, where only the general property of stability entered. The entire analysis bears a strong similarity to that of Section 26 of O.

It thus appears that in many classification problems a stage is reached in which one must carry out a local group-theoretic analysis for certain primes for which the corresponding Sylow subgroups have small depth. Unfortunately this analysis seems to depend in each case upon special properties of the subgroups of G specified by the given problem and so does not lend itself easily to a general conceptual formulation.

4. C-GROUPS

The statement of Suzuki's main result on C-groups involves two families of simple groups that we have not previously considered. The first of these is the family $Sz(q)$ discovered by Suzuki and named after him. It is defined only for $q = 2^{2m+1}$, with $m = 1, 2, 3, \ldots$. Some properties of Suzuki groups will be discussed below. The second family is the three-dimensional projective unitary group $PGU(3, q)$, q any prime power, which by definition is the factor group of the general unitary group $GU(3, q)$ modulo its center. Here $GU(3, q)$ consists of all 3×3 unitary matrices with entries in $GF(q^2)$. A matrix X of $GL(3, q^2)$ is said to be unitary provided $X^{-1} = (X^\sigma)^t$, where X^σ is the matrix obtained from X by applying to each of its entries the automorphism $x^\sigma = x^q$ of $GF(q^2)$ and where t denotes transpose. It is a theorem that for $q > 2$ the group $PGU(3, q)$ possesses a simple subgroup $U_3(q)$ of index 1 or 3 according as $q \not\equiv -1 \pmod 3$ or $q \equiv 1 \pmod 3$. In fact, $U_3(q) = PSU(3, q)$, the factor group of the special unitary group $SU(3, q)$ modulo its center.

We wish to point out that the groups $Sz(q)$, $PGU(3, q)$, and $U_3(q)$, $q > 2$, are doubly transitive of respective degrees $q^2 + 1$ and $q^3 + 1$. In fact, $Sz(q)$ is a Zassenhaus group of type (H, S) with H cyclic of order $q - 1$ and S a nonabelian special 2-group of order q^2 with elementary abelian center of order q. Although $U_3(q)$ is not a Zassenhaus group, it is close to being one and has a structure very similar to that of $Sz(q)$. Indeed, the subgroup M fixing a letter is a semidirect product $M = HS$, where S is a nonabelian special 2-group of order q^3 with elementary abelian center of order q and H is a subgroup fixing two letters. Moreover, no element of $S^\#$ leaves any of the remaining letters fixed (equivalently S is disjoint from its conjugates). In addition, H is abelian of order $(q^2 - 1)/d$, where $d = 1$ or 3 according as $q \not\equiv -1 \pmod 3$ or $q \equiv 1 \pmod 3$ and H contains a cyclic subgroup H_0 of order $q - 1$ such that $H_0 S$ is a Frobenius group. However, $U_3(q)$ is not a Zassenhaus group, for the subgroup H_1 of H fixing three letters is cyclic of order $(q + 1)/d > 1$ (as $q > 2$). Similar remarks apply to $PGU(3, q)$.

We can now state Suzuki's theorem:

Theorem

A nonabelian simple C-group G is isomorphic to one of the groups of the following list:

(i) $L_2(p)$, *p a Fermat or Mersenne prime.*

(ii) $L_2(9)$.

(iii) $L_2(q)$, $Sz(q)$, $U_3(q)$, *or* $L_3(q)$, *where* $q = 2^n$, $n \geqslant 2$.

As in the case of groups with dihedral S_2-subgroups, to proceed by induction it is necessary to establish a stronger theorem classifying all

C-groups and to derive the result on simple C-groups as a corollary. To simplify the exposition, we shall not state Suzuki's general result explicitly.

The local group-theoretic analysis involved in the proof of this theorem differs considerably from that of the odd-order and dihedral theorems, for the latter two are "odd characteristic" problems, whereas this result is a "characteristic 2" problem, as can be seen from the above list. Indeed, G turns out to be of characteristic 2 except when its S_2-subgroups are dihedral. However, even in that case only those $L_2(q)$, q odd, can arise in which the centralizer of an involution is a 2-group, for this is equivalent to the condition $q = 9$ or $q = p$, p a Fermat or Mersenne prime.

In Parts I and II we established two closely related theorems which can be viewed as characteristic 2 results. The first was Suzuki's Theorem 9.3.2 concerning a group G that contains a strongly embedded nilpotent subgroup K of even order and provides a condition for G to be a Zassenhaus group. The second was that part of Theorem 13.1.4 which dealt with Zassenhaus groups of type (H, K) in which $|K|$ is even. Examination of the proofs will show that they focus on two major themes:

(a) Analysis of involutions: their conjugacy, number, and distribution in appropriate cosets.
(b) Properties of strongly real elements.

These same kinds of considerations underlie the local group-theoretic analysis involved in determining the structure and embedding of the maximal 2-local subgroups of the general simple C-group G. For example, an important property of G, which follows easily from the C-group assumption, is the fact that for any real element v of $G^{\#}$, $C_G(v)$ has odd order (compare Exercise 9.1).

Unfortunately these two theorems are far less satisfactory than those on CN-groups of odd order and on groups with a self-centralizing S_2-subgroup of order four in revealing the depth and complexity of the corresponding general problem. Despite this deficiency, we shall try to make our discussion detailed enough to provide the reader with as full a picture of characteristic 2 problems as he may have of the odd characteristic case. At the same time, this discussion should give him a much greater understanding of the role of the generator-relation method in classification problems. Finally, it should also help to clarify the discussion on N-groups, which we shall present in the next section, where both characteristic 2 and odd characteristic problems will be combined in a yet more complex situation.

To begin, we note that in the special theorems mentioned above, the subgroup K of G contains an S_2-subgroup S of G and we are given that $C_G^*(u) \subseteq K$ for any u in $K^\#$. This means that we have complete control over the centralizers $C_G(x)$ of any involution x of S and also over the centralizers $C_G(y)$ of any element y of $C_G(x)^\#$, these subgroups all being forced to lie in the nilpotent group K. However, in the case of an arbitrary simple C-group G, corresponding assertions about such centralizers $C_G(x)$ and $C_G(y)$ are in general false and so we do not know a priori the structure of these subgroups. Clearly this is a major complication. Moreover, it is evident that our induction hypothesis must be brought into play to give us some preliminary hold on their structure. As in the dihedral problem, specific properties of the groups in our list enter into the subsequent analysis.

Of the possibilities that can occur, four major subcases emerge. To describe these, we need a few preliminary remarks. Note that if the S_2-subgroup S of the group G is disjoint from its conjugates, then G is a C-group. Indeed, if x is an involution of S, this condition implies at once that $C_G(x) \subseteq M = N_G(S)$. Since M is 2-closed, so therefore is $C_G(x)$, which proves the assertion. If, in addition, G is simple, Theorem 9.1.4 tells us that G has only one class of involutions. In particular, it follows that these all lie in $\Omega_1(Z(S))^\#$. Observe also that S has a complement H of odd order by the Schur-Zassenhaus theorem; H is therefore solvable by Feit-Thompson. This fact is crucial for Suzuki in demonstrating in case B below that H is metacyclic.

Now let G be a simple C-group with S_2-group S. Then we have:

Type A   (a) S is disjoint from its conjugates.
          (b) If x is an involution of S and y an element of $C_G(x)^\#$, then $C_G(y) \subseteq M$.

Type B   (a) S is disjoint from its conjugates.
          (b) If x is an involution of S, then there is an element y in $C_G(x)^\#$ such that $C_G(y) \nsubseteq M$.

Type C   (a) S is not disjoint from its conjugates.
          (b) $Z(S)$ is cyclic.

Type D   (a) S is not disjoint from its conjugates.
          (b) $Z(S)$ is noncyclic.

The more precise formulation of Suzuki's theorem is the following:

Theorem

Let G be a simple nonabelian C-group. Then
  (i) *If G is of type* A, *it is isomorphic to $L_2(q)$ or $Sz(q)$, $q = 2^n$, $n \geqslant 2$.*
  (ii) *If G is of type* B, *it is isomorphic to $U_3(q)$, $q = 2^n$, $n \geqslant 2$.*

(iii) *If G is of type* C, *it is isomorphic to* $L_2(9)$ *or to* $L_2(p)$, *p a Fermat or Mersenne prime.*

(iv) *If G is of type* D, *it is isomorphic to* $L_3(q)$, $q = 2^n$, $n \geqslant 2$.

We shall comment briefly on each of these four cases.

Type A   In this case, by essentially the same argument that we used to prove Theorem 14.4.1, it is shown that G is a Zassenhaus group of type (H, S) when acting on the right cosets of $M = HS$. Then H is cyclic of odd order by Theorem 13.1.4(i). Since G has only one class of involutions and $S_0 = \Omega_1(Z(S))$ contains all the involutions of S, H must permute the elements of $S_0^{\#}$ transitively. In particular, $|H| = q - 1$, where $q = |S_0|$.

If S is abelian, Theorem 14.1.4 yields the conclusion that G is isomorphic to $L_2(q)$. Hence we may assume that S is nonabelian. In this case we must show that G is isomorphic to $Sz(q)$.

We are led at once to an extremely interesting question concerning 2-groups: What is the structure of a nonabelian 2-group S which admits a fixed-point-free automorphism of order $q - 1$ transitively permuting the $q - 1$ involutions of S? Using the methods of the associated Lie ring discussed in Section 5.6, Graham Higman [3] has completely solved this problem and has shown that for each $q > 2$, S must be of exponent 4 and order q^2 or q^3. Moreover, if $|S| = q^2$, then S is uniquely described in terms of the integer q together with an automorphism θ of the field $GF(q)$. We denote the corresponding group by $S(q; \theta)$.

Higman's theorem thus yields the possible structures of the S_2-subgroup S of our Zassenhaus group G. Using delicate arithmetic counts of the elements of G in conjunction with properties of the strongly real elements of G, Suzuki is able to establish that the order of G is not divisible by 3 [otherwise G would be isomorphic to $L_2(q)$ and S would be abelian]. This in turn implies that q is an odd power of 2 and that $|S| = q^2$, so that, in particular, S is isomorphic to $S(q; \theta)$ for some θ.

It now follows easily that $M = HS$ is uniquely determined up to isomorphism by q and θ. However, we cannot yet assert that G has a generalized Bruhat structure identical to that of $Sz(q)$, for in $Sz(q)$ the automorphism θ is not arbitrary, but is specified by the condition

$$(4.1) \qquad\qquad\qquad \theta^2 = 2.$$

[Actually there are two solutions of (4.1), θ and θ^{-1}, but either possibility can be used in defining $Sz(q)$.] Thus we have still to prove that the automorphism θ of our Zassenhaus group G satisfies (4.1). However, it does not seem to be possible to do this except in the process of determining the uniqueness of the multiplication functions α, β, and γ of G by means of generators and relations. All that Suzuki can show in advance is that the mapping $\theta - 1$ is an automorphism of $GF(q)$. This fact, which is critical for the final determination of θ, is not trivial to establish, but relies on a property of the elements of G of order 4 which is derived by means of character theory. Thus at this point we may say that G has a generalized Bruhat structure "identical" to that of $Sz(q)$.

The proof that G is, in fact, isomorphic to $Sz(q)$ is very analogous to that of Zassenhaus's theorem in Chapter 13. Once again a key structural identity is established on the basis of which a canonical set of generators of G is constructed. Indeed, very near the beginning of the entire argument, it is shown that for a given involution w of G inverting H there exists a unique element z in S^* and a unique power z^k of z with z^k an involution such that

$$(4.2) \qquad\qquad wzw = z^k w z^k.$$

Once it is known that $|G|$ is not divisible by 3, the case $|z| = 2$ is excluded, for then $(wz)^3 = 1$ as $z^{-1} = z$. Since S is of exponent 4, this forces $|z| = 4$ and $k = 2$. A direct consequence of this is the fact that

$$(4.3) \qquad\qquad (wz)^5 = 1.$$

The final step is to show that the multiplication functions α, β, and γ of G with respect to (H, S, w) and also the automorphism θ are uniquely determined. This argument proves that any two simple Zassenhaus groups of the same odd degree with nonabelian S_2-subgroups are isomorphic.

We must emphasize that this argument does not at all resolve the question of whether such Zassenhaus groups actually exist. This is a completely independent problem which Suzuki had to face, and part of his great achievement lies in the fact that he was able to construct a family of simple groups fulfilling the required conditions. Indeed, let q be an odd power of 2 and let θ be an automorphism of $GF(q)$ such that $\theta^2 = 2$. Consider the 4×4 matrices over $GF(q)$ of the form

$$\begin{pmatrix} 1 & 0 & 0 & 0 \\ a & 1 & 0 & 0 \\ a^{1+\theta} + b & a^\theta & 1 & 0 \\ a^{2+\theta} + ab + b^\theta & b & a & 1 \end{pmatrix} \quad \text{and} \quad \begin{pmatrix} c^{1+\theta-1} & 0 & 0 & 0 \\ 0 & c^{\theta-1} & 0 & 0 \\ 0 & 0 & c^{-\theta-1} & 0 \\ 0 & 0 & 0 & c^{-1-\theta-1} \end{pmatrix},$$

where a, b, $c \in GF(q)$ and $c \neq 0$. The first set forms a group S^* isomorphic to $S(q; \theta)$ and the second form a cyclic group H^* of order $q - 1$ which normalizes S^*. Moreover, if

$$w^* = \begin{pmatrix} 0 & 0 & 0 & 1 \\ 0 & 0 & 1 & 0 \\ 0 & 1 & 0 & 0 \\ 1 & 0 & 0 & 0 \end{pmatrix},$$

then w^* inverts H^*. Suzuki has shown that S^*, H^*, and w^* generate a group having all the desired properties.

Type B The complete analysis in this case is by far the longest. Since the argument resembles that of type A in many respects, we shall limit ourselves to presenting a "flow diagram" of the proof:

1. With y as in condition (b) of type B, it is first shown that $L = C_G(y)$ has the following structure: $L/O(L)$ is isomorphic to a subgroup of Aut X, where $X = L_2(q)$, $U_3(q)$, or $Sz(q)$, $q > 2$.

2. Properties of L, including the fact that there exists a structure identity in L, form an integral part of an exceedingly delicate argument which proves that

   (a) G acts doubly transitively on the cosets of M.
   (b) M possesses a normal Hall subgroup Q with $S \subseteq Q$ such that no element of $Q^\#$ fixes any coset of $G - M$.

3. H contains a cyclic subgroup H_0 of order $q - 1$ such that

   (a) $H_0 Q$ is a Frobenius group.
   (b) H_0 acts transitively on the $q - 1$ involution of S.
   (c) H_0 is the subset of H inverted by an involution w of $N_G(H)$.

4. By the structure of a Frobenius group, Q is nilpotent. Moreover, Higman's theorem implies that S is either homocyclic abelian or nonabelian special of order q^2 or q^3.

5. There exists a unique involution z of S and a unique element y of M such that

$$w^{-1}zw = y^{-1}wy.$$

As a consequence,

$$(wz)^p = 1$$

for some odd prime p. The integer p, which depends only upon G, is denoted by $\chi(G)$.

6. $\chi(G) = 3$ or 5. The structure identity for L has the corresponding integer $\chi(L) = 3$ or 5 and we must have $\chi(L) = \chi(G)$.

7. A particular class of groups of the general type under consideration

is shown to satisfy the condition $Q = S$. The argument is very difficult and involves the structure of S_3-subgroups of G.

8. $\chi(G) = 3$. If $\chi(G) = 5$, it is proved that H_0, S, and w generate a subgroup G_0 of G isomorphic to $Sz(q)$. Then the conditions of (7) are shown to hold, which yields $Q = S$ and $G = G_0$, so G is of type A, contrary to assumption.

9. S is nonabelian of order q^3. Higman's classification theorem gives three possible structures for S when $|S| = q^3$. However, Suzuki's argument shows that only one of these types is permissible. As in the case of $Sz(q)$, S can be completely described in terms of the integer q and an automorphism θ of $GF(q)$. The argument of (9) also yields:

10. $H \supset H_0$. In particular, M is not a Frobenius group with kernel Q.

11. $Q = S$. The proof parallels that of Feit's theorem very closely and depends upon the coherence of suitable characters of M.

12. H is cyclic of order dividing $q^2 - 1$. At this point we may say that G has a generalized Bruhat structure of the same type as $U_3(q)$, even though HS is not necessarily isomorphic to the corresponding subgroup of $U_3(q)$. In fact, in the present case there are *two* degrees of indeterminancy for the structure of H: First, the automorphism θ which determines the structure of S and, second, the actual order of H. In $U_3(q)$ itself we have $\theta = 1$ and $|H| = (q^2 - 1)/d$ with $d = 1$ or 3. As in the case of $Sz(q)$, these properties of G are deduced during the generator-relation analysis.

13. G is isomorphic to a subgroup of $PGU(3, q)$. As in the case of a Zassenhaus group, the multiplication table of G can be completely described in terms of HS, w, and three functions α, β, and γ from $S^\#$ to $S^\#$, $S^\#$, and H, respectively. The generator-relation analysis yields that $\theta = 1$ and that α, β, and γ are uniquely determined and have the same form as in the group $PGU(3, q)$.

14. G is isomorphic to $U_3(q)$. A comparison of orders tells us that G has the same number of S_2-subgroups as $PGU(3, q)$ and so its image must be a normal subgroup of $PGU(3, q)$.

Type C   In this case it is not difficult to prove that an S_2-subgroup S of G must be of maximal class and so is either cyclic, generalized quaternion, semi-dihedral, or dihedral. Under the present conditions the simplicity of G forces S to be dihedral, in which case the general dihedral classification theorem yields that G is isomorphic to one of the groups $L_2(q)$, q odd, or A_7. The actual possibilities for G are now easily determined.

Type D   The local group-theoretic analysis of this case differs considerably from those of the preceding cases and resembles in spirit certain arguments that occur in more complex form in Thompson's work on N-groups. If D is a maximal intersection of two S_2-subgroups of G, and if P is an S_2-subgroup of $N_G(D)$, then a delicate analysis of the weak closure of $Z(S)$ in P relative to G is undertaken, where S is an S_2-subgroup of G containing P. The analysis depends rather crucially upon the following general property of G: If R and T are S_2-subgroups of G such that $Z(R) \cap T \neq 1$, then $\{Z(R), Z(T)\} \subseteq R \cap T$.

This analysis, which is not unduly long, establishes that $S = P$ is of order q^3, $q = 2^n$, $n > 1$, that D is elementary abelian of order q^2, and that $N_G(D)/D$ contains a normal subgroup of odd index isomorphic to $L_2(q)$.

We now set $B = N_G(S)$ and let H be a complement of S in B. If $N = N_G(H)$, the next stage of the local analysis is aimed at proving that $W = N/H$ is isomorphic to the symmetric group S_3 and that the group $G_0 = \langle B, N \rangle$ has the form $G_0 = BNB$, and that all the intersections $B \cap B^y$, $y \in N$, are determined. These conditions together amount to the fact that G_0 is a (B, N)-pair of rank 2 with "Weyl group" W isomorphic to S_3 (rank 2 because W can be generated by *two* involutions).

If $\bar{G}_0 = G_0/O(G_0)$, it is not difficult to show that $\bar{G}_0$ possesses a normal subgroup $\bar{G}_1$ of odd index in $\bar{G}_0$ which is also a (B, N)-pair with S_3 as Weyl group, but whose Borel subgroup $\bar{B}_1$ is isomorphic to that of $L_3(q)$— to the group of all 3×3 matrices over $GF(q)$ of determinant 1 of the form

$$\begin{pmatrix} * & 0 & 0 \\ * & * & 0 \\ * & * & * \end{pmatrix}.$$

Thus $\bar{G}_1$ has a Bruhat structure identical to that of $L_3(q)$. D. Higman and McLaughlin [1] have shown by a geometric argument that $\bar{G}_1$ must then be isomorphic to $L_3(q)$. The method of generators and relations will also yield the same conclusion.

The final step in the proof is to establish that $G = G_0$ by application of Theorem 9.2.1(iii), as was discussed in Section 1. Now the simplicity of G implies that $G = \bar{G}_1$ is isomorphic to $L_3(q)$.

5. N-GROUPS

We recall that a group G is called an N-group provided each of its local subgroups is solvable. Thompson's remarkable classification theorem asserts the following:

Theorem

A nonabelian simple N-group G is isomorphic to one of the groups of the following list:

   (i) $L_2(q), q > 3$;
   (ii) $Sz(q), q = 2^{2n+1}, n \geqslant 1$; or
   (iii) $A_7, L_3(3), U_3(3), M_{11}$.

Note that (iii) consists of four specific groups, the last one denoting the smallest of the five simple permutation groups on 11, 12, 22, 23, and 24 letters, respectively, discovered by Mathieu; M_{11} is quadruply transitive of order $8 \cdot 9 \cdot 10 \cdot 11$. As usual, this result is a corollary of a more general theorem classifying all nonsolvable N-groups.

In establishing this theorem, Thompson actually obtains important characterizations of two other specific simple groups of rank 2: the groups $E_2(3)$ and $S_4(3)$. However, each of these possesses a nonsolvable 2-local subgroup, so is not an N-group. A fuller discussion of these characterizations will be given below. We note here only that $E_2(3)$ and $S_4(3)$ are members of the respective families $E_2(q)$ and $S_4(q)$, defined for each prime power q. The first of these is the exceptional family discovered by Dickson; it can be realized as the group of automorphisms of the "Cayley numbers" of trace 0 defined over $GF(q)$ and so has a natural representation by 7×7 matrices over $GF(q)$. On the other hand, $S_4(q)$ is the factor group modulo its center of the group of 4×4 matrices of determinant 1 with entries in $GF(q)$ which leave invariant a nondegenerate alternate form in four variables.

The characterization of N-groups constitutes a much broader problem than that of groups with dihedral S_2-subgroups or of C-groups, and its solution would seem to reflect characteristics of much more general classification problems. Indeed, in each of the preceding two problems very strong hypotheses were imposed on the 2-local subgroups—in the first case, we were actually given the S_2-subgroup of G, while in the second the centralizer of every involution was a solvable group with a normal S_2-subgroup. In the case of N-groups no such a priori conditions are given. To begin with at least, our group G may have completely arbitrary S_2-subgroups and the 2-local subgroups may be completely arbitrary solvable groups.

Thompson makes three major subdivisions in the over-all problem, according as $2 \in \pi_2$, π_3, or π_4, respectively. Here if $p \in \pi(G)$, we say

$p \in \pi_1$ if an S_p-subgroup of G is cyclic.

$p \in \pi_2$ if an S_p-subgroup of G is noncyclic, but $SCN_3(p)$ is empty.

$p \in \pi_3$ if $SCN_3(p)$ is nonempty and an S_p-subgroup of G normalizes some nontrivial p'-subgroup of G.

$p \in \pi_4$ if $SCN_3(p)$ is nonempty and an S_p-subgroup of G normalizes no nontrivial p'-subgroup of G.

The identical breakup of $\pi(G)$ was considered in O and D. Clearly $\pi(G) = \pi_1 \cup \pi_2 \cup \pi_3 \cup \pi_4$. In particular, the simplicity of G together with Theorem 7.6.1 implies that $2 \notin \pi_1$. Thus 2 lies in exactly one of the subsets π_2, π_3, or π_4.

In the first case, Thompson proves:

Theorem 1

If G is a nonabelian simple N-group in which $2 \in \pi_2$, then G is isomorphic to one of the following groups:

    (i) $L_2(q), q$ *odd*, $q > 3$.

    (ii) $A_7, L_3(3), U_3(3), M_{11}$.

Most of the analysis is taken up with the task of pinning down the precise possibilities for the S_2-subgroups of G. A result of Glauberman's [2] to the effect that an S_2-subgroup of a simple group cannot possess a weakly closed subgroup of order 2 is of great help in the argument. Glauberman's result relies on modular character theory, but on the basis of it, Thompson is able to proceed by purely local group-theoretic considerations.

Let S be an S_2-subgroup of G. Then the argument yields that S has one of the following four structures:

    (a) S is dihedral;

    (b) S is semi-dihedral of order 16;

    (c) $|S| = 2^6$, S has exactly 3 involutions, each of which lies in $Z(S)$; or

    (d) $|S| = 2^5$, S contains the direct product of two cyclic groups T_i of order 4, $1 \leqslant i \leqslant 2$, and an involution which interchanges T_1 and T_2 under conjugation.

Moreover, in each case G possesses only one conjugate class of involutions.

If (a) holds, then G is isomorphic to $L_2(q)$, q odd, $q > 3$, or to A_7 by D. Suppose (b) holds. Then a further argument shows that $C_G(Z(S)) = SA$, where A is abelian of odd order. But these are the exact conditions under which Wong has characterized $L_3(3)$ and M_{11} (see Section 7). When (c) holds, Thompson argues that two elements of S conjugate in G are already conjugate in $N_G(S)$. Another result of Glauberman's [6] contradicts the simplicity of G. Finally, in case (d), with $N = C_G(\Omega_1(Z(S)))$, it follows easily that $N/O(N)$ is isomorphic to the centralizer of an involution in $U_3(3)$. But now a result of Fong's, which we shall also mention in Section 7, yields that G is isomorphic to $U_3(3)$.

In the π_3 case, Thompson proves

Theorem 2

If G is a simple N-group in which $2 \in \pi_3$, then an S_2-subgroup of G is disjoint from its conjugates.

The proof of this theorem is in the same spirit as the assertion in the dihedral problem that the set of primes σ_4 was empty, but of course it is much more complicated. Assuming the conclusion to be false, a contradiction is ultimately derived from the existence of a strongly embedded subgroup M of G. Difficult problems concerning the nature of the $\{2, p\}$-subgroups of G for $p \geqslant 5$ must be resolved to carry out this analysis. It is an interesting and fortunate fact that the arguments do not require a detailed investigation of the more formidable problem of the $\{2, 3\}$-subgroups of G.

If Theorem 2 is combined with Suzuki's classification of C-groups, we obtain the stronger conclusion that, in fact, $2 \notin \pi_3$, for it is easily checked that no group in Suzuki's list has the property that $2 \in \pi_3$.

We come now to the case $2 \in \pi_4$, which represents approximately three-fourths of the entire paper. The local group-theoretic analysis is almost overwhelming in its complexity and the number of technical difficulties involved in the determination of the structure of the maximal 2-local subgroups reaches staggering proportions. We shall not attempt to present a detailed outline but shall content ourselves with a brief discussion of some salient points. To do this, we need a preliminary concept, which is actually basic for the entire paper.

For odd primes p and q, the relation $p \sim q$ has been defined earlier in terms of the existence of a solvable $\{p, q\}$-subgroup D of G which contains elementary abelian subgroups of both orders p^3 and q^3. A verbatim extension of this definition to the case $q = 2$ turns out to be less satisfactory than a somewhat weaker condition. Indeed, we shall say that $p \sim 2$ (or $2 \sim p$), p odd, provided there exists a solvable $\{p, 2\}$-subgroup D which contains

  (a) A noncyclic abelian 2-subgroup of order 8.

  (b) An element of $T(p)$.

Here $T(p)$ is defined to be the set of elementary abelian subgroups T of G of type (p, p) such that for each x in T^{*}, $C_G(x)$ contains an element of

$U(p)$; and $U(p)$ in turn is defined to be the set of elementary abelian subgroups U of type (p, p) such that U is normal in some S_p-subgroup P of G with $U \subseteq Z(P)$ if $Z(P)$ is noncyclic.

Moreover, if 2 is not related in this fashion to any odd prime, we shall say that 2 is *isolated*.

It is easy to see that an elementary abelian p-group of order p^3 always contains an element of $T(p)$, so this definition is, in fact, weaker than our earlier one. We note also that the assumption $p \sim 2$ implies only that $SCN_2(p)$ and $SCN_2(2)$ are nonempty, whereas the definition for odd p and q requires $SCN_3(p)$ and $SCN_3(q)$ to be nonempty, as follows from Theorem 5.4.15(i). Finally, we remark that the definition of $T(p)$ is very analogous to that of the set $A_3(p)$ which occurs in the statement of the Maximal Subgroup theorem.

In the groups $E_2(3)$ and $S_4(3)$, $3 \sim 2$ in the present sense, but not in the earlier sense, which explains in part why the present definition is more satisfactory for Thompson.

The first major portion of Thompson's argument in the π_4 case can be summarized as follows:

Theorem 3
If G is a simple N-group in which $2 \in \pi_4$, then one of the following holds:
(i) *G is a C-group; or*
(ii) *$2 \sim 3$ and $3 \in \pi_4$.*

The proof of Theorem 3 is itself divided into three main parts, corresponding to the possible values of a certain integer $e(G)$ which we proceed to define. For each odd p, let $e(p)$ be the largest integer n for which there exists an elementary abelian p-subgroup E of G of order p^n which normalizes a nontrivial 2-subgroup of G. Then set

$$e(G) = \max \{e(p) | p \text{ ranging over all odd primes in } \pi(G)\}.$$

Since G is simple, the Frobenius normal p-complement theorem shows that $N_G(T)$ is not a 2-group for some nontrivial 2-subgroup T of G. Hence $e(p) \geqslant 1$ for any odd p dividing $|N_G(T)|$ and so $e(G) \geqslant 1$. Thompson's subdivision corresponds to the three possibilities:
(a) $e(G) \geqslant 3$,
(b) $e(G) = 2$,
(c) $e(G) = 1$.

One should not be too surprised that the treatment of these three subcases is very difficult. Indeed, it is a fact that the known simple groups of characteristic 2 all satisfy $2 \in \pi_4$ [provided $SCN_3(2)$ is nonempty, as is almost always the case]. Assuming Theorem 3 to be false, why cannot G be isomorphic to some other known simple group G^* of characteristic 2? Obviously, because such a group G^* necessarily possesses a nonsolvable local subgroup. Thus in essence Thompson's task is to show that G must contain a nonsolvable local subgroup. But this may be almost as difficult as classifying G^* and may very well require an almost complete determination of the structure of the 2-local subgroups before this nonsolvability can be forced. Phrased somewhat differently, if the hypotheses on the local subgroups were slightly weaker, Thompson's analysis might very well provide the major portion of the argument needed to characterize the group G^*. In fact, it is precisely this that he has done in the case of $E_2(3)$ and $S_4(3)$. By the time he can force a nonsolvable 2-local subgroup to exit in G under the assumption $2 \sim 3$ and $3 \in \pi_4$, he has sufficient knowledge of the subgroup structure of G so that it is about as easy to relax his conditions slightly and to continue the analysis to obtain a characterization of these two groups. Almost certainly then, the proof of Theorem 3 contains a basis for characterizations of other known simple groups, including possibly some of the Mathieu groups.

For convenience, let us call a group G in which $\{2, 3\} \subseteq \pi_4$ and $2 \sim 3$ a *weak N*-group if every 3-local subgroup is solvable, every 2-local subgroup is 2-constrained, and the centralizer of every involution is solvable. Thus we demand solvability of only certain of the 2-local subgroups. The classification of N-groups is completed once the following theorem is established:

Theorem 4

Let G be a simple weak N-group and let P be an S_3-subgroup of G. If $Z(P)$ is noncyclic, then G is isomorphic to $E_2(3)$; if $Z(P)$ is cyclic, then G is isomorphic to $S_4(3)$.

As remarked earlier, $E_2(3)$ and $S_4(3)$ are not N-groups. Hence Theorems 1 to 4, together with Suzuki's classification of C-groups, give a complete determination of all simple N-groups.

A critical portion of the classification of simple C-groups was devoted to the determination of the exact structure of the maximal 2-local subgroups. We recall that for groups of type D, which gave rise to groups of rank 2, the analysis depended upon weak closure arguments. Likewise the proof of Theorem 4 requires a knowledge of the precise structure of the maximal 3-local subgroups, which is again accomplished by weak closure arguments. This analysis forces G to possess a non-3-stable maximal 3-local subgroup (otherwise a contradiction is reached using strongly embedded subgroups).

The problem here is considerably more complicated than that of C-groups of type D, for the analysis now depends upon the interaction of the 2-subgroups and 3-subgroups of G and involves some very delicate configurations of subgroups, whereas in the previous case our attention was essentially limited to the prime 2. Moreover, the present analysis requires a simultaneous determination of the structure of the centralizer of an involution and, in particular, of the S_2-subgroups of G. As in the case of Suzuki's characterization of $L_3(2^n)$, the ultimate objective is to construct a subgroup G_0 of G which is a (B, N)-pair of rank 2. As usual, $B = N_G(P)$, P an S_3-subgroup of G, and $N = N_G(H)$, where H is a complement of H in B. Again the problem is to determine the Weyl group $W = N/H$, which in the case of $E_2(3)$ is a dihedral group of order 12 and in the case of $S_4(3)$ is a dihedral group of order 8. This argument requires all the information concerning the maximal 3-local subgroups and the centralizers of involutions that it is possible to derive by local group-theoretic analysis.

In the process of establishing the fact that BNB is actually a group G_0, a canonical set of generators and relations is constructed for G_0. This means that G_0 is uniquely determined independently of G; more precisely, if G' is any other simple group satisfying the same initial conditions as G and if G_0' is the corresponding subgroup of G', then G_0 and G_0' are isomorphic. Since $E_2(3)$ and $S_4(3)$ can be shown to satisfy the respective hypotheses of the theorem, one is able to conclude that G_0 is isomorphic to $E_2(3)$ or $S_4(3)$, as the case may be. The final step, that $G = G_0$, is carried out in the same way as for C-groups of type D.

We conclude with a few final comments of the over-all proof. In each of the groups $L_2(q)$, $Sz(q)$, $U_3(q)$, and $L_3(q)$, $q = 2^n$, $n \geqslant 3$, it is not difficult to show that not only does $2 \in \pi_4$, but also that 2 is isolated in the sense defined earlier in this section. Thus Thompson's proof, although not so organized, actually establishes the following result:

If G is a simple N-group (or weak N-group), then one of the following holds:

    I. $2 \in \pi_2$;

    II. $2 \in \pi_4$ and 2 is isolated;

    III. $\{2, 3\} \subseteq \pi_4$ and $2 \sim 3$.

Clearly this indicates the importance of classifying all simple groups of type I and II. The known simple groups with these properties are all of low rank, and so these classification problems fall within the scope of the discussion of this chapter. As we have noted above, Thompson's proof of Theorem 3 will undoubtedly have considerable bearing on the study of groups of type II.

6. GROUPS WITH ABELIAN SYLOW 2-SUBGROUPS

In recent years a considerable amount of work has been done towards obtaining a complete classification of simple groups with abelian S_2-subgroups. At this writing, it appears that only a single problem connected with generators and relations remains for this classification to be completed. In this section we present a brief summary of the known results.

Besides the groups $L_2(q)$, $q \equiv 3, 5 \pmod 8$ or $q = 2^n$ with $q > 3$, there is one other infinite family of simple groups, discovered by Ree, and one single exceptional simple group, discovered by Janko, which have abelian S_2-subgroups. Ree constructed his family and also a second infinite family of new simple groups (which does not have abelian S_2-subgroups) shortly after Suzuki's discovery of the groups $Sz(q)$, using a more-or-less well-known procedure for constructing subgroups of known simple groups as the set of fixed elements of certain automorphisms.

Indeed, the unitary groups $GU(3, q)$ can be constructed by just such a process from the groups $GL(3, q^2)$. Let σ be the automorphism of $GL(3, q^2)$ induced from the automorphism of order 2 of $GF(q^2)$ and define a mapping ϕ of $GL(3, q^2)$ into itself by the rule

$$\phi(X) = ((X^\sigma)^t)^{-1} \qquad X \in GL(3, q^2).$$

Then ϕ is an automorphism of $GL(3, q^2)$ and we see that $\phi(X) = X$ if and only if X is a unitary matrix. Thus $GU(3, q)$ is realized as the fixed points of the automorphism ϕ.

This procedure has been studied in general by Steinberg and gives rise to a number of families of finite simple groups, which are known as the "twisted" matrix groups, the unitary groups being the simplest such example. Steinberg's groups are defined in each case for arbitrary values of the parameter $q = p^n$. However, it was known for some time that there were three families of simple matrix groups that possessed an "extra" automorphism for specified values of the characteristic p—$O_4(2^n)$, $E_2(3^n)$, and $F_4(2^n)$—where $O_4(q)$ and $F_4(q)$ are two well-defined families of matrix groups which we shall describe somewhat more explicitly in Chapter 17.

Ree observed that from Suzuki's description of them the groups $Sz(2^n)$

could be alternatively constructed as the fixed points of the extra auto-morphism of $O_4(2^n)$. He then investigated the extra automorphisms of $E_2(3^n)$ and $F_4(2^n)$ and found that their fixed points gave rise to two new families of simple groups, of ranks 1 and 2, respectively, which we shall denote by $R_1(3^n)$ and $R_2(2^n)$. Here n must be odd and at least 3 to obtain simple groups. For $n = 1$, $R_1(3)$ contains a normal subgroup of index 3 isomorphic to $L_2(8)$, while $R_2(2)$ contains a normal subgroup of index 2 which is also a new simple group.

For our purposes the critical fact about the groups $R_1(q)$ is that they have elementary abelian S_2-subgroups of order 8. Moreover, they can be realized as doubly transitive groups of degree $q^3 + 1$ in which the subgroup N fixing a letter is the semidirect product of an S_3-subgroup P of order q^3 which is disjoint from its conjugates and a cyclic subgroup H of order $q - 1$ which is a subgroup fixing two letters. In addition, H possesses a subgroup H_0 of index 2 such that $H_0 P$ is a Frobenius group and so a subgroup fixing three letters is of order 2. Thus the groups $R_1(q)$ closely resemble both the groups $Sz(q)$ and $U_3(q)$. However, they present an added difficulty because P has class 3, whereas in the latter two families the corre-sponding Sylow subgroups have class 2.

If x is an involution of $R_1(q)$ (all involutions are, in fact, conjugate), then the centralizer of x has the form $\langle x \rangle \times L$, where L is isomorphic to $L_2(q)$. In particular, we see that for $q > 3$, $R_1(q)$ is neither a C-group nor an N-group. Given this structure of the centralizer, it is natural to consider the following classification problem:

Determine all simple groups G in which

   (a) S_2-subgroups are elementary abelian of order 8; and
   (b) For any involution x, $C_G(x) = \langle x \rangle \times L$, where L is isomorphic to $L_2(q)$, $q > 3$.

We do not assume here to begin with that q is a power of 3. However, condition (a), together with the fact that $L_2(4)$ and $L_2(5)$ are isomorphic forces $q \equiv 3, 5 \pmod 8$.

H. N. Ward was the first one to investigate this situation. He imposed certain additional restrictions on the centralizers of the elements of odd order in L. In particular, we note that his conditions directly forced $q > 5$. On the basis of his assumptions, he was able to prove, using almost exclusively character-theoretic methods, that $q = 3^n$, $n > 1$, and that G had to be a doubly transitive group satisfying all the conditions which we have listed above for $R_1(q)$. This clearly represented a major step in obtain-ing a characterization of the groups $R_1(q)$ from purely local group-theoretic conditions. Janko and Thompson considered the general situation and, under the assumption that $q > 5$, they have shown that Ward's hypothesis can be deduced from conditions (a) and (b) above. The argument involves both local group-theoretic and character-theoretic analysis.

The case $q = 5$ turns out to be a fascinating exception. Indeed, Janko has established that there exists a unique simple group which satisfies conditions (a) and (b) with $q = 5$, its order being 175,560. In a remarkable paper he proves that the two matrices

(6.1)

$$
\begin{pmatrix}
0 & 1 & 0 & 0 & 0 & 0 & 0 \\
0 & 0 & 1 & 0 & 0 & 0 & 0 \\
0 & 0 & 0 & 1 & 0 & 0 & 0 \\
0 & 0 & 0 & 0 & 1 & 0 & 0 \\
0 & 0 & 0 & 0 & 0 & 1 & 0 \\
0 & 0 & 0 & 0 & 0 & 0 & 1 \\
1 & 0 & 0 & 0 & 0 & 0 & 0
\end{pmatrix}
\quad \text{and} \quad
\begin{pmatrix}
-3 & 2 & -1 & -1 & -3 & -1 & -3 \\
-2 & 1 & 1 & 3 & 1 & 3 & 3 \\
-1 & -1 & -3 & -1 & -3 & -3 & 2 \\
-1 & -3 & -1 & -3 & -3 & 2 & -1 \\
-3 & -1 & -3 & -3 & 2 & -1 & -1 \\
1 & 3 & 3 & -2 & 1 & 1 & 3 \\
3 & 3 & -2 & 1 & 1 & 3 & 1
\end{pmatrix}
$$

with entries in $GF(11)$ generate this simple group, which we denote by $J(11)$. The calculation which establishes that these two matrices generate a group of the required order 175,560 is not at all easy and is due to M. A. Ward. We remark that $J(11)$ has no doubly transitive permutation representations. Moreover, W. A. Coppel has shown that $J(11)$ is a subgroup of $E_2(11)$.

The bulk of Janko's paper consists of the investigation of an arbitrary group G satisfying (a) and (b) with $q = 5$. Although some local group-theoretic analysis enters, his primary task is character-theoretic. Ultimately he obtains complete information concerning the order, subgroup structure, conjugacy classes, and irreducible characters of such a group G; in particular, he shows that G must be simple. With these results at his disposal, he analyzes the p-modular characters of G for the prime $p = 11$ and derives the fundamental fact that G possesses one and only one absolutely irreducible representation of degree 7 in a finite field of characteristic 11 and that it can be written in the prime field $GF(11)$. It is this crucial result which is used to prove the uniqueness of G and at the same time to arrive at the matrices (6.1) as a possible set of generators for G.

Indeed, G turns out to have a generalized Bruhat structure, which may be described as follows. If $B = N_G(S)$, S an S_2-subgroup of G, then $B = HS$, where H is a Frobenius group with kernel Y of order 7 and complement U of order 3. Also $C_S(U) = \langle x \rangle$ has order 2. Moreover,

$N_G(H)$ contains an involution w which centralizes U, inverts Y, and together with x satisfies the structure identity

$$(6.2) \qquad\qquad (xw)^5 = 1.$$

Finally $G = \langle y, xw \rangle$, where $Y = \langle y \rangle$.

Now Janko considers the seven-dimensional representation of G on a vector space V over $GF(11)$, choosing the basis so that y is represented by the first matrix of (6.1). But then a computational argument, using (6.2), together with the fact that w is an involution normalizing H, shows that xw must be represented by the second matrix of (6.1). In this way Janko is able to conclude that G is necessarily isomorphic to $J(11)$.

Returning to the general discussion let us for convenience say that a group G is of *Ree type* if G is doubly transitive of degree $q^3 + 1$ and satisfies all the conditions listed above for $R_1(q)$. Then the combined work of Janko, Thompson, and H. N. Ward can be summarized as follows:

Theorem

If G is a simple group which satisfies conditions (a) *and* (b) *above, then either G is of Ree type or G is isomorphic to $J(11)$.*

Presumably the groups $R_1(q)$ are the only simple groups of Ree type, but this is not yet known. Thompson has shown that in a group G of Ree type, the structure of $B = N_G(P)$, P an S_3-subgroup of G, can be uniquely described in terms of the integer q together with an automorphism θ of $GF(q)$. In $R_1(q)$ itself, this automorphism satisfies the condition $\theta^2 = 3$. As in the case of $L_2(q)$, $Sz(q)$, and $U_3(q)$, the multiplication table of a group of Ree type is completely determined by three analogous functions α, β, and γ defined on $P^\#$.

The problem that still remains to show that the groups $R_1(q)$ are the only simple groups of Ree type is to prove that α, β, γ, and θ are uniquely determined for a given value of q. Because P has class 3, the required generator-relations computations are very difficult to carry out, and it appears that the expressions for α, β, and γ are unbelievably involved. In fact, even in the groups $R_1(q)$ themselves, using Ree's description of them, it does not seem to be an easy task to compute these functions. Thompson has made considerable progress (unpublished), but as of this writing a complete solution does not exist. If one could show, as in Janko's case, that G must possess a seven-dimensional representation over $GF(q)$ [which is true of $R_1(q)$], one could undoubtedly obtain the desired conclusions along the same lines as Janko; but unfortunately this also appears to be very difficult to establish.

By making special assumptions one can avoid the Ree groups and can obtain characterizations of the groups $L_2(q)$. For example, we have

Theorem

Let G be a nonabelian simple group with abelian S_2-subgroups in which $SCN_3(2)$ is empty. Then G is isomorphic to $L_2(q)$, $q \equiv 3, 5 \,(\text{mod } 8)$ and $q > 3$.

Under these assumptions Brauer has shown, using the techniques of modular character theory, that an S_2-subgroup of G must be elementary abelian of order 4 and so must be dihedral. But then the theorem follows from D.

Furthermore, the author has obtained the following result:

Theorem

Let G be a nonabelian simple group with abelian S_2-subgroups in which the centralizer of every involution is solvable. Then G is isomorphic to $L_2(q)$, $q > 3$, with either $q \equiv 3, 5 \,(\text{mod } 8)$ or $q = 2^n$.

The proof of this result amounts to a simpler version of the proof of Theorem 2 of the section on N-groups, its aim being to show, when $SCN_3(S)$ is nonempty, S an S_2-subgroup of G, that S is disjoint from its conjugates, in which case Suzuki's classification of C-groups can be invoked to complete the proof. Let σ be the set of odd primes p in $\pi(G)$ such that S normalizes, but does not centralize, some p-subgroup of G. The disjointness of S from its conjugates follows directly if σ is empty. If σ is nonempty, one ultimately derives a contradiction by constructing a strongly embedded subgroup in G and applying a variation of Theorem 9.3.1.

At first glance it might seem that the last theorem represents a significant step toward a general classification of groups with abelian S_2-subgroups, but, in fact, its hypothesis is designed specifically to avoid the central difficulty of the general problem. How does one handle non-p-constrained p-local subgroups? In all the classification problems discussed so far, the critical p-local subgroups involved in the local group-theoretic analysis related to the Maximal Subgroup theorem, and to the existence of strongly embedded subgroups have always been p-constrained. However, this has been entirely a consequence of the restrictions which our induction assumptions placed upon the structure of the p-local subgroups and will no longer be true in more general classification problems. The abelian S_2-subgroup problem is the first case in which this difficulty must be faced head on.

J. H. Walter has been studying this problem for a considerable period of time and has recently announced the following fundamental result:

Theorem

   If G is a nonabelian simple group with abelian S_2-subgroups, then one of the following hold:
   (i) *G is isomorphic to $L_2(q)$, $q > 3$, $q \equiv 3$, 5 (mod 8) or $q = 2^n$;*
   (ii) *G is isomorphic to $J(11)$; or*
   (iii) *G is of Ree type.*

It is very interesting that for the purposes of the proof of this theorem, Walter does not need to know that the groups $R_1(q)$ are the only ones of Ree type. The point is that a subgroup of G of Ree type is almost as easy to work with as $R_1(q)$ itself.

As usual, this theorem comes as a corollary of a more general result. To state it, let us call a group H an *A-group* provided H contains a normal subgroup K with $O(H) \subseteq K$ such that
   (a) H/K has odd order, and
   (b) $K/O(H)$ is the direct product of a 2-group and a finite number of simple groups of types (i), (ii), and (iii) above.

Walter's main result asserts that every group with abelian S_2-subgroups is an *A*-group. By induction the problem reduces to the study of a simple group G all of whose proper subgroups are *A*-groups, and one must show that G has the structure of one of the groups listed in the preceding theorem. The aim of the argument is to show that one of the following three statements must hold:
   A. $SCN_3(S)$ is empty,
   B. S is disjoint from its conjugates, or
   C. S is elementary abelian of order 8 and for any x in $S^\#$,

$$C_G(x) = \langle x \rangle \times L,$$

where L is isomorphic to $L_2(q)$, $q > 3$, $q \equiv 3$, 5 (mod 8).

The desired conclusion concerning the structure of G follows from this together with earlier results.

Assuming that neither A, B, nor C hold, one considers the same set of odd primes σ as in the special case in which centralizers of involutions were assumed solvable which we discussed above. Again σ is nonempty, since otherwise B would hold, and again the object is to derive a contradiction by constructing a strongly embedded subgroup in G. But now the local subgroups may involve the direct product of arbitrarily many simple groups. This is in sharp contrast to the dihedral problem, where each local subgroup could possess at most one nonsolvable composition factor. This fact made it easy for us to subdivide σ effectively and to concentrate first on eliminating the subsets σ_3 and σ_4. Primarily we were able to carry this out because the p-local subgroups were both p-constrained and p-stable. Even though the p-local subgroups for p in σ_2 did not have to be p-constrained, we were not forced to deal with them until after we had shown that σ_3 and σ_4 were empty. In the abelian S_2-subgroup problem, on the other hand, non-p-constrained p-local subgroups must be considered right from the beginning. The essential problem is how does one control the weak closure of certain p-subgroups in the absence of p-constraint? For one thing one can at best hope to establish some weaker form of the transitivity theorem1 and this alone adds a serious complication to the situation. Fortunately A-groups are at least p-stable for all odd p; for as we have pointed out in the discussion on N-groups, the lack of p-stability also gives rise to formidable problems. Thus one can anticipate some major difficulties in more general classification problems when the p-local subgroups need be neither p-constrained nor p-stable.

7. OTHER CLASSIFICATION THEOREMS

Work has only just begun on groups with semi-dihedral S_2-subgroups and with one other closely related family of S_2-subgroups, which for brevity we shall refer to as *wreathed* groups. A 2-group S will be said to be wreathed if it contains the direct product of two cyclic groups T_i of order 2^n, $n \geqslant 2$, $1 \leqslant i \leqslant 2$, as a subgroup of index 2 and possesses an involution which interchanges T_1 and T_2 under conjugation. In terms of the general notion of a wreathed product, S is thus the wreathed product of a cyclic group of order 2^n and a group of order 2. Note that $SCN_3(S)$ is empty if S is wreathed.

These two families of 2-groups are important because they occur as S_2-subgroups of the following known simple groups:
   (a) The S_2-subgroups of $L_3(q)$ are semi-dihedral if $q \equiv -1 \pmod 4$ and are wreathed if $q \equiv 1 \pmod 4$.

(b) The S_2-subgroups of $U_3(q)$ are semi-dihedral if $q \equiv 1 \pmod 4$ and are wreathed if $q \equiv -1 \pmod 4$.

(c) The S_2-subgroups of the Mathieu group M_{11} on 11 letters are semi-dihedral of order 16.

We note also that an S_2-subgroup of $GL(2, q)$ is semi-dihedral if $q \equiv -1 \pmod 4$ and is wreathed if $q \equiv 1 \pmod 4$.

Characterizations of the groups $L_3(q)$, q odd, and M_{11} have been obtained by Brauer:

Theorem

Let G be a simple group which contains an involution x such that $C_G(x)$ is isomorphic to $GL(2, q)/K$, q odd, where K is a normal subgroup of $GL(2, q)$ of odd order. Then one of the following holds:

(i) *G is isomorphic to $L_3(q)$, or*

(ii) *$q = 3$ and G is isomorphic to M_{11}.*

Moreover, $K = 1$ if $q \equiv -1 \pmod 3$ and $|K| = 3$ if $q \equiv 1 \pmod 3$.

Here we have hypotheses analogous to those of the Brauer-Suzuki-Wall theorem: The centralizer of an involution in G is assumed to satisfy conditions similar to those which hold in the known groups that one wishes to characterize. As usual, character-theoretic methods are used to show that G is doubly transitive with the appropriate generalized Bruhat structure. One of Brauer's methods of completing the proof is geometric: He constructs a Désarguesian projective plane over $GF(q)$ out of the group G, on which G acts as a group of collineations (the case M_{11} is, of course, exceptional). The (B, N)-pair approach can also be used.

Most likely a corresponding characterization of $U_3(q)$ can also be obtained. However, the final generator-relation problem that one encounters when $q \equiv -1 \pmod 3$ appears to be quite difficult. Suzuki has solved this problem only in the case of $PGU(3, q)$ [which contains $U_3(q)$ as a subgroup of index 3 when $q \equiv -1 \pmod 3$]. Suzuki's result is the following:

Theorem

Let G be a doubly transitive permutation group of degree $q^3 + 1$, $q = p^n$, p an odd prime, such that the subgroup N fixing a letter is the semidirect product of an S_p-subgroup P of G of order q^3 which is disjoint from its conjugates and a cyclic subgroup H of order $q^2 - 1$ which fixes two letters. Then G is isomorphic to $PGU(3, q)$.

It is interesting to note that when $p = 2$ and $q \equiv -1 \pmod 3$, Suzuki was able to resolve the corresponding generator-relation problem and hence was able to obtain a characterization of the groups $U_3(2^n)$ for all values of n.

In addition to these results, there are a few other characterization theorems involving groups of low rank:

1. As remarked in Section 14.4, the combined work of Zassenhaus, Feit, Suzuki, and Ito establishes that the groups $L_2(q)$, $q > 3$, and $Sz(q)$ are the only simple Zassenhaus groups.

2. Wong has shown that $L_3(3)$ and M_{11} are the only simple groups having semi-dihedral S_2-subgroups in which the centralizers of involutions are solvable.

3. Fong has shown that $U_3(3)$ is the only simple group having a wreathed S_2-subgroup of order 2^5 in which centralizers of involutions are solvable.

4. Brauer and Fong have obtained a characterization of M_{12} as the only simple group having an S_2-subgroup isomorphic to that of M_{12} and possessing more than one class of involutions. The proof utilizes an earlier result of Stanton, who showed that M_{12} is the only simple group of order 95,040.

5. The combined works of Wong and Held give characterizations of the alternating groups A_8 and A_9 in terms of conditions on the centralizers of involutions.

6. Fong and the author have obtained preliminary characterizations of the groups $E_2(q)$, q odd, for certain congruences on q.

8. SOME OPEN PROBLEMS

The foregoing survey should indicate the state of our knowledge of the simple groups of low rank at the present time. It seems appropriate to conclude this chapter with a list of a number of questions that still remain to be answered. We shall phrase each solely in terms of simple groups, but in most instances a classification of all groups satisfying the given condition would be required to be able to proceed by induction.

1. Characterize the Ree groups of characteristic 3 as doubly transitive permutation groups.

2. Characterize the groups $U_3(q)$, q odd, $q \equiv -1 \pmod 3$, as doubly transitive permutation groups.

3. Determine all simple groups with semi-dihedral or wreathed Sylow 2-subgroups.

4. Determine all simple groups in which $SCN_3(2)$ is empty. Apart from

A_7 and M_{11}, there appear to be eight distinct infinite families of known simple groups of Lie type of odd characteristic q satisfying this condition. In addition to those with dihedral, semi-dihedral, or wreathed S_2-subgroups, there are $L_4(q)$, $q \not\equiv 1 \pmod 8$, $U_4(q)$, $q \not\equiv 1 \pmod 8$, $S_4(q)$, $q \equiv \pm 1 \pmod 8$, $E_2(q)$, $q \equiv -1 \pmod 8$, and the "triality twisted $D_4(q)$" with $q \equiv \pm 1 \pmod 8$.

5. Determine all simple groups whose orders are not divisible by 3. The Suzuki groups are the only known groups with this property.

6. Determine all simple groups whose orders are divisible by exactly three distinct primes. Thompson's results on minimal simple groups imply that these three primes must be either $\{2, 3, 5\}$, $\{2, 3, 7\}$, $\{2, 3, 13\}$ or $\{2, 3, 17\}$. The only known simple groups with this property are $L_2(q)$ with $q = 5, 7, 8, 9$, or 17, $L_3(3)$, and the group $U_3(2)$ [which is also isomorphic to $S_4(3)$].

7. Determine all simple groups in which $2 \in \pi_4$ and 2 is isolated. The Mathieu groups M_{12}, M_{22}, M_{23}, and M_{24} all appear to satisfy these conditions.

8. Determine all simple groups in which the centralizer of every involution is solvable. Unfortunately this condition is not inductive; hence either one would have to impose some reasonable assumption on the proper subgroups of the given simple group or else strengthen the condition slightly in order to have an inductive hypothesis.

9. Finally, there is the general problem mentioned in the introduction of the chapter: Determine all simple groups in which the nonsolvable composition factors of any local subgroup lie in the family $L_2(q)$. (Obviously one can modify this condition by allowing other simple groups of rank 1 as composition factors.)

CHAPTER 17

REMARKS ON
CLASSIFICATION OF SIMPLE GROUPS

We should like to conclude our expository account on simple groups with a few comments on classification problems in general. First, in the course of Chapter 16 we mentioned all the known simple groups of rank 1 as well as some of those of higher rank. To put that discussion in proper perspective, it will be useful to present a complete list of the known simple groups. After doing this, we shall define the term "general classification problem" and shall discuss possible generalizations of some of the concepts and results we have considered in connection with groups of low rank, especially with the classification of N-groups.

1. THE FAMILIES OF KNOWN SIMPLE GROUPS

Unfortunately there have developed over the years several notational conventions for listing the simple groups, no one of which is entirely satisfactory. When presenting a complete list, it is perhaps most convenient to follow the Lie notation. As Chevalley has shown, each of the so-called families of matrix groups is associated with one of the complex simple Lie algebras A_n, B_n, C_n, D_n, G_2, F_4, E_6, E_7, and E_8 of rank n. (Do not confuse A_n here with the corresponding alternating group.) We shall therefore adopt the notation $A_n(q)$, etc., for the corresponding finite group defined relative to $GF(q)$. For example, $A_n(q) = SL(n + 1, q)$. We shall also write $^2A_n(q)$ for the unitary group $SU(n + 1, q)$. Here the superscript is meant to indicate the order of the automorphism of the Dynkin diagram of A_n relative to which the unitary group is defined. A similar convention will apply to the other twisted matrix groups. Furthermore, the groups we list may not be simple; the integer d in the table below will designate the order of the central subgroup that must be factored out to obtain a simple group. At the end of the table we shall indicate the correspondence with our earlier notation.

Known Finite Simple Groups

G	order of G	d
$A_n(q)$	$q^{n(n+1)/2} \prod_{i=1}^{n} (q^{i+1} - 1)$	$(n+1, q-1)$
$B_n(q), n > 1$	$q^{n^2} \prod_{i=1}^{n}(q^{2i} - 1)$	$(2, q-1)$
$C_n(q), n > 2$	$q^{n^2} \prod_{i=1}^{n}(q^{2i} - 1)$	$(2, q-1)$
$D_n(q), n > 3$	$q^{n(n-1)}(q^n - 1) \prod_{i=1}^{n-1}(q^{2i} - 1)$	$(4, q^n - 1)$
$G_2(q)$	$q^6(q^6 - 1)(q^2 - 1)$	1
$F_4(q)$	$q^{24}(q^{12} - 1)(q^8 - 1)(q^6 - 1)(q^2 - 1)$	1
$E_6(q)$	$q^{36}(q^{12} - 1)(q^9 - 1)(q^8 - 1)(q^6 - 1)(q^5 - 1)(q^2 - 1)$	$(3, q-1)$
$E_7(q)$	$q^{63}(q^{18} - 1)(q^{14} - 1)(q^{12} - 1)(q^{10} - 1)(q^8 - 1)(q^6 - 1)(q^2 - 1)$	$(2, q-1)$
$E_8(q)$	$q^{120}(q^{30} - 1)(q^{24} - 1)(q^{20} - 1)(q^{18} - 1)$ $(q^{14} - 1)(q^{12} - 1)(q^8 - 1)(q^2 - 1)$	1
$^2A_n(q), n > 1$	$q^{n(n+1)/2} \prod_{i=1}^{n}(q^{i+1} - (-1)^{i+1})$	$(n+1, q+1)$
$^2B_2(q), q = 2^{2m+1}$	$q^2(q^2 + 1)(q - 1)$	1
$^2D_n(q), n > 3$	$q^{n(n-1)}(q^n + 1) \prod_{i=1}^{n-1}(q^{2i} - 1)$	$(4, q^n + 1)$
$^3D_4(q)$	$q^{12}(q^8 + q^4 + 1)(q^6 - 1)(q^2 - 1)$	1
$^2G_2(q), q = 3^{2m+1}$	$q^3(q^3 + 1)(q - 1)$	1
$^2F_4(q), q = 2^{2m+1}$	$q^{12}(q^6 + 1)(q^4 - 1)(q^3 + 1)(q - 1)$	1
$^2E_6(q)$	$q^{36}(q^{12} - 1)(q^9 + 1)(q^8 - 1)(q^6 - 1)(q^5 + 1)(q^2 - 1)$	$(3, q+1)$

Known Finite Simple Groups

G	order of G	d
Z_p	p	1
Alternating group $\mathscr{A}_n$, $n > 2$	$\frac{1}{2}(n!)$	1
M_{11}	$7920 = 2^4 \cdot 3^2 \cdot 5 \cdot 11$	1
M_{12}	$95040 = 2^6 \cdot 3^3 \cdot 5 \cdot 11$	1
M_{22}	$443520 = 2^7 \cdot 3^2 \cdot 5 \cdot 7 \cdot 11$	1
M_{23}	$10200960 = 2^7 \cdot 3^2 \cdot 5 \cdot 7 \cdot 11 \cdot 23$	1
M_{24}	$244823040 = 2^{10} \cdot 3^3 \cdot 5 \cdot 7 \cdot 11 \cdot 23$	1
$J(11)^{(*)}$	$175560 = 2^3 \cdot 3 \cdot 5 \cdot 7 \cdot 11 \cdot 19$	1

Comparison with Previous Notation

$$A_n(q) = SL(n+1, q), \ C_n(q)/Z(C_n(q)) = S_{2n}(q), \ B_n(q) = O_{2n}(q), \ G_2(q) = E_2(q),$$
$$^2A_n(q) = SU(n+1, q), \ ^2B_2(q) = Sz(q), \ ^2G_2(q) = R_1(q), \ ^2F_4(q) = R_2(q)$$

Exceptions

G	Nature of exception
$\mathscr{A}_n$, $n = 3, 4$	G is solvable
$A_1(q)$, $q = 2, 3$	G is solvable
$B_2(2)$	G is isomorphic to symmetric group S_6
$G_2(2)$	$\|G : G'\| = 2$ and G' is isomorphic to $^2A_2(3)$
$^2A_2(2)$	G is solvable
$^2B_2(2)$	G is solvable
$^2G_2(3)$	$\|G : G'\| = 3$ and G' is isomorphic to $A_1(8)$
$^2F_4(2)$	$\|G : G'\| = 2$ and G' is a simple group not appearing elsewhere in the table

The types B_1, C_1, C_2, D_1, D_2, D_3, $^2D_2$, and $^2D_3$ have been excluded from the table inasmuch as they are isomorphic to other groups:

$$C_1 \cong B_1 \cong A_1 \qquad C_2 \cong B_2 \qquad D_1(q) \cong Z_{q-1}$$

$$D_2 \cong A_1 \times A_1 \qquad D_3 \cong A_3 \qquad {}^2D_2(q) \cong A_1(q^2)$$

$$^2D_3 \cong {}^2A_3$$

Finally there are some isomorphisms which exist among the group

(*)Added in proof: Two new simple groups have just been discovered, the first by M. Hall and Janko and the second by D. Higman and Sims. Both are transitive permutation groups of degree 100 (and rank 3), in which the subgroups fixing a letter are respectively isomorphic to $U_3(3)$ and M_{22}. The first one arose in the study of groups that contain an involution whose centralizer is isomorphic to a split extension of an extra-special group of order 2^5 by $\mathscr{A}_5$; its permutation representation then led to the discovery of the second.

listed. We shall write G^* for $G/Z(G)$:

$$A_1(2) \cong S_3 \qquad\qquad A_1(9)^* \cong \mathscr{A}_6$$

$$A_1(4) \cong A_1(5)^* \cong \mathscr{A}_5 \qquad A_3(2) \cong \mathscr{A}_8$$

$$A_1(7)^* \cong A_2(2) \qquad\qquad {}^2A_3(2) \cong B_2(3)^*$$

We should like also to describe explicitly the Bruhat decomposition [equivalently the (B, N)-pair] structure of the groups of Lie type. To do this, we need a preliminary definition.

A group W will be said to be a *Coxeter group* or to be *generated by reflections* provided:

(1) W is generated by distinct involutions w_i, $1 \leqslant i \leqslant t$.

(2) If $w_i w_j$ has order k_{ij}, then the relations

$$(w_i w_j)^{k_{ij}} = 1 \qquad 1 \leqslant i, j \leqslant t$$

are a complete set of defining relations for W.

For example, the symmetric group S_{t+1} is generated by the transpositions $w_i = (i, i+1)$, $1 \leqslant i \leqslant t$, which satisfy the relations $(w_i w_j)^{k_{ij}} = 1$, where $k_{ii} = 1$, $k_{ii+1} = 3$, and $k_{ij} = 2$ if $j \geqslant i+2$. Moreover, these are a complete set of defining relations for S_{t+1}, in the sense that any other relation satisfied by the generators w_i is a consequence of these relations. Note also that $|W| = 2$ if $t = 1$ and that W is a dihedral group if $t = 2$.

The integer t is called the *rank* of W. We shall call the involutions w_i a *defining set* for W.

Now let $G = G(q)$ be a group of Lie type from the above list with $q = p^r$, p a prime. Let P be an S_p-subgroup of G, set $B = N_G(P)$, and let H be a complement of P in B. Then there exists a subgroup N of G with the following properties:

(1) $B \cap N = H \lhd N$ and $W = N/H$ is a group generated by reflections.

(2) $G = \bigcup_{u \in N} BuB$; equivalently $G = BNB$.

(3) Let w_i, $1 \leqslant i \leqslant t$, be a defining set for W and let u_i be a representative of w_i in N. Then for each u in N and all i, $1 \leqslant i \leqslant t$, we have

$$BuBu_i B \subseteq (BuB) \cup (Buu_i B).$$

(4) $B^{u_i} \neq B$, $1 \leqslant i \leqslant t$.

It is not difficult to see that (3) implies (2). The integer t is also called the *rank* of G, the group W is called the *Weyl* group of G, and B is called a *Borel* subgroup of G. In the case of the nontwisted groups of Lie type the subscript indicates the rank: $A_n(q)$ has rank n. In fact, its Weyl group is isomorphic to S_{n+1}. The twisted groups have the following ranks: $^2A_{2n}$ has rank n, $^2A_{2n-1}$ has rank n, $^2B_2$ has rank 1, ^2D_n has rank $n - 1$, $^3D_4$ has rank 2; $^2G_2$ has rank 1, $^2F_4$ has rank 2, and $^2E_6$ has rank 4.

Finally, the subgroup H is called a *Cartan* subgroup of G and is always abelian. Moreover, if $G = G(q)$ is nontwisted of rank t, then H is the direct product of t cyclic groups of order $q - 1$ [each thus being isomorphic to the multiplicative group of $GF(q)$]. The exact structure of P, H, B, and W is known for all the groups of Lie type, but we shall not attempt to list them.

It is also possible to introduce a workable definition of the rank of $\mathscr{A}_n$ and the six exceptional groups. For example, since $\mathscr{A}_7$ and $J(11)$ arise as exceptional cases within a rank 1 problem, it is reasonable to assign them a rank of 1. Similarly, as M_{11} occurs as an exception in a rank 2 problem, it may be given a rank of 2.

2. GENERAL CLASSIFICATION PROBLEMS

We shall call a group a *K-group* if each of its composition factors appears in the list of known simple groups given in the preceding section. In this terminology each of the classification problems discussed in Chapter 16 dealt with a simple group G, all (or some) of whose local subgroups were K-groups of some restricted type. More generally, any problem involving the determination of all simple groups G whose local subgroups are all members of some specified family $\mathscr{F}$ of K-groups will be called a *general classification problem*.

As we have seen, many classification problems, not initially stated in these terms, reduce by induction to general classification problems. An objection may be raised to the definition of a K-group and by implication to that of a general classification problem since these concepts appear to depend upon time. For clearly any new simple group discovered in the future will enlarge the family of K-groups. This criticism is, however, a superficial one, for there appears to be no more effective way of studying simple groups than by means of assumptions of this type on the proper subgroups. Moreover, it actually provides a significant way of discovering new simple groups. Indeed, both the groups $Sz(q)$ and $J(11)$ arose organically out of particular configurations of subgroups within just such a general classification problem. Although it might be argued that Suzuki's groups could also have been discovered by means of the Lie theory, no such claim can be made for Janko's group. Furthermore, the procedure for constructing new twisted simple groups from known groups by means of automorphisms has been exhausted. Conceivably there are other as yet unknown algebraic or geometric processes for constructing new simple groups, but we emphasize in the meantime that among these undiscovered simple groups (if any) that one G_0 of least order necessarily has local subgroups that are all K-groups. Should these subgroups lie in the family $\mathscr{F}$ under consideration in a given problem, then any results we might establish would, in effect, represent properties of the unknown group G_0.

Obviously the broader the family $\mathscr{F}$, the wider will be the list of simple groups that our problem embraces. The ultimate general classification problem is, of course, that in which $\mathscr{F}$ consists of all K-groups, and the ultimate question is: Must G then be a K-group? If true, the list in the preceding section includes all simple groups.

It is natural to wonder how effective the concepts and techniques that worked for the study of groups of low rank will be for the classification of groups of higher rank. It is not unreasonable to hope that with suitable modifications they can be adapted to these more difficult problems. Thus one may first ask what the objective might be of the initial local group-theoretic analysis. The entire discussion of Chapter 16 points unmistakenly toward the kind of subdivision that occurs in the classification of N-groups and which is summarized in the final paragraph of Section 16.6.

The concepts which enter into that summary are π_2, π_4, and $\sim$ (isolation being defined in terms of $\sim$). In particular, it includes the statement that either $2 \in \pi_2$ or $2 \in \pi_4$; in other words, if $SCN_3(2)$ is nonempty in a simple N-group, then an S_2-subgroup normalizes no nontrivial subgroups of odd order. We cannot expect to establish the identical result in more general problems, since $2 \in \pi_3$ in many of the known simple groups. However, there do appear to be possible modifications of the concept of π_4 under which it becomes a universal property of the known simple groups. We should like to discuss briefly some of the factors that must be taken into account in formulating the appropriate generalization.

To begin with, there are two critical points to be made concerning our present definition of π_4. First, our subdivision of $\pi(G)$ had a certain degree of arbitrariness, for we could just as well have defined π_4 as the set of primes p in $\pi(G)$ such that $SCN_3(p)$ is nonempty and an S_p-subgroup of G centralizes every p'-subgroup that it normalizes. No significant changes in the arguments result from this weaker definition of π_4. Second, our definition was made without reference to p-local subgroups of G. The following typical example shows the significance of these two points.

Consider $G = L_n(q)$, q odd, n odd, $n \geq 5$. Then $SCN_3(2)$ is nonempty. We study the subgroups of odd order normalized by an S_2-subgroup S of G. We may choose S to consist of the images of matrices of the form $\begin{pmatrix} A & 0 \\ 0 & \lambda \end{pmatrix}$ in $SL(n, q)$, where A is $(n-1) \times (n-1)$ and $\lambda \in GF(q)$. Then S normalizes the elementary abelian group Q of order q^{n-1} which consists of the images of the matrices $\begin{pmatrix} I & 0 \\ B & 1 \end{pmatrix}$, where B is $1 \times (n-1)$. Moreover, the central involution x of S, represented by the matrix $\begin{pmatrix} -I & 0 \\ 0 & 1 \end{pmatrix}$ inverts Q, so that, in particular, S does not centralize Q. Hence certainly $2 \in \pi_3$ in our original definition. On the other hand, if we limit ourselves to 2-local subgroups H containing S, then S centralizes $O(H)$. For example, if $H = C_G(x)$, then H is isomorphic to $GL(n-1, q)$, and $O(H)$ consists of the scalar matrices in $GL(n-1, q)$, whence $O(H) \subseteq Z(H)$. Clearly $O(H)$ need not be 1 and so the weaker condition seems to be more appropriate.

Unfortunately this centralizing condition in the p-local subgroups is itself inadequate. Indeed, in $\mathcal{A}_n$ with $n \equiv 3 \pmod 4$, $n \geq 10$, we have $SCN_3(2)$ nonempty, yet there exists a 2-local subgroup H containing an S_2-subgroup S of $\mathcal{A}_n$ such that $O(H)$ does not centralize S. In fact, $|O(H)| = 3$ and $|H : C_H(O(H))| = 2$. [Here $H = N_{\mathcal{A}_n}(X)$, where $X = \langle x_1, x_2, \ldots, x_k \rangle$, $k = \frac{1}{4}(n-3)$, and $x_i = (4i-3, 4i-2)(4i-1, 4i)$.] However, this is not a serious objection, for one would presumably be satisfied with a condition of the form $H/C_H(O(H))$ being cyclic.

A more serious problem occurs in $G = E_2(q)$ with $q \equiv -1 \pmod 4$. Let H be a Cartan subgroup of G and let N be the usual subgroup of G such that $N/H = W$ is the Weyl group of G. Then H is the direct product of two cyclic groups of order $q-1$ and N/H is dihedral of order 12. Moreover, $C_N(O(N)) = H$ in this case. On the other hand, with this congruence on q, N is a maximal 2-local subgroup and contains an S_2-subgroup of G. Furthermore, $SCN_3(2)$ is nonempty in G. This example strongly indicates that to obtain a satisfactory extension of the concept of $p \in \pi_4$, one may be forced to impose conditions on the centralizers of p-elements rather than on all p-local subgroups.

There is still another aspect of the concept that should be considered. In the case of N-groups, all local subgroups are constrained and so the Thompson transitivity theorem holds for all primes in $\pi_3 \cup \pi_4$. In particular, Theorem 8.5.6 shows that when $p \in \pi_4$, any element A of $SCN_3(p)$ normalizes no nontrivial p'-subgroup. Clearly one could have made this stronger condition the basis of the definition of π_4 in the N-group case without affecting any of the arguments. Obviously it would be preferable if the general definition could be given by conditions on appropriate p-local subgroups of our group G which contain an element of $SCN_3(p)$ rather than only on those which contain a full Sylow p-subgroup of G. However, as the transitivity theorem does not hold in general in the absence of p-constraint, it will be a more difficult task to reach these conditions.

The proper extension of the notion of π_4 will emerge only after the investigation of further general classification problems. In any event, the initial local group-theoretic analysis will presumably be taken up with the following question:

How general is the statement: Either $2 \in \pi_2$ or $2 \in \pi_4$?

If we continue with the N-group summary, the second phase of the local group-theoretic analysis of general classification problems will presumably be concerned with the following question:

If $2 \in \pi_4$, how general is the statement: Either 2 is isolated or $2 \sim p$ and $p \in \pi_4$ for some odd prime p?

As in the case of the concept of π_4, some modification in the definition of $\sim$ would seem to be required for more general classification problems. Indeed, consider $G = E_2(p^m)$, p odd. If $p^m = 3$, then $2 \sim 3$ and the required $\{2, 3\}$-subgroup D may be taken to be the centralizer of an involution in G. Moreover, for all values of p^m for which $2 \sim p$, the subgroup D necessarily lies in the centralizer C of an involution of G. Now C has the following structure: It contains a normal subgroup K of index 2 which is the central product of two copies of $SL(2, p^m)$. One can verify directly that C possesses a $\{2, 3\}$-subgroup D with the required properties if and only if $p^m \equiv 1$ (mod 4). Rather than say that 2 and p are not related when $p^m \equiv -1$ (mod 4), it would seem to be preferable to allow D to be nonsolvable in formulating a general definition of $2 \sim p$.

A second point occurs in connection with the requirement that D contain a noncyclic abelian subgroup of order 8, which is possibly of type (4, 2). This is entirely satisfactory for the characterizations of $E_2(3)$ and $S_4(3)$, owing to the fact that a cyclic group of order 3 does not possess an automorphism of order 4. However, the corresponding argument would break down in attempting to characterize $E_2(p^m)$ when $p^m \equiv 1 \pmod 4$. Thus the general definition that $2 \sim p$ will at times require D to contain an elementary abelian subgroup of order 8.

This discussion suggests a somewhat related problem in connection with π_2, since for some of the groups $G(q)$ of Lie type the question of whether $SCN_3(2)$ is empty or nonempty reduces to a congruence on $q \pmod 8$ (compare Section 16.8). Obviously it would be desirable, whenever possible, to obtain single characterization theorems for a given family which do not depend upon a particular congruence for $q \pmod 8$. We note that for the families in question an S_2-subgroup of $G(q)$ always contains a noncyclic abelian normal subgroup of order 8 (but not necessarily an elementary abelian one). Perhaps it is possible to develop the initial group-theoretic arguments in such a way that the definition of $2 \in \pi_2$ can be made to encompass all these groups, independent of the congruence on q.

If, in a given classification problem, one is able to accomplish these two major steps, one will have reached a division entirely analogous to that of the N-group problem. Cases I and II, corresponding to $2 \in \pi_2$ and $2 \in \pi_4$, 2 isolated, respectively, will involve only groups of low rank, whereas case III, $\{2, p\} \subseteq \pi_4$ and $2 \sim p$, may involve groups of arbitrary rank and so represents the "general case." Thus we would be led to a fundamental problem:

Determine all simple groups in which $\{2, p\} \subseteq \pi_4$ and $2 \sim p$, p an odd prime.

Of course, it is understood we also assume that the 2-local and p-local subgroups of G are K-groups of the type prescribed by the particular classification problem under consideration.

Obviously this is a vast problem. We should note, however, that these conditions involve the "characteristic" of G in an explicit way and hence the subgroup structure of G is much more sharply limited under this hypothesis than at the very outset of our problem. For brevity, let us call a simple group satisfying these conditions an *L-group*.

Now the "general" known simple groups fall into three categories:

    A. Lie type of odd characteristic p.

    B. Lie type of characteristic 2.

    C. Alternating type, no characteristic.

Remarkably enough, it seems that the groups of each of these types of suitably high rank are, in fact, L-groups, for some appropriate odd prime p (which is not necessarily unique in types B and C). Moreover, these three types of groups can themselves be distinguished by means of the property of constraint. Indeed, the following appears to be the case:

1. In a group of Lie type of characteristic p, the p-local subgroups are p-constrained.
2. In a group of Lie type of characteristic 2, the 2-local subgroups are 2-constrained, but not all the p-local subgroups are p-constrained.
3. In an alternating group, neither are all the 2-local subgroups 2-constrained nor are all the p-local subgroups p-constrained.

These three mutually exclusive conditions suggest a natural subdivision in the over-all problem of the classification of L-groups and lead to the following refinement of the general problem:

1. If G is an L-group whose p-local subgroups are p-constrained, is G isomorphic to a group of Lie type of characteristic p?
2. If G is an L-group whose 2-local subgroups are 2-constrained but whose p-local subgroups are not all p-constrained, is G isomorphic to a group of Lie type of characteristic 2?
3. If G is an L-group whose 2-local subgroups are not all 2-constrained and whose p-local subgroups are not all p-constrained, is G isomorphic to $\mathscr{A}_n$ for some n?

The reader will certainly realize that the preceding discussion represents no more than educated speculation. Whether the classification of the simple groups will actually continue to develop along the lines we have suggested is by no means certain, for either some unforeseen difficulty or some powerful new method may radically alter the direction in which that development will proceed. Our purpose has been rather to indicate the breadth and generality of the various concepts that we have studied throughout the book and at the same time to show that they do provide a satisfactory conceptual framework in which to analyze general classification problems.

In one respect, however, there can be no uncertainty: For no matter how the analysis of a particular general classification problem will actually proceed, it is abundantly evident that specific properties of the proper subgroups of G will necessarily enter into the course of the arguments. In the problems we have treated above, either completely or in outline, we were concerned primarily with solvable subgroups or with groups involving $L_2(q)$, and it was specific properties of these families of groups that were used. In more general classification problems, it will obviously be properties of wider classes of K-groups that will be needed.

It should therefore be apparent that some kind of general theory of K-groups is called for, similar in spirit to that of the theory of solvable groups. The known simple groups have very sharply defined structures. Moreover, their automorphisms and central extensions are essentially completely known and are of very limited types. In addition, a great deal is known about their representations. All this information, which is clearly needed for such a theory, should make it possible to establish useful general properties of K-groups.

As an illustration of the kind of properties we have in mind, we may consider the question of p-stability, which will obviously be of vital concern in any general classification problem. Hence let H be a K-group in which $O_{p'}(H) = 1$, p odd, and suppose H possesses a faithful representation on a vector space V over $GF(p)$ in which some p-element x of H has a quadratic minimal polynomial. What does this imply about H? About the representation? About the position of x in a normal series of H? In fact, it is possible to reduce the problem by general considerations to the special case that H is either p-solvable (in which case necessarily $p = 3$) or is what we may call a *near-* or *quasi*-simple K-group: that is, $Z(H) \subseteq H'$ and $\bar{H} = H/Z(H)$ is a subgroup of Aut $\bar{K}$, where $\bar{K} \lhd \bar{H}$ and $\bar{K}$ is a simple K-group. It is a very reasonable conjecture, which has actually been established for a number of families of simple K-groups, that $\bar{K}$ must be of Lie type of characteristic p, that x must lie in the inverse image K of $\bar{K}$ in H, and that the representation of K on any composition factor of V is either trivial or "fundamental" in the sense of Steinberg [all irreducible representations of K over $GF(p)$ being obtained in an explicit way from the tensor products of the so-called "fundamental" ones].

The fundamental property of p-solvable groups which subsequently formed the basis of our definition of p-constraint is the condition

(2.1) $$C_H(O_p(H)) \subseteq O_p(H) \qquad \text{provided } O_{p'}(H) = 1.$$

Whenever this condition holds, $\bar{H} = H/O_p(H)$ is faithfully represented as a subgroup of Aut $O_p(H)$ and hence by Theorem 5.1.4 is faithfully represented on the vector space $V = O_p(H)/\Phi(O_p(H))$. Much of the group-theoretic analysis in the classification problems we have studied, and also the basic result of Glauberman, reduces ultimately to considerations of this type.

When H is an arbitrary K-group [with $O_{p'}(H) = 1$], condition (2.1) certainly need not hold; in fact, it may very well happen that $O_p(H) \subseteq Z(H)$. However, this condition is too vital to let the matter drop there. We can at least investigate the structure of a minimal subgroup K of H containing $O_p(H)$ which satisfies the condition $C_H(K) \subseteq K$. In this connection, there exists a general result which does not require H to be a K-group. To state it, we introduce the following term:

A group L will be called *semisimple* provided L is the product of subgroups L_i, $1 \leqslant i \leqslant r$, such that
   (a) $[L_i, L_j] = 1$ if $i \neq j$ and $[L_i, L_i] = L_i$, and
   (b) $L_i/Z(L_i)$ is a simple group.
(This extends the usual definition of semisimple, which requires each L_i itself to be simple.)

It is not difficult to establish the following general result:

Theorem

Let H be a group and let π be a set of primes such that $O_{\pi'}(H) = 1$. Then H possesses a unique characteristic subgroup K with the following properties:
   (i) $O_\pi(H) \subseteq K$.
   (ii) $C_H(K) \subseteq O_\pi(H)$,
   (iii) $K = LO_\pi(H)$, where L is semisimple and characteristic in K.
   (iv) $[L, O_\pi(H)] = 1$ and $L \cap O_\pi(H) = Z(L)$.

We denote this subgroup K by $O_\pi^*(H)$. The above theorem shows that, whereas $H/O_p(H)$ is faithfully represented as a subgroup of Aut $O_p(H)$ under the assumption of p-constraint, in the general case it is faithfully represented as a subgroup of Aut $O_p^*(H)$. This theorem makes it quite apparent that the structure of the simple groups related to the semisimple part of $O_p^*(H)$ will greatly influence the over-all structure of H. At the same time it is clear that it provides a convenient tool with which to investigate properties of K-groups—for example, in the general analysis of p-stability discussed above.

We should like to conclude with two other general points of consideration. The Brauer-Suzuki-Wall theorem (Theorem 15.4.1) gives a characterization of the family $L_2(q)$ in terms of conditions on the centralizers of involutions. Brauer's theorem of Section 16.7 provides a similar characterization of the family $L_3(q)$, and Janko's characterization of his group is made in similar terms. There exist a number of other results of the same nature, characterizing some single known simple group or family of known simple groups by conditions on the centralizers of their involutions.

One may formulate the general problem as follows: Let G be a simple group, let S be an S_2-subgroup of G, let x be an involution of $Z(S)$, and suppose that $C_G(x)$ is isomorphic to the centralizer of an involution in some simple group G^*. Must then G and G^* be isomorphic? [If G has more than one conjugate class of involutions, one can, of course, also assume the structure of the centralizers of involutions of S not conjugate to x and, if one wishes, even how these centralizers intersect each other. J. H. Walter [1] has given just such a characterization of suitable n-dimensional linear and projective linear groups defined over $GF(q)$. However, for the applications to general classification problems, it is much more useful to have available characterization theorems made in terms of the centralizer of a single involution x.]

Since distinct known simple groups may possess involutions whose centralizers, are themselves isomorphic—for example, M_{11} and $L_3(3)$ or $\mathscr{A}_8$ and $\mathscr{A}_9$—it will be necessary in some instances to replace the known simple group G^* by a pair of known simple groups G_1^*, G_2^*, if one is to hope for an affirmative answer to our question.

Starting with the given assumption on the structure of $C_G(x)$, the aim is to show by means of local group-theoretic arguments and, in some cases, also of character-theoretic methods, that G has a generalized Bruhat structure identical to that of G^* (correspondingly G_1^* or G_2^*). Then the generator-relation method can be used to attempt to show that G and G^* (correspondingly G and G_1^* or G_2^*) are, in fact, isomorphic. It is not unreasonable to believe that all the known simple groups may ultimately be characterized in these terms.

However, the exact role which such characterization theorems will play in general classification problems concerning groups of rank greater than one is not yet clear. The reason for this can be seen in Thompson's characterization of $E_2(3)$ and $S_4(3)$ as L-groups. On the one hand, a large part of his analysis can be viewed as a proof that the centralizer of an involution in the given L-group G is isomorphic to that of $E_2(3)$ or $S_4(3)$, as the case may be. On the other hand, this stage of the argument is reached almost simultaneously with that in which it is shown that G has a generalized Bruhat structure. Hence an independent proof that G has a generalized Bruhat structure, based solely upon the structure of these centralizers, would not provide a significant reduction in Thompson's argument. There is some indication that this same situation may continue to prevail in the analysis of L-groups in general.

On the other hand, it is entirely possible that the centralizer-of-an-involution method may provide an alternative approach to general classification problems distinct from that of L-groups. In this approach the objective of the initial group-theoretic analysis would be aimed at pinning down the structure of the centralizer of an involution in the center of a Sylow 2-subgroup of G rather than in trying to establish that G is an

L-group. In the case of characterization theorems involving groups of rank one, this has indeed been the approach that has invariably been used. Whether it can be adapted to general classification problems concerning the simple groups of higher rank remains to be seen.

The second and final topic we wish to discuss concerns the concept of strongly embedded subgroup which plays such a fundamental role in the various general classification problems that have been successfully solved to date. As we have seen in the proof of Theorem 15.3.1 and at several points in the discussion of Chapter 16, a major step in the initial local group-theoretic analysis of each of these problems has been the construction in the given simple group G of a strongly embedded subgroup M which is also a uniqueness subgroup for some odd prime p, the existence of such a subgroup M being in contradiction to Theorem 9.3.1 or a suitable variant thereof. In each case a considerable simplification in the structure of the centralizers of the involutions of G was thereby effected.

The question arises whether this same line of argument will continue to be useful in general classification problems involving groups of rank greater than one. For one thing the construction of such a subgroup in each of the group G above was extremely difficult to accomplish, even though the local subgroups in question were either stable or both stable and constrained. When neither of these conditions is present, as will be the case in more general situations, the technical problems involved in constructing M may be insurmountable. Furthermore, there is also strong reason to feel that in these higher rank classification problems such a subgroup M may not even be the right one to attempt to construct. Indeed, the existence of a strongly embedded subgroup M in G forces both M and G to have only one conjugate class of involutions by Theorem 9.2.1 and so would seem to be somewhat artificial if the members of the family being classified themselves possess more than one class of involutions. (However, this does not *ipso facto* preclude the possibility of our constructing a strongly embedded subgroup M in G, since our purpose in any event is to derive a contradiction from its existence.)

There are definite indications that the existence in a simple group G of a subgroup M satisfying certain conditions weaker than strong embedding and considerably easier to achieve may in some circumstances suffice to yield a contradiction. These conditions are incorporated into the following definition:

A subgroup M of even order of the simple group G will be said to be *weakly embedded* in G provided:

(a) $O(M) \neq 1$;

(b) Any two 2-elements of M that are conjugate in G are conjugate in M;

(c) For any involution x of M, we have

$$C_G(x) = O(C_G(x))(M \cap C_G(x)).$$

Thus in weak embedding we do not require M to contain the centralizer of each of its involutions, but only to *cover* these centralizers modulo their largest normal subgroups of odd order. Should M actually contain each $C_G(x)$, then it is easy to see that M is, in fact, strongly embedded in G.

The essential distinction between the construction of a weakly embedded and a strongly embedded subgroup of G can be summed up as follows: In the first case one can limit oneself to an analysis of p-local subgroups of G for a *single* prime p in $\pi(O(C_G(x))$, x an involution of G, whereas in the second case one must investigate p-local subgroups for a *set* of such primes p. (Compare the proof of Theorem 15.3.1, in which it was necessary to consider p-local subgroups for all primes p in the set β.) Because of this difference, the task of constructing a weakly embedded subgroup is very much simpler than that of constructing a strongly embedded one.

On the other hand, the problem of deriving a contradiction from the existence of such a weakly embedded subgroup is unfortunately vastly more difficult than from a strongly embedded one. Indeed, it has so far been accomplished by Brauer only in the case of groups with semi-dihedral or wreathed Sylow 2-subgroups. In each of these cases Brauer has carried out a detailed analysis of the characters of an arbitrary simple group G with S_2-subgroups of either of these types *without* reference to the existence of a weakly embedded subgroup in G. Then, assuming the existence of such a subgroup M, he is able to show that there is an irreducible character χ of G whose restriction to M remains irreducible. Moreover, χ is in the principal 2-block of G and $\chi \mid_M$ is in the principal 2-block of M. The latter fact implies directly that $O(M)$ is in the kernel of $\chi \mid_M$ and hence is in the kernel of χ. Since $O(M) \neq 1$ by condition (a) above, the simplicity of G is thus contradicted.

Except in cases of simple groups whose Sylow 2-subgroups are of very restricted types, it is extremely unlikely that a corresponding character analysis can be successfully carried out *ab initio* for more general simple groups. There seems to be a greater promise that such an analysis can possibly be achieved when the given group G possesses a weakly embedded subgroup M. For the conditions which define such a subgroup M are closely related to those of a tamely embedded subset and the primary problem which must be resolved is the analogous one of constructing a coherent isometry of a suitable submodule $I'(M)$ of ch(M) into ch(G).

We have seen in the proofs of Feit's theorems (Theorems 4.6.5 and 13.2.1) and in a portion of the Brauer-Suzuki-Wall theorems (Theorem 4.4.4) how substantial a task it is to carry this out even in the very much simpler situations which these theorems embody.

In the present case the submodule $I'(M)$ consists by definition of those elements of ch(M) which vanish on all elements of $M^{\#}$ of odd order and which are constant on the 2-classes of M whose elements are of even order (see Section 4.7 for the definition of a 2-class). If such a coherent isometry can be constructed, it will then be possible to obtain values of certain irreducible characters of G on the 2-elements of G. Then formula (9.4.2) (more exactly, an analogous formula related to the principal 2-block of G) may hopefully yield in many cases bounds for the degree of a suitable irreducible character χ of G which will enable one to show that $\chi|_M$ is irreducible and contains $O(M)$ in its kernel, thereby contradicting the simplicity of G. (Glauberman [6] has given a characterization of the Suzuki groups which involves some of these ideas, but under very restricted conditions—the centralizer of every involution is assumed to have a normal 2-complement.)

The fact that in a general classification problem the proper subgroups of the given simple group are K-groups will naturally imply that our weakly embedded subgroup M is, in fact, a K-group. It is not unreasonable to hope that properties of the characters of K-groups may enable us to carry through the program just outlined in at least some significant cases.

If the speculations of this section stimulate an interest in any of the specific questions we have raised, they will have served their purpose well.

BIBLIOGRAPHY

The following bibliography is not intended as a comprehensive list of papers in finite group theory but is limited primarily to topics discussed or referred to in the text. We first give a number of general references which supplement some of our material.

GENERAL REFERENCES

Artin, E.
[1] Geometric algebra, Wiley-Interscience (New York, 1957).
Blichfeldt, H. F.
[1] Finite collineation groups, University of Chicago (Chicago, 1917).
Brauer, R., and Weiss, E.
[1] Non-commutative rings, Part I (lecture notes, Harvard University, Cambridge, Mass.).
Burnside, W.
[1] Theory of groups, 2nd edition, 1911, Dover (New York, 1955).
Curtis, C. W., and Reiner, I.
[1] Representation theory of finite groups and associative algebras, Wiley-Interscience (New York, 1962).
Dickson, L. E.
[1] Linear groups with an exposition of the Galois field theory, 1901, Dover (New York, 1958).
Dieudonné, J.
[1] La Géométrie des groupes classiques, Springer (Berlin, 1955).

Feit, W.
 [1] Characters of finite groups (lecture notes, Yale University, New Haven, Conn.).
Hall, M., Jr.
 [1] The theory of groups, Macmillan (New York, 1959).
Hall, P.
 [1] Lecture notes, unpublished.
Herstein, I. N.
 [1] Theory of rings (lecture notes, University of Chicago, Chicago).
Huppert, B.
 [1] Endliche Gruppen, Springer (Berlin, to appear).
Lang, S.
 [1] Algebra, Addison-Wesley (Reading, Mass., 1965).
Schenkman, E.
 [1] Group theory, Van Nostrand (Princeton, N.J., 1965).
Scott, W. R.
 [1] Group theory, Prentice-Hall (Englewood Cliffs, N.J., 1964).
Speiser, A.
 [1] Die Theorie der Gruppen von endlicher Ordnung, Dritte Auflage, Dover (New
     York, 1945).
Waerden, B. L. van der
 [1] Modern algebra, two volumes, Ungar (New York, 1949).
Wielandt, H.
 [1] Finite permutation groups, Academic Press (New York, 1964).
Zassenhaus, H.
 [1] Theory of groups, 2nd edition, Chelsea (New York, 1958).

JOURNAL ARTICLES

Alperin, J. L.
 [1] Centralizers of abelian normal subgroups of p-groups, *Jour. Alg.*, **1** (1964),
     110–113.
 [2] System normalizers and Carter subgroups, *Jour. Alg.*, **1** (1964), 355–366.
 [3] Sylow intersections and fusion, *Jour. Alg.*, **6** (1967), 222–241.
Alperin, J. L., and Gorenstein, D.
 [1] The multiplicators of certain simple groups, *Proc. Amer. Math. Soc.*, **17** (1966),
     515–519.
 [2] Transfer and fusion in finite groups, *Jour. Alg.*, **6** (1967), 242–255.
Artin, E.
 [1] The orders of the classical simple groups, *Comm. Pure Appl. Math.*, **8** (1955),
     455–472.
Baer, R.
 [1] Classes of finite groups and their properties, *Ill. Jour. Math.*, **1** (1957), 115–187.
 [2] Partitionen endlicher Gruppen, *Math. Zeit.*, **75** (1961), 333–372.
 [3] Einfache Partitionen endlicher Gruppen mit nicht-trivialer Fittingscher Unter-
     gruppe, *Arch. Math.*, **12** (1961), 81–89.

[4] Einfache Partitionen nicht-einfacher Gruppen, *Math. Zeit.*, **77** (1961), 1–37.

Bauman, S. F.

[1] The Klein group as an automorphism group without fixed points, *Pac. Jour. Math.*, **18** (1966), 9–13.

Blackburn, N.

[1] On a special class of p-groups, *Acta Math.*, **100** (1958), 45–92.

[2] Generalizations of certain elementary theorems on p-groups, *Proc. London Math. Soc.*, **11** (1961), 1–22.

[3] Automorphisms of finite p-groups, *Jour. Alg.*, **3** (1966), 28–29.

Brauer, R.

[1] On groups whose order contains a prime number to the first power, I, II, *Amer. Jour. Math.*, **64** (1942), 401–440.

[2] On permutation groups of prime degree and related classes of groups, *Ann. Math.*, **44** (1943), 57–79.

[3] Representations of groups of finite order, *Proc. Int. Cong. Math.*, **II** (1950), 33–36.

[4] A characterization of the characters of groups of finite order, *Ann. Math.*, **57** (1953), 357–377.

[5] Zur Darstellungstheorie der Gruppen endlicher Ordnung, I, II, *Math. Zeit.*, **63** (1956), 406–444; **72** (1959), 25–46.

[6] Investigations on groups of even order, I, II, *Proc. Nat. Acad. Sci.*, **47** (1961), 1891–1893; **52** (1966), 254–259.

[7] On some conjectures concerning finite simple groups, in the Studies in Math. Anal. and Related Topics Series, Stanford University Press (Stanford, Calif. 1962), 58–61.

[8] On quotient groups of finite groups, *Math. Zeit.*, **83** (1964), 72–84.

[9] Some applications of the theory or blocks of characters of finite groups I, II, III, *Jour. Alg.*, **1** (1964), 152–167, 307–334; **3** (1966), 225–255.

[10] On finite Desarguesian planes, I, II, *Math. Zeit.*, **90** (1966), 117–151.

Brauer, R., and Fong, P.

[1] A characterization of the Mathieu group M_{12}, *Trans. Amer. Math. Soc.*, **122** (1966), 18–47.

Brauer, R. and Fowler, K. A.

[1] On groups of even order, *Ann. Math.*, **62** (1955), 565–583.

Brauer, R., and Leonard, H. S., Jr.

[1] On finite groups with an abelian Sylow subgroup, *Can. Jour. Math.*, **14** (1962), 436–450.

Brauer, R., and Reynolds, W. F.

[1] On a problem of E. Artin, *Ann. Math.*, **68** (1958), 713–720.

Brauer, R., and Suzuki, M.

[1] On finite groups of even order whose 2-Sylow subgroup is a quaternion group, *Proc. Nat. Acad. Sci.*, **45** (1959), 1757–1759.

Brauer, R., Suzuki, M., and Wall, G. E.

[1] A characterization of the one-dimensional unimodular groups over finite fields, *Ill. Jour. Math.*, **2** (1958), 718–745.

Brauer, R., and Tate, J.

[1] On the characters of finite groups, *Ann. Math.*, **62** (1955), 1–7.

Brauer, R., and **Tuan, H. F.**

[1] On simple groups of finite order, *Bull. Amer. Math., Soc.* **51** (1945), 756–766.

Carter, R. W.

[1] Nilpotent self-normalizing subgroups of soluble groups, *Math. Zeit.*, **75** (1961), 136–139.

[2] Nilpotent self-normalizing subgroups and system normalizers, *Proc. London Math. Soc.*, **12** (1962), 535–563.

[3] Simple groups and Lie algebras, *Jour. London, Math. Soc.*, **40** (1965), 193–240.

Carter, R. W., and **Fong, P.**

[1] The Sylow 2-subgroups of the finite classical groups, *Jour. Alg.*, **1** (1964), 139–151.

Chevalley, C.

[1] Sur certains groupes simples, *Tohoku Math. Jour.*, **7** (1955), 14–66.

Clifford, A. H.

[1] Representations induced in an invariant subgroup, *Ann. Math.*, **38** (1937), 533–550.

Coxeter, H. S. M.

[1] Discrete groups generated by reflections, *Ann. Math.*, **35** (1934), 558–621.

[2] The complete enumeration of finite groups of the form $R_i^2 = (R_i R_j)^{k_{ij}} = 1$, *Jour. London Math. Soc.*, **35** (1935), 21–25.

Dade, E. C.

[1] Lifting group characters, *Ann. Math.*, **79** (1964), 590–596.

[2] Blocks with cyclic defect groups, *Ann. Math.*, **84** (1966), 20–48.

Feit, W.

[1] On the structure of Frobenius groups, *Can. Jour. Math.*, **9** (1957), 587–596.

[2] On groups which contain Frobenius groups as subgroups, *Proc. Symp. Pure Math., Amer. Math. Soc.*, **1** (1959), 22–27.

[3] On a class of doubly transitive permutation groups, *Ill. Jour. Math.*, **4** (1960), 170–186.

[4] A characterization of the simple groups $SL(2, 2^a)$, *Amer. Jour. Math.*, **82** (1960), 281–300.

[5] Group characters; exceptional characters, *Proc. Symp. Pure Math., Amer. Math. Soc.*, **6** (1962), 67–70.

[6] Groups which have a faithful representation of degree less than $p - 1$, *Trans. Amer. Math. Soc.*, **112** (1964), 287–303.

[7] Groups with a cyclic Sylow subgroup, *Nag. Math. Jour.*, **27** (1966), 571–584.

Feit, W., Hall, M., Jr., and **Thompson, J. G.**

[1] Finite groups in which the centralizer of any non-identity element is nilpotent, *Math. Zeit.*, **74** (1960), 1–17.

Feit, W., and **Higman, G.**

[1] On the nonexistence of certain generalized polygons, *Jour. Alg.*, **1** (1964), 114–131.

Feit, W., and **Thompson, J. G.**

[1] A solvability criterion for finite groups and some consequences, *Proc. Nat. Acad. Sci.*, **48** (1962), 968–970.

[2] Solvability of groups of odd order, *Pac. Jour. Math.*, **13** (1963), 775–1029.

[3] On groups which have a faithful representation of degree less than $(p - 1)/2$, *Pac. Jour. Math.*, **4** (1961), 1257–1262.

[4] Finite groups which contain a self-centralizing subgroup of order 3, *Nag. Math. Jour.*, **21** (1962), 185–197.

Fischer, B.

[1] Frobeniusautomorphismen endlicher Gruppen, *Math. Ann.*, **163** (1966), 273–298.

[2] A characterization of the symmetric groups on 4 and 5 letters, *Jour. Alg.*, **3** (1966), 88–98.

[3] Finite groups admitting a fixed-point-free automorphism of order 2*p*, I, II, *Jour. Alg.*, **3** (1966), 98–114; **5** (1967), 25–40.

Fitting, H.

[1] Beiträge zur Theorie der Gruppen endlicher Ordnung, *Jahr. Deutsch. Math. Ver.*, **48** (1938), 77–141.

Fong, P.

[1] Some Sylow subgroups of order 32 and a characterization of $U(3, 3)$, *Jour. Alg.*, **6** (1967), 65–76.

Gäschutz, W.

[1] Über die Φ-Untergruppen endlicher Gruppen, *Math. Zeit.*, **58** (1953), 160–170.

[2] Nichtabelsche *p*-Gruppen besitzen äussere *p*-Automorphismen, *Jour. Alg.*, **4** (1966), 1–2.

Glauberman, G.

[1] Fixed points in groups with operator groups, *Math. Zeit.*, **84** (1964), 120–125.

[2] Central elements in core-free groups, *Jour. Alg.*, **4** (1966), 403–420.

[3] Subgroups of finite groups, *Bull. Amer. Math. Soc.*, **73** (1967), 1–12.

[4] A characteristic subgroup of a *p*-stable group (to appear).

[5] Weakly closed elements of Sylow groups (to appear).

[6] A characterization of the Suzuki groups (to appear).

Gorenstein, D.

[1] A class of Frobenius groups, *Can. Jour. Math.*, **11** (1959), 39–47.

[2] Finite groups which admit an automorphism with few orbits, *Can. Jour. Math.*, **12** (1960), 73–100.

[3] On finite groups of the form ABA, *Can. Jour. Math.*, **14** (1962), 195–236.

[4] Some topics in the theory of finite groups, *Rend. di Mat.*, **23** (1964), 298–315.

[5] Finite groups in which Sylow 2-subgroups are abelian and centralizers of involutions are solvable, *Can. Jour. Math.*, **17** (1965), 860–896.

[6] On a theorem of Philip Hall, *Pac. Jour. Math.*, **19** (1966), 77–80.

[7] *p*-Constraint and the transitivity theorem (to appear).

Gorenstein, D., and Herstein, I. N.

[1] A class of solvable groups, *Can. Jour. Math.*, **11** (1959), 311–320.

[2] Finite groups admitting a fixed-point-free automorphism of order 4, *Amer. Jour. Math.*, **83** (1961), 71–78.

Gorenstein, D., and Hughes, D. R.

[1] Triply transitive groups in which only the identity fixes four letters, *Ill. Jour. Math.*, **5** (1961), 486–491.

Gorenstein, D., and Walter, J. H.

[1] On finite groups with dihedral Sylow 2-subgroups, *Ill. Jour. Math.*, **6** (1962), 553–593.

[2] On the maximal subgroups of finite simple groups, *Jour. Alg.*, **1** (1964), 168–213.

[3] The characterization of finite groups with dihedral Sylow 2-subgroups, I, II, III, *Jour. Alg.*, **2** (1965), 85–151, 218–270, 334–393.

Grün, O.

[1] Beiträge zur Gruppentheories, I, II, *Crelle Jour.*, **174** (1936), 1–14; **186** (1948), 165–169.

Hall, P.

[1] A note on soluble groups, *Jour. London Math. Soc.*, **3** (1928), 98–105.

[2] A contribution to the theory of groups of prime power order, *Proc. London Math. Soc.*, **36** (1933), 29–95.

[3] On a theorem of Frobenius, *Proc. London Math. Soc.*, **40** (1935), 468–501.

[4] A characteristic property of soluble groups, *Jour. London Math. Soc.*, **12** (1937), 198–200.

[5] On the Sylow systems of a soluble group, *Proc. London Math. Soc.*, **43** (1937), 316–323.

[6] On the system normalizers of a soluble group, *Proc. London Math. Soc.*, **43** (1937), 507–528.

[7] Theorems like Sylow's, *Proc. London Math. Soc.*, **6** (1956), 286–304.

[8] Some sufficient conditions for a group to be nilpotent, *Ill. Jour. Math.*, **2** (1958), 787–801.

Hall, P., and Higman, G.

[1] The p-length of a p-soluble group and reduction theorems for Burnside's problem, *Proc. London Math. Soc.*, **7** (1956), 1–42.

Held, D.

[1] A characterization of the alternating groups of degrees eight and nine (to appear).

Higman, D. G.

[1] Focal series in finite groups, *Can. Jour. Math.*, **5** (1953), 477–497.

Higman, D. G., and McLaughlin, J. E.

[1] Geometric ABA-groups, *Ill. Jour. Math.*, **5** (1961), 382–397.

Higman, G.

[1] Groups and rings which have automorphisms with no non-trivial fixed elements, *Jour. London Math. Soc.*, **32** (1957), 321–334.

[2] Finite groups in which every element has prime order, *Jour. London Math. Soc.*, **32** (1957), 335–342.

[3] Suzuki 2-groups, *Ill. Jour. Math.*, **7** (1963), 79–96.

Hoffman, F.

[1] Nilpotent height of finite groups admitting fixed-point-free automorphisms. *Math. Zeit.*, **85** (1964), 260–267.

Hughes, D. R., and Thompson, J. G.

[1] The H_p-problem and the structure of H_p-groups, *Pac. Jour. Math.*, **9** (1959), 1097–1101.

Huppert, B.

[1] Monomiale darstellung endlicher Gruppen, *Nag. Math. Jour.*, **6** (1953), 93–94.

[2] Normalteiler und maximale Untergruppen endlicher Gruppen, *Math. Zeit.*, **60** (1954), 409–434.

[3] Zweifach, transitive, auflosbare Permutationsgruppen, *Math. Zeit.*, **68** (1957), 126–150.

[4] Subnormale Untergruppen und Sylowgruppen, *Acta Szeged.*, **22** (1961), 46–61.

[5] Gruppen mit modularer Sylowgruppen, *Math. Zeit.*, **75** (1961), 140–153.

[6] Scharf dreifach transitive Permutationsgruppen, *Arch. Math.*, **13** (1962), 61–72.

Huppert, B., and Wielandt, H.

[1] Arithmetical and normal structure of finite groups, *Proc. Symp. Pure Math.*, *Amer. Math. Soc.*, **6** (1962), 17–38.

Ito, N.

[1] On a theorem of H. F. Blichfeldt, *Nag. Math. Jour.*, **5** (1954), 75–77.

[2] Zur Theorie der Permutationsgruppen von Grad *p*, *Math. Zeit.*, **74** (1960), 299–301.

[3] On a class of doubly transitive permutation groups, *Ill. Jour. Math.*, **6** (1962), 341–352.

[4] On transitive simple groups of degree 2*p*, *Math. Zeit.*, **78** (1962), 453–468.

[5] On transitive simple groups of degree 3*p*, *Nag. Math. Jour.*, **21** (1962), 123–158.

Iwahori, N.

[1] On a property of finite groups, *Jour. Fac. Sci. Tokyo*, **11** (1964), 47–64.

Iwahori, N., and Kondo, T.

[1] On a finite group admitting a permutation representation *P* such that tr $P(\sigma) = 3$ for all $\sigma \neq 1$, *Jour. Fac. Sci. Tokyo*, **11** (1964), 113–144.

[2] A criterion for the existence of a non-trivial partition of a finite group with applications to finite reflection groups, *Jour. Math. Soc. Japan*, **17** (1965), 207–215.

Iwasawa, K.

[1] Über die endlichen Gruppen und die Verbände ihrer Untergruppen, *Jour. Univ. Tokyo*, **43** (1941), 171–199.

Janko, Z.

[1] A new finite simple group with abelian 2-Sylow subgroups, *Proc. Nat. Acad. Sci.*, **53** (1965), 657–658.

[2] A new finite simple group with abelian Sylow 2-subgroups and its characterization, *Jour. Alg.*, **4** (1966), 147–186.

Janko, Z., and Thompson, J. G.

[1] On a class of finite simple groups of Ree, *Jour. Alg.*, **4** (1966), 274–292.

Kegel, O. H,

[1] Producte nilpotenter Gruppen, *Arch. Math.*, **12** (1961), 90–93.

[2] Die Nilpotenz der H_p-Gruppen, *Math. Zeit.*, **75** (1961), 373–376.

[3] Nicht-einfache Partitionen endlicher Gruppen, *Arch. Math.*, **12** (1961), 170–175.

[4] Aufzahlung der Partitionen endlicher Gruppen mit trivialer Fittingscher Untergruppe, *Arch. Math.*, **12** (1961), 409–412.

Kegel, O. H., and Wall, G. E.

[1] Zur Structur endlicher Gruppen mit nicht-trivialer Partition, *Arch. Math.*, **12** (1961), 255–261.

Leonard, H. S., Jr.

[1] On finite groups which contain a Frobenius factor group, *Ill. Jour. Math.*, **9** (1965), 47–58.

Leonard, H. S., Jr., and McKelvey, K. K.

[1] On lifting characters in finite groups (to appear).

Mazarov, V. D.
[1] On finite groups with a given Sylow 2-subgroup, *Dokl. Akad. Nauk SSSR*, **168** (1966), 519–522.
Neumann, B. H.
[1] Groups with automorphisms that leave only the neutral element fixed, *Arch. Math.*, (1956), 1–5.
Ree, R.
[1] On some simple groups defined by Chevalley, *Trans. Amer. Math. Soc.*, **84** (1957), 392–400.
[2] A family of simple groups associated with the simple Lie algebra of type (F_4), *Amer. Jour. Math.*, **83** (1961), 401–420.
[3] A family of simple groups associated with the simple Lie algebra of type (G_2), *Amer. Jour. Math.*, **83** (1961), 432–462.
Reynolds, W. F.
[1] Sections, isometries, and generalized group characters (to appear).
Sah, C. H.
[1] A class of finite groups with abelian 2-Sylow subgroups, *Math. Zeit.*, **82** (1963), 335–346.
Schur, I.
[1] Untersuchen uber die Darstellung der endlichen Gruppen durch gebrochenen linearen Substitutionen, *Crelle Jour.*, **132** (1907), 85–137.
[2] Über darstellung der symmetrischen und der alternieren Gruppen durch gebrochenen linearen Substitutionen, *Crelle Jour.*, **139** (1911), 155–250.
Shult, E.
[1] On groups admitting fixed point free operator groups, *Ill. Jour. Math.*, **9** (1965), 701–720.
[2] Nilpotence of the commutator subgroup in groups admitting fixed point free operator groups, *Pac. Jour. Math.*, **17** (1966), 323–347.
Sims, C.
[1] Graphs and finite permutation groups (to appear).
Stanton, R.
[1] The Mathieu groups, *Can. Jour. Math.*, **3** (1951), 164–174.
Steinberg, R.
[1] Variations on a theme of Chevalley, *Pac. Jour. Math.*, **9** (1959), 875–891.
[2] The simplicity of certain groups, *Pac. Jour. Math.* **10** (1960), 1039–1041.
[3] Automorphisms of finite linear groups, *Can. Jour. Math.*, **12** (1960), 606–615.
[4] Generators for simple groups, *Can. Jour. Math.*, **14** (1962), 277–283.
[5] Générateurs, relations, et revêtements de groupes algébriques, Colloque sur la théorie des groupes algébriques, C.B.R.M. (Brussels, 1962), 113–127.
[6] Representations of algebraic groups, *Nag. Math. Jour.*, **22** (1963), 33–56.
Suzuki, M.
[1] On finite groups with a complete partition, *Jour. Math. Soc. Japan*, **2** (1950), 165–185.
[2] A characterization of the simple groups $LF(2, p)$, *Jour. Fac. Sci. Univ. Tokyo*, **6** (1951), 259–293.
[3] On finite groups with cyclic Sylow subgroups for all odd primes, *Amer. Jour. Math.*, **77** (1955), 657–691.

[4] The nonexistence of a certain type of simple group of odd order, *Proc. Amer. Math. Soc.*, **8** (1957), 686–695.

[5] On characterizations of linear groups, I, II, III, *Trans. Amer. Math. Soc.*, **92** (1959), 191–219; *Nag. Math. Jour.*, **21** (1961), 159–183.

[6] On finite groups containing an element of order 4 which commutes only with its own powers, *Ill. Jour. Math.*, **3** (1959), 255–271.

[7] Applications of group characters, *Proc. Symp. Pure Math.*, *Amer. Math. Soc.*, **1** (1959), 88–99.

[8] A new type of simple group of finite order, *Proc. Nat. Acad. Sci.*, **46** (1960), 868–870.

[9] Finite groups with nilpotent centralizers, *Trans. Amer. Math. Soc.*, **99** (1961), 425–470.

[10] On a finite group with a partition, *Arch. Math.*, **12** (1961), 241—254.

[11] On generalized (ZT)-groups, *Arch. Math.*, **13** (1962), 199–202.

[12] On a class of doubly transitive groups, I, II, *Ann. Math.*, **75** (1962), 105–145; **79** (1964), 514–589.

[13] On the existence of a Hall normal subgroup, *Jour. Math. Soc. Japan*, **15** (1963), 387–391.

[14] Two characteristic properties of (ZT)-groups, *Osaka Math. Jour.*, **15** (1963), 143–150.

[15] Finite groups of even order in which Sylow 2-groups are independent, *Ann. Math.*, **80** (1964), 58–77.

[16] A characterization of the 3-dimensional projective unitary group over a finite field of odd characteristic, *Jour. Alg.*, **2** (1965), 1–14.

[17] Finite groups in which the centralizer of any element of order 2 is 2-closed. *Ann. Math.*, **82** (1965), 191–212.

Thompson, J. G.

[1] Finite groups with fixed-point-free automorphisms of prime order, *Proc. Nat. Acad. Sci.*, **45** (1959), 578–581.

[2] Normal p-complements for finite groups, *Math. Zeit.*, **72** (1960), 332–354.

[3] A special class of non-solvable groups, *Math. Zeit.*, **72** (1960), 458–462.

[4] 2-Signalizers of finite groups, *Pac. Jour. Math.*, **14** (1964), 363–364.

[5] Normal p-complements for finite groups, *Jour. Alg.*, **1** (1964), 43–46.

[6] Fixed points of p-groups acting on p-groups, *Math. Zeit.*, **86** (1964), 12–13.

[7] Factorizations of p-solvable groups, *Pac. Jour. Math.*, **16** (1966), 371–372.

[8] Vertices and sources, *Jour. Alg.*, **6** (1967), 1–6.

[9] Non-solvable finite groups all of whose local subgroups are solvable (to appear).

[10] A replacement theorem for p-groups and a conjecture (to appear).

Tits, J.

[1] Les Groupes simples de Suzuki et de Ree, *Sem. Bour.*, expose 210 (Paris, 1960).

[2] Théorème de Bruhat et sous-groupes paraboliques, *C. R. Acad. Sci. Paris*, **254** (1962), 2910–2912.

[3] Groupes simples et géométries associées, *Proc. Int. Cong. Math.* (1962), 197–221.

[4] Algebraic and abstract simple groups, *Ann. Math.*, **80** (1964), 313–329.

Tuan, H. F.

[1] On groups whose orders contain a prime to the first power, *Ann. Math.*, **45** (1944), 110–140.

Wall, G. E.

[1] On the conjugacy classes in the unitary, symplectic, and orthogonal groups, *Jour. Austral. Math. Soc.*, **3** (1963), 1–62.

Walter, J. H.

[1] On the characterization of linear and projective linear groups, I, II, *Trans. Amer. Math. Soc.*, **100** (1961), 481–529; **101** (1961), 107–123.

[2] Character theory of finite groups with trivial intersection sets, *Nag. Math. Jour.* **27** (1966), 515–524.

[3] Finite groups with abelian Sylow 2-subgroups of order 8 (to appear).

[4] The characterization of finite groups with abelian Sylow 2-subgroups (to appear).

Wielandt, H.

[1] Zur Theorie der einfach transitiven Permutationsgruppen, *Math. Zeit.*, **40** (1935), 582–587.

[2] Eine Verallgemeinerung der invarianten Untergruppen, *Math. Zeit.*, **45** (1939), 209–244.

[3] *p*-Sylowgruppen und *p*-Factorgruppen, *Crelle Jour.*, **182** (1940), 180–193.

[4] Zur Theorie einfach transitiven Permutationsgruppen, II, *Math. Zeit.*, **52** (1949), 384–393.

[5] Uber das Produkt paarweise vertauschbarer nilpotenter Gruppen, *Math. Zeit.*, **55** (1951), 1–7.

[6] Zum Satz von Sylow, *Math. Zeit.*, **60** (1954), 407–408.

[7] Primitive Permutationsgruppen von Grad 2*p*, *Math. Zeit.*, **63** (1956), 478–485.

[8] Über die Existenz von Normalteilern in endlichen Gruppen, *Math. Nachr.*, **18** (1958), 274–280.

[9] Über Producte von nilpotenten Gruppen, *Ill. Jour. Math.*, **2** (1958), 611–618.

[10] Beziehungen zwischen den Fixpunktzahlen von Automorphismengruppen einer endlichen Gruppe, *Math. Zeit.*, **73** (1960), 146–158.

[11] Über den Transitivitatsgrad von Permutationsgruppen, *Math. Zeit.*, **74** (1960), 297–298.

[12] Subnormale Hüllen in Permutationsgruppen, *Math. Zeit.*, **79** (381–388).

[13] Gedanken fur eine allgemeine Theorie der Permutationsgruppen, *Rend. Sem. Mat. Torino*, **21** (1962), 31–39.

Ward, H. N.

[1] On Ree's series of simple groups, *Trans. Amer. Math. Soc.*, **121** (1966), 62–89.

Weir, A.

[1] Sylow *p*-subgroups of the classical groups over finite fields with characteristic prime to *p*, *Proc. Amer. Math. Soc.*, **6** (1955), 529–533.

Witt, E.

[1] Die 5-Fach transitiven Gruppen von Mathieu, *Hamb. Abh.*, **12** (1938), 256–264.

[2] Spiegelungsgruppen unde Aufzahlung halbeinfacher Liescher Ringe, *Hamb. Abh.*, **14** (1941), 289–337.

Wong, W. J.

[1] A characterization of the alternating group of degree 8, *Proc. London Math. Soc.*, **50** (1963), 359–383.

[2] On finite groups whose Sylow 2-subgroups have cyclic subgroups of index 2, *Jour. Austral. Math. Soc.*, **4** (1964), 90–112.

[3] A characterization of the Mathieu group M_{12}, *Math. Zeit.*, **84** (1964), 378–388.

[4] On finite groups with semi-dihedral groups, *Jour. Alg.*, **4** (1966), 363–379.

[5] Exceptional character theory and the theory of blocks, *Math. Zeit.*, **91** (1966), 363–379.

Zassenhaus, H.

[1] Kennzeichnung endlicher linearer Gruppen als Permutationsgruppen, *Hamb. Abh.*, **11** (1936), 17–40.

LIST OF SYMBOLS

Symbols are shown in order of initial use.

INDEX

67 68 69 70   7 6 5 4 3 2 1